06/03

MOTHS

of Hampshire and the Isle of Wight

MOTHS

of Hampshire and the Isle of Wight

Barry Goater and Tim Norriss

Sponsored by
Hampshire County Council, Butterfly Conservation, English Nature and the Isle of Wight Council

Published by Pisces Publications
in association with Hampshire County Council

First published 2001 by Pisces Publications in association with Hampshire
County Council. Pisces Publications is the imprint of the **Nature**Bureau.

British Library-in-Publication Data
A catalogue record for this book is available from the British Library

ISBN 1-874357-21-8

Designed and produced by the **Nature**Bureau,
36 Kingfisher Court, Hambridge Road, Newbury, Berkshire RG14 5SJ, UK

Printed by Information Press, Oxford, UK

Contents

Foreword

This book, written by local lepidopterists Barry Goater and Tim Norriss, describes the status and distribution of the moth species of Hampshire and the Isle of Wight at the beginning of the 21st century. It updates earlier accounts by Barry Goater published in 1974 and 1992 and, as with the recently produced *Flora of Hampshire*, *Birds of Hampshire*, and *Butterflies of Hampshire*, it now provides distribution maps which give instant and graphic pictures of the occurrence of the Macro and Pyralid moth species recorded during the past 20 years and 50 years. From these maps it is possible to detect changes in their distribution and as with many other taxonomic groups the general picture is one of decline and loss with only a few species showing an expansion in range.

The production of such a book is only made possible by the dedicated work of numbers of highly competent amateur recorders, coordinated by the authors and organisations such as Butterfly Conservation. Voluntary work of this kind has enabled the recently published Biodiversity Action Plans for Hampshire and the Isle of Wight to identify those moth species which are of particular concern, for which action is now planned to arrest their decline and bring about their conservation.

Hampshire County Council was extremely pleased to be asked to take on the task of getting the *Moths of Hampshire and the Isle of Wight* published. The County Council is proud of its record in nature conservation and is leading both the Biodiversity Action Plan programme in Hampshire and the forthcoming establishment of a Hampshire Biodiversity Information Centre in partnership with many other organisations, including Butterfly Conservation. It sees the publication of this book as a tribute to the recorders for their valuable work.

The County Council would like to thank English Nature, Butterfly Conservation and the Isle of Wight Council for responding so positively to its appeals for additional financial assistance towards the *Moths of Hampshire and the Isle of Wight*, and also to Pisces Publications for making the publication process appear so painless!

It will be the intended role of the Hampshire Biodiversity Information Centre to support biological recording in the county. The Centre will collate and manage information to disseminate to those that need it so that more informed decisions can be made about the environment to prevent further loss and decline. The publication of similar atlases for other taxa will also be encouraged and supported.

Nicky Court
Principal Ecologist
Hampshire County Council

Acknowledgements

First and foremost, it is our pleasure and privilege to acknowledge the enthusiasm with which Hampshire County Council have supported this Project. Not only have they identified the need for an authoritative account of the status of the Moths of Hampshire and the Isle of Wight at the turn of the century, but have accepted the onerous tasks associated with the printing and publication of the work, given much practical advice and encouragement and have themselves made a generous financial grant towards publication. Welcome support and a financial contribution has also come from the Isle of Wight Council, and we are very pleased to be able to continue the tradition of treating the mainland and the Island as a single biogeographical unit. English Nature has also provided a generous grant.

Hampshire and Isle of Wight Branch of Butterfly Conservation has shown great interest in the Project from its inception; many personal contributions of records have come from Branch members. Our warm appreciation is therefore extended not only to individual members for their time and effort but to the Branch itself for a major financial Grant.

Without the flood of records sent in over the past decade, this Project would have been still-born. As it is, it is but a stepping-stone, and it is hoped that in future years records will continue to enter the data-bases held by the Councils and by Hampshire and Isle of Wight Branch so that the well-being of our lepidopterous fauna can continue to be monitored and its diversity conserved.

The compilation of the data set out in this book would have been impossible but for the enthusiasm and persistence of over 150 contributors, whose names are listed in full in Appendix 2. The contributions of all of them are warmly acknowledged. Whereas the authors themselves take full responsibility for the accuracy or otherwise of the records that have been included, they are greatly indebted to the expertise of others, most especially Dr John Langmaid, for the verification of many of the records of microlepidoptera, and to the forbearance of all contributors whose records have been queried prior to their acceptance or, occasionally, rejection. Everyone has invariably seen the point, and in so doing has helped in imparting the best possible accuracy to the records.

Considerable help over certain determinations has also been received from staff in the Department of Entomology at the Natural History Museum, London, in particular Messrs D.J. Carter, M.R. Honey, M. Shaffer and K. Tuck, and more locally from Dr Phil Sterling.

The work has been greatly enhanced by the inclusion of colour photographs of representative species, and we have tried to include contributions from as many sources as possible. Photographs have been generously contributed by Dr Jim Asher, Alan Barnes, Andy Butler, Peter Creed, Barry Duffin, Pete Durnell, David Green, Paul Harris, Terry Heathcote, Tony Mundell, Tim Norriss, Dr Phil Sterling, John Taverner, Dr Paul Waring and Ken Willmott (see Appendix 3).

We are also extremely grateful to Nicky Court (Hampshire County Council), Colin Pope (Isle of Wight Council), David Green and Tony Davis for checking drafts and proof-reading and to the many people, especially Ian Thirwell, who have been pestered at unreasonably short notice with last-minute queries.

All the above are sincerely thanked.

The distribution maps in this book have been produced using DMAP written by Dr Alan Morton. Further information on this software programme can be found at http://www.dmap.co.uk

Preface

The return of one of the authors (Barry Goater) to residence in Hampshire in 1991 more or less coincided with a widening of the interests of the Hampshire and Isle of Wight Branch of Butterfly Conservation to include the moths. With the close of the 20th century approaching, we decided that it would be an opportune time to map the distribution of all the larger moths of Hampshire and the Isle of Wight and to provide a short commentary on their current status, while at the same time updating the records of the smaller Lepidoptera. Future generations of conservationists and lepidopterists would then have a base-line at a logical date upon which to monitor future changes. The involvement of Butterfly Conservation Branch Members brought a highly significant increase in the number of recorders, many of whom started from scratch and have since become highly competent general lepidopterists.

The Project received a tremendous boost following the launch, by Hampshire County Council and the Hampshire Biodiversity Partnership, of the Hampshire Biodiversity Action Plan. The County Council's subsequent support for the work is deeply appreciated, and it is fair to say that the Project is as much theirs as that of the authors and recorders. The County Council fully concurred with our desire to include maps for all the larger moths, together with an update of information on the "micros", and it was their fundraising efforts which led to the inclusion of so many colour photographs.

The first serious attempt to present a picture of the status of the whole of the Lepidoptera of Hampshire and the Isle of Wight was made in 1974 (Goater, 1974). Enough new information was gathered during the following 15 years to justify a Supplement which came out in 1992 (Goater, 1992). In the first of these books, an outline was given of the geology and geography of the area, but recently two new books on Hampshire wildlife have been published, both of which contain detailed and authoritative background for the lepidopterist which we therefore deemed unnecessary to repeat here. The *Flora of Hampshire* (Brewis, *et al.*, 1996) contains chapters written by Dr Francis Rose on the Structure and Geology of Hampshire, the Climate of Hampshire and the History of the Vegetation of Hampshire, and a very important and interesting chapter on Botanical Recording using the vice-county system, by the late Paul Bowman. *Birds of Hampshire* (Clark and Eyre, 1993) contains an equally fascinating chapter by the late Colin Tubbs, called An Introduction to Hampshire, emphasising changes in land use and the human impact on the countryside and its inhabitants. Both of these works are considered to be essential background reading for the student of Lepidoptera. While cognisant of some of the reasons for doing so, we consider it regrettable that the Isle of Wight, so much part of the biogeographical area under study, was omitted from both these treatises.

During the last decade of the 20th century, Hampshire and Isle of Wight Branch of Butterfly Conservation embarked on an extremely thorough survey of the butterflies, which led to their decision to write their own book on the subject, and for this reason, the Rhopalocera have been omitted from this otherwise complete coverage of the Lepidoptera of Hampshire and the Isle of Wight.

Introduction

The area covered by this Atlas is based on the vice-county system and comprises the Isle of Wight (vc10), South Hants (vc11) and North Hants (vc12). Disparities between the immutable boundaries of Watson's vice-counties and the present political boundaries are explained by Bowman *in* Brewis *et al.* (1996), to whom the reader is referred. The most significant areas in this context are:

- the south-western extremity of vc11, including Stanpit Marsh and Hengistbury Head, now politically part of Dorset
- Martin Down, now politically Hampshire but in the Watsonian vice-county 8, South Wilts
- Tidworth, now politically Wiltshire but in the Watsonian vice-county 12, North Hants
- a small area of vc22, Berks, annexed by Hampshire in 1979, around Mortimer West End.

Hampshire County Council has asked us to also include records from everywhere that is the political Hampshire of today, while agreeing that we include the areas that have been acceded to neighbouring counties – a classic example of us having it both ways! The species distribution maps mark all these areas that have changed hands between adjacent counties, except where these are too small to plot (see Figure 1 below). Those areas that have been "lost" to adjacent counties are shaded grey within boundaries whilst the current political area of Hampshire is shown white.

Residents of the Isle of Wight are fortunate in many respects, and being surrounded by water is one of them. They can only lose land to the sea, maybe gaining a little in return.

Much time was spent deciding on the scale of the units for mapping, and we eventually came to the conclusion that the 2 × 2 km grid (tetrad) was about right. Here we envy the botanists who can go systematically "square-bashing" throughout the year and in any weather, except perhaps deep snow, and butterfly and dragonfly recorders who can take advantage of the motor car and the occasional fine day to do likewise. The unfortunate 'moth-er', largely reliant on light as a source of records, really needs at least two fine nights per month throughout the year in a single site in order to obtain a reasonable picture of what that site contains. To some extent, our maps reflect the positions of lepidopterists' homes and of well-known localities, and many of them look dreadfully incomplete. However, safe extrapolations can, we believe, be made, and the accompanying species accounts are intended to provide a summary of the present status of our moths.

We also hope that publication will stimulate future search in under-worked areas, notably that extensive "silent area" south of Basingstoke in the east of vc12.

A map showing the tetrad distibution of all records received and used in the compilation of this book is shown in Figure 2.

Where new county and vice-county records are referred to in the species accounts that follow, they represent new records not previously published in Goater, 1974 and 1992.

Figure 1. Map showing vice-county and administrative boundaries with major areas of change.

VC12 (part) from Hampshire to Berkshire
VC22 (part) from Berkshire to Hampshire
VC12 (part) from Hampshire to Wiltshire
VC12
VC8 (part) from Wiltshire to Hampshire
VC11
VC12 (part) from Hampshire to Surrey
VC11 (part) from Hampshire to Dorset
VC10

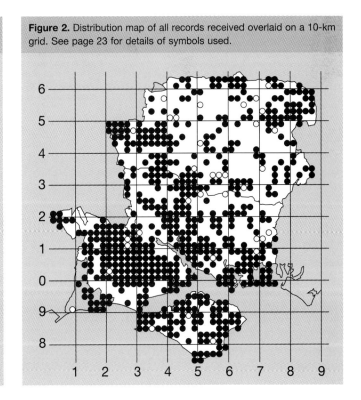

Figure 2. Distribution map of all records received overlaid on a 10-km grid. See page 23 for details of symbols used.

Changes in Distribution

Despite the changes that have been wrought, especially since the end of the Second World War, Hampshire and the Isle of Wight remain one of the richest regions in Britain for wildlife, and it is incumbent on us all to help it remain so. Its varied geology provides substrates for heath and downland, deciduous and coniferous woodland on light and heavy soils, and a variety of cultivated ground from the centres of the large towns out into deep countryside. There are notable reedbeds, mainly on the Hampshire coast and at Freshwater Marsh, small but important dune systems on Hayling Island and to a lesser extent near Hengistbury and at St Helens Duver on the Isle of Wight, and other kinds of wetland both on the Island and on the mainland. The extensive shingle at Browndown is unique in Hampshire and contains several unusual species, and, of course, there is the New Forest, itself a varied mix of heath and bog, ancient deciduous woodland and conifer plantation. It has always been a naturalist's Mecca. Geographically, Hampshire and the Isle of Wight are exceptionally well-placed for the interception of migrant species, some of which manage to establish temporary or more permanent breeding populations. One delightful consequence of this feature is the keen but always good-natured competition for records of rarities between the "yokels" on the Island and the "townies" of the mainland. The former are usually the winners!

While it is absolutely certain that our moth population, along with those of other organisms, has decreased dramatically, the reasons for this are not easy to define. Younger lepidopterists are unable to comprehend the sheer numbers of insects which we took for granted in our youth. The countryside in summer was a continual hum of insects on the wing, bramble bushes in the New Forest had up to a dozen White Admirals *Ladoga camilla* and Silver-washed Fritillaries *Argynnis paphia* on them in early July, and fields teemed with a variety of butterfly and diurnal moth species. The senior author was introduced to moths from his push-chair, and a line of palings viewed from this would produce Spring Usher *Agriopis leucophaearia*, Engrailed *Ectropis bistortata*, Broad-barred White *Aetheria bicolorata*, Grey Arches *Polia nebulosa*, Dark Arches *Apamea monoglypha*, Willow Beauty *Peribatodes rhomboidaria* and many others species in their season. As a student in the early 1950s, a cycle ride down Southampton Avenue in September was invariably productive of several Red Underwings *Catocala nupta* and once, it is recalled, a Convolvulus Hawk-moth *Agrius convolvuli*. The mixed deciduous woods locally around Chandlers Ford had the occasional large yew, on the trunk of which several Geometridae would habitually shelter from the heat of the day, and would fly off at one's approach. Trunk-hunting was a profitable way of collecting, and tapping hedgerow vegetation with a light cane resulted in scores of geometers and smaller moths flying out. Not today. Having returned to the same garden after some 40 years, a trap is operated in precisely the same spot. The fall in numbers is depressing, but some encouragement is gained by finding that most of the species just about survive, and there are some newcomers.

In many areas of south Hampshire and elsewhere, housing development and new roads have destroyed and fragmented many habitats; trees have been cut down, heathland turned into housing estates, and wild country has been turned into industrial parks. On the Isle of Wight, one of the most scandalous destructions occurred in the early 1950s, when Freshwater Marsh, the recently-discovered home of Blair's Wainscot *Sedina buettneri*, was drained and burned. *S. buettneri* has not been recorded from the site since that time although the reedbed has since regenerated. It is also disturbing to go into the New Forest and find the tree-trunks and fences bereft, to hear no more the hum of countless insects, to search hard and usually in vain for the sight of a bee hawk-moth on the rhododendrons. The fences over the downland were reliable resting places for many a moth. Where are they now? It is hard indeed not to lay the blame on human activity – pesticides, fertilisers, the internal combustion engine – but proof is elusive. There are clear cases where a foodplant has been eliminated by the use of spray, but the effect appears to extend well beyond the boundaries of farms and cultivated ground.

The one Hampshire speciality the loss of which may fairly be blamed on collectors is the New Forest Burnet *Zygaena viciae ytensis*, last seen in 1927. Professional collectors are said to have stood over the very localised breeding-grounds, waiting for the moths to emerge. Another to have disappeared, but manifestly not at the hands of collectors, is the Speckled Beauty *Fagivorina arenaria*, a lichen-feeder which apparently spent its adult life high in the forest trees, occasionally being dislodged therefrom by a rainstorm. On the downs, the phycitine moth, *Eurhodope cirrigerella*, was last seen in 1961. The reason for these losses is unclear.

We will not lengthen this list, though we could. Instead, on a more optimistic note, we will remark on some of the numerous species that have become established in the area in recent years. Perhaps the first to have been noticed was the Golden Plusia *Polychrisia moneta* which appeared towards the end of the 19th century. The larva feeds on garden *Delphinium*, and the moth is less common than formerly, probably on account of the attentions of the spray-wielding gardener. Blair's Shoulder-knot *Lithophane leautieri* was first reported at Freshwater in 1951, and is now one of the commonest autumnal moths at light, coming even in the most inclement weather. Varied Coronet *Hadena compta* came from the north-east, entering Hampshire near Basingstoke in 1983; nowadays, a plantation of sweet-williams *Dianthus barbatus* in a Hampshire garden will almost guarantee the appearance of larvae, and of moths at light. Black-streaked or Cypress Pug *Eupithecia phoeniceata* began to appear in the 1970s and is now all along the coast and has penetrated some distance inland, even to South Wonston in vc12. Jersey Tiger *Euplagia quadripunctaria* now has a strong and apparently established colony on the Isle of Wight. It is not clear whether the species spread from its British stronghold in South Devon or whether it arrived from the Continent. Recently, three astonishing recruits to our fauna have become established: to the west of Southampton and on Purbeck, the Cypress Carpet *Thera cupressata* is now well-established on *Cupressus* spp., mostly in gardens, while to the east, chiefly around Hayling Island but also now on the Isle of

Wight, larvae of the Channel Islands Pug *Eupithecia ultimaria* are locally abundant on tamarisk. In the New Forest, Southern Chestnut *Agrochola haematidea* is now locally common although this may just have been previously overlooked. All these are southern European species. A glance through the text will reveal many other new county or vice-counties records since the publication of the Supplement in 1992.

What of the future? The attractive pyrale, *Evergestis limbata*, is now taken regularly on the Isle of Wight and there are to date two mainland records. It is considered likely to settle here. Two one-time breeding species, Flame Brocade *Trigonophora flammea* and Orache Moth *Trachea atriplicis* show signs of returning. It is possible that Tree-lichen Beauty *Cryphia algae* is already in residence in south-east Hampshire. Other predominantly southern European species are turning up as migrants with increasing frequency, and could colonise. Again,

we are unsure of the true reasons for these northward extensions of range. It is too easy to explain everything in terms of global warming – yet this is the most likely cause for many species although only time will tell.

For the amateur lepidopterist, there is much to do and much to discover. The life cycles of many species, mostly microlepidoptera, have still to be worked out. Systematic field work, often in "unlikely" places, continues to produce new records and it is still largely the domain of the amateur to monitor regularly the status and wellbeing of the fauna we know, and to make sure that our records reach the depositories where they will be most useful for conservation. Openness, not secrecy, will help take care of the creatures we delight in studying, and it is hoped fervently that future legislation will encourage, not frown upon, moth-hunting and, in moderation, their collection for serious enquiry.

Moths and their Habitats

One reason for the richness of the fauna and flora of Hampshire and the Isle of Wight lies in the diversity of habitat, itself a reflection of the diverse geology of the region. Almost all lowland habitat types are represented, with the exception of hard-rock cliffs, and they all support a characteristic lepidopterous fauna.

Chalk cliffs are a prominent feature of the Island, particularly in West Wight, and their fauna includes the region's only locality for the plume moth, *Pterophorus spilodactyla*, the larva of which feeds on the very local white horehound, *Marrubium vulgare*. Three special noctuids occur here, Square-spot Dart *Euxoa obelisca*, Crescent Dart *Agrotis trux* and Beautiful Gothic *Leucochlaena oditis*, as well as a silvery-green form of Feathered Ranunculus *Eumichtis lichenea*. Here, too, is a white form of the Annulet *Gnophos obscuratus*, and it is the classic locality for the long-lost Isle of Wight Wave *Idaea humiliata*.

There is a strong colony of Dew Moth *Setina irrorella*, also present on the shingle of Hurst Point, which juts out from the mainland opposite the Isle of Wight. The best stretch of shingle, however, is at Browndown, where a large population of the very local Nottingham catchfly is host to a colony of White Spot *Hadena albimacula*. Tawny Shears *H. perplexa* and Marbled Coronet *H. confusa* are also frequent, with another local species, White Colon *Sideridis albicolon*. The nearby Browndown Marsh, partially lost to landfill in the Alver Valley, has an extremely interesting group of species which include *Cosmopterix lienigiella*, the tortricid *Acleris lorquiniana*, the pyrale *Nascia cilialis* and the Mere Wainscot *Photedes fluxa*.

Reedbeds occur at Browndown, but are more extensive at Keyhaven, Lymington and Titchfield Haven, and there are other smaller sites, chiefly along the coast. Among the reeds may be found Obscure Wainscot *Mythimna obsoleta*, Twin-spotted Wainscot *Archanara geminipuncta*, Brown-veined Wainscot *A. dissoluta*, Fen Wainscot *Arenostola phragmitidis* and Silky Wainscot *Chilodes maritimus*, as well as the Crescent *Celaena leucostigma* and much else. The famous reedbed at Freshwater, once the home of Blair's Wainscot *Sedina buettneri* still contains these other species.

Sand-dunes are more or less confined to the southern tip of Hayling Island. Here, there are strong colonies of Grass Eggar *Lasiocampa trifolii*, Sand Dart *Agrotis ripae* and the pyrale *Cynaeda dentalis*. Smaller and less productive dunes occur at St Helens on the Isle of Wight and at Hengistbury.

Much of the Hampshire coast consists of tidal mudflats covered with cord-grass *Spartina anglica*, but where more generalised salterns occur, notably on North Hayling, Mathew's Wainscot *Mythimna favicolor* and Crescent-striped *Apamea oblonga* may be found. In a more specialised habitat on Hayling Island, the larval cases of *Coleophora deviella* and *C. aesturiella* have recently been discovered on annual sea-blite *Suaeda maritima*, and *Monochroa moyses* on sea club-rush *Bulboschoenus maritimus*, which is also found on Farlington Marsh.

Before leaving the coast, mention should be made of Hengistbury Head, virtually an island with a mixture of sandy cliffs, dry heathland, deciduous woodland, coniferous plantations and, on the Christchurch Harbour side, reedbeds and salterns. Though rather inaccessible for night work, its diversity makes it a fascinating small area for intensive study. Portland Moth *Actebia praecox* occurred here at one time, Sand Dart *Agrotis ripae* and Archer's Dart *A. vestigialis* are common and many of the woodland and reedbed species are present in good numbers.

The most famous of Hampshire's localities is surely however the New Forest. It was once renowned for its butterflies and the large areas of mature oak woodland are still visited in early autumn for the two nationally rare crimson underwings *Catocala sponsa* and *C. promissa* both of which are sometimes quite common at sugar. Earlier in the year, Scarce Merveille du Jour *Moma alpium* attracts attention, and the woodlands of oak and beech contain many other interesting species such as Rosy Marbled *Elaphria venustula* and White-line Snout *Schrankia taenialis*. On the dry heaths, specialities include the phycitines, *Pempelia genistella* and *Apomyelois bistriatella*, Purple-bordered Gold *Idaea muricata*, Dotted Border Wave *I. sylvestraria*, Grey scalloped Bar *Dyscia fagaria*, Grass Wave *Perconia strigillaria*, Dark Tussock *Dicallomera fascelina*, Clouded Buff *Diacrisia sannio*, Autumnal Rustic *Eugnorisma glareosa*, Neglected Rustic *Xestia castanea*, Heath Rustic *X. agathina* and many others, including the remarkable recent discovery, Southern Chestnut *Agrochola haematidea*. Speckled Footman *Coscinia cribraria* used to occur on the western heaths, but seems to have disappeared from Hampshire. As the heaths descend into valley bog, bog-myrtle becomes abundant and is the host to the "red" form of Powdered Quaker *Orthosia gracilis*. The tortricid *Sparganothis pilleriana* is locally common in this zone. Crambids of the damp heaths include *Crambus hamella*, mostly in the drier parts, *C. silvella*, *C. pascuella*, *C. perlella* and, in the wet areas, *C. uliginosella*. The valley bogs support good populations of Brown China-mark *Elophila nymphaeata*, *Eudonia pallida*, the sundew-feeding plume moth *Buckleria paludum*, Rosy Wave *Scopula emutaria* which also occurs on the coast, Round-winged Muslin *Thumatha senex* and, in places, colonies of Webb's Wainscot *Archanara sparganii*.

The acid heathland is colonised in places by birch *Betula* spp. and Scots pine *Pinus sylvestris*. Moths which are particularly associated with the former are Yellow Horned *Achlya flavicornis*, the hook-tips *Falcaria lacertinaria* and *Drepana falcataria* and Orange Underwing *Brephos parthenias*. The Scarce Prominent *Odontosia carmelita* is not uncommon in many of the Hampshire birch-woodlands, and also occurs near Cranmore on the Isle of Wight. Characteristic pine species are Bordered White *Bupalus piniarius*, Pine Beauty *Panolis flammea* and several species of tortricid of the genera *Clavigesta*, *Pseudococcyx*, *Rhyacionia* and *Cydia*. The Pine Hawk-moth *Hyloicus pinastri* spread across Hampshire from Purbeck in the 1940s and became very common. It is still present, though less frequent.

The very rare tortricid, *Archips oporana*, has recently been rediscovered in the extreme west of vc11. In the same type of country, and also in the river valleys, sallows *Salix* spp. are common, and support a number of notable species, among which may be mentioned the Sallow Clearwing *Synanthedon flaviventris*, first discovered in Britain by the late W. Fassnidge in 1924, in Hampshire. Slender, fusiform galls on small sallows on heathland are made by the larva of *Cydia servillana*. Larvae of Dingy Mocha *Cyclophora pendularia* were found regularly on sallow bushes in parts of the New Forest, but have become very rare. Aspen *Populus tremula* is very local and more or less confined to the clays, sands and gravels in the county. Where it occurs, Light Orange Underwing *Brephos notha*, Poplar Lutestring *Tethea* or and the tortricids *Pseudosciaphila branderiana* and *Epinotia maculana* may be found, along with more general poplar-feeders.

Other extensive woodlands occur outside the New Forest, notably Parkhurst Forest on the Isle of Wight, Botley Wood in south Hampshire, Harewood Forest towards the north-west, Pamber Forest and Ashford Hill in the north of the county and Bentley Wood in the west lying largely just over the border in Wiltshire. In some of these woodlands are found the very rare oecophorids *Esperia oliviella* and *Oecophora bractella*, the tortricids *Olindia schumacherana*, *Olethreutes arcuella* and the day-flying Argent and Sable *Rheumaptera hastata* and Drab Looper *Minoa murinata*. In the south-east, the once-extensive Forest of Bere and also Havant Thicket, which was at one time a stronghold of the Double-line *Mythimna turca*, have been damaged by fragmentation, coniferisation and development.

The heathlands in the north-east of Hampshire have also been damaged by coniferisation and many areas are under threat from housing developments. On them are found many of the heathland species of the New Forest, but bog-myrtle is largely absent and so, therefore, is the "red" form of Powdered Quaker *O. gracilis*. This area is thought of particularly as home territory of Dotted Chestnut *Dasycampa rubiginea* and Waved Black *Parascotia fuliginaria*, though both have become much more widespread recently. On the Isle of Wight, true heathland is confined to Headon Warren; there are no boggy areas, and it seems far less rewarding as a locality than the mainland heaths. However the Reddish Buff *Acosmetia caliginosa* survives in its only native British site on relict clay heath in the north-west of the Island.

Wonderful chalk downland once swept across the centre of Hampshire up to the time of the Second World War, and was extremely rich in species. The same may be said of the central spine of chalk that traverses the Isle of Wight. During the War, most of the Hampshire downland was ploughed up, pesticide sprays and fertilisers were introduced, and the whole area severely fragmented. Besides the pristine stretch of downland on the Isle of Wight which reaches from east of Freshwater to the Needles, where Five-spot Burnet *Zygaena trifolii palustrella*, *Pyrausta ostrinalis* and *Mecyna flavalis* continue to thrive, some good downland remains further east

along the Island's "spine"; at one of these sites, Knighton Down, Chalk Carpet *Scotopteryx bipunctaria* has a strong colony. On the mainland, St Catherine's Hill near Winchester is being carefully restored by the Wildlife Trust and the Hampshire and Isle of Wight Branch of Butterfly Conservation are making an excellent job of revitalising Yew Hill and Magdalen Hill Down. Moths should benefit from this treatment, and already the larvae of Striped Lychnis *Shargacucullia lychnitis* have appeared at Magdalen Hill Down where there is also a strong colony of Orange-tailed Clearwing *Synanthedon andrenaeformis*.

It is, however, the great unspoilt downland area which straddles the Hampshire/Wiltshire border at Porton Down which is of particular merit for many noteworthy species. Here, the nationally scarce Lunar Yellow Underwing *Noctua orbona* has a strong colony, there is another of *Mecyna flavalis* and here, we believe, is the only place where *Eurhodope cirrigerella* may still be located. Although not restricted to downland habitat it was in this area that Pale Shining Brown *Polia bombycina* was last seen in numbers in the county. Its rapid national decline and our lack of knowledge on its ecological requirements are a cause of great concern. Nearby, the military area around Tidworth still has some excellent downland, where Scarce Forester *Jordanita globulariae* was discovered in the year 2000 and Five-spot Burnet *Zygaena trifolii palustrella* remains common.

Noar Hill near Selborne is still very rich in plant-life and supports a good moth fauna, notably White-marked *Cerastis leucographa*, which has been well-studied, particularly by Tony James. The Butser Hill/Oxenbourne Down complex in the east of Hampshire, south of Petersfield, is extensive but relatively depauperate for moths. Regrettably, all these areas exist as islands, surrounded by heavily sprayed fields of monocrops. During and after the War, Brighton Wainscot *Oria musculosa* became established in the wheat-fields on the north Hampshire chalk and was locally common for a time. Now, it has disappeared from the county and is on the verge of extinction nationally.

Most of us lepidopterists can only enjoy the privilege of visiting many of the attractive sites mentioned above and are destined to reside in suburbia, or in the towns. Even so, our garden moth traps and flower-beds produce interesting species and it is important to continue to monitor their presence. Some species, indeed, are seldom if ever reported away from towns and gardens. Marbled Green *Cryphia muralis* is more common in Southsea than anywhere else in the county, Buttoned Snout *Hypena rostralis* is regularly recorded about Southampton, *Udea fulvalis* is a Christchurch speciality and both Cypress Pug *Eupithecia phoeniceata* and Cypress Carpet *Thera cupressata* are to be expected more in large suburban gardens than out in the countryside.

Moth Conservation

It is vital that the large amount of information being diligently collected by the growing number of recorders listed in Appendix 2 is put to good use in order to benefit the very species being observed. Not only can this data be used to identify general trends in numbers and distribution but it can also be used to detect those species which are, or are becoming, of particular concern, and so be used ultimately to bring about their conservation, both through appropriate site management and protection from development. The appointment of two full-time Moth Conservation Officers by Butterfly Conservation in May 1999 was an important milestone and whilst their appointment was national their local contribution has been significant.

In 1996 a review of the UK Priority moth species by Dr Paul Waring for the UK Biodiversity Action Plan listed 54 species of macro-moths of conservation concern. From this list 27 species (see below), which occur in fewer than 15 10-km squares nationally, or else have their national stronghold in the region, have been selected by Butterfly Conservation for inclusion in a Species Action Plan for the Hampshire Biodiversity Action Plan (Johnson 1999) – based on their presence in the county or in neighbouring counties close to the border. Some of these species have only been recorded occasionally over the last few decades, and it is doubtful if viable populations still exist. However, even a slight possibility that such species may still be present is sufficient enough reason for their inclusion. Future survey work should establish their true status.

The 27 high-priority macro-moth species in Hampshire are:

0174 The Triangle *Heterogenea asella*
1675 Dingy Mocha *Cyclophora pendularia*
1731 Chalk Carpet *Scotopteryx bipunctaria*
1785 Barberry Carpet *Pareulype berberata*
1787 Argent and Sable *Rheumaptera hastata*
1878 Drab Looper *Minoa murinata*
1880 Barred Tooth-striped *Trichopteryx polycommata*
1982 Narrow-bordered Bee Hawk-moth *Hemaris tityus*
2053 Speckled Footman *Coscinia cribraria*
2108 Lunar Yellow Underwing *Noctua orbona*
2148 Pale Shining Brown *Polia bombycina*
2153 Bordered Gothic *Heliophobus reticulata*
2172 White Spot *Hadena albimacula*
2219 Striped Lychnis *Shargacucullia lychnitis*
2257 Orange Upperwing *Jodia croceago*
2264a Southern Chestnut *Agrochola haematidea*
2277 Scarce Merveille du Jour *Moma alpium*
2315 Heart Moth *Dicycla oo*
2378 Brighton Wainscot *Oria musculosa*
2393 Reddish Buff *Acosmetia caliginosa*
2401 Marbled Clover *Heliothis viriplaca*
2402 Shoulder-striped Clover *Heliothis maritima*
2454 Light Crimson Underwing *Catocala promissa*
2455 Dark Crimson Underwing *Catocala sponsa*
2480 Buttoned Snout *Hypena rostralis*
2482 White-line Snout *Schrankia taenialis*
2488 Common Fan-foot *Pechipogo strigilata*

The Hampshire Biodiversity Action Plan being written for these species (to be published at the end of 2001) will summarise what is known of their ecology and habitat requirements, population and distribution, status, factors affecting their population and distribution, and current and future actions. Current action in the main tends to concentrate on detailed surveys of the species at specific sites in order to determine much of the above. Recent examples include:

- English Nature Species Recovery Programme for the Reddish Buff *Acosmetia caliginosa*.
- English Nature Species Recovery Programme for the Barberry Carpet *Pareulype berberata*.
- English Nature funded surveys of the Dingy Mocha *Cyclophora pendularia* in the New Forest.
- National Trust initiated surveys of the Chalk Carpet *Scotopteryx bipunctaria* on the Isle of Wight.
- Hampshire Wildlife Trust surveys of the Chalk Carpet *S. bipunctaria* and Barred Tooth-striped *Trichopteryx polycommata* at Broughton Down.
- A larval survey of the White Spot *Hadena albimacula* at Browndown.
- English Nature 'pre-species recovery project' surveys for Marbled Clover *Heliothis viriplaca* and Shoulder Striped Clover *Heliothis maritima*.

Thirteen UK Priority moth species have been identified as having been recorded from the Isle of Wight and are therefore the high priority species for the Island.

The 13 high-priority macro-moth species in the Isle of Wight are:

1675 Dingy Mocha *Cyclophora pendularia*
1731 Chalk Carpet *Scotopteryx bipunctaria*
1982 Narrow-bordered Bee Hawk *Hemaris tityus*
2148 Pale Shining Brown *Polia bombycina*
2153 Bordered Gothic *Heliophobus reticulata*
2257 Orange Upperwing *Jodia croceago*
2317 White-spotted Pinion *Cosmia diffinis*
2378 Brighton Wainscot *Oria musculosa*
2393 Reddish Buff *Acosmetia caliginosa*
2465 Four-spotted *Tyta luctuosa*
2480 Buttoned Snout *Hypena rostralis*
2482 White-line Snout *Schrankia taenialis*
2488 Common Fan-foot *Pechipogo strigilata*

In addition, 62 macro-moth species have been identified as being of local concern and these are listed in the *Wildlife of the Isle of Wight: BAP Audit* (2000). It is intended that Species Action Plans will be produced in due course for those species not otherwise catered for within the Habitat Action Plans.

Current action for most species is principally confined to surveying. The notable exception is that of the English Nature Species Recovery programme for the Reddish Buff *Acosmetia caliginosa* where habitat management has secured the population in its sole native locality.

Hengistbury Head has a fine range of different habitats including heathland, woodland, freshwater pools, saltmarsh and reedbed, as well as a strip of sand-dune with such specialities as Sand Dart *Agrotis ripae* (2093) and Bird's Wing *Dypterygia scabriuscula* (2301) (inset).

The heathland of Latchmore Bottom lying to the south of Hampton Ridge in the west of the New Forest is home to the recently discovered Southern Chestnut *Agrochola haematidea* (2264a) (inset), and other heathland species.

Mark Ash Wood on the Ornamental Drive contains many enormous beech trees favoured by species such as Barred Hook-tip *Watsonalla cultraria* (1647), Clay Triple-lines *Cyclophora linearia* (1681) and Lobster Moth *Stauropus fagi* (1999) (inset).

The extensive woodland of Frame Wood contains many old spreading oak trees up to 300 years old and is home to many New Forest specialities including Scarce Merveille du Jour *Moma alpium* (2277) and Dark Crimson Underwing *Catocala sponsa* (2455) (inset).

Looking west along the edge of Compton Down, Isle of Wight towards the Needles. This is a locality for the Beautiful Gothic *Leucochlaena oditis* (2226) (inset), the pyralids *Pyrausta ostrinalis* (1363) and *Mecyna flavalis* (1396), and Square-spot Dart *Euxoa obelisca* (2080).

Clearance of evergreen oak at Bonchurch Down, Isle of Wight has resulted in colonisation of the cut stumps by the Yellow-legged Clearwing *Synanthedon vespiformis* (0374) (inset).

Amongst the diverse woodland habitats to be found in Harewood Forest are many Hampshire specialities including Argent and Sable *Rheumaptera hastata* (1787) and the Drab Looper *Minoa murinata* (1878) (inset).

At the mouth of the River Meon lies Titchfield Haven NR with its extensive reedbeds, meadows and carr woodland. Several species of wainscot moth occur here, and others such as Drinker *Euthrix potatoria* (1640) (inset).

Browndown ranges are still used as a military training area and the shingle beach contains areas of heath and stunted oak. The White Spot *Hadena albimacula* (2172) (inset) is found where the foodplant Nottingham catchfly grows.

Hayling Island contains excellent maritime habitats at Sandy Point (far right) and Sinah dunes where the Grass Eggar *Lasiocampa trifolii* (1636) (inset) still thrives in its only Hampshire locality. It is the only place in Hampshire where there are extensive sand-dunes.

Odiham Common is now the last known site in Hampshire for the Forester *Adscita statices* (0163) (inset).

Noar Hill, near Selborne, is famous for its butterflies but also has a wide variety of moth species including the day-flying Burnet Companion *Euclidia glyphica* (2463) (inset).

▲ 0077 *Stigmella tityrella* – vacated mine in beech *Fagus sylvatica*

▼ 0129 *Incurvaria pectinea* – tenanted mines in birch *Betula* sp.

0014 *Hepialus humuli* Ghost Moth (female) ▲

0148 *Nemophora degeerella* ▼

▲ 0161 *Zeuzera pyrina* Leopard Moth

▼ 0162 *Cossus cossus* Goat Moth

0163 *Adscita statices* Forester ▲

0173 *Apoda limacodes* Festoon (male) ▼

▲ 0171 *Zygaena lonicerae* Narrow-bordered Five-spot Burnet

▼ 0192 *Pachythelia villoselia* – larval case

0174 *Heterogenea asella* Triangle (male) ▲

0196 *Morophaga choragella* ▼

0374 *Synanthedon vespiformis* Yellow-legged Clearwing (female) ▲

▲ 0377 *Synanthedon flaviventris* Sallow Clearwing

0530 *Coleophora lixella* ▼

▼ 0538 *Coleophora vibicella* – larval case on dyer's greenweed *Genista tinctoria*

0651 *Oecophora bractella* ▲

0809 *Pexicopia malvella* ▼

▼ 0925 *Phtheochroa rugosana*

1073 *Olethreutes schulziana* ▲

▲ 1288 *Alucita hexadactyla* Twenty-plume Moth

1359 *Cynaeda dentalis* ▼

▼ 1362 *Pyrausta purpuralis*

1398 *Nomophila noctuella* Rush Veneer ▲

▲ 1405 *Pleuroptya ruralis* Mother of Pearl

1438 *Trachycera (Numonia) suavella* ▼

▼ 1513 *Pterophorus pentadactyla* White Plume Moth

1633 *Eriogaster lanestris* Small Eggar – larval nest ▲

▲ 1637 *Lasiocampa quercus* Oak Eggar (male)

▼ 1640 *Euthrix potatoria* Drinker (male)

1643 *Saturnia pavonia* Emperor Moth (male) ▲

▲ 1645 *Falcaria lacertinaria* Scalloped Hook-tip

1648 *Drepana falcataria* Pebble Hook-tip ▼

▼ 1651 *Cilix glaucata* Chinese Character

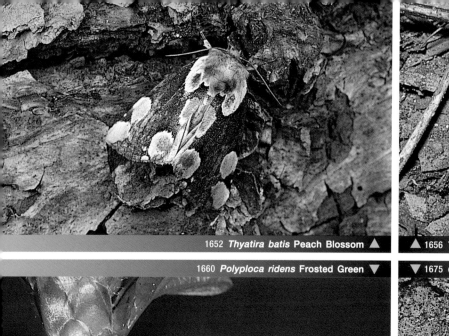

1652 *Thyatira batis* Peach Blossom ▲

▲ 1656 *Tetheella fluctuosa* Satin Lutestring

1660 *Polyploca ridens* Frosted Green ▼

▼ 1675 *Cyclophora pendularia* Dingy Mocha

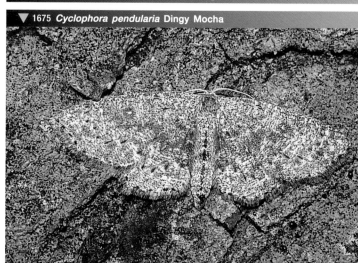

▲ 1680 *Cyclophora punctaria* Maiden's Blush

1682 *Timandra griseata* Blood-vein ▼

▼ 1747 *Anticlea derivata* The Streamer

1750 *Lampropteryx suffumata* Water Carpet ▲

1787 *Rheumaptera hastata* Argent and Sable ▼

▲ 1771a *Thera cupressata* Cypress Carpet

1825 *Eupithecia centaureata* Lime-speck Pug ▲

▲ 1852 *Eupithecia abbreviata* Brindled Pug

1878 *Minoa murinata* Drab Looper ▼

▼ 1919 *Selenia tetralunaria* Purple Thorn

1947 *Ectropis bistortata* The Engrailed ▲

▲ 1979 *Mimas tiliae* Lime Hawk-moth

1982 *Hemaris tityus* Narrow-bordered Bee Hawk-moth ▼

▼ 1994 *Phalera bucephala* Buff-tip

1999 *Stauropus fagi* Lobster Moth ▲

▲ 2010 *Odontosia carmelita* Scarce Prominent

2019 *Clostera curtula* Chocolate-tip ▼

▼ 2026 *Orgyia antiqua* The Vapourer (male left, female right)

2028 *Calliteara pudibunda* Pale Tussock (male left, female right) ▲

▲ 2033 *Lymantria monacha* Black Arches

037 *Miltochrista miniata* Rosy Footman ▼

▼ 2050 *Eilema lurideola* Common Footman

▼ 2069 *Tyria jacobaeae* Cinnabar

2057 *Arctia caja* Garden Tiger ▲

2068 *Callimorpha dominula* Scarlet Tiger ▼

2172 *Hadena albimacula* White Spot

2077 *Nola cucullatella* Short-cloaked Moth ▲

2214 *Cucullia chamomillae* Chamomile Shark – larva ▼

2107 *Noctua pronuba* Large Yellow Underwing ▼

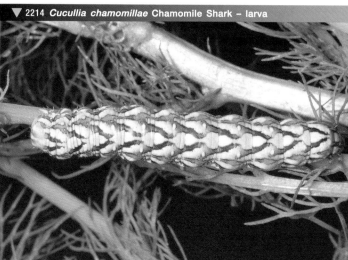

2219 *Shargacucullia lychnitis* Striped Lychnis – larva ▼

2142 *Anarta myrtilli* Beautiful Yellow Underwing ▼

2226 *Leucochlaena oditis* Beautiful Gothic ▲

▲ 2247 *Dichonia aprilina* Merveille du Jour

2264a *Agrochola haematidea* Southern Chestnut ▼

▼ 2301 *Dypterygia scabriuscula* Bird's Wing

2421 *Bena bicolorana* Scarce Silver-lines ▼

▼ 2437 *Polychrysia moneta* Golden Plusia

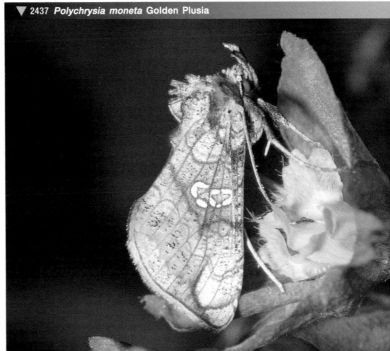

2441 *Autographa gamma* Silver Y ▲

2463 *Euclidia glyphica* Burnet Companion ▼

2477 *Hypena proboscidalis* The Snout ▼

▲ 2455 *Catocala sponsa* Dark Crimson Underwing – larva

▼ 2455 *Catocala sponsa* Dark Crimson Underwing

▲ 2475 *Parascotia fuliginaria* Waved Black

▼ 2480 *Hypena rostralis* Buttoned Snout

Maps and Systematic Accounts

Distribution maps have been compiled for all the generally-accepted macro-moths (*sensu* Skinner, 1998) and Pyralidae, with the exception of a small number of casuals which have been recorded on very few occasions; reference is made to them in the text. No attempt has been made to present maps of the distribution of the so-called Microlepidoptera, but a text has been provided which updates the distributional data already published (Goater, 1974, 1992). In some instances the recorded occurrences of extreme rarities are reiterated in full.

Three different symbols are used on the maps:
● A solid dot represents records from 1981 to date
○ An open circle shows records between 1951 and 1980
× A cross indicates historic records from before 1950 for which it has been possible to work out an accurate grid reference. In the case of many of the old records, this has not been possible, and the reader must refer to the text in the present work or in previous publications (Goater, 1974, 1992).

The text accompanying the maps attempts to give an assessment of the present status of all species in the area under consideration. Individual records are given for the rarer species and selected unusual records of species outside their normal range are also included, especially those from nature reserves.

The national status of the rarer macro-moth species is given, according to the system devised by Waring (1994), viz.:
- **RDB1** Endangered; currently known from five or fewer 10-km squares in Britain, and in danger of extinction.
- **RDB2** Vulnerable; currently known from between six and ten 10-km squares in Britain. Populations declining and considered likely to become endangered.
- **RDB3** Rare; currently known from between 11 and 15 10-km squares in Britain. Small, thinly scattered local populations, but not at present considered to be vulnerable or endangered.
- **RDBK** Recently-discovered species believed to be rare, but currently of uncertain status.
- **Notable/Na** Nationally scarce, Grade A. Very restricted national distribution, recorded from 16–30 10-km squares in Britain since 1980.
- **Notable/Nb** Nationally scarce Grade B. Restricted national distribution, recorded from 31–100 10-km squares in Britain since 1980.

Of course, these categories must be interpreted on a local scale otherwise they may be misleading. For instance, species which are common in some other parts of the country, such as Juniper

Table 1. Number of species of Lepidoptera (excluding butterflies) recorded in vice-counties 10 (Isle of Wight), 11 (South Hants) and 12 (North Hants).

Family	Vice-county 10	11	12	Family	Vice-county 10	11	12
Micropterigidae	3 + [1]	4 + [1]	5	Blastobasidae	2	3	2
Eriocraniidae	5	8	8	Batrachedridae	0	2	2
Hepialidae	5	5	5	Momphidae	10	13	11
Nepticulidae	55 + [1]	79	66 + [1]	Cosmopterigidae	4	14 + [1]	10
Opostegidae	1	2	2	Scythrididae	2	4	3
Tischeriidae	4	4	3	Cochylidae	31 + [1]	36	31
Incurvariidae	18	22	21	Tortricidae	187 + [3]	253	213 + [1]
Heliozelidae	4 + [1]	6	6	Epermeniidae	4 + [1]	6	5
Cossidae	2	2	2	Schreckensteiniidae	1	1	1
Zygaenidae	4	4 + 2†	6	Alucitidae	1	1	1
Limacodidae	1	2	2	Pyralidae	128 + 1† + [3]	139 + 4† + [1]	109 + 1†
Psychidae	5	13	7	Thyrididae	0	1	0
Tineidae	25	27	24	Pterophoridae	20 + [3]	27	21
Bucculatricidae	5 + [1]	10	7	Lasiocampidae	8 + 2†	8 + 1†	7 + 1†
Douglasiidae	0	1	1	Saturniidae	1	2	1
Roeslerstammiidae	1	1	1	Endromidae	0	0	1 †
Gracillariidae	55 + [1]	72 + [2]	67	Drepanidae	5	6	5
Sesiidae	5	12	11	Thyatiridae	8	9	9
Choreutidae	2 + [2]	4	3	Geometridae	220 + 1† + [5]	245 + 2†	234 + 1† + [2]
Glyphipterigidae	5 + [1]	6	5	Sphingidae	16	16 + [1]	16
Yponomeutidae	39	63 + [1]	62 + [1]	Notodontidae	18	22	20
Lyonetiidae	6	8	6	Thaumetopoeidae	1	0	0
Coleophoridae	50 + [3]	77	60	Lymantriidae	7	8 + 1†	7 + 1† + [1]
Elachistidae	23	36	27 + [1]	Arctiidae	25	28 + 2†	23
Oecophoridae	47 + [1]	64 + [1]	55 + [1]	Ctenuchidae	0	1	0
Ethmiidae	1	2 + [1]	1	Nolidae	4	4	4
Gelechiidae	59 + [1]	103 + [2]	69	Noctuidae	287 + 2† + [3]	302 + 4† + [3]	262 + 1† + [0]
Autostichidae	1	1	2	**TOTAL**	**1421 + 6† + [32]**	**1789 + 16† + [14]**	**1531 + 5† + [8]**

Note: Totals are inflated by the inclusion of scarce migrants, several of which have been recorded once only. Species believed to be extinct are marked †. Doubtful records have been placed in square brackets. The totals that follow each Family name within the text are the totals that have occurred within all three vice-counties. The same symbols have been used.

Carpet *Thera juniperata*, have an extremely restricted distribution in Hampshire, and Striped Lychnis *Shargacucullia lychnitis,* nationally Notable/Na, is probably commoner in mid-Hampshire than anywhere else in the country. Angle-striped Sallow *Enargia paleacea* is given as Notable/Nb for its resident populations from the Midlands northwards, but in Hampshire it is an extremely rare migrant. There are many other species which are common or merely local in Britain as a whole, but which are absent or very rare in Hampshire and the Isle of Wight. Conversely, our two counties boast several species which are found nowhere else in Britain.

Table 1 details the number of species of each family that has been recorded in each of the three vice-counties to date, illustrating the rich diversity of the moth fauna within our two counties. It is our duty to maintain that diversity.

In the accounts which follow, the numbering of species accords with that of Bradley and Fletcher (1979) but the sequence and nomenclatural changes which have been incorporated follow Bradley (1998). In cases where the generic or specific name has changed since the publication of the previous work (Goater, 1992), the names used here are included in parenthesis, or as synonyms. As our understanding of the taxonomy of lepidoptera has developed and evolved, a realignment of the systematic order has occurred, resulting in the movement of some species within and between families. The Bradley and Fletcher number remains the same in such instances to maintain continuity, but this inevitably results in some minor changes to the numerical sequence. This can be confusing for the layman not familiar with these changes, and the reader is referrred to the index in such circumstances.

The Moths of Hampshire and the Isle of Wight

Systematic list

Micropterigidae (5)

Small, primitive Lepidoptera with functional mandibles, which fly by day and feed on pollen of a variety of plant species. They are seldom observed on the wing but are frequently seen, often in numbers, on flower-heads in late spring and summer. The early stages of the British species are largely unknown.

0001 *Micropterix tunbergella* (Fabricius, 1787)
Locally common in woodland.
- vc8 Martin Down, 29.4.90 (S. Nash).
- vc10 Osborne, 25.5.96, DTB conf. JRL (Agassiz *et al.*, 1998); Luccombe Chine, 3.6.78 (RJD). **New vc record.**

0002 *Micropterix mansuetella* Zeller, 1844
Apart from some old and unsubstantiated records given in Goater (1974), the only more recent and detailed ones are from Leckford vc12 (Goater, 1992).

0003 *Micropterix aureatella* (Scopoli, 1763)
Local in woodland and on heaths.

0004 *Micropterix aruncella* (Scopoli, 1763)
Local on downland and in other dry localities. The moth flies throughout the summer.
- vc8 Martin Down, 6.5.90 (S. Nash).
- vc10 Tolt Down, 1.6.96 (DTB).
- vc11 Merrietown Heath, 2.6.95, common (PHS); Fletchwood Meadows, 10.6.99, very common (BE); The Moors NR, Bishop's Waltham; Place Wood, Southwick, 31.5.98, one in flight; Oxenbourne Down NR (RJD); Hookheath Meadows NR, Southwick, 9.6.92 (JRL, DHS).
- vc12 Winnall Moors NR (DHS); Pamber, 1994 (GJD); Conford Moor, 21.6.95, many (JRL, RM Palmer).

0005 *Micropterix calthella* (Linnaeus, 1761)
Locally abundant. The moth often swarms on flowers of buttercup, sedges, etc., feeding on the pollen.

Eriocraniidae (8)

Adults of this genus fly in spring sunshine and rest on twigs in dull weather. Confirmation of identity by dissection of genitalia is often necessary, especially with regard to the birch-feeding species.

0006 *Eriocrania subpurpurella* (Haworth, 1828)
Common to abundant throughout the mainland vice-counties wherever deciduous oaks occur (JRL). The larva mines in leaves of oak and the moth flies in April and May.
- vc8 Martin Down, 29.4.90 (S. Nash), 8.6.92, mines (JRL, RMP).
- vc10 Parkhurst Forest, 17.5.95, mines with larvae (DTB); Gatcombe, 6.6.98, mine with larva (DTB); Shanklin; SE of Northwood (JMC).

0007 *Eriocrania chrysolepidella* Zeller, 1851
Very local amongst hazel *Corylus avellana* in the mainland vice-counties. The larva mines in leaves of hazel and hornbeam *Carpinus betulus* in April and May, and the moth flies in March and April.

0008 *Eriocrania unimaculella* (Zetterstedt, 1839)
Local and evidently rather uncommon amongst birch *Betula* spp. in the mainland vice-counties but still unrecorded from the Isle of Wight. The larva makes blotches in the leaves of birch during May and the moth flies in March and April.
- vc11 Sopley Common, 1.4.97, frequent by day (PD); Chandlers Ford, 4.4.95, det. JRL (BG); Emer Bog; Baddesley Great Covert; Hut Wood; Botley Wood; Warsash; West Walk; Rowner Wild Grounds (RJD); Victoria Country Park, Netley, 3.6.99 (PAB).
- vc12 Silchester Common (RJD); Bartley Heath NR; Bramley Frith Wood NR (AHD).

0009 *Eriocrania sparrmannella* (Bosc, 1791)
Uncommon, and unrecorded from the Isle of Wight. The larva makes mines in leaves of birch *Betula* spp. during the summer months and the moth flies amongst the foodplant in April and May.
- vc11 Merrietown Heath, 12.4.94, common (PHS); Weston Shore, 21.7.99 (PAB); Botley Wood, 6.6.93, a few tenanted mines (JRL); Emer Bog; Wickham Common, 9.5.89, one at m.v. light (RJD).
- vc12 Pamber, 1994 (GJD); Bartley Heath NR (AHD); Eelmoor Marsh, 5.7.98, tenanted mines (DGG).

0010 *Eriocrania salopiella* (Stainton, 1854)
Uncommon, but probably under-recorded, and no record from the Isle of Wight. The larva mines in leaves of birch *Betula* spp. in May and June, and the moth flies in birch woodland in April and May.
- vc11 Warsash, 20.5.94, a few tenanted mines (JRL).
- vc12 Abbotstone Down, 1.6.93, many tenanted mines (RJBH, JRL, DHS); Bartley Heath NR; Bramley Frith Wood NR (AHD); Fleet Pond LNR, 8.5.98, one by day (DGG); Bramshott Common, 23.5.98, several tenanted mines (JRL, IRT).
- vc22 Benyon's Inclosure, 3+ flying, 24.4.76, caught by DMA, in coll. RJD.

0011 *Eriocrania cicatricella* (Zetterstedt, 1839)
= *haworthi* Bradley, 1966
Common, and recorded in all three vice-counties. The larva makes blotches in leaves of birch *Betula* spp. in May, and the moth flies amongst birch in April.

0012 *Eriocrania sangii* (Wood, 1891)
Now recorded from all three vice-counties, but rare or overlooked. Larva makes blotch mines on birch *Betula* spp. in spring. The moth flies in March and April.
- vc10 Afton Marsh, 17.5.96, several tenanted mines on *B. pendula*, DTB conf. JRL (Agassiz *et al.*, 1998). **New vc record.**
- vc11 Sopley Common, 13.5.00, larva on *B. pendula* (PHS); Parnholt Wood, 1.5.98, a few tenanted mines on *B. pubescens* (RJBH, JRL); Thornhill, 4.4.76 (RJD),

3.5.99, tenanted mine in birch leaf (PAB); Botley Wood, 5.4.76 (RJD).
■ vc12 Pamber, 3.4.75 (RJD), 1994, genit det. (GJD).

0013 *Eriocrania semipurpurella* (Stephens, 1835)
The most abundant of the birch-feeding *Eriocrania*. Habits and life cycle similar to those of *E. sangii*.
■ vc10 Fattingpark Copse, many mines with larvae on *Betula pendula*, 4.5.94 (DTB).
■ vc12 Wildhern, 10.4.97; Fleet Pond, 21.4.98, adults beaten and swept from birch (DGG); Pamber, 1994 (GJD); Bartley Heath NR; Bramley Frith Wood NR (AHD).

Hepialidae (5)

The Swift moths. The five British species have traditionally been included among the Macrolepidoptera, although they are a very primitive group with a type of wing-coupling found in no other family. The moths are nocturnal, though some species are on the wing by early dusk. The larvae are subterranean, feeding on roots.

0014 *Hepialus humuli* (Linnaeus, 1758)
Ghost Moth

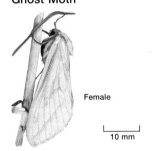

Female

10 mm

Widespread but local. The males have "leks" in grassy places on downland and in meadows where they fly in numbers at dusk, and the females wander, presumably on egg-laying missions, and come occasionally to light. Larva polyphagous in root systems of many herbaceous plants. Moth in June–July.
■ vc12 Winnall Moors NR (DHS).

0015 *Triodia sylvina* (Linnaeus, 1761)
Orange Swift
Common in woodlands where bracken *Pteridium aquilinum* grows. Larva in rhizomes of bracken and other root-systems. Moth in July and August.

0016 *Phymatopus hecta* (Linnaeus, 1758)
Gold Swift
Locally common amongst bracken. The males sometimes swarm just before dusk over grassy places adjacent to stands of foodplant. Larva in rhizomes of bracken. Moth in June.

0017 *Hepialus lupulinus* (Linnaeus, 1761)
Common Swift
Locally common to abundant. Larva polyphagous in root systems of grasses and many other herbaceous plants. The

moth flies in May and June and is one of the first arrivals in the evening at light.
■ vc12 Winnall Moors NR (DHS).

0018 *Hepialus fusconebulosa* (de Geer, 1778)
Map-winged Swift
Very local amongst bracken. No recent record from the Isle of Wight. In Hampshire, the strongholds are Crab Wood vc11 and Pamber Forest vc12. The larva feeds in rhizomes of bracken and the moth flies at dusk in June and July.
■ vc11 Sloden Inclosure, 10.6.00, six male and one female at m.v. light (DGG).
■ vc12 Selborne, 11.6.97, 27.5 and 15.6.98, 1.6.99 (AEA); Noar Hill, first recorded 14.6.94, 11 in 1995 (AMJ).

Nepticulidae (81)

Larvae of these small species mine the parenchyma of leaves, occasionally in bark. The appearance of the mines is usually diagnostic, and many species have been identified with confidence from the mines alone. A reference collection of

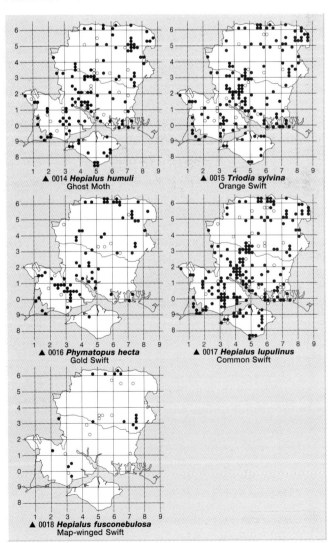

▲ 0014 *Hepialus humuli*
Ghost Moth

▲ 0015 *Triodia sylvina*
Orange Swift

▲ 0016 *Phymatopus hecta*
Gold Swift

▲ 0017 *Hepialus lupulinus*
Common Swift

▲ 0018 *Hepialus fusconebulosa*
Map-winged Swift

leaves containing mines can be made by drying and storing them in plastic envelopes. The moths are sometimes recorded at light or netted during the day.

0019 *Bohemannia quadrimaculella* (Boheman, 1851)
Apparently a rare species for which there is only one recent record, given below. Associated with alder *Alnus glutinosa*.
■ vc12 Farnborough, 11.8.97, det. JRL (RWP). **New vc record**.

0033 *Bohemannia auriciliella* (de Joannis, 1908)
The only record is that detailed in Goater (1992), from Southampton, 11.7.37.

0040 *Bohemannia pulverosella* (Stainton, 1849)
Scattered records from all three vice-counties are given by Goater (1974, 1992). Mines on apple *Malus* spp.
■ vc10 Parkhurst Forest, 19.9.97, a few vacated mines on *M. sylvestris*; Newtown, 18.9.97, a few vacated mines (AME, JRL).
■ vc11 Roydon Woods, 3.10.98, old vacated mines (RJD, JRL); Botley Wood, 20.9.92, long-vacated mines on *M. sylvestris* (JRL, PHS); Portsdown, 3.5.93, one; Hookheath Meadows NR, Southwick, 14.7.96, one mine; The Moors NR, Bishops Waltham, 18.10.96, one vacated mine; Swanwick, 14.6.97, one tenanted mine (JRL).
■ vc12 Wildhern, nr Andover, 6.10.96, 28.9.97, mines on cultivated *Malus* (DGG); Pamber, 1994 (GJD).

0020 *Etainia decentella* (Herrich-Schäffer, 1855)
Recorded from Bournemouth, 1957 (Goater, 1974), Winchester and Southsea (Goater, 1992), all in vc11. Most specimens have been taken at light, but one mine was reported from Winchester, in a sycamore "key", by DHS in 1977.
■ vc11 Fareham, 1.7.94, 11.8.98, singles at m.v. light (RJD); Milton Common, Southsea, 12.8.99, one at m.v. light, det. JRL (IRT).

0021 *Etainia sericopeza* (Zeller, 1839)
Very little is known of this species in Britain, the larva of which in restricted to Norway maple *Acer platanoides*. Genuine Hampshire records are given in Goater (1992) for Winchester vc11 and Itchen Valley vc12.
■ vc11 Southsea, 4.8.96, one at m.v.light, genitalia det. 2nd vc record (JRL).

0022 *Etainia louisella* (Sircom, 1849)
= *sphendamni* (Hering, 1937)
Recorded from St Helens, Isle of Wight, in 1973 and 1987 (Goater, 1974, 1992). Mines on field maple *Acer campestre*.
■ vc12 Wildhern, nr Andover, 6.10.96, mines; adult to actinic light on 20.6.98 (DGG); Magdalen Hill Down, 30.8.00, one larval mine (PAB). **New vc record**.

0023 *Ectoedemia argyropeza* (Zeller, 1839)
The few records, from all three vice-counties, are set out in Goater (1974, 1992). There has been only one recent record. Mines on aspen *Populus tremula*.

■ vc11 Wickham Common, 31.5.99, a female amongst aspen, genitalia det. (RJD).

0025 *Ectoedemia intimella* (Zeller, 1848)
Mines, from which moths have been bred, have been recorded in October and November from all three vice-counties (Goater, 1992). Associated with sallows and willows, chiefly goat willow *Salix caprea*.
■ vc11 Roydon Wood, 6.10.99, several mines (BE); Horsebridge, 11.10.90, mines common on *Salix caprea*, three bred (RJBH); Lower Titchfield Haven, NR, 21.10.96, a few tenanted mines on *S. cinerea*; Farlington Marshes NR, 14.9.93, tenanted mines on *S. fragilis*; Havant Thicket, 10.11.92, many tenanted mines on fallen leaves of *S. caprea* (JRL).

0026 *Ectoedemia agrimoniae* (Frey, 1858)
Records from the Isle of Wight and S Hants are given in Goater (1974, 1992). Unrecorded from N Hants. The larva mines leaves of agrimony *Agrimonia eupatoria*.

0027 *Ectoedemia spinosella* (de Joannis, 1908)
Recorded from Christchurch, S Hants in Goater (1974) and from Ventnor, Isle of Wight in Goater (1992). These are the only records. The larva mines the leaves of blackthorn *Prunus spinosa*.

0028 *Ectoedemia angulifasciella* (Stainton, 1849)
Mines have been reported on rose *Rosa* spp. in late autumn in all three vice-counties (Goater, 1992).
■ vc10 Cowes, 6.11.95, mines with larvae; Nunneys Wood, 17.11.97, empty mine (DTB).
■ vc11 Merrietown Heath, 18.10.93, two mines (PHS); Roydon Woods, 3.10.98, several early mines (RJD, JRL); Pennington, 8.11.93, a few vacated mines; Holbury, 23.10.00, mines (JEC); Hursley Park, 1.11.98, mines (PAB); Curbridge (RJD); Hookheath Meadows NR, Southwick, 17.10.92, many tenanted mines; West Meon, 8.10.96, several tenanted mines; Stubbington, 21.10.96, several tenanted mines; Fareham, 17.9.97, one tenanted mine (JRL, *et al.*); Waterlooville, 1996–1999 (RJM).
■ vc12 Isle of Wight Woods, Porton Down, 3.10.94, one tenanted mine (RJBH, JRL); Wildhern, nr Andover, 27.10.96, 28.9.97, mines; Harewood Forest, 26.10.97, mines; Fleet Pond LNR, 7.10.97, mines (DGG); Bramdean Common, 8.10.96, several tenanted mines (AME, JRL, IRT); Ashford Hangers NR, 18.10.93, a few tenanted mines (JRL).

0029 *Ectoedemia atricollis* (Stainton, 1857)
Mines common on apple, hawthorn and pear throughout the three vice-counties (JRL).

0030 *Ectoedemia arcuatella* (Herrich-Schäffer, 1855)
Single records from each of the mainland vice-counties are given in Goater (1974). There have been none since.

0031 *Ectoedemia rubivora* (Wocke, 1860)
Local in the mainland vice-counties, the mines on dewberry

Rubus caesius (Goater, 1974, 1992). Unrecorded from the Isle of Wight.
■ vc12 Noar Hill, 13.10.96, mines (GJD).

0032 *Ectoedemia erythrogenella* (de Joannis, 1907)
Recorded from vc's 10 and 11 (Goater, 1992) but so far not from N Hants. It appears to be a strictly coastal species, the larva mining leaves of bramble (Emmet *in* Heath, 1976).
■ vc11 Hamble Common, 3.11.99, mines (PAB); Titchfield Haven, 26.12.77, vacated mines; Portchester Castle, 13.11.90, mines; Fareham, 17.9.97, several tenanted mines (RJD); Great Salterns NR, Portsmouth; Portsdown, 19.4.92, mines; Hilsea, 17.1.92, many tenanted early mines; Havant Thicket, 9.5.00, one mine, the only inland record to hand (BE, JRL, IRT); Hayling Island, 19.3.93 a few mines with larvae (JRL).

0034 *Ectoedemia occultella* (Linnaeus, 1767)
= *argentipedella* (Zeller, 1839)
Mines on birch *Betula* spp., sometimes abundant, in all three vice-counties (JRL).

0035 *Ectoedemia minimella* (Zetterstedt, 1839)
Scattered records of mines on birch *Betula* spp. in September and October from all three vice-counties (Goater, 1992).
■ vc10 Fort Victoria Country Park; Firestone Copse (JMC).
■ vc11 Merrietown Heath, 18.10.93, two tenanted mines (PHS); Mudeford Wood North, 17.9.99, mines on *Betula pubescens* (PAB); Upper Hamble Country Park, 7.10.96, one tenanted mine on *B. pubescens* (AME, AMD, JRL); West Walk, mines; Rowner Wild Grounds, mines (RJD).
■ vc12 Bartley Heath NR, 22.5.99, one det. DGG (AHD); Yateley, 23.9.94, a few tenanted mines (AMD, JRL).

0036 *Ectoedemia quinquella* (Bedell, 1848)
Scattered records of mines on oak *Quercus* spp. from the mainland vice-counties but not, so far, from the Isle of Wight (Goater, 1992).
■ vc11 Merrietown Heath, 16.11.93, several tenanted mines (PHS); Pennington, 8.11.93, several tenanted mines (JRL); Holbury, 23.10.00, mines (JEC); Winchester, mines common on oak in garden, several bred 1991 (RJBH); Riverside Park, Swaythling, 26.10.99, egg and mines seen (PAB); Stubbington, 21.10.96, several tenanted mines (JRL, IRT); Curbridge, mines (RJD).
■ vc12 Wildhern, 26.11.97, mines (DGG).

0037 *Ectoedemia albifasciella* (Heinemann, 1871)
Mines on oak *Quercus* spp. in September and October. Hitherto, only one old record from the Isle of Wight (Goater, 1974).
■ vc10 Parkhurst Forest, 18.9.97, many mines, some with larvae; Newtown, 18.9.97, several tenanted mines (AME, JRL); Shalfleet, 10.9.97, mines (DTB).
■ vc11 Merrietown Heath, 18.10.93, a few vacated mincs (PHS); Roydon Woods, 3.10.98 (RJD, JRL); Chessel Bay, Southampton, 6.10.99, mines; Botany Bay, Sholing,

5.10.99, mines; Stoke Park Wood, 19.10.99, mines; Royal Victoria Country Park, 2000, mines; Holly Hill Park, Warsash, 16.9.00, mines (PAB); Marchwood, 8.9.98, several vacated mines; Crab Wood, 20.9.97, a few tenanted mines; Upper Hamble Country Park, 7.10.96, many vacated mines on *Q. robur*; Bursledon, 8.9.98, several vacated mines; Purbrook, 28.9.98, a few vacated mines; Lower Titchfield Haven, NR, 21.10.96, several vacated mines; Fareham, 17.9.97, many vacated mines; West Meon, 8.10.96, many vacated mines (JRL, *et al.*); Hookheath Meadows, 1999 (RJD).
■ vc12 Wildhern, nr Andover, 18.10.97, mines; Harewood Forest, 26.10.97, mines (DGG); Pamber, 1994 (GJD); Yateley, 23.9.94, many tenanted mines; Bramdean Common, 8.10.96, many vacated mines (AME, JRL, IRT).

0038 *Ectoedemia subbimaculella* (Haworth, 1828)
Mines abundant on oak *Quercus* spp. throughout the three vice-counties (JRL).

0039 *Ectoedemia heringi* (Toll, 1934)
Mines on oak *Quercus* spp. in autumn. Very few records are given by Goater (1974, 1992).
■ vc11 Roydon Woods, 10.7.96 (PRD, JRL); Holbury, 23.10.00, mines (JEC); Hookheath Common NR, Southwick, 17.10.92, one tenanted mine; West Meon, 8.10.96, one tenanted mine; Stubbington, 21.10.96, a few tenanted mines (JRL *et al.*); Milton Common, Southsea, occupied mines (IRT); Havant Thicket, 10.11.96, a few tenanted mines on fallen oak leaves (JRL).
■ vc12 Wildhern, 26.11.97, mines (DGG).

0041 *Ectoedemia atrifrontella* (Stainton, 1851)
First recorded in Hampshire in 1976 (Goater, 1983), and subsequently at Ashurst and Botley Wood (Goater, 1992). Larva mines in young, green bark of oak *Quercus* spp.
■ vc10 Newtown Ranges, mines, 18.9.77 (AME); Lock's Copse, mines, 18.9.77 (ECP-C). **New vc record.**
■ vc11 Upper Pennington, 12.10.99, old larval mines; Hamble Common, 3.11.99, mines (PAB); West Walk, 29.1.94, several mines in bark of oak saplings (RJH, JRL); Creech Wood, Denmead, 8.2.97, several mines; Wickham Common, 8.4.00, mines (RJD, JRL, IRT).
■ vc12 Yateley Common, 26.3.94, one mine in bark of oak sapling, det. JRL (AMD).

0042 *Fomoria septembrella* (Stainton, 1849)
Local in all three vice-counties, larvae mining St John's-wort *Hypericum* spp. most often *H. perforatum*, but also recorded from *H. androsaemum* and *H. pulchrum* (Goater, 1974).
■ vc10 Newtown, 18.9.97, a few tenanted mines on *Hypericum* spp. (AME, JRL); Osborne, 16.9.95, mines; Bonchurch, 9.9.98, mines (DTB).
■ vc11 Roydon Wood, 6.10.99, several mines (BE); Kings Copse Inclosure, 24.10.00, mines (JEC); Crab Wood, 20.9.97, tenanted mines on *Hypericum* spp.; Otterbourne, 4.1.99, mines; Chessel Bay, Southampton, 6.10.99, mines; Woolston, 4.12.98, old mines; Itchen Valley Country Park, 11.10.99, mines; Holly Hill Park, Warsash, 16.9.00,

mines (PAB); Catisfield, occasional on evergreen cultivated *Hypericum*; Portsdown, on *H. perforatum* (RJD); Beacon Hill NNR, 20.9.96, mine on *H. perforatum* (AMD); West Meon, 8.10.96, a few tenanted mines; Alver Valley NR, Gosport, 22.9.97, one mine on *H. perforatum*; Clanfield, 4.10.97, one mine on *H. perforatum*; Sandy Point NR, Hayling Island, 17.10.96, one mine (JRL, *et al.*).

■ vc12 Eelmoor Marsh SSSI, 19.10.97, mines on *H. perforatum*; Harewood Forest, 26.10.97, mines on *H. perforatum*; Fleet Pond LNR, 7.10.97, mines on *H. perforatum* (DGG); Bramdean Common, 8.10.96, many mines on *Hypericum* sp. (AME, JRL, IRT); Ashford Hangers NR, 18.10.93, a few tenanted mines on *H. androsaemum* (JRL *et al.*).

0044 *Trifurcula headleyella* (Stainton, 1854)

First reported for the area in Goater (1983) and now known very sparingly from all three vice-counties (Goater, 1992). There have been no more recent records, but the following old one has come to hand. Larva mines the leaves of self-heal *Prunella vulgaris*.

■ vc11 Oxenbourne Down, 22.5.74, one on wild basil *Clinopodium vulgare* (RJD).

0046 *Trifurcula immundella* (Zeller, 1839)

Old records from Bournemouth, Christchurch, Bucklers Hard and Baddesley Great Covert, all in vc11, are given by Goater (1974); since then, it has been found commonly in Botley Wood vc11 and from Leckford and Itchen Valley, vc12, but none of the old records have been confirmed (Goater, 1992). The larva mines the young twigs of broom *Cytisus scoparius*.

■ vc12 Bramdean Common, 8.10.96, one tenanted mine (JRL *et al.*); Yateley, 23.9.93, a few tenanted mines (AMD, JRL).

0047 *Trifurcula beirnei* Puplesis, 1984

■ vc11 Southampton, 20.8.1935 by Wm Fassnidge (see Goater, 1992); Southsea, 20.8.00 (JRL) appears to be the first British specimen recorded since that date, exactly 65 years later.

0048 *Trifurcula cryptella* (Stainton, 1856)

Old records for Bournemouth and Lymington vc11 are given in Goater (1974).

0049 *Trifurcula eurema* (Tutt, 1899)

The very few records, from all three vice-counties, are given in Goater (1974, 1992). The larva mines the leaves of bird's-foot-trefoil *Lotus corniculatus*.

0050 *Stigmella aurella* (Fabricius, 1775)

Common to abundant throughout all three vice-counties (JRL). The larva makes long, sinuous mines in leaves of bramble. Probably bivoltine (see Emmet *in* Heath, 1976).

(0051) *Stigmella aurella* (Fabricius, 1775) f. *nitens* Fologne, 1862
= *S. fragariella* (Heinemann, 1862)

Now considered to be conspecific with *S. aurella*; larvae

mine leaves of herbaceous Rosaceae, including agrimony *Agrimonia eupatoria*, wild strawberry *Fragaria vesca*, wood avens *Geum urbanum* and tormentil *Potentilla erecta*.

■ vc10 Alverstone (JMC); Shalfleet, 14.10.95, mines on *Geum* (DTB).

■ vc11 Peartree Green, Southampton, 9.10.99, mines on *Agrimonia* (PAB).

■ vc12 Wildhern, nr Andover, 21.8.97, mines on *Fragaria vesca* (DGG).

0053 *Stigmella splendidissimella* (Herrich-Schäffer, 1855)
= *dulcella* Heinemann, 1862

Mines on bramble *Rubus fruticosus* agg. and wood avens *Geum urbanum*. Probably bivoltine (Emmet *in* Heath, 1976). The few records given by Goater (1974, 1992) are supplemented as follows below.

■ vc10 Parkhurst Forest, 18.9.97, one vacated mine on bramble; Newtown, 5.9.97, mines on *Rubus* spp. (DTB), 18.9.97, one vacated mine on *G. urbanum* (AME, JRL).

■ vc11 Roydon Woods, 3.10.98, one vacated mine on *G. urbanum* (RJD, JRL); Crab Wood, 20.9.97, vacated mines on *R. caesius* (JRL, *et al.*); Mudeford Wood North, 27.8.00, mines on *R. idaeus*; Southampton Common, 14.9.99, mines on *R. idaeus*; Sholing, 5.10.99, mines; Weston Common, 5.10.99, and other localities in and around Southampton, mines; Royal Victoria Country Park, 2000, mines on *Rubus* spp.; Hamble Common, 3.11.99, mines on *R. idaeus*. (PAB); Wickham Common, 9.10.98, mines very locally common in *R. caesius* (RJD); Warsash, 20.5.94, one; Bursledon, 8.9.98, several vacated mines on *R. idaeus*; West Meon, 8.10.96, a few vacated mines on *R. idaeus*; Alver Valley NR, Gosport, 22.9.97, one vacated mine on *R. idaeus*; Clanfield, 4.10.97, a few vacated mines on *G. urbanum* and bramble (JRL *et al.*).

■ vc12 Wildhern, nr Andover, 28.9.96, 2.10.97, mines on *R. caesius*; Tangley, 2.10.97, mines on *R. caesius*; Harewood Forest, 26.10.97, mines on *R. caesius*; Fleet Pond LNR, 7.10.97, mines on *Rubus* spp., not *R. caesius*; Noar Hill, 13.10.96, mines on *R. caesius* (DGG); Pamber, 1994 (GJD).

0055 *Stigmella aeneofasciella* (Herrich-Schäffer, 1855)

The only records received since Goater (1974) are given below.

■ vc12 Bramdean Common, 8.10.96, two tenanted mines on agrimony *Agrimonia eupatoria* (AME, JRL, IRT); Bentley Station Meadow, mines on tormentil *Potentilla erecta*, 28.8 and 10.10.98 (DGG).

0057 *Stigmella filipendulae* (Wocke, 1871)

Recorded only from Teg Down, Winchester, vc11 up to 1991, Leckford, up to 1986 and Chilbolton, 1973, both vc12. Mines on dropwort *Filipendula vulgaris* on chalk downland. Bivoltine.

0058 *Stigmella ulmariae* (Wocke, 1879)

Recorded from a few localities in N Hants (Goater, 1974, 1992). The record from Tennyson Down vc10 is considered to be questionable. Mines on meadowsweet

Filipendula ulmaria. Bivoltine (Emmet *in* Heath, 1976).

0059 *Stigmella poterii* (Stainton, 1857)
The only records of this species are given in Goater (1974, 1992). It inhabits downland on which the larva mines the leaves of salad burnet *Sanguisorba minor.* Bivoltine (Emmet *in* Heath, 1976).
    f. *serrella* Stainton, 1866
Recorded from Burley vc11 and Hook Common vc12 in Goater (1974). No record since. Larva mines the leaves of tormentil *Potentilla erecta.*

0063 *Stigmella lemniscella* (Zeller, 1839)
    = *marginicolella* (Stainton, 1853)
Mines common on elm *Ulmus procera,* rarely on *U. glabra,* in all three vice-counties (JRL). Bivoltine, larvae in July and in the autumn.
■ vc10 Osborne, 16.9.95, mines (DTB).

0064 *Stigmella continuella* (Stainton, 1856)
Widespread amongst birch *Betula* spp. in the three vice-counties, although most records are of vacated mines. Partially bivoltine (see Emmet *in* Heath, 1976).
■ vc11 Norleywood, 2.9.94, a few vacated (JRL); Rowner Wild Grounds, mines (RJD); Browndown, 18.6.93, one vacated mine; Sandy Point NR, Hayling Island, 3.11.92, a few vacated mines (JRL).
■ vc12 Eelmoor Marsh SSSI, 19.10.97, mines; Fleet Pond LNR, 7.10.97, mines (DGG); Yateley, 23.9.94, a few vacated mines (AMD, JRL).

0065 *Stigmella speciosa* (Frey, 1858)
Very local (Goater, 1974, 1992). Mines occur in leaves of sycamore in July and August, with a small second generation in the autumn. (Emmet *in* Heath, 1976).
■ vc11 Mudeford Wood North, 17.9.99, mines; Chessel Bay, Sholing and Peartree Green, Southampton, 5.10 to 6.10.99, mines; Telegraph Woods, West End, 25.9.99, mines; Royal Victoria Country Park, 23.8.00, mines (PAB); Crab Wood, 20.9.97, vacated mine (JRL *et al.*).
■ vc12 Winchester, 1975 (Goater, 1992); Bentley Station Meadow, 28.8.98, mines (DGG).

0066 *Stigmella sorbi* (Stainton, 1861)
A very few records, all from S Hants (Goater 1974, 1992). Mines in June on rowan *Sorbus aucuparia.*

0067 *Stigmella plagicolella* (Stainton, 1854)
Common in all three vice-counties wherever blackthorn occurs (JRL). Bivoltine; larvae in July and in the autumn (Emmet *in* Heath, 1976).
■ vc8 Martin Down, 24.8.90 (MFVC and S. Nash).

0068 *Stigmella salicis* (Stainton, 1854)
    = *auritella* (Skala, 1939)
Mines common on rough-leaved sallows *Salix* spp. throughout the three vice-counties (JRL). Bivoltine, larvae in summer and autumn generations.

■ vc10 Hurst Stake, N of Newport, 9.10.96, mines on *S. cinerea* (DTB). First recent record for Isle of Wight.

0070 *Stigmella obliquella* (Heinemann, 1862)
The very few records for the area are given in Goater (1974, 1992) – single localities on the Isle of Wight and in S Hants, two localities in N Hants. Mines on various species of sallow and willow *Salix* spp. in summer and as a second generation in autumn.
■ vc10 Alverstone, 8.7.00, mine with larva on *S. fragilis* (DTB).
■ vc11 Mudeford Wood North, 17.9.99, mines on crack willow *S. fragilis* (PAB); Hookheath Meadows, 21.8.99, vacated mine on *S. fragilis,* det. JRL (RJD).

0072 *Stigmella myrtillella* (Stainton, 1857)
Old records for Burley and Beaulieu vc11 and Woolmer Forest vc12 are given in Goater (1974). The larva mines leaves of bilberry *Vaccinium myrtillus,* in summer and autumn, in two generations (Emmet *in* Heath, 1976).

0073 *Stigmella trimaculella* (Haworth, 1828)
No recent record from the Isle of Wight. Mines on poplars in summer and autumn.
■ vc11 Stanpit Marsh, 27.8.00, mines; Riverside Park, Southampton, 26.10.99, mines on Lombardy poplar *Populus nigra* 'italica' (PAB); Lower Titchfield Haven NR, 21.10.96, a few vacated mines; Fareham, 17.9.97, a few vacated mines; Portsmouth, 26.7.92, vacated mines on *Populus* × *canadensis*; Great Salterns NR, Portsmouth; Hilsea Lines, 11.9.90, vacated mines (RJD); Gutner Point NR, Hayling Island, 11.9.96, vacated mines on *P. nigra* var. *italica* (JRL *et al.*); Milton Common, Southsea, 1994, mines (IRT).
■ vc12 Overton Mill, mines on *Populus* spp., 1996 (DGG).

0074 *Stigmella assimilella* (Zeller, 1848)
No record from either the Isle of Wight or N Hants since 1973. Mines on poplars between July and November, probably in one protracted generation (Emmet *in* Heath, 1976).
■ vc11 Riverside Park, Southampton, 26.10.99, mines on white poplar *P. alba* (PAB); Fareham, 10.10.97, two vacated mines on *P. canescens* (DJLA, JRL).

0075 *Stigmella floslactella* (Haworth, 1828)
Fairly widespread in all three vice-counties. Mines on hazel and hornbeam, in summer and between September and November.
■ vc10 Borthwood (JMC); Newtown, 18.9.97, several vacated mines; Parkhurst Forest, 18.9.97, a few vacated mines on hazel (AME, JRL); Parkhurst Forest, Cowes, Whitefield Wood, 1995, mines found (DTB).
■ vc11 Holbury, 23.10.00, mines (JEC); Lower Test Marshes NR, 1996; Crab Wood, 20.9.97, vacated mines; Lordswood, 26.10.99, mines; Peartree Green, Southampton, 9.10.99, mines on hornbeam; Royal Victoria Country Park, 23.8.00, mines (PAB); Hookheath Meadows NR, Southwick, 12.6.92, a few tenanted mines; Hen Wood, East Meon, 10.10.94, a few vacated mines;

Alver Valley NR, Gosport, 22.9.97, one vacated mine (JRL, *et al.*); Titchfield Haven, mines on hazel; Havant Thicket, mine on hornbeam (RJD).
■ vc12 Harewood Forest, 26.10.97, mines on hazel; Oakley, 18.6.99; Fleet Pond LNR, 7.10.97, mines on hazel (DGG), 23.9.00, mines; Church Crookham, 8.10.00, mines (RE); Pamber, 1994 (GJD); Pamber Forest Farm, 18.10.00, a few empty mines (AHD).

0077 *Stigmella tityrella* (Stainton, 1854)
Mines common on beech throughout the three vice-counties (JRL). Bivoltine.

0078 *Stigmella incognitella* (Herrich-Schäffer, 1855)
= *pomella* (Vaughan, 1858)
Recorded from all three vice-counties (Goater, 1974, 1992) but sparsely. Mines on apple *Malus* spp. in summer and autumn, in two generations.
■ vc11 Winchester, mines common in garden, two bred from mines coll. 28.10.90 (RJBH); Botley Wood, mines; Wickham Common, 18.7.98, vacated mine; Rowner Wild Grounds, mines (RJD).
■ vc12 Wildhern, nr Andover, 21.7.96, mines on cultivated *Malus* (DGG).

0079 *Stigmella perpygmaeella* (Doubleday, 1859)
Mines common to abundant on hawthorn throughout the three vice-counties (JRL). Larvae in July and in the autumn, in two generations.

0080 *Stigmella ulmivora* (Fologne, 1860)
Very few records are given by Goater (1974, 1992), so all recent ones are included below. Mines on elm *Ulmus* spp. in autumn.
■ vc10 Firestone Copse (JMC); Parkhurst Forest, Billingham, Carisbrooke, 19.7.95, mines (DTB).
■ vc11 Mudeford Wood North, 17.9.99, mines; Peartree Green, Southampton, 9.10.99, mines (PAB); Catisfield, 24.4.90, vacated mines; Hilsea Lines, 12.9.90, vacated mine (RJD); Lower Titchfield Haven NR, 21.10.96, a few vacated mines on; Fareham, 17.9.97, many vacated mines; Alver Valley NR, Gosport, 22.9.97, several tenanted mines; Gutner Point NR, Hayling Island, 6.10.96, a few tenanted mines (JRL *et al.*); Great Salterns NR, Portsmouth (JRL); Milton Common, Southsea, 1994, mines (IRT).
■ vc12 Wildhern, nr Andover, 1.9.96, 12.10.97, mines on *U. glabra*, 3.7.98, by day (DGG); Ashford Hangers NR, 18.10.93, several vacated mines on *U. glabra* (JRL).

0081 *Stigmella hemargyrella* (Kollar, 1832)
Local in all three vice-counties. Mines on beech, in two generations, summer and autumn.
■ vc10 Carisbrooke, 19.7.95, mines (DTB); Parkhurst Forest, 18.9.97, a few vacated mines (AME, JRL).
■ vc11 Roydon Woods, 3.10.98, vacated and tenanted mines (RJD, JRL); Matley Heath, 11.10.98, mines (DGG); Ashurst, 12.7.93, a few vacated mines; Holbury, 23.10.00, mines (JEC); Parnholt Wood, 1.5.98, a few; Crab Wood, 20.9.97, vacated mine; Fareham, 14.8.97, a few vacated mines; Clanfield, 4.10.97, several vacated

mines; West Meon, 8.10.96, a few vacated mines (JRL, *et al.*); Royal Victoria Country Park, 23.8.00, mines (PAB); Botley Wood, mines; Wickham Common, 9.10.98, vacated mines common (RJD).
■ vc12 Wildhern, nr Andover, 26.9.97, mines; Eelmoor Marsh SSSI, 19.10.97; Tangley, 2.10.97, mines; Harewood Forest, 26.10.97, mines; Fleet Pond LNR, 7.10.97, mines (DGG); Pamber, 1994 (GJD); Bramdean Common, 8.10.96, a few vacated mines; Yateley, 23.9.94, a few vacated mines (JRL *et al.*); Wick Hill Hanger, 5.7.99, mines (PAB).

0083 *Stigmella atricapitella* (Haworth, 1828)
[The record in Goater (1992) of mines on sweet chestnut *Castanea sativa* at Wickham vc11, 26.7.86 from which moths were bred is erroneous: on dissection, they proved to be *S. samiatella* (Zeller) (JRL).] Other records given there are correct. All recent records are included below. Mines on oak *Quercus* spp. in June and July and in autumn.
■ vc10 Locksgreen, 18.9.77, vacated mine (ECP-C); Godshill, 17.8.96, vacated mines on *Q. robur*; Gurnard, 26.10.96, mines, all conf. JRL (DTB); Newtown, 18.9.97, a few vacated mines (AME, JRL). **New vc record.**
■ vc11 Stanpit Marsh, 27.8.00, mines (PAB); Merrietown Heath, 18.10.93, a few tenanted mines (PHS); Pennington, 8.11.93, a few tenanted mines; Roydon Woods, 3.10.98, vacated mines (RJD, JRL); Royal Victoria Country Park, 23.8.00, mines (PAB); Crab Wood, Sparsholt, 20.9.97, vacated mines; Bursledon, 8.9.98, a few vacated mines; Purbrook, 28.9.98, a few vacated mines; Hamble Country Park, 7.10.96, many vacated mines; Lower Titchfield Haven NR, 21.10.96, a few vacated mines; Clanfield, 4.10.97, a few vacated mines; Fareham, 17.9.97, a few vacated mines; West Meon, 8.10.96, several vacated mines; Havant Thicket, 10.11.92, a few tenanted mines (JRL, *et al.*).
■ vc12 Wildhern, nr Andover, 28.9.96, 26.9.97, mines; Anton Lakes, Andover, 19.8.98; St John's Copse, Oakley, 5.8.98, mines; Eelmoor Marsh SSSI, 19.10.97; Harewood Forest, 26.10.97, mines; Fleet Pond LNR, 7.10.97, mines (DGG); Chilbolton, 22.6.92, vacated mine (JRL, DHS); Pamber, 1994 (GJD); Winchfield Hurst, 15.10.00, mines on *Quercus* spp., det. J. Robbins (RE); Bramdean Common, 8.10.96, several vacated mines; Shortheath Common, 20.8.98, a few vacated mines; Yateley, 23.9.94, a few vacated mines (JRL *et al.*).

0084 *Stigmella ruficapitella* (Haworth, 1828)
The first confirmed records of this species in our area were given by Goater (1983). All subsequent records are included below. This is another species the larva of which mines the leaves of oak *Quercus* spp. Bivoltine, larvae in summer and autumn, moths in late spring and again in late summer.
■ vc10 Gurnard, Whitecroft, 1995, mines; Godshill, 17.8.96, mine, conf. JRL; Ricket's Hill, 14.11.99, mines; Priory Bay, 4.7.99, mines (JMC); Parkhurst Forest, 18.9.97, a few vacated mines (AME, JRL); Gurnard, 26.10.96, mine (DTB).
■ vc11 Roydon Woods, 3.10.98, a few vacated mines (RJD, JRL); Matley Heath, 11.10.98, mines (DGG);

Marchwood, 8.9.98, a few vacated mines; Crab Wood, 20.9.97, vacated mines (JRL, *et al.*); Royal Victoria Country Park, 23.8.00, mines (PAB); Curbridge; Chilling Copse, 1996, mines; Warsash shore, 7.10.98, one mine; Wickham Common, 1998 (RJD); Hookheath Meadows NR, Southwick, 4.8.92, vacated mines; Upper Hamble Country Park, 7.10.96, many vacated mines; West Meon, 8.10.96, several vacated mines; Lower Titchfield Haven NR, 21.10.96, a few tenanted mines; Clanfield, 4.10.97, several vacated mines; Fareham, 17.9.97, a few vacated mines; Great Salterns NR, Portsmouth (JRL *et al.*).

■ vc12 Chilbolton, 22.6.92, vacated mines (JRL, DHS); Wildhern, nr Andover, 20.9.97, mines; Eelmoor Marsh SSSI, 19.10.97, mines; Tangley, 2.10.97, mines; Harewood Forest, 26.10.97, mines; Fleet Pond LNR, 7.10.97, mines (DGG); Pamber, 1994 (GJD); Bramdean Common, 8.10.96, several tenanted mines; Yateley, 23.9.94, several tenanted mines (JRL *et al.*).

0085 *Stigmella suberivora* (Stainton, 1869)
Locally abundant in coastal localities in the Isle of Wight and S Hants, the mines on evergreen oak *Quercus ilex*. Bivoltine, moths in May and September, and larvae in late summer and through the winter months.
■ vc10 Cowes, 13.1.96, empty mines on *Quercus × turneri* (DTB).
■ vc11 Pennington, 8.11.93, a few vacated mines on *Q. ilex*; Browndown, 18.6.93, several vacated mines (JRL); Royal Victoria Country Park, 23.8.00, mines (PAB); Botany Bay, Sholing, 5.10.99, mines (PAB); Gilkicker Point, 1999 (RJD).

0086 *Stigmella roborella* (Johansson, 1971)
The first records for the area are given in Goater (1983), and all subsequent ones are included below. Mines on oak *Quercus* spp. in two generations.
■ vc10 Dodnor, 15.10.96, empty mine on *Q. robur*, conf. JRL (DTB).
■ vc11 Ashurst, 12.7.93, a few tenanted mines (JRL); Bitterne Park, Southampton, 24.10.99, mines; Botany Bay, Sholing, 5.10.99, mines; Weston Common, 5.10.99, mines Royal Victoria Country Park, 23.8.00, mines (PAB); Hookheath Meadows NR, Southwick, 17.10.92, a few mines; Lower Titchfield Haven NR, 21.10.96, a few tenanted mines; Purbrook, 28.9.98, one vacated mine; Browndown, 7.11.94, several tenanted mines, moths bred; Great Salterns NR, Portsmouth; Sandy Point NR, Hayling Island, 3.11.92, many tenanted mines (JRL).
■ vc12 Wildhern, nr Andover, 25.8.96, 17.8.97, mines; St John's Copse, Oakley, 5.8.98, mines; Eelmoor Marsh SSSI, 24.8.97, mines; Tangley, 2.10.97, mines; Fleet Pond LNR, 7.10.97, mines (DGG); nr Fleet Station, 15.10.00, mines on *Quercus*, det. J. Robbins (RE). **New vc record.**

0087 *Stigmella svenssoni* (Johansson, 1971)
First recorded from Botley Wood in 1985 (Goater, 1992). The few other records are given below. Mines on oak *Quercus* spp.
■ vc11 Anses Wood, mines, 22.8.98; Ladycross Inclosure, mines, 23.9.00 (DGG); Fareham, 6.6.95, one at m.v.

light, genitalia det. (RJD); Upper Hamble Country Park, 7.10.96, two vacated mines; Southsea, 28.7.92, one at m.v. light, genitalia det.; Havant Thicket, 7.10.94, one vacated mine (JRL *et al.*).
■ vc12 Redenham, nr Andover, mines, 1998; Wildhern, nr Andover, mines, 16.10.00; Bentley Station Meadow, mines, 10.10.98 (DGG); Shortheath Common, 20.8.98, two tenanted mines (JRL, IRT). **New vc record.**

0088 *Stigmella samiatella* (Zeller, 1839)
■ vc10 Parkhurst Forest, 18.9.97, a few vacated mines on sweet chestnut *Castanea sativa* (AME, SAK-J, JRL). **New vc record.**
■ vc11 Winchester, vacated mines under sweet chestnut in garden, October 1988, submitted to AM Emmet who confirmed their identity; vacated mines each autumn since 1988; one moth bred in 1994 from a tenanted mine coll. 24.9.93 (RJBH); West End, 27.10.99, mines; Netley Common, 25.10.99, mines (PAB); Wickham Common, 9.10.98, one vacated mine (RJD); Wickham, 26.7.86, mines, moth bred and genitalia det. (see under 0083 *S. atricapitella*); Southsea, 25.5.92, one at m.v.light (Langmaid, 1993). **New county record.**
■ vc12 Yateley Common, 15.10.00, mines common on sweet chestnut, three mines with larvae (AMD). **New vc record.**

0089 *Stigmella basiguttella* (Heinemann, 1862)
The meagre records given in Goater (1974, 1992) are supplemented below. Mines on oak *Quercus* spp. in two generations.
■ vc11 Merrietown Heath, 18.10.93, a few vacated mines (PHS); Norleywood, 2.9.94, a few vacated mines; Marchwood, 8.9.98, one vacated mine; Crab Wood, 20.9.97, vacated mine; Curbridge, mines; Upper Hamble Country Park, 7.10.96, several vacated mines; West Meon, 8.10.96, several vacated mines; Lower Titchfield Haven NR, 21.10.96, a few vacated mines; Alver Valley NR, Gosport, 22.9.97, a few vacated mines Fareham, 17.9.97, several vacated mines (JRL *et al.*); Southampton area, October, 1999, mines found in several localities (PAB); Milton Common, Southsea, at light in garden, 1998 (IRT), 29.6.95, one at light, genitalia det.; Havant Thicket, 10.11.92, one tenanted mine; Gutner Point NR, Hayling Island, 6.10.96, a few vacated mines (JRL *et al.*).
■ vc12 Wildhern, nr Andover, 28.9.96, 29.9.97, mines; Eelmoor Marsh SSSI, 19.10.97, mines; Harewood Forest, 26.10.97, mines; Fleet Pond LNR, 7.10.97, mines; Noar Hill, 13.10.96, mines (DGG); Magdalen Hill Down, 20.7.00, mines (PAB); Pamber, 1994 (GJD); Bramdean Common, 8.10.96, several vacated mines; Yateley, 23.9.94, several vacated mines (JRL *et al.*).

0091 *Stigmella minusculella* (Herrich-Schäffer, 1855)
Recorded from Bournemouth in 1943 (Goater, 1974) but not since. The larva mines the leaves of pear *Pyrus* spp.

0092 *Stigmella anomalella* (Goeze, 1783)
Mines common on rose *Rosa* spp. in all three vice-counties (JRL). Bivoltine, larvae in July and October.

■ vc10 Cowes, Hurst Stake, Bembridge, 1995, mines (DTB).

0093 *Stigmella centifoliella* (Zeller, 1848)

The presence of this species in Hampshire was confirmed in 1975 (Goater, 1983), since when it has been found in several places in both the mainland vice-counties. Mines on wild and cultivated roses *Rosa* spp., in two generations.

■ vc10 Parkhurst Forest, 24.11.92, mine on *Rosa* spp. (DTB). **New vc record.**

■ vc11 Marchwood, 8.9.98, a few vacated mines (JRL); Botley Wood, mines (RJD); Lower Titchfield Haven NR, 21.10.96, one vacated mine; Alver Valley NR, Gosport, 29.9.97, a few vacated mines on *R. rugosa* and *Rosa* spp.; Fareham, 10.10.97, a few tenanted mines; Portsmouth, 16.8.92, many mines and cocoons, moths bred; Great Salterns NR, Portsmouth; Gutner Point NR, Hayling Island, 11.9.96, a few vacated mines, and cocoons (JRL *et al.*); Milton Common, Southsea, 1994, mines (IRT). **New vc record.**

■ vc12 Wildhern, nr Andover, 28.9.97, mines; Harewood Forest, 26.10.97, mines; Fleet Pond LNR, 7.10.97, mines (DGG); Bramdean Common, 8.10.96, several vacated mines (AME, JRL).

0095 *Stigmella viscerella* (Stainton, 1853)

Recorded from scattered localities in all three vice-counties. Larva single-brooded on elm *Ulmus* spp., in early autumn.

■ vc10 Newtown, 18.9.97, one vacated mine on *U. procera* (AME, JRL); Parkhurst Forest, Priory Woods, 1995, mines (DTB).

■ vc11 Mudeford Wood North, 17.9.99, mines; Upper Pennington, 12.10.99, mines; several places in Southampton area, autumn 1999, mines; Royal Victoria Country Park, 23.8.00, mines; Hamble Common, 3.11.99, mines (PAB); Fort Brockhurst (RJD); Hookheath Meadows NR, Southwick, 17.10.92, a few vacated mines; Lower Titchfield Haven NR, 21.10.96, a few tenanted mines; Fareham, 10.10.97, several tenanted mines (JRL *et al.*).

■ vc12 Wildhern, nr Andover, 12.10.96, 27.10.97, mines on *U. procera* (DGG).

0097 *Stigmella malella* (Stainton, 1854)

Scattered records from the two mainland vice-counties (Goater 1974, 1992). Larvae mine leaves of apple *Malus* spp. in July and in the autumn.

■ vc10 Yarmouth, mine, 18.9.76 (RJD); Newtown Ranges, 18.9.77 (AME); Lock's Copse, mines, 18.9.77 (ECP-C). **New vc record.**

■ vc11 The Moors NR, Bishops Waltham, 19.10.96, a few vacated mines on *M. sylvestris* (JRL); Royal Victoria Country Park, 23.8.00, mines (PAB); Hamble Common, 1996, mines; Rowner Wild Grounds (RJD).

■ vc12 Wildhern, nr Andover, 12.10.96, 13.10.98, mines on cultivated *Malus* (DGG); Pamber, 1994 (GJD).

0098 *Stigmella catharticella* (Stainton, 1853)

Associated with buckthorn *Rhamnus cathartica*, and therefore found mostly on or near the chalk downs, in the two mainland vice-counties. Unrecorded from the Isle of Wight. In addition to the records given in Goater (1974, 1992) there are the following.

■ vc11 Merrietown Heath, 18.10.93, two tenanted mines on *R. cathartica* (PHS); Corhampton, mines on alder buckthorn *Frangula alnus*; Portsdown, mines on *Rhamnus* (RJD); Upper Hamble Country Park, 7.10.96, a few vacated mines on *Rhamnus*; Hen Wood, East Meon, 10.10.94, a few tenanted mines; Oxenbourne Down NR, 13.8.93, a few vacated mines (JRL *et al.*).

■ vc12 Wildhern, nr Andover, 5.10.96, 29.9.97, mines (DGG); Micheldever, 30.7.99, mines (PAB).

0099 *Stigmella hybnerella* (Hübner, 1796)

Mines common on hawthorn *Crataegus* spp. throughout the three vice-counties (JRL), in early summer and again in early autumn.

■ vc8 Martin Down, 24.8.90 (MFVC and S. Nash).

0100 *Stigmella oxyacanthella* (Stainton, 1854)

Widespread. Mines most commonly on hawthorn *Crataegus* spp but also sometimes on apple *Malus sylvestris*. Single-brooded, the larvae in September and October.

■ vc10 Yarmouth (JMC); Parkhurst Forest, 18.9.97, one vacated mine on hawthorn; Newtown, 18.9.97, one vacated mine (AME, JRL).

■ vc11 Kings Copse Inclosure, 24.10.00, mines (JEC); Roydon Woods, 3.10.98, a few tenanted mines on hawthorn and one on apple; Upper Hamble Country Park, 7.10.96, many tenanted mines on hawthorn; Lower Titchfield Haven NR, 21.10.96, one vacated mine; Gutner Point NR, Hayling Island, 6.10.96, a few tenanted mines (JRL); Royal Victoria Country Park, 23.8.00, mines (PAB); Wickham Common, 7.10.98, one tenanted mine (RJD).

■ vc12 Winnall Moors NR (DHS); Wildhern, nr Andover, 12.10.96, 28.9.97, mines on hawthorn and apple; Harewood Forest, 26.10.97, mines; Fleet Pond LNR, 7.10.97, mines; Noar Hill, 13.10.96, mines (DGG); Pamber, 1994 (GJD); Bramdean Common, 8.10.96, one tenanted mine on hawthorn; Ashford Hangers NR, 18.10.93, a few vacated mines; Yateley, 23.9.94, one vacated mine (JRL *et al.*).

0101 *Stigmella pyri* (Glitz, 1865)

Recorded new to the county from a vacated mine found on pear *Pyrus* at Portsmouth, 27.10.85 (see Goater, 1992). No further record.

0102 *Stigmella aceris* (Frey, 1857)

So far, recorded from a single area near Winchester, where it was first discovered in 1985 (see Goater, 1992). The larva mines the leaves of field maple *Acer campestre*.

■ vc11 Winchester, St James's Lane, mines fairly common; an adult found on a leaf of field maple, 10.9.92, nr Teg Down (RJBH).

0103 *Stigmella nylandriella* (Tengström, 1848)

Recorded from all three vice-counties, where the mines are locally plentiful on rowan *Sorbus aucuparia*. Univoltine, the larvae in July to September.

■ vc10 Hurst Stake, N of Newport, 14.7.95, mines (DTB).

■ vc11 Roydon Woods, 3.10.98, one vacated mine (JRL *et al.*); Botany Bay, Sholing, 5.10.99, mines; Royal Victoria Country Park, 23.8.00, mines (PAB).

■ vc12 Wildhern, nr Andover, 19.7.97, mines; St John's Copse, Oakley, 5.8.98, mines; Fleet Pond LNR, 7.10.97, mines; Eelmoor Marsh, 25.7.98, mines (DGG); Pamber, 1994 (GJD); Shortheath Common, 20.8.98, one vacated mine; Yateley, 23.9.98, one vacated mine (JRL *et al.*).

0107 *Stigmella regiella* (Herrich-Schäffer, 1855)

Mines found on hawthorn, usually sparsely and often empty, in a few localities in mainland Hampshire (Goater 1974, 1992).

■ vc11 Roydon Woods, 3.10.98, vacated and tenanted mines (RJD, JRL); Holbury, 23.10.00, mines (JEC); Botley Wood; Wickham Common, 7.10.98, a few mines (RJD).

■ vc12 Wildhern, nr Andover, 12.10.96, mines; Noar Hill, 13.10.96, mines (DGG).

0108 *Stigmella crataegella* (Klimesch, 1936)

Mines common on hawthorn in all three vice-counties (JRL). Larvae in a single brood from late June to August (Emmet *in* Heath, 1976).

■ vc11 Roydon Woods, 3.10.98, vacated and tenanted mines on hawthorn and apple *Malus sylvestris* (RJD, JRL); Lower Test Marshes NR, 1996 (JRL); Crab Wood, 20.9.97, vacated mines on hawthorn (JRL, *et al.*); Chilling Copse, 1996, mines (RJD); Great Salterns NR, Portsmouth (JRL).

■ vc12 Winnall Moors NR (DHS); Wildhern, nr Andover, 28.9.96, 4.10.97, mines on hawthorn; Harewood Forest, 26.10.97, mines on hawthorn; Anton Lakes, Andover, 19.8.98; Fleet Pond LNR, 7.10.97, mines on hawthorn; Noar Hill, 13.10.96, mines on hawthorn (DGG); Pamber, 1994 (GJD).

0109 *Stigmella prunetorum* (Stainton, 1855)

There has been no acceptable record since the one given in Goater (1974).

0110 *Stigmella betulicola* (Stainton, 1856)

Apparently very local amongst birch *Betula* spp. in the mainland vice-counties.

■ vc11 Roydon Woods, 3.10.98, tenanted mines on *B. pubescens* on heathland (RJD, JRL); Botley Wood; Wickham Common, 7.10.98, mines fairly common on *B. pubescens* seedlings (RJD).

■ vc12 Eelmoor Marsh SSSI, 24.8.97, mines on *B. pendula*; Fleet Pond LNR, 7.10.97, mines on *Betula* (DGG); The Warren NR, Oakshott, 18.10.93, a few tenanted mines on *B. pubescens*; Yateley, 23.9.94, a few tenanted mines (JRL *et al.*).

0111 *Stigmella microtheriella* (Stainton, 1854)

Widespread and common in the mainland vice-counties and on the Isle of Wight. Mines on hazel and hornbeam. Larvae in two broods, in summer and autumn.

■ vc10 Osborne, Cowes, 1995, mines (DTB).

0112 *Stigmella luteella* (Stainton, 1857)

Locally common in mainland Hampshire, and mines found commonly in Parkhurst Forest in 1975 (Goater, 1992). Mines on birch *Betula* spp., probably in a single protracted brood (Emmet *in* Heath, 1976).

■ vc11 Merrietown Heath, 18.10.93, mines common (PHS); Roydon Woods, 3.10.98, mines (JRL); Crab Wood, 20.9.97, vacated mine on *B. pubescens*; Upper Hamble Country Park, 7.10.96, a few vacated mines; Alver Valley NR, Gosport, 22.9.97, one vacated mine; West Meon, 8.10.96, several tenanted mines (JRL, *et al.*); Wickham Common, 1998; Titchfield Haven; Rowner Wild Grounds (RJD).

■ vc12 Wildhern, nr Andover, 27.10.96, mines; Eelmoor Marsh SSSI, 19.10.97, mines; Fleet Pond LNR, 7.10.97, mines (DGG); Pamber, 1994 (GJD); Yateley, 23.9.94, a few vacated mines (AMD, JRL).

0113 *Stigmella sakhalinella* Puplesis, 1984

= *distinguenda* auctt.

Occurs in all three vice-counties amongst birch *Betula* spp. Probably univoltine, in a single protracted generation (Emmet *in* Heath, 1976).

■ vc10 Parkhurst Forest, 3.10.95, mines (DTB), 18.9.97, one vacated mine on *Betula pubescens* (AME, JRL).

■ vc11 Roydon Woods, 3.10.98, mines frequent on birch (RJD, JRL); Kings Copse Inclosure, 24.10.00, mines (JEC); Southampton area, autumn 1999, mines found in several localities; Royal Victoria Country Park, 23.8.00, mines (PAB); Norleywood, 2.9.94, a few vacated mines; Purbrook, 28.9.98, one tenanted mine; Hamble Common, 1996, mines; Wickham Common, 27.9.98, mines; Rowner Wild Grounds (RJD); Upper Hamble Country Park, 7.10.96, several vacated mines; Lower Titchfield Haven NR, 21.10.96, one vacated mine; Sandy Point NR, Hayling Island, 17.10.96, a few vacated mines (JRL *et al.*); Waterlooville, 1996–1999 (RJM).

■ vc12 Eelmoor Marsh SSSI, 24.8.97, mines on *B. pendula* (DGG); Pamber, 1994 (GJD); Shortheath Common, 20.8.98, a few vacated mines; Yateley, 23.9.94, several vacated mines (JRL *et al.*).

0114 *Stigmella glutinosae* (Stainton, 1858)

The following may be added to the few records given in Goater (1974, 1992). Mines on alder *Alnus glutinosa*.

■ vc10 Shide, 26.9.95, mines with larvae; Hurst Stake, N of Newport, 6.11.96, one vacated mine, conf. JRL (DTB). **New vc record.**

■ vc11 Hookheath Meadows NR, Southwick, 17.10.92, a few tenanted mines; Lower Titchfield Haven NR, 23.10.93, a few vacated mines (JRL).

■ vc12 Pamber, 1994 (GJD); Fleet Pond LNR, 7.10.97, mines (DGG).

0115 *Stigmella alnetella* (Stainton, 1856)

The single acceptable record for the Isle of Wight is given in Goater (1974). The larva of this species also mines the leaves of alder *Alnus glutinosa*.

■ vc11 Upper Pennington, 12.10.99, mine with larva (PAB); Roydon Woods, 3.10.98, one tenanted mine, larva

examined (RJD, JRL); Lower Test Marshes NR, 1.10.96, a few vacated mines; Hookheath Meadows NR, Southwick, 17.10.92, a few tenanted mines; Upper Hamble Country Park, 7.10.96, a few mines, one with larva; Lower Titchfield Haven NR, 21.10.96, a few tenanted mines; (JRL *et al.*).
■ vc12 Pamber, 1994 (GJD); Fleet Pond LNR, 7.10.97, mines (DGG).

0116 *Stigmella lapponica* (Wocke, 1862)
Mines fairly common on birch *Betula* spp. throughout the three vice-counties (JRL).
■ vc10 Parkhurst Forest, 18.9.75, vacated mines (RJD); Fort Victoria Country Park (JMC).
■ vc11 Merrietown Heath, 18.10.93, one vacated mine (PHS); Roydon Woods, 3.10.98, one vacated mine (RJD, JRL); Matley Heath, 11.10.98, mines (DGG); Hamble Common, 1996, mines; Wickham Common, 18.7.98, vacated mine (RJD); Waterlooville, 1996–1999 (RJM).
■ vc12 Wildhern, 14.7.98, mines (DGG); Pamber, 1994 (GJD); Harewood Forest, 26.10.97, mines; Fleet Pond LNR, 7.10.97, mines (DGG).

0117 *Stigmella confusella* (Wood, 1894)
Mines common on birch *Betula* spp. throughout the three vice-counties (JRL).

0118 *Enteucha acetosae* (Stainton, 1854)
The only recent record, from Longmoor vc12, is given in Goater (1992). The larva mines the leaves of sheep's sorrel *Rumex acetosella* and common sorrel *R. acetosa*.

Opostegidae (2)

The early stages of these small, whitish moths are unknown in Britain; the moths are nocturnal and come to light.

0119 *Opostega salaciella* (Treitschke, 1833)
Taken occasionally at light in all three vice-counties (see Goater, 1974, 1992).
■ vc11 Winchester, Sarum Road, 16.7.93, one at m.v. light (RJBH); Hamble Common, 30.6.74, 1996 (RJD); Sinah Common, Hayling Island, 15.8.98, one at m.v. light (JRL, IRT, *et al.*).
■ vc12 Farnborough, 11.7.94, two in 1995 (RWP).

0121 *Pseudopostega (Opostega) crepusculella* (Zeller, 1839)
Very occasional specimens have been taken in the Winchester area – Winchester vc11, Itchen Valley and Winnall Moors NR vc12.

Tischeriidae (4)

This is another family of small moths with leaf-mining larvae.

0123 *Tischeria ekebladella* (Bjerkander, 1795)
Mines common to abundant on deciduous oaks *Quercus* spp., and sometimes sweet chestnut *Castanea sativa*, in all three vice-counties (JRL).

■ vc8 Martin Down, 29.4.90 (S. Nash).
■ vc10 Parkhurst Forest, Osborne, 1995, mines (DTB).

0124 *Tischeria dodonaea* Stainton, 1858
Local in S Hants and N Hants. Moths are taken occasionally at dusk, but more often, mines are found on oak *Quercus* spp. in autumn. Records are given in Goater (1974, 1992).
■ vc10 Parkhurst Forest, 19.9.77, mines found by A.M. Emmet (comm. IRT); Bouldnor Forest, 14.10.00, one mine with larva (DTB, conf. JRL). **New vc record.**
■ vc11 Merrietown Heath, 18.10.93, a few tenanted mines (PHS); Lower Test Marshes NR, 1.10.96, a few mines on *Q. robur* (JRL); Peartree Green, Southampton, 9.10.99, mines; Round Coppice, Park Gate, 9.9.00, mines (PAB); Chilling Copse; Fort Fareham, 9.7.98 (RJD); Wickham Common, 30.9.00, one mine (JRL, IRT).

0125 *Emmetia (Tischeria) marginea* (Haworth, 1828)
Mines common on bramble *Rubus* spp. in all the three vice-counties (JRL).
■ vc8 Martin Down, 29.4.90 (S. Nash), 24.8.90 (MFVC and S. Nash).

0127 *Emmetia (Tischeria) angusticollella* (Duponchel, 1843)
The very few records for the mainland vice-counties are set out in Goater (1974, 1992). The larva mines the leaves of rose *Rosa* spp. in autumn.
■ vc10 Parkhurst Forest, 9.8.96, mines, DTB conf. JRL (Agassiz *et al.*, 1998). **New vc record.**

Incurvariidae (23)

This family includes the familiar long-horn moths *Nematopogon* and *Adela*, the males of which have extravagantly long antennae. Some of them fly in swarms around the upper branches of trees or nearer the ground in woodland rides. The larvae of many of the species in this family live in flat cases made from cut-outs from leaves of the foodplant or other plant debris.

0128 *Phylloporia bistrigella* (Haworth, 1828)
A few records from all three vice-counties (Goater, 1974, 1992).
■ vc11 Sopley Common, 12.5.00, one at m.v. light (PHS); Botley Wood, 30.5.75, 18.5.76 (RJD).
■ vc12 Shortheath Common, 20.8.98, one vacated mine and cut-out on birch *Betula* spp. (JRL, IRT).

0129 *Incurvaria pectinea* Haworth, 1828
Common amongst birch *Betula* spp. and hazel *Corylus avellana* throughout the mainland vice-counties (JRL).

0130 *Incurvaria masculella* ([Denis & Schiffermüller], 1775)
Common on the Hampshire mainland, but only one recent record from the Isle of Wight, given below. Associated with hawthorn *Crataegus* spp. in this country.
■ vc8 Martin Down, 29.4.90 (S. Nash).
■ vc10 Tennyson Down, 18.5.92, one (JRL, DHS, PHS).

0131 *Incurvaria oehlmanniella* (Hübner, 1796)

Fairly widespread on the mainland, but so far unrecorded from the Isle of Wight. The moth is usually seen by day or at light, and there is only one record of a larval case being found in Hampshire (Goater, 1992).

■ vc11 Roydon Woods, 10.7.96, one at m.v. light (PRD, JRL); Sparsholt College (AHD); Botley Wood, 1999; Wickham Common, 1999 (RJD); Hookheath Meadows NR, Southwick, 23.5.92, one; Warsash, 20.5.94, one; Titchfield, 20.5.94, several (JRL).

■ vc12 Pamber, 1994 (GJD); Wick Hill Hanger, Selborne, 20.5.99 (PAB); Farnborough, 30.5.96 (RWP); Yateley Common, 1996 (AMD).

0132 *Incurvaria praelatella* ([Denis & Schiffermüller], 1775)

A few records from the mainland vice-counties, but only one record from the Isle of Wight. All records are of moths taken by day or at light.

■ vc10 Parkhurst Forest, 28.5.73 (RJD). **New vc record.**

■ vc11 Botley Wood, 12.7.94, one at m.v. light (JRL); Park Gate; Kite's Croft (RJD).

■ vc12 Harewood Forest, Burnt Lodge Copse, 7.6.97, by day (DGG).

0133 *Lampronia capitella* (Clerck, 1759)

Reported in the past from the New Forest, Southampton and Botley (Goater, 1974), but no recent record except for the following.

■ vc10 Brighstone Forest, 6.6.78 (RJD). **New vc record.**

0134 *Lampronia flavimitrella* (Hübner, 1817)

A specimen taken, new to Britain, at Martyr Worthy vc12 on 18.5.74 (see Goater, 1983).

0135 *Lampronia luzella* (Hübner, 1817)

A few records from all three vice-counties (Goater, 1974, 1992).

■ vc10 Bouldnor, 5.6.78, two; Firestone Copse, 10.6.78 (RJD).

■ vc11 Botley Wood, 29.5.76 (RJD); Warsash, 20.5.94, one (JRL).

■ vc12 Bramley Frith Wood NR (AHD); Selborne hanger, 26.7.77 (RJD).

0136 *Lampronia corticella* (Linnaeus, 1758)

= *rubiella* (Bjerkander, 1781)

Recorded only from S Hants, where it is local, and associated with raspberry *Rubus idaeus*, from the stems of which it has been bred (see Goater, 1974, 1992).

■ vc11 Portchester, 11.6.72; Oxenbourne Down, 1.6.74 (RJD).

0137 *Lampronia morosa* (Zeller, 1852)

A very few records from S Hants, and one from N Hants (Goater, 1992).

■ vc10 Bouldnor, 5.6.78, det. J.D. Bradley (RJD). **New vc record.**

■ vc11 Warsash, 20.5.94, a few (JRL); Portsdown, 19.5.99, two moths det. JRL (RJD).

0138 *Lampronia fuscatella* (Tengström, 1848)

There are several old records from vc11 (Goater, 1974), and more recently, galls have been found on birch *Betula* spp. at Newtown Common vc12 (Goater, 1992). The larva makes a gall in a twig of birch, and is best collected in early spring.

■ vc11 Dockens Water, Ringwood, 18.4.92, one gall; 15.3.93, three galls, one moth bred (JRL, DHS).

0140 *Nematopogon swammerdamella* (Linnaeus, 1758)

Widespread and often fairly common in deciduous woodland. Larva in a flat case amongst dead leaves.

■ vc10 Parkhurst Forest, 17.5.95; Gurnard 4.5.95 (DTB).

■ vc11 Sinah Common, Hayling Island, 29.5.95, one (JRL).

0141 *Nematopogon schwarziellus* (Zeller, 1839)

Frequent in deciduous woodland and amongst scrub in all three vice-counties. Larva in a flat case constructed from dead leaves.

■ vc10 Tennyson Down, 18.5.92, one (JRL, DHS, PHS); Bembridge Down (JMC).

0143 *Nematopogon metaxella* (Hübner, 1813)

Scattered records from all three vice-counties (Goater 1992), in woodland, marshes and bogs.

■ vc11 Botley Wood; Catisfield; Hazel Holt; Titchfield Haven (RJD); Soberton, 10.6.95, one at m.v. light; Titchfield, 20.5.94, one (JRL).

■ vc12 Chilbolton Down, 25.5.92, one; Abbotstone Down, 1.6.93, one (JRL, DHS); Oakley; Bramley Frith Wood NR (AHD); Selborne, four in 1995 (AEA); Noar Hill, 26.6.96 (AMJ).

0145 *Nemophora minimella* ([Denis & Schiffermüller], 1775)

Local and uncommon on downland and in boggy areas where the foodplants devil's-bit scabious *Succisa pratensis* or field scabious *Knautia arvensis* grow.

■ vc11 Ashurst, 1.8.99, common, swept by day (BE); Beacon Hill NNR, Warnford, 7.8.98, two by day (CA); Botley Wood, 12.8.74; Oxenbourne Down, 18.8.72 (RJD).

■ vc12 Leckford, 29.7.89, two on *Knautia* heads (DHS, MJS, PHS) (see Agassiz, 1991); Harewood Forest (RJD).

0146 *Nemophora cupriacella* (Denis & Schiffermüller, 1775)

A rare species in the two counties, associated with *Knautia*, *Succisa* and small scabious *Scabiosa columbaria*. To the two recent records given in Goater (1992), the following can be added.

■ vc11 Oxenbourne Down, 14.7.98, six females at rest on heads of teasel *Dipsacus fullonum* (JRL, IRT).

0147 *Nemophora metallica* (Poda, 1761)

Very local on the remaining downland in the mainland vice-counties; unrecorded from the Isle of Wight. Associated with field scabious *Knautia arvensis* and small scabious *Scabiosa columbaria*.

■ vc12 Porton Down, 24.7.94, one (JRL).

0148 *Nemophora degeerella* (Linnaeus, 1758)

Colonies occur in deciduous woodland throughout the

three vice-counties. Larva in a case amongst leaf litter.
■ vc8 Martin Down, 16.6.95 (MCH).

0149 *Adela cuprella* ([Denis & Schiffermüller], 1775)

Very local in damp areas amongst grey sallow *Salix cinerea*. Recorded as new to vc's 10 and 12 in Goater (1992). All more recent records are given below.
■ vc10 Tolt Down, 1.6.96; Osborne, 5.5.97; Whitefield Wood, 4.5.97 (DTB).
■ vc11 Matchams, 9.4.97, in flight around tops of sallows; Sopley Common, 9.4.97, flying around sallows; St Catherine's Hill, Christchurch, 7.4.95, flying around tops of sallows (PD); Ashurst, 1.8.99, common, swept by day (BE); Wickham Common, 8.4.00, many flying round tops of sallow bushes (RJD, JRL, IRT).
■ vc12 Bartley Heath NR (AHD); Fleet Pond, 21.4.98, one at rest on *Salix* spp. (DGG).

0150 *Adela reaumurella* (Linnaeus, 1758)

10 mm

Abundant in deciduous woodland throughout the three vice-counties, the males often swarming about the tips of branches of oak *Quercus* spp., sycamore *Acer pseudoplatanus* and other deciduous trees.

0151 *Adela croesella* (Scopoli, 1763)

Very local (Goater 1974, 1992). All records received since 1992 are given below.
■ vc8 Martin Down, 8.6.92 (JRL, RMP).
■ vc10 Tennyson Down, 15.6 and 21.6.85, 19.6.89 (SAK-J); Afton Down, 10.6.78 (RJD).
■ vc11 Merrietown Heath, 2.6.95, one by day (PHS).
■ vc12 Pamber, 5.6.95, small numbers on flowers of germander speedwell *Veronica chamaedrys* (GJD), 16.6.96 (MCH).

0152 *Adela rufimitrella* (Scopoli, 1763)

Local; associated with cuckooflower *Cardamine pratensis* and garlic mustard *Alliaria petiolata*. All recent records are included.
■ vc8 Martin Down, 6.5.90 (S. Nash).
■ vc11 Botley Wood, 4.6.93, one (JRL), 11.5.98, one at actinic light; Catisfield; Titchfield Haven (RJD); Waterlooville, 14.5.00, in flight by day in woods (RJM).
■ vc12 Harewood Forest, 26.5.96, by day (DGG); Pamber, 19.5.95, small numbers on flowers of *Alliaria* (GJD); Bramley Frith Wood NR; Greywell Moors NR (AHD); Selborne, 13.5.93 (AEA); Hawkley Warren (RJD); Ashford Hangers NR, 21.5.93, a few (JRL).

0153 *Adela fibulella* ([Denis & Schiffermüller], 1775)

Locally frequent, especially amongst germander speedwell *Veronica chamaedrys* growing amongst downland scrub, but no recent record from the Isle of Wight.
■ vc10 Apes Down; Parkhurst Forest; Knowles Farm (RJD).
■ vc11 Old Winchester Hill NNR, 3.5.1.93, a few; Beacon

Hill NNR, Warnford, 11.6.94, one; Botley Wood, 29.5.98, one (JRL); Cherque (RJD).
■ vc12 Magdalen Hill Down, 22.5 and 29.5.00, singletons (PAB); Abbotstone Down, 1.6.93, a few (RJBH, JRL, DHS); Pamber, 5.6.95, common on flowers of *Veronica chamaedrys*, with *A. croesella*; 17.6.95, one at light (GJD).

Heliozelidae (5)

The moths of this family fly by day in sunshine. The larvae make mines in leaves, petioles or young stems, later living in a portable case excised from the foodplant.

0154 *Heliozela sericiella* (Haworth, 1828)
= *stannella* (Fischer von Röslerstamm, 1841)

Common in the two mainland vice-counties, but no recent record from the Isle of Wight. The young larva lives in a twig of oak *Quercus* spp., later mining a leaf and then excising a case.
■ vc11 Royal Victoria Country Park, 23.8.00, on *Q. robur* (PAB).
■ vc12 Eelmoor Marsh SSSI, 19.10.97, mines and cut-outs; Harewood Forest, 26.10.97, mines and cut-outs; Fleet Pond LNR, 7.10.97, mines and cut-outs (DGG).

0156 *Heliozela resplendella* (Stainton, 1851)

All but a handful of the records are from S Hants, and most have been made recently by JRL and his co-workers. Associated with alder *Alnus glutinosa*.
■ vc10 Alverstone, 21.9.97, vacated mine (RJD). **New vc record.**
■ vc11 Upper Hamble Country Park, 7.10.96, a few mines, one tenanted (AMD, AME, JRL); Swanwick, 14.6.97, one tenanted mine; Hookheath Meadows NR, Southwick, 17.10.92, a few vacated mines and cut-outs; Purbrook Common, 28.9.98, a few tenanted mines; Farlington Marshes NR, 6.9.93, many tenanted mines (RJD, JRL).
■ vc12 Leckford, 1981 (Goater, 1992).

0157 *Heliozela hammoniella* (Sorhagen, 1885)

Recorded from all three vice-counties, where it is associated with birch *Betula* spp.
■ vc10 Firestone Copse and Parkhurst, 1997, (AME). **New vc record.**
■ vc11 Norleywood, 2.9.94, a few vacated mines and cut-outs; Havant Thicket, 10.10.94, a few vacated mines and cut-outs on *B. pubescens* (JRL).

0158 *Antispila metallella* ([Denis & Schiffermüller], 1775)
= *pfeifferella* (Hübner, 1813)

Recorded from all three vice-counties, mostly as vacated mines and cut-outs on dogwood *Cornus sanguinea*.
■ vc10 Ningwood, 5.7.95, mine with larva (DTB).
■ vc11 Crab Wood, 20.9.97; Botley Wood, 4.5.93, one; Hen Wood, East Meon, 10.10.94; Clanfield, 4.10.97 (JRL, *et al.*); Waterlooville, 20.5.00, swept by day in woodland, conf. JRL (RJM).
■ vc12 Wildhern, nr Andover, 19.10.96, 4.10.97; Tangley, 2.10.97 (DGG); Old Alresford Pond, 17.4.76 (RJD).

0159 *Antispila treitschkiella* (Fischer von Röslerstamm, 1840)
= *petryi* Martini, 1898
This species, also associated with dogwood *Cornus sanguinea*, appears to be as common as *A. metallella* where the foodplant grows, in all three vice-counties, and is usually recorded in the same manner.
■ vc11 Botany Bay, Sholing, 5.10.99, on ornamental dogwood (PAB); Hookheath Meadows NR, Southwick, 17.10.92; Botley Wood, 29.9.94; Clanfield, 4.10.97; Oxenbourne Down NR, 13.8.93 (JRL *et al.*).
■ vc12 Wildhern, nr Andover, 12.10.96, 27.10.97 (DGG); Magdalen Hill down, 4.11.99 (PAB).

Cossidae (2)

Being large, conspicuous moths, species in this family have been traditionally included by students among the Macrolepidoptera. The larvae feed internally in living wood or pith, often taking several years to mature. The adults lack functional mouthparts and do not feed, but their bodies carry abundant fat reserves.

0161 *Zeuzera pyrina* (Linnaeus, 1761)
Leopard Moth

Widespread and still fairly common. The males come freely to light, but females are seldom seen.

0162 *Cossus cossus* (Linnaeus, 1758)
Goat Moth   **Notable/Nb**
Full-fed larvae are occasionally found wandering, and there are a few records of moths at light, chiefly near the coast and in the New Forest.
■ vc10 Whitwell, three-quarter grown larva found in elm *Ulmus* spp. by Miss Somerville, August 1992; subsequently died (*comm.* SAK-J).
■ vc11 Hengistbury Head, September 1997, one larva (MJ); Thorns Beach, 5.9.96, one female at m.v. light (BG); larval workings found in the trunk of an oak, Ladycross, 26.8.99 (DGG); Beaulieu, 28.6.95, one at m.v. light (BI-J); nr Lyndhurst, 10.7.98 (RAB); Brockenhurst, 3.5.99 (JEC); Fareham, 1993, at least one *Cossus*-oak in Trinity Street (RJD).
■ vc12 Wildhern, 24.8.98, larvae in cultivated *Prunus*: trees cut down and burned before colony could be saved (DGG); a larva was seen near Fleet in May 1999 (DPD).

Zygaenidae (7)

All members of this family fly by day, in sunshine. The black-and-red burnets, though sometimes difficult to distinguish from one another, are familiar and conspicuous insects, and so, too, are the shiny, fusiform cocoons on grass-stems, which are constructed by some species. The green foresters, on the other hand, are less conspicuous and require looking for. All are local, some extremely so.

0163 *Adscita statices* (Linnaeus, 1758)
Forester

Since the 1950s, this species has disappeared from many localities, sometimes as a result of habitat loss, elsewhere for unknown reasons. It is now known from but a single locality, in vc12. The larva feeds on sorrel *Rumex acetosa*.
■ vc12 Odiham Common, 2.6.94, fairly common (BG), 17.6.98, c.100 seen in 10 minutes (PHC).

0164 *Adscita geryon* (Hübner, 1813)
Cistus Forester   **Notable/Nb**
Local on chalk downland, but gone from many localities where it was once plentiful. Larva on rock-rose *Helianthemum chamaecistus*.

0165 *Jordanita globulariae* (Hübner, 1793)
Scarce Forester   **Notable/Na**
A very local species which was detected in Hampshire for the first time in 2000. The larva feeds on greater knapweed *Centaurea scabiosa*.

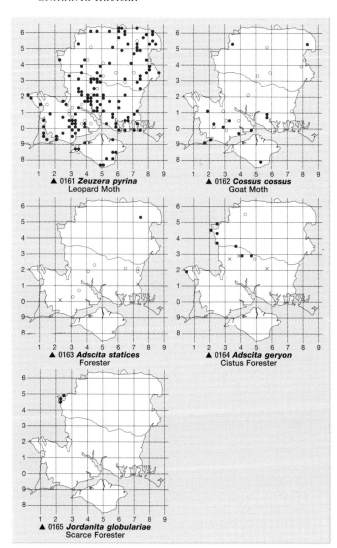

▲ 0161 *Zeuzera pyrina*
Leopard Moth

▲ 0162 *Cossus cossus*
Goat Moth

▲ 0163 *Adscita statices*
Forester

▲ 0164 *Adscita geryon*
Cistus Forester

▲ 0165 *Jordanita globulariae*
Scarce Forester

■ vc12 Shipton Bellinger, 10.6 to 11.6.00, at least three small colonies on chalky slopes (BG); Perham Down, Tidworth, 18.6.95, one male, det. BG from photograph (ARGM). **New county record.**

0168 *Zygaena viciae* ([Denis & Schiffermüller],1775)
New Forest Burnet
Small colonies were known in the New Forest between 1872 and 1927 (see Goater, 1974). The map shows these localities, several of which had ceased to exist by the turn of the century.

0169 *Zygaena filipendulae* (Linnaeus, 1758)
Six-spot Burnet
Scattered colonies, some of them vigorous, throughout the three vice-counties.

0170/0171 *Zygaena trifolii/lonicerae*
■ vc10 Tennyson Down, 30.7.94, with SAK-J, five-spot burnets taken; Afton Down, 24.6.93, two taken (BJW).

0170 *Zygaena trifolii palustrella* Verity, 1926
Five-spot Burnet
Lost from many localities where it was formerly common, with present strongholds only on Martin Down (vc8) and the Isle of Wight.
■ vc8 Martin Down, 8.6.92 (JRL, RMP).
■ vc10 Ashey, 31.5.95, det. BG., a good colony there (BJW); Nunwell, West Down, 4.6.97, det. BG (BJW).
■ vc11 Farley Mount, 18.6.95 (PAB); Oxenbourne Down, 8.6.00, many; not seen in this part of Hampshire since the 1950s or 1960s (JRL, IRT).
■ vc12 Shipton Bellinger, 10.6.00, locally common, several confluent forms (BG); Perham Down, 29.6.95, eight seen, again in 1996, det. RAB (TJN).

0170a *Zygaena trifolii decreta* Verity, 1926
There have been no recent confirmed records of this ssp. See Goater (1974).

0171 *Zygaena lonicerae* (Scheven, 1777)
Narrow-bordered Five-spot Burnet

Much more common and widespread than *Z. trifolii*, and colonies of "five-spot burnets" off the chalk downs are far more likely to be this species than *Z. trifolii decreta*.
■ vc10 Cridmoor Bog, 8.7.95, a colony; specimens seen by BG (C. Pope); Long Lane, Newport, 10.6.97, several specimens by T. Redfern, det. BG.
■ vc11 Moorgreen, 22.6.95; Swaythling Grange, 3.7.95; Monks Brook, 3.7.95; Hum Hole, Bitterne, 4.7.95; Frogs Copse, 4.7.95 (PAB).
■ vc12 Noar Hill, 1994 (AMJ).

Limacodidae (2)

This is another family that has always been embraced by students of the Macrolepidoptera. Both the British species are local and mainly nocturnal, and inhabit deciduous woodland. The humped larvae could be mistaken for those of a lycaenid butterfly.

0173 *Apoda limacodes* (Hufnagel, 1766)
Festoon   **Notable/Nb**

Recorded occasionally in all three vice-counties. This moth appears to have a very short emergence-period and may thus be overlooked, but single specimens also appear from time to time in places where moth-traps are operated regularly.
■ vc10 Cranmore, fairly common: eight in May 1993 (SAK-J).
■ vc11 St Ives, Ringwood, 1987, at m.v. light (JHC); Roydon Woods, 19.7.91, 20.6.98 (PAB); Studley Wood,

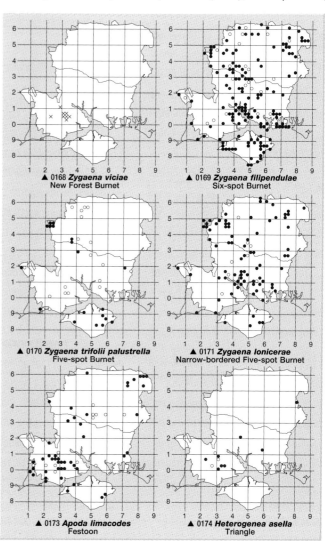

▲ 0168 *Zygaena viciae*
New Forest Burnet

▲ 0169 *Zygaena filipendulae*
Six-spot Burnet

▲ 0170 *Zygaena trifolii palustrella*
Five-spot Burnet

▲ 0171 *Zygaena lonicerae*
Narrow-bordered Five-spot Burnet

▲ 0173 *Apoda limacodes*
Festoon

▲ 0174 *Heterogenea asella*
Triangle

8.6.98 (NB); Kings Somborne, 30.6.98 (TJN); Southwick, 10.7.91, one at m.v.light (Townsend and Wynne, 1992); Havant Thicket, 23.6.98, several at m.v. light (RJD); Leigh Park, Havant, 10.7 and 18.7.95, singletons at light, 8.7.97, six (CBC).

■ vc12 Crawley, 2.8.95, one at m.v. light (RAB); Longstock, 5.7.98, five at m.v. light (WRLG); Monxton, 7.7.98 (NB, TJN); Yateley Common, 9.6 and 8.7.94, singles at light (AMD).

0174 *Heterogenea asella* ([Denis & Schiffermüller], 1775)
Triangle   **RDB3**
The New Forest is a well-known locality for this very local species, but it is now scarce there. Elsewhere in Hampshire it has been seen at Chandlers Ford (see below), Wickham, and once in vc12, at Alice Holt (Goater, 1992).

■ vc11 Chandlers Ford, 29.6.92, female at m.v. light (BG).

Psychidae (13)

Increased interest in this family by Hampshire microlepidopterists has resulted in a spate of new records from the mainland. The adult moths are seen occasionally, but most records are of larval cases. On the Continent, these moths are usually regarded as "Macros", but in Britain they have always been included among the Microlepidoptera.

0175 *Narycia monilifera* (Geoffroy, 1785)
Locally common; cases found most often on old trunks of hawthorn *Crataegus* spp., oak *Quercus* spp. and yew *Taxus baccata*, in spring. Records have been received from the following.

■ vc11 Picket Post, 10.5.99, many cases on oak trunk (BE); Crab Wood, 17.3.92, a few cases; Lower Test Marshes NR, 3.4.96, a few cases; The Moors NR, Bishops Waltham, 19.4.93, one case; Hookheath Meadows NR, Southwick, 6.3.92, a few cases (JRL *et al.*).

■ vc12 Bartley Heath NR, 22.5.99, cases on tree trunks det. DGG (AHD).

0177 *Dahlica inconspicuella* (Stainton, 1849)
■ vc11 Denny Wood, 6.4.74, one flying by day (RJD); Bramshaw Woods, 4.4.90, male at rest on a beech trunk, conf. DHS (RJBH). **Presence in county confirmed.**

0179 *Dahlica lichenella* (Linnaeus, 1761)
Cases recorded from Denny Wood and Havant Thicket in 1979 and from Emer Bog in 1987 (Goater, 1992), there has been only one recent record, given below. No record from the Isle of Wight or from N Hants.

■ vc11 Matley Passage, 10.5.99, a few cases (BE).

0180 *Diplodoma herminata* (Geoffroy, 1785)
The following records are in addition to the few given in Goater (1974, 1992).

■ vc11 Rowbarrow, 20.5.00, one larval case (PAB); Clanfield, 1.4.97, one case on a beech trunk (JRL, IRT).

■ vc12 Silchester Common, 30.5.93, a few cases on tree-

trunks (JRL); Bartley Heath NR, 22.5.99, cases on tree trunks det. DGG (AHD).

0181 *Taleporia tubulosa* (Retzius, 1783)
Widespread and common in the mainland vice-counties, but no recent record from the Isle of Wight.

0178 *Bankesia douglasii* (Stainton, 1854)
The rediscovery of this species by Dr Dickson close to its original locality after exactly 100 years was a triumph (R.J. Dickson, 1995). Some of the details are given below.

■ vc11 Fareham, 20.3.94, one male; 12.3.95, 7+ males; 13.3.95, four males; 19.3.95, one male; 27.1.96, very many cases found, attached to *Buddleia* trunk, on fence and saw-bench, moths emerging during February, mostly females; 24.2.98, the old site destroyed, but cases found all along the wall of a work-shed (RJD, JRL); Segensworth, 10.3.95, one male, 10.4.96 (DMA); all caught in sunshine between 0700 and 0850 hrs; conf. JRL. (comm. RJD).

0183 *Bacotia sepium* (Speyer, 1846)
Fassnidge recorded this species from several localities in S Hants up to 1936. Cases were found, new to N Hants, at Stockbridge Down between 1979 and 1984 (see Goater, 1992), but since then only one report has been received.

■ vc11 Havant Thicket, 20.3.96, one case on tree-trunk; 14.3.97, one case (JRL, IRT).

0185 *Luffia ferchaultella* (Stephens, 1850)
Cases common to abundant on tree-trunks, fences and old walls throughout the mainland vice-counties (JRL).

0186 *Psyche casta* (Pallas, 1767)
Widespread and common in all three vice-counties (JRL).

0189 *Epichnopterix plumella* ([Denis & Schiffermüller], 1775)
Recorded only from Beaulieu Road, Rowner Wild Grounds and Sinah Common, Hayling Island (Goater, 1992), all vc11, in addition to a few old records from the Isle of Wight given in Goater (1974).

0190 *Epichnopterix retiella* (Newman, 1847)
An inhabitant of saltmarshes, and recorded in the past from Cracknore Hard, Bursledon and Hayling Island. The most recent record, given in Goater (1992), is of a single male netted at the last-named locality in 1986.

■ vc11 Hound coast, 4.6.74, swept (RJD).

0191 *Acanthopsyche atra* (Linnaeus, 1767)
Nothing had been seen of this species in Hampshire since the old records given in Goater (1974), and the comment on distribution given in Heath and Emmet (eds) (1985) is misleading. However, the following record, which is of great interest, reached the authors just prior to printing.

■ vc12 Castle Bottom NR, 2.4.01, one case found, identity confirmed by PHS (AMD).

0192 *Pachythelia villosella* (Ochsenheimer, 1810)
Reported from a number of heathy areas of the New Forest, sometimes commonly, but not since 1986 (Goater,

1992). Recently rediscovered in vc11; records are given below.

■ vc11 Merrietown Heath, occasional cases found between July 1994 and August 1997 (PHS); 20+ cases, some with active larvae, found on dry heathland at Hincheslea Moor on 28.6.00 and another 20+ found in similar circumstances SE of Dorridge Hill, Gorley on 1.7.00. (Mrs P Davis and Mrs C Giles, comm. PAB); Ocknell Plain 6.5.99, six larval cases; Stephill Bottom, 9.5.00, one larval case (DGG, MSP); Beaulieu Road, 17.6.00, four male and one female case (DGG, TJN).

Tineidae (30 + [1])

Many adults of this family lead secretive lives and the species are most often bred. Some of the house moths belong to this family, and others are pests of stored products. The larvae of another large group feed in bracket fungi or rotten wood, and others are inhabitants of old birds'-nests. Others live in cases and feed on lichens, and species of the genus *Psychoides* feed amongst the sori of ferns.

0196 *Morophaga choragella* ([Denis & Schiffermüller], 1775)

10 mm

Widespread and fairly common, but only recently recorded from the Isle of Wight (see below). The moth comes to light, and the larva lives in various species of bracket fungus.

■ vc10 Parkhurst Forest, 22.7.96 (SAK-J). **New vc record.**

■ vc11 Merrietown Heath, 25.4.95, many larvae in the fungus *Ganoderma* (PHS); Rufous (sic.) Stone, March, 1995, reared from *Ganoderma adspersum* (Sims, 1997); Chandlers Ford, 1.8.95, one at light, det. JRL (BG); Bitterne, 25.7.99 (PAB); Southwick, 29.7.96, one at m.v. light (JRL, EAP); Fareham, 16.8.98 (RJD); Havant Thicket, 8.7.97, a few at m.v. light (JRL, IRT, *et al.*).

■ vc12 Cholderton, 15.7.95, one at light (HE); Wildhern, 1.8.98 (DGG); Silchester Common, 30.5.93, one; Monkwood, 2.4.97, larvae in the fungus, *Pseudotrametes gibbosa*, moth bred (JRL, IRT); Selborne, regularly since 1992 (AEA); Farnborough, 23.7.96 (RWP).

0199 *Psychoides verhuella* Bruand, 1853

The larvae of this species feed amongst the sori of hart's-tongue fern *Phyllitis scolopendrium* and seem to occur wherever that plant is established, in all three vice-counties.

0200 *Psychoides filicivora* (Meyrick, 1937)

Very local, and recorded only from Bournemouth, Highcliffe and Southsea, all on the coast of S Hants. The moth has been bred from larvae on male-fern *Dryopteris* spp. (see Goater (1992).

■ vc10 Tennyson Down, Freshwater, 18.5.92, pupae on hart's tongue (DHS, PHS, JRL); Totland Bay, 18.6.78 (RJD). **New vc record.**

0203 *Infurcitinea argentimaculella* (Stainton, 1849)

Local but probably overlooked, especially on the Isle of Wight. The larva feeds in a silken tube amongst lichens growing on shaded walls and rocks, sometimes on tree-trunks.

■ vc11 Merrietown Heath, 14.1.94, larval feedings on *Lepraria* on oak bark (PHS); Sandy Balls, Godshill, 20.4.94, many larval tubes; Parnholt Wood, 1.5.95, many larval tubes; Hookheath Meadows NR, Southwick, 6.3.92, larvae in tubes on *Lepraria* on tree-trunks; West Walk, 29.1.94, many larval tubes; Havant Thicket, 2.4.95, many larval tubes (JRL *et al.*); Rowner Wild Grounds, 27.7.76 (RJD).

■ vc12 Leckford, 27.3.89, larval tubes (DHS, MJS) (see Agassiz, 1991); Abbotstone Down, 30.7.92, one at rest on an oak trunk (RJBH); Selborne, 28.3.96, larval tubes on *Lepraria* on beech trunks (JRL). **New vc record.**

0206 *Stenoptinea cyaneimarmorella* (Millière, 1854)

There is one ancient record of this species of this extremely scarce species from Liss vc12 (see Goater, 1992).

[0207 *Myrmecozela ochraceella* (Tengström, 1848)

The old records given in Goater (1974) are now considered to be unreliable, and this species should be deleted from the Hampshire List.]

0212 *Haplotinea insectella* (Fabricius, 1794)

There are but two records of this species in Hampshire, one from Southampton, and two in a garden at Winchester (see Goater, 1974, 1992). It is likely to be resident but overlooked.

0215 *Nemapogon granella* (Linnaeus, 1758)

Apart from the old records given in Goater (1974), there has been only one other, given below.

■ vc11 Fordingbridge, 26.10.96 by NH, det. G. Robinson, BM (NH) (Agassiz *et al.*, 1998). **New vc record.**

0216 *Nemapogon cloacella* (Haworth, 1828)

Widespread and common in the two mainland vice-counties (JRL), but no recent record from the Isle of Wight.

0217 *Nemapogon wolffiella* Karsholt & Nielsen, 1976

■ vc11 Chandlers Ford, 8.6.00, one (BE); Wickham Common, bred from the fungus *Hypoxylon multiforme* in 1997 (RJD); Havant Thicket, reared from larvae and pupae on *Hypoxylon multiforme* on dead birch, collected 5.5.97, moths began to emerge on 8.5.97 (Langmaid, 1998). **New county record.**

0219 *Nemapogon ruricolella* (Stainton, 1849)

There are a few records from all three vice-counties but no recent ones from the Isle of Wight.

■ vc11 Rufous (sic.) Stone, March, 1995, larvae in the fungus *Coriolus versicolor* (Sims, 1997b); Brockenhurst, 23.7.98, one; Soberton, 30.6.95, one at m.v. light (JRL); Wickham Common, 12.8.98; Hamble Common, 1996; Warsash shore; Old Winchester Hill; all genitalia det. (RJD); Hookheath Meadows NR, Southwick, 12.6.92, one by day; Southsea, 5.6.98, first for garden (JRL).

■ vc12 Wildhern, nr Andover, 25.7.99, to house lights (DGG); Bramshill Plantation, Eversley, April, 1995, larvae on the fungus *Bjerkandera adjusta* (Sims, *ibid.*); Selborne, 18.7 and 20.7.95 and 16.6 and 27.6.96, at light (AEA); 28.3.96, larvae on fungus on dead branches, moths emerged May–June (JRL). **New vc record.**

0220 *Nemapogon clematella* (Fabricius, 1781)

Widespread but apparently uncommon; probably overlooked.

■ vc11 Parnholt Wood, 14.5.96, larval workings on the fungus *Diatrype disciformis* on dead hazel *Corylus avellana* (JRL, D. O'Keefe); Chandlers Ford, 25.6.00, one (BE); Dur Wood; The Moors NR, Bishop's Waltham (RJD); Hookheath Meadows NR, Southwick, 14.7.96, many larval workings; Creech Wood, Denmead, 8.2.97, a few larval workings (JRL).

■ vc12 Wildhern, nr Andover, 20.8.96, to house lights; Harewood Forest, 23.6.00, larval workings in *D. disciformis* on decaying hazel, two moths bred (DGG); Bramley Frith Wood, 29.7.99, three at m.v. light (AHD); Selborne, 1994 (AEA).

0223 *Nemaxera betulinella* (Paykull, 1785)

There have been no records of this species since those given in Goater (1974, 1992). In the past, it has been reported from all three vice-counties.

0224 *Triaxomera parasitella* (Hübner, 1796)

The older records (Goater, 1974) indicate that this species is locally frequent on the Isle of Wight, but all recent reports have come from the mainland vice-counties. Larvae on bracket fungi and dead wood.

■ vc11 Merrietown Heath, 4.6.98, one at m.v. light (PHS); Sparsholt College (AHD); Chandlers Ford, 28.5.95, one at light, det. JRL (BG), July, 1999, several at m.v. light (BE); Crab Wood; Hound coast; Hook-with-Warsash; Hamble Common, 1996; Fareham; Titchfield Haven; Old Winchester Hill; Havant Thicket (RJD); Waterlooville, 22.6.00, at m.v. light, conf. JRL (RJM).

■ vc12 Wildhern, nr Andover, 27.5.97, at dusk (DGG); Oakley; Bramley Frith Wood NR (AHD); Pamber, 1994 (GJD); Farnborough, 21.6.95 (RWP); Selborne, 14.6.97, 1.7.99 (AEA).

0225 *Triaxomera fulvimitrella* (Sodoffsky, 1830)

Similarly recorded in the past from the Isle of Wight, but again, all recent records are from the mainland.

■ vc11 Hookheath Meadows NR, Southwick, 9.4.94, larvae in fungus-infested twigs, moth bred (JRL, PHS).

■ vc12 Selborne, 20.4.93, det. JRL from photograph (AEA).

0227 *Monopis laevigella* ([Denis & Schiffermüller], 1775)
= *rusticella* (Hübner, 1813)

Probably common throughout, but no recent records from the Isle of Wight. The moth has been bred from old birds'-nests, owl pellets and dead animal material.

■ vc10 Parkhurst Forest 5.6.78, one at m.v. light (RJD); Wildcliff, 3+ moths, 17 to 23.9.77 (AME *et al.*).

■ vc11 Sparsholt College (AHD); Hook-with-Warsash, 1996 (RJD); Hookheath Meadows NR, Southwick, 24.5.94, one at m.v. light; Creech Wood, Denmead, 16.5.97 (JRL); Warsash; Catisfield; Fareham; Titchfield Haven; Portsdown (RJD); Milton Common, Southsea, at light in garden, 1998, 2000 (IRT); Waterlooville, 20.9.00, netted at 1830hrs (RJM).

■ vc12 Bramley Depot, 1994 (GJD); Brighton Hill, Basingstoke, 1996; Bramley Frith Wood NR (AHD); Selborne, 10.6 and 16.7.97 (AEA); Noar Hill, 7.6.96 (AMJ); Shortheath Common, 13.8.97 (AMD).

0228 *Monopis weaverella* (Scott, 1858)

There are scattered records from all three vice-counties, but no recent ones from the Isle of Wight. The larva feeds on dead animal material.

■ vc11 Sopley Common, 12.5.00, several at m.v. light (PHS); Anses Wood, New Forest, 22.8.98 (DGG); Botley Wood, 1999 (RJD); Swanwick NR., 20.8.96, two at m.v. light; Old Winchester Hill NNR, 23.7.97, one at m.v. light; Southsea, 18.8.97, one at m.v. light (JRL), Milton Common, 1998, at light in garden, (IRT); Oxenbourne Down (RJD).

■ vc12 Abbotstone Down, 27.7.94, one at m.v. light (RJBH, JRL); Pamber, 1994 (GJD); Yateley Common, 11.8.98, det. JRL (AMD); Selborne, from 1987 (12.8.96 conf. JRL) (AEA); Farnborough, 3.8.97 (RWP).

0229 *Monopis obviella* ([Denis & Schiffermüller], 1775)
= *ferruginella* (Hübner, 1813)

There are a few records from all three vice-counties, but the only recent ones are from S Hants.

■ vc11 Botley Wood; Catisfield; Fareham (RJD), Milton Common, Southsea, 24.8.97, at light (IRT).

0230 *Monopis crocicapitella* (Clemens, 1859)

Recorded occasionally, though sometimes in abundance, in flour mills and chicken-houses. The moth is also taken at light from time to time.

■ vc10 Freshwater, 20.10.98, at m.v. light, first Island record since 1931 (Knill-Jones, 1999).

■ vc11 Sparsholt College (AHD); Fareham; Hamble Common, 1996; Browndown; Portsdown, 30.5.98, one at dusk (RJD); Milton Common, Southsea, 1996, 1998, 1999, 2000, conf. JRL (IRT).

■ vc12 Wildhern, nr Andover, 29.9.96, in stables (DGG).

0231 *Monopis imella* (Hübner, 1813)

Apparently rare. Recorded in the past from all three vice-counties (Goater, 1974, 1992.

■ vc11 Milton Common, Southsea, 30.8.99, 6.6 and 8.8.00, singletons at m.v. light, all conf. JRL (IRT).

0234 *Trichophaga tapetzella* (Linnaeus, 1758)

No record since Goater (1974). Most of the old records were from the Isle of Wight, but it has occurred in both the mainland vice-counties.

0236 *Tineola bisselliella* (Hummel, 1823)

Called "Common Clothes Moth" in the literature, this

species is evidently by no means common in Hampshire or the Isle of Wight. There have been no recent records.

0237 *Niditinea fuscella* (Linnaeus, 1758)
= *fuscipunctella* (Haworth, 1828)
Recorded from vice-counties 11 and 12, where it is very locally common. The first records for the Isle of Wight are given below. The moth is found indoors and in chicken-houses and out-buildings, and occasionally comes to light. Larva in birds'-nests, on dead animal material such as feathers, and on stored plant material.
■ vc10 Freshwater, 18.1.99, bred from a larva, conf. JRL (SAK-J); Shanklin, 19.9.99, one dead indoors (JMC).
New vc record.
■ vc12 Wildhern, nr Andover, 11.7.96, in house; Fleet Pond LNR, 8.5.98, one at m.v. light (DGG).

0238 *Niditinea striolella* (Matsummura, 1931)
= *piercella* (Bentinck, 1935)
Single specimens, the genitalia of which were checked, have been reported from Emery Down and Holmhill in the New Forest, and from Itchen Abbas in vc12 (see Goater, 1983, 1992).

0239 *Tinea columbariella* Wocke, 1877
Recorded only from Southsea vc11 and Itchen Abbas vc12 (Goater, 1983).
■ vc11 Southsea, 22.5.89, 23.5.89 (RJD), 10.7.95, 18.7.96, singletons at m.v. light, genitalia det. (JRL).

0240 *Tinea pellionella* Linnaeus, 1758
Probably the commonest tineid clothes moth, but owing to possible confusion with other species the genitalia need to be checked. Hence, verified records are rather few (see Goater, 1974, 1992).
■ vc11 Fareham (RJD).
■ vc12 Wildhern, 18.8.98, in house, genitalia det. (DGG); Farnborough, 5.4.97, det. JRL (RWP).

0243 *Tinea dubiella* Stainton, 1859
= *turicensis* Müller-Rutz, 1920
One record from N Hants is given in Goater (1974). This and the following are the only ones for the county.
■ vc12 Wildhern, nr Andover, 29.9.96, in stables (DGG).

0244 *Tinea flavescentella* Haworth, 1828
Recorded by Blair as fairly common at Freshwater, vc10 (Goater, 1974). No other record apart from the vague reference in the Victoria County History.

0245 *Tinea pallescentella* Stainton, 1851
In Goater (1974) a few old records are given for the Isle of Wight, and in 1992, three vc11 records were reported. It is surprisingly rare.
■ vc12 Wildhern, 1.4.98, in house, genitalia det. (DGG).
New vc record.

0246 *Tinea semifulvella* Haworth, 1828
Recorded widely from each of the three vice-counties, though not recently from the Isle of Wight. Systematic

collection of old birds'-nests during the winter months would likely result in many more reports of this and related species.
■ vc11 Merritown Heath, 4.6.98, 18.6.99, at m.v. light (PHS); Brockenhurst, common (JEC); Sparsholt College (AHD); Hilliers Arboretum, Ampfield, 1998 (NB,TJN); Chandlers Ford, July, 1998, several at m.v. light (BE); Botley Wood; Hook Common; Wickham Common; Catisfield; Oxenbourne Down (RJD).
■ vc12 Conford Moor, 21.6.95, one (JRL, RMP); Wildhern, nr Andover, 25.5.97, at dusk, 14.7.98 (DGG); Overton; Oakley; Bramley Frith Wood NR (AHD); Pamber, 1994 (GJD); Selborne, 21.6.95, 3.7 to 9.8.97, four at light (AEA); Rye Common, 5.8.96; Yateley Common, 11.6.94, one (AMD).

0247 *Tinea trinotella* Thunberg, 1794
Most of the records have been from vc11, but recent work by several microlepidopterists in the north has resulted in a number of vc12 records, the majority of which are given below.
■ vc8 Martin Down, 29.4.90 (S. Nash).
■ vc10 Shanklin (JMC).
■ vc11 Dilton Meadows, Roydon Woods, 12.7.97, by day (DGG); Sparsholt College (AHD); Chandlers Ford, 5.5.95, one at light, det. JRL (BG), July, 1998, common at m.v. light (BE); Bitterne, 19.5.99 (PAB); Widley, Portsdown (PMP); Catisfield; Fareham, 15.5, 5.6 and 16.7.98; Brownwich; Portsdown (RJD); Milton Common, Southsea, 1996, 1998, 2000 (IRT); Waterlooville, 14.5 and 20.6.00, at m.v. light (RJM).
■ vc12 Wildhern, nr Andover, 31.8.96, in stables, 15.7.98 (DGG); Overton; Bramley Frith Wood NR; Mapledurwell Fen; (AHD); Selborne, 1993, 1994, 1995 and 1997 (AEA); Farnborough, 15.5.94 (two), 23.5.95 (RWP); Yateley Common, 8.8.96 (AMD).

Bucculatricidae (10)

Treated by Heath and Emmet (1985) as a subfamily of Lyonetiidae. The modern view, expressed by Karsholt and Razowski (1996) is to assign full family status to this group of rather inconspicuous moths, the larvae of which are leaf-miners, at least in the early stages of development, and to place them in the superfamily Gracillarioidea. The adult moths, though small, can sometimes be found in numbers flying around their foodplant in the evening.

0265 *Bucculatrix cristatella* (Zeller, 1839)
There are a few records from the mainland vice-counties, but none for the Isle of Wight since the Victoria County History. Larva on yarrow *Achillea millefolium*, at first mining the leaves then feeding externally.
■ vc11 Portsdown, 29.4.97, larval feedings (JRL, IRT).

0266 *Bucculatrix nigricomella* (Zeller, 1839)
Local in the mainland vice-counties, but unrecorded on the Isle of Wight. The larva mines the leaves of ox-eye daisy *Leucanthemum vulgare*.

■ vc11 Botley Wood, 20.5.98, two (RJD), 29.5.98, one (JRL, IRT); Fareham, 15.5.98, 8.8.98; Wickham Common (RJD); Milton Common, Southsea, at light in garden, 27.7.98, 6.8.00, both det. JRL (IRT).

0267 *Bucculatrix maritima* Stainton, 1851

A coastal species, the larva of which feeds on sea aster *Aster tripolium* in the saltmarshes of S Hants and the Isle of Wight.

■ vc10 Freshwater, 10.8.00 (SAK-J); Yarmouth, 18.5.92, mines abundant (JRL, DHS, PHS).

■ vc11 Marchwood, 8.9.98, several old mines; Bursledon, 8.9.98, several old mines (JRL); Hound coast; Curbridge; Fareham, 17.8.98 (RJD); Milton Common, Southsea, 12.8.97, at light (IRT).

0270 *Bucculatrix frangulella* (Goeze, 1783)

No recent record from the Isle of Wight, but in the mainland vice-counties it is found in boggy areas where the foodplant is alder buckthorn *Frangula alnus* and on the chalk, where the larva is associated with buckthorn *Rhamnus cathartica*.

■ vc8 Martin Down, 24.8.90 (MFVC and S. Nash).

■ vc11 Merrietown Heath, 18.10.93, several mines on *Rhamnus* (PHS); Norleywood, 2.9.92, mines abundant on *Frangula*; Crab Wood, 20.9.97, vacated mines and cones on *Rhamnus*; Hen Wood, East Meon, 10.10.94, many vacated mines and a few larvae on *Rhamnus* (JRL, *et al.*); Lordswood, 26.10.99, mines; Stoke Park Wood, 19.10.99, mines (PAB).

■ vc12 Conford Moor, 21.6.95, one (JRL, RMP); Wildhern, nr Andover, 29.9.97, mines on *Rhamnus*; Eelmoor Marsh, 2.7 and 24.7.98, at m.v. light (DGG); Stockbridge Down, September, 1999, many larvae seen (BE); north of Itchen Wood, Micheldever, 10.11.98, mines (PAB); Magdalen Hill Down, 25.5.00, imago (PAB); Bramdean Common, 8.10.96, a few vacated mines and moulting-cocoons on *Rhamnus* (AME, JRL, IRT); Yateley, 23.9.94, many vacated mines on *Frangula* (AMD, JRL).

0271 *Bucculatrix albedinella* (Zeller, 1839)

Recorded from Cracknore Hard, Southampton and Farley Mount in Goater (1974). No additions were made in 1992, so the following records, all from vc11, are of particular interest. The larva mines, then makes windows, in the leaves of elm *Ulmus* spp.

■ vc11 Testwood, 17.10.99, mines; Peartree Green, 9.10.99, mines; Royal Victoria Country Park, 23.8.00, mines (PAB); Lower Test Marshes NR, 1.10.96, a few vacated mines; Alver Valley NR, Gosport, 22.9.97, a few vacated mines; Fareham, 10.10.97, a few vacated mines; Great Salterns NR, Portsmouth, 9.12.95, several vacated mines on *Ulmus procera*, and subsequently cocoons found on trunks and moths bred; Gutner Point NR, Hayling Island, 6.10.96, a few vacated mines (JRL *et al.*).

0272 *Bucculatrix cidarella* Zeller, 1839

Very local in the two mainland vice-counties. The larva mines and then makes windows in the leaves of alder *Alnus glutinosa* and bog-myrtle *Myrica gale*.

■ vc11 Sopley Common, 13.5.97, in flight by day (PD); Roydon Woods, 3.10.98, one mine and one moulting cocoon on *Myrica* (RJD, JRL); Flexford Meadows NR, October, 1999, larvae (BE); Lower Test Marshes NR, 1.10.96, a few vacated mines and moulting-cocoons on alder; Upper Hamble Country Park, 7.10.96, mines and moulting-cocoons abundant; Hookheath Meadows NR, Southwick, 17.10.92, one mine and moulting-cocoon on alder; Lower Titchfield Haven NR, 23.10.93, a few mines and moulting-cocoons on alder (JRL).

■ vc12 Winnall Moors NR (DHS); Eelmoor Marsh, 4.7.98, at m.v. light (DGG).

0273 *Bucculatrix thoracella* (Thunberg, 1794)

The first confirmed records of this species in Hampshire were given in Goater (1983). Since then, the species has been found in some other localities in S Hants. The preferred foodplant, small-leaved lime *Tilia cordata* is very local in Hampshire (Brewis *et al.*, 1996: 126), and systematic search in these localities is likely to produce more records.

■ vc11 Roydon Woods, 23.8.00, mines; Itchen, Bitterne Park and Riverside Park, Southampton, autumn 1999, mines (PAB); Upper Hamble Country Park, 7.10.96, several mines and moulting-cocoons (AMD, AME, JRL); Fareham, 29.9.97, a few larval feedings and moulting-cocoons; Southsea, frequent at m.v. light and larvae common on *Tilia* × *vulgaris* since 1992, and in 2000, moths were found resting on lime trunks on 25 April, a very early date; Langstone, 29.7.97, larval feedings and moulting-cocoons (JRL), Milton Common, at light in garden (IRT).

0274 *Bucculatrix ulmella* Zeller, 1848

Despite the specific name, this insect is associated with deciduous oaks *Quercus* spp. and not elm *Ulmus* spp. It occurs widely in all three vice-counties, with many more records in recent years, given below.

■ vc10 Newtown, 18.9.97, a few vacated mines; Parkhurst Forest, 18.9.97, a few vacated mines on *Q. robur* (AME, JRL).

■ vc11 Roydon Woods, 10.7.96, one at m.v. light (PRD, JRL); Pennington, 8.11.97, one vacated mine and moulting-cocoon; Balmer Lawn (RJD); Lower Test Marshes NR, 1.10.96, many vacated mines (JRL); Crab Wood, 20.9.97, vacated mines on *Quercus* spp. (JRL, *et al.*); Peartree Green, Southampton, 9.10.99, mines; Botany Bay, Sholing, 5.10.99, mines; Royal Victoria Country Park, 23.8.00, mines; Hamble Common, 3.11.99, mines (PAB); Fareham, 17.8.98; Hook-with-Warsash, 1996, (RJD); Upper Hamble Country Park, 7.10.96, many vacated mines; Bursledon, 8.9.98, a few vacated mines; Lower Titchfield Haven NR, 21.10.96, several vacated mines; Swanwick NR, 20.8.96, one at m.v. light; Curbridge NR, 10.10.98, a few vacated mines; The Moors NR, Bishops Waltham, 19.10.96, a few vacated mines; West Meon, 8.10.96, many vacated mines; Purbrook, 28.9.98, many vacated mines; Alver Valley NR, Gosport, 22.9.97, a few vacated mines; Great Salterns NR, Portsmouth (JRL).

■ vc12 Wildhern, nr Andover, 26.9.97, mines on *Quercus* spp; Fleet Pond LNR, 7.10.97, mines on *Quercus*;

St John's Copse, Oakley, 5.8.98 (DGG); Farnborough, 6.5.95 (RWP); Bramdean Common, 8.10.96, many vacated mines; Yateley, 23.9.94, many vacated mines and moulting-cocoons; Shortheath Common, 20.8.98, a few vacated mines and one cocoon (JRL *et al.*).

0275 *Bucculatrix bechsteinella* (Bechstein & Scharfenberg, 1805)
= *crataegi* Zeller, 1839

On the mainland, the species is widespread; its presence on the Isle of Wight was confirmed recently by RJD. When specified, the mines have always been on hawthorn *Crataegus* spp.

■ vc8 Martin Down, 5.5.90 (S. Nash).

■ vc10 Yarmouth, a female, genitalia det. (RJD). **First confirmed record.**

■ vc11 Lower Titchfield Haven NR, 20.8.93, larval feedings and moulting-cocoons on hawthorn (JRL); Portsdown; Oxenbourne Down (RJD); Sandy Point NR, Hayling Island, 30.7.96, several vacated mines (JRL, RMP).

■ vc12 Wildhern, nr Andover, 24.7.97, mines on hawthorn (DGG); Harewood Forest, 26.10.97, mines on hawthorn; Noar Hill, 13.10.96, mines on hawthorn (DGG).

0276 *Bucculatrix demaryella* (Duponchel, 1840)

There are very few records of this species. It has been reported in the past from all three vice-counties, but seen in any number only in Botley Wood, vc11. The larva mines and later makes windows in the leaves of birch *Betula* spp.

■ vc12 Pamber, 1994 (GJD).

Douglasiidae (1)

A family of small, dark moths which rest with their front legs "on tiptoe". The larvae of both British species feed among the flowers of viper's bugloss *Echium vulgare*.

0398 *Tinagma ocnerostomella* (Stainton, 1850)

The distribution of this species is limited by that of its foodplant, viper's bugloss. It is now known from several localities along the coast of S Hants and has recently been relocated at Micheldever (see below), whence it was recorded in the early 1970s by D.W.H. Ffennell (Goater, 1974).

■ vc11 Hamble Common, 21.6.93, two; 19.6.95, at least four; confined to a small area on western edge where some buildings had been demolished and *Echium* present; Portsdown Hill, 19.6.98, several beaten from *Echium* (RJD); Browndown, 5.7.97, many at m.v. light (JRL, IRT, *et al.*); Milton Common, Southsea, at light in garden, 1998 (IRT); Queen Elizabeth Country Park; Sinah Common, Hayling Island (RJD).

■ vc12 Micheldever, 7.4.97, larvae in old stems of *Echium* (JRL, IRT).

Roeslerstammiidae (1)

Another small family, the systematic position of which remains somewhat controversial. It is currently (Karsholt and Razowski, 1996) placed in the superfamily Gracillarioidea near Douglasiidae and Bucculatricidae.

0447 *Roeslerstammia erxlebella* (Fabricius, 1787)

Recorded for the first time for both Isle of Wight and N Hants in Goater (1992). It is probably widespread but overlooked. The larva feeds on lime *Tilia* and birch *Betula*.

■ vc11 Upper Hamble Country Park, 7.10.96, a few vacated mines on *Tilia* sp. and *Betula* sp. (AMD, AME, JRL); Chandlers Ford, May and August, 1999, very common (BE); Botley Wood; Catisfield; Havant Thicket, 30.4.93, one at m.v. light (JRL).

■ vc12 Wildhern, 24.5.98, disturbed by day; Fleet Pond LNR, 8.5.98, one by day (DGG); Oakley (AHD); Castle Bottom NR, 11.5.98; Yateley Common, 11.8.98 (AMD); Farnborough, 30.6.95, one at light, det. BR Baker (RWP).

Gracillariidae (75 + [3])

The features defining this family are clear-cut but subtle: the larvae, when young, feed on sap within the epidermal cells of leaves, but later they mine the leaves and consume the parenchyma cells, or spin leaves or construct a cone from a leaf, in which they live. This involves considerable structural changes to the head and mouthparts, a step referred to as hypermetamorphosis. The moths are small, but often with elegantly patterned forewings, especially perhaps in the large genus *Phyllonorycter*.

0280 *Caloptilia cuculipennella* (Hübner, 1796)

Recorded from the Isle of Wight and S Hants, but not since 1948.

0281 *Caloptilia populetorum* (Zeller, 1839)

■ vc12 Farnborough, 31.3.95, det JRL (RWP). **New county record.**

0282 *Caloptilia elongella* (Linnaeus, 1761)

Recorded from numerous localities in all three vice-counties. The larva on alder *Alnus glutinosa*, at first mining the leaves and feeding initially on sap, later on the parenchyma; later it spins part of a leaf into a cone and lives and feeds therein.

0283 *Caloptilia betulicola* (Hering, 1927)

Widespread on birch *Betula* spp. in the mainland vice-counties, but unrecorded from the Isle of Wight. The imago can be distinguished with certainty from the last species only by examining the genitalia.

0284 *Caloptilia rufipennella* (Hübner, 1796)

First recorded in vc11 in 1990 and 1991 (Goater, 1992). The species has now been found in all three vice-counties, mostly in the form of larval spinnings on the foodplant, sycamore *Acer pseudoplatanus*, and occasionally other species of maple.

■ vc10 Freshwater, 23.9.00, one at m.v. light (SAK-J); Newtown, 18.9.97, one spinning; Parkhurst Forest, 18.9.97, many spinnings (AME, JRL). **New vc record.**

■ vc11 Marchwood, 8.9.98, a few spinnings; Lower Test Marshes NR, 1.10.96, several vacated spinnings; Crab Wood, 20.9.97, several spinnings (JRL, *et al.*); Chessel Bay and Peartree Green, Southampton, 1999, spinnings; Royal Victoria Country Park, 23.8.00, spinnings (PAB); Winchester, nr Teg Down, larvae on *Acer saccharinum*, three moths bred (RJBH); Fareham, genit. checked; Titchfield Haven (RJD); Botley Wood, 29.9.94, a few spinnings; Fareham, 29.9.97, a few spinnings; Clanfield, 4.10.97, a few vacated spinnings; Great Salterns NR, Portsmouth; Langstone, 29.7.97, a few spinnings (JRL, IRT); Milton Common, Southsea, 1994, larva in a cone; 9.8, 14.8 and 22.8.97, at light, also in 2000, when 12 were recorded between 18.7 and 27.8 (IRT); Waterlooville, 1996–2000, at m.v. light (RJM).

■ vc12 Danebury Hillfort, 11.9.91, larva, em. 28.9.91 (RJBH); Wildhern, nr Andover, 20.9.97, mines; Tangley, 2.10.97, mines (DGG); Basingstoke, 23.9.98, vacated cones and larva (AHD); Farnborough, 16.4.95, det. JRL (RWP). **New vc record.**

0285 *Caloptilia azaleella* (Brants, 1913)

An introduced species which occurs in the wild amongst *Azalea* spp. in several of the southern counties, and more widely in greenhouses. In Hampshire, early stages were first reported in a garden at Bournemouth, and subsequently from Southampton, Hilliers Arboretum, Ampfield. A few adult specimens have been taken at light elsewhere in S Hants (Goater, 1974, 1992).

■ vc11 Hursley Park, 1.11.98, mines; Bitterne, 11.7.99, imago in garden (PAB); Chandlers Ford, 7.5.95, one at light, det. JRL (BG), October, 1999, a few cones in garden on evergreen azaleas (BE); Funtley, 2 to 9.5.99 (MLO, comm. RJD).

■ vc12 Farnborough, 21.10.94, one at m.v.light (RWP). **New vc record.**

0286 *Caloptilia alchimiella* (Scopoli, 1763)

The records given in Goater (1974) may refer to this or the next species, but those in Goater (1992) and the ones given below are correct. Both species feed on oak *Quercus* spp. The present species is univoltine, *C. robustella* bivoltine. Structurally, the two species are very similar and can be separated by dissection of the genitalia. The presence of *C. alchimiella* on the Isle of Wight requires confirmation.

■ vc11 Hound coast; Hamble Common, 1996; Browndown; Rowner Wild Grounds; Oxenbourne Down (RJD); West Walk, Wickham, 25.8.95 (JRL); Southsea, 5.10.96, one at m.v. light (JRL), 16.8.97, 31.7 and 27.8.00, singletons at light (IRT); Havant Thicket, 8.7.97, at m.v. light (JRL, IRT, *et al.*).

■ vc12 Wildhern, nr Andover, 23.5.99, at m.v. light (DGG); Pamber, 1994 (GJD); Bramley Frith Wood NR; Mapledurwell Fen (AHD); Selborne, 25.7 and 26.7.95, at light (AEA); Farnborough, 21.7.94 (RWP); Yateley Common, 11.6.94, one (AMD).

0287 *Caloptilia robustella* Jäckh, 1972

The records given in Goater (1992) and below indicate that this species is widespread in the mainland vice-

counties, and probably also on the Isle of Wight, amongst oak *Quercus* spp.

■ vc10 Newtown, 18.9.97, one vacated spinning on *Q. robur* (AME, JRL); Gurnard, 15.6.95, mines, conf. JRL (DTB). **New vc record.**

■ vc11 Anses Wood, New Forest, 22.8.98 (DGG); Roydon Woods, 10.7.96, a few at m.v. light (PRD, JRL); Balmer Lawn (RJD); Sparsholt College (AHD); Crab Wood, 20.9.97, vacated spinnings (JRL, *et al.*); Chandlers Ford, 18.8.95, det. JRL (BG); Bitterne, 1999; Gull Coppice, Whitley, 25.8.00 (PAB); Fareham, 17.8.98; West Walk; Rowner Wild Grounds (RJD); Marchwood, 8.9.98, a few old spinnings; Swanwick, 20.8.96, one at m.v. light; Upper Hamble Country Park, 7.10.96, one old spinning on *Q. robur*; Purbrook, 28.9.98, one old spinning; Creech Wood, Denmead, 22.8.97, one at m.v. light; Sandy Point NR, Hayling Island, 14.7.92, one at m.v. light (JRL *et al.*).

■ vc12 Wildhern, nr Andover, 20.9.97, mines; Anton Lakes, Andover, 19.8.98, mines and cones; St John's Copse, Oakley, 5.8.98; Eelmoor Marsh SSSI, 19.10.97, mines; Tangley, 2.10.97, mines; Harewood Forest, 26.10.97, mines; Fleet Pond LNR, 7.10.97, mines, 22.4.98, one at m.v. light (DGG); Abbotstone Down, 27.7.94, one at m.v. light; Bramdean Common, 8.10.96, a few vacated spinnings (JRL *et al.*); Oakley; Bartley Heath NR (AHD); Yateley Common, 11.8.98, det. JRL (AMD); Selborne, 1994 (AEA); Noar Hill NR, 23.8.95 (AMJ).

0288 *Caloptilia stigmatella* (Fabricius, 1781)

Mines and spinnings common on sallow, willows and poplars in all three vice-counties (JRL).

■ vc10 Yarmouth (RJD); Cranmore, 13.7.97; Freshwater, 24.5.98, at m.v. light (SAK-J); Parkhurst Forest, 13.11.96, mines (DTB).

0289 *Caloptilia falconipennella* (Hübner, 1813)

Apart from the records for the New Forest given in Goater (1974, 1992), the following are the only other ones received. The larva makes characteristic cones on alder *Alnus glutinosa*.

■ vc11 Matley Bog, 6.10.99, several cones, moths bred (BE); Lower Test Marshes NR, 1.10.96, one cocoon, moth bred (JRL).

0290 *Caloptilia semifascia* (Haworth, 1828)

This species appears to be fairly widespread in all three vice-counties, amongst the foodplant, field maple *Acer campestre*.

■ vc11 Sparsholt College (AHD); Crab Wood, 20.9.97, vacated spinnings (JRL, *et al.*); Hookheath Common, 1999, spinnings, moth bred (RJD).

■ vc12 Wildhern, nr Andover, 20.9.97, mines; Tangley, 2.10.97, mines; Harewood Forest, 26.10.97, mines (DGG); St John's Copse, Oakley, 5.8.98, mines and cones (DGG).

0295 *Caloptilia (Calybites) hauderi* (Rebel, 1906)

In Britain, known only from the Isle of Wight, where it was discovered in 1933 near St Helens, and now from S Hants. The most recent record from St Helens is of cones on field maple *Acer campestre*, 11.6.81, from which moths were bred (Goater, 1992).

■ vc11 Waterlooville, 25.7.00, at m.v. light, conf. JRL (RJM). **New vc record.**

0292 *Caloptilia leucapennella* (Stephens, 1835)
Recorded from the Isle of Wight and S Hants. The overwintering moth is occasionally beaten from yew *Taxus baccata* or gorse *Ulex europaeus*. Larva on oak *Quercus* spp. including *Q. ilex*.

■ vc11 Southsea, 28.6.95, one at m.v. light; Sandy Point NR, Hayling Island, 29.5.95, a few larvae on *Quercus robur*, moth bred (JRL).

0293 *Caloptilia syringella* (Fabricius, 1794)
Common amongst the foodplants ash, privet and lilac throughout the three vice-counties (JRL).

0294 *Aspilapteryx tringipennella* (Zeller, 1839)
Common throughout vice-counties 11 and 12, mines on ribwort plantain *Plantago lanceolata* (JRL).

■ vc8 Martin Down, 24.8.90 (MFVC and S. Nash), 8.6.92 (JRL, RMP).

■ vc10 Apes Down (RJD).

0296 *Calybites phasianipennella* (Hübner, 1813)
Recorded from all three vice-counties but evidently rare and taken mostly as single specimens.

■ vc12 Magdalen Hill Down, 12.8.00, imago (PAB); Farnborough, 7.8.97 (RWP).

0297 *Eucalybites (Calybites) auroguttella* (Stephens, 1835)
Locally common in the two mainland vice-counties. The moth is sometimes taken at light, and mines and spinnings occur on St John's-wort *Hypericum* spp.

■ vc10 Newtown, 18.9.97, several mines and spinnings (AME, JRL).

■ vc11 Merrietown Heath, 21.7.93, by day (PHS); Chandlers Ford, August, 1999, several (BE); Crab Wood, 20.9.97, mines and spinnings; Knapp, 25.9.99; Chessel Bay and Peartree Green, 1999; Bitterne, 27.10.99; Alver Valley NR, Gosport, 22.9.97, several mines; Clanfield, 4.10.97, many mines and spinnings on *H. perforatum*; Oxenbourne Down NR, 13.8.93, a few spinnings; Farlington Marshes NR, 17.8.93, a few mines and spinnings (JRL, *et al.*); Hookheath Common (RJD).

■ vc12 Winnall Moors NR (DHS); Magdalen Hill Down, 17.9.99, 12.8.00; Northington, 3.10.99 (PAB); Eelmoor Marsh SSSI, 19.10.97, mines on *H. perforatum*; Harewood Forest, 26.10.97, mines on *H. perforatum*; Fleet Pond LNR, 7.10.97, mines on *H. perforatum* (DGG); Pamber Forest, 2000 (GJD); Farnborough, 1.8.97 (RWP); Bramdean Common, 8.10.96, one mine; Ashford Hangers NR, 18.10.93, a few mines and spinnings on *H. perforatum* (JRL *et al.*).

0299 *Parectopa ononidis* (Zeller, 1839)
Described by Emmet *et al. in* Heath and Emmet (eds), (1985) as "an inconspicuous and evasive insect which may have been overlooked in many areas". This is almost certainly true in Hampshire. In S Hants, the moth and its early stages have been found recently in several places, but there is still only one record, of an empty mine, for N Hants and nothing since the Victoria County History for the Isle of Wight.

■ vc11 Fareham; Wickham Common, 8.7.98, one vacated mine on clover *Trifolium* spp. (RJD); Browndown, 2.5.92, a few tenanted mines on *T. pratense*, moths bred; Hilsea, 16.5.92, tenanted mines, and regularly since (JRL); Milton Common, Southsea, at light in garden, 1998 (IRT), 26.5.98, one by day (JRL, RMP).

[0300 *Parornix loganella* (Stainton, 1848)
The record given in Goater (1974) from Minstead is almost certainly in error. Although associated with birch *Betula* spp., this is a northern species occurring mainly from Lancashire and Yorkshire to the north of Scotland.]

0301 *Parornix betulae* (Stainton, 1854)
Common amongst birch *Betula* spp. in all three vice-counties (JRL). The larva mines a leaf, then lives in a folded-down leaf-margin or tip.

0302 *Parornix fagivora* (Frey, 1861)
■ vc11 West Wood, ix.89, two cocoons in upturned edges of beech leaves, moths em. 27.4.90 (RJBH); Crab Wood, 20.9.97, a few spinnings on beech; West Walk, 6.11.92, one vacated spinning on beech (JRL, *et al.*); Sparsholt College (AHD).

■ vc12 Wildhern, nr Andover, 20.9.97, mines on beech; Tangley, 2.10.97, mines on beech; Fleet Pond LNR, 7.10.97, mines on beech (DGG).

0302a *Parornix carpinella* (Frey, 1863)
■ vc12 Tangley, 2.10.97, 2.12.00, mines on *Carpinus*; Bentley Station Meadows, 28.8.98. These were originally identified as *P. fagivora* but redetermined and verified as *P. carpinella* in 2000, using criteria given by Emmet (1986, 1987) (DGG). **New county record.**

0303 *Parornix anglicella* (Stainton, 1850)
Abundant amongst hawthorn *Crataegus* spp., and wild service-tree *Sorbus torminalis* where it occurs, in all three vice-counties (JRL).

■ vc8 Martin Down, 29.4 and 5.5.90 (S. Nash), 8.6.92, spinnings on hawthorn (JRL, RMP).

0304 *Parornix devoniella* (Stainton, 1850)
Widespread and common amongst hazel in all three vice-counties (JRL).

0305 *Parornix scoticella* (Stainton, 1850)
Scattered records from the mainland vice-counties (Goater, 1974, 1992).

■ vc10 Parkhurst Forest, 18.9.97, a few vacated mines on rowan *Sorbus aucuparia* (AME, JRL). **New vc record.**

■ vc11 Roydon Woods, 3.10.98, one vacated mine on rowan (RJD, JRL); several localities in Southampton area, autumn 1999 and 2000, mines on apple *Malus* sp. and rowan; Royal Victoria Country Park, 23.8.00, mines on

apple *Malus* spp. (PAB); Crab Wood, 20.9.97, a few mines on whitebeam *S. aria*; Alver Valley NR, 22.9.97, one vacated mine on rowan; Oxenbourne Down NR, 13.5.3.93, a few mines, one with larva, on whitebeam (JRL, *et al.*); Wickham Common, 7.10.98, mines; Milton Common, Southsea, at light in garden, 1998 (IRT).
■ vc12 Wildhern, nr Andover, 28.9.97, mines on apple *Malus* spp. (DGG); Yateley, 23.9.94, a few mines on rowan (AMD, JRL).

0308 *Parornix finitimella* (Zeller, 1850)
Widespread in all three vice-counties. Larval mines and spinnings on blackthorn *Prunus spinosa*.
■ vc10 Tennyson Down, 18.5.92, one, genitalia det. (JRL, DHS, PHS); Newtown, 18.9.97, a few vacated mines and spinnings; Parkhurst Forest, 18.9.97, a few vacated mines and spinnings (AME, JRL). **New vc record.**

0309 *Deltaornix (Parornix) torquillella* (Zeller, 1850)
Frequent in all three vice-counties. The larva makes mines and spinnings in leaves of blackthorn *Prunus spinosa*, and also in wild plum *Prunus domestica* and apple *Malus* spp.
■ vc8 Martin Down, 24.8.90 (MFVC and S. Nash).
■ vc10 Alum Bay, 14.10.96, mines; Roud, 4.9.96, mines (DTB).

0310 *Callisto denticulella* (Thunberg, 1794)
Widespread throughout the three vice-counties, mining and spinning leaves of apple *Malus domestica* in orchards and gardens and also on crab apple *M. sylvestris*.
■ vc10 Newtown, 18.9.97, one vacated spinning on *M. sylvestris* (AME, JRL); Gurnard, 10.7.95, tenanted mines (DTB).

0311 *Dialectica (Acrocercops) imperialella* (Zeller, 1847)
There have been no records of this insect from the Isle of Wight or mainland Hampshire since Goater (1974). The larva feeds on the very local narrow-leaved lungwort *Pulmonaria longifolia*, but is stated also to use comfrey *Symphytum* spp. by Emmet *et al.* (1985).

0313 *Acrocercops brongniardella* (Fabricius, 1798)
Only two records are given in Goater (1974). Since then, this species has been found quite widely in all three vice-counties (Goater, 1992). The larva mines the leaves of oak *Quercus* spp. including evergreen oak *Q. ilex*.
■ vc8 Martin Down, 8.6.92, mine on deciduous oak *Quercus* spp. (JRL, RMP).
■ vc10 St Boniface Down, 22.4.94, empty mines on *Q. ilex* (JMC); Totland, 10.6.96, mines with larvae; Locks Copse, 11.8.96, mines with larvae on *Q. robur*; Gurnard, 15.6.95, mines, all conf. JRL (DTB). **New vc record.**
■ vc11 Teg Down, Winchester, 25.5.92, several tenanted mines on deciduous *Quercus* spp.; Swanwick, 14.6.97, a few vacated mines; Hookheath Meadows NR, Southwick, 9.6.92, one tenanted mine (JRL *et al.*); Fareham (RJD); Titchfield Haven NR, 24.5.93, a few mines on *Q. robur*; Sandy Point NR, Hayling Island, 14.7.92, one at m.v. light (JRL).
■ vc12 Harewood Forest, 29.7.99, one (BE); Silchester

Common, 1995, mine on deciduous *Quercus*, moth em. (MCH); Bramdean Common, 8.10.96, one vacated mine; Bramshott Common, 23.5.98, one tenanted mine; Yateley, 23.9.94, a few vacated mines (JRL *et al.*).

0314 *Leucospilapteryx omissella* (Stainton, 1848)
Recorded from all three vice-counties, but not recently from the Isle of Wight (Goater, 1974, 1992). The larva mines the leaves of mugwort *Artemisia vulgaris*, and has also been found on the extremely local Chinese mugwort *A. verlotiorum*.
■ vc11 Peartree Green, Southampton, 9.10.99, mines in *A. vulgaris* and *A. verlotiorum* (PAB); Fareham, 17.9.97, a few mines on *A. vulgaris* (AME, JRL); Browndown, September, 1999, larvae locally abundant (BE); Alver Valley NR, Gosport, 22.9.97, one mine on *A. verlotiorum* (JRL, IRT); Milton Common, Southsea, 1994, mines; four between 16.8 and 7.9.97, at light (IRT).
■ vc12 Harewood Forest, 26.10.97, mines on *A. vulgaris* (DGG); Pamber Forest, 21.5.74 (RJD).

The large genus *Phyllonorycter* has excited considerable attention among microlepidopterists in recent years, and the fauna of Hampshire and the Isle of Wight is probably as well-known as anywhere in the British Isles, and 43 of the 54 British species have been found here.

0315 *Phyllonorycter harrisella* (Linnaeus, 1761)
Widespread and common in the two mainland vice-counties, mines on deciduous oaks *Quercus* spp. (JRL).
■ vc8 Martin Down, 29.4.90 (S. Nash).
■ vc10 Apes Down; Parkhurst Forest; Borthwood; Firestone Copse (RJD).

[0316 *Phyllonorycter roboris* (Zeller, 1839)
The record given in Goater (1974) remains unconfirmed.]

0317 *Phyllonorycter heegeriella* (Zeller, 1846)
Not recorded in Hampshire until 1976 (Langmaid, 1976), but now known to be widespread in the two mainland vice-counties (Goater, 1983, 1992). There is still no record from the Isle of Wight. The larva mines the leaves of deciduous oak *Quercus* spp.
■ vc11 Stanpit Marsh, 27.8.00, mines, larva seen (PAB); Matley Heath, 11.10.98, mines (DGG); Emer Bog, 27.3.93, mines in fallen leaves of *Quercus*, moths bred (JRL, DHS); Weston Common, 5.10.99, larva seen (PAB); Upper Hamble Country Park, 7.10.96, one mine (JRL *et al.*); Botley Wood, 20.5.98, two beaten from oak; Wickham Common; Shedfield Common (RJD).
■ vc12 Wildhern, nr Andover, 31.8.96, 17.10.97, mines; Eelmoor Marsh SSSI, 19.10.97, mines; Harewood Forest, 26.10.97, mines; St John's Copse, Oakley, 5.8.98, mines; Fleet Pond LNR, 7.10.97, mines; Noar Hill, 13.10.96, mines; Eelmoor Marsh, 25.7.98, mines (DGG); Pamber Forest Farm, 18.10.00, a few mines; Bramley Frith NR; Bartley Heath NR, 22.10.94, mines fairly common, moths bred (AHD); Yateley Common, 26.3.94, mines in leaf-clothed young oaks, moths bred (AMD, BG, JRL). **New vc record.**

0318 Phyllonorycter tenerella (de Joannis, 1915)

There appears to be only one record, from Alice Holt, N Hants, in 1963 (Goater, 1974). The larva mines the leaves of hornbeam *Carpinus betulus*, a local plant in the county.

[0319 Phyllonorycter kuhlweiniella (Zeller, 1839)
= *saportella* (Duponchel, 1840)

The only record of this oak-feeding species is that in the manuscript of the late Wm Fassnidge, for "Southampton" (Goater, 1974). It is a very local species, perhaps overlooked, but its presence in Hampshire is best regarded as requiring confirmation.]

0320 Phyllonorycter quercifoliella (Zeller, 1839)

Widespread and locally common to abundant in all three vice-counties, though perhaps less so in the last five years. The larva mines the leaves of deciduous oaks *Quercus* spp.

■ vc10 Freshwater; Parkhurst Forest (RJD); Locks Copse, 28.8.96, mines, conf. JRL (DTB).

0321 Phyllonorycter messaniella (Zeller, 1846)

Abundant in all three vice-counties, mines on oak *Quercus* spp., especially *Q. ilex*, and on beech *Fagus sylvatica*, hornbeam *Carpinus betulus* and sweet chestnut *Castanea sativa* (JRL).

0321a Phyllonorycter platani (Staudinger, 1870)

This species was discovered new to Britain in 1990 (Emmet, 1991), and has since spread from London, where it was first found (Nash *et al.*, 1995). Mines should be sought on plane *Platanus × hispanica* growing in the Hampshire towns.

■ vc11 Southampton, 7.11.98, mines found, conf. JRL; Southampton Cemetery, 4.8.00, mines (PAB). **New county record.**

0323 Phyllonorycter oxyacanthae (Frey, 1856)

Mines common and widespread on hawthorn in all three vice-counties (JRL).

0324 Phyllonorycter sorbi (Frey, 1855)

The authors have records of this species from several localities in S and N Hants, but none from the Isle of Wight, where it is shown as present on the map (Emmet *et al. in* Heath and Emmet, 1985). The larva mines the leaves of rowan *Sorbus aucuparia*.

■ vc11 Mudeford Wood, 17.9.99, mines; Holbury, 23.10.00, mines on *Sorbus* sp., **not** *S. aucuparia* (JEC); Lordswood, Bitterne Park and Botany Bay, Sholing, autumn, 1999, mines; Southampton Cemetery, 4.8.00, mines; Royal Victoria Country Park, 23.8.00, mines (PAB); Roydon Woods, 3.10.98, mines; Lower Titchfield Haven NR, 21.10.96, a few mines (JRL).

■ vc12 Pamber, 1994 (GJD); Ludshott Common (RJD); Yateley, 23.9.94, several mines (AMD, JRL).

0325 Phyllonorycter mespilella (Hübner, 1805)

The larva of this species is associated particularly with wild service-tree *Sorbus torminalis*, and the moth, like its

foodplant, is very local in Britain. The only records are those given in Goater (1974).

0326 Phyllonorycter blancardella (Fabricius, 1781)

Recorded from all three vice-counties, but not recently from the Isle of Wight (Goater, 1974, 1992). The larva mines the leaves of crab apple *Malus sylvestris* and cultivars.

■ vc11 Roydon Wood, 6.10.99, mines on *M. sylvestris* (BE); Mallard Wood; Catisfield; Titchfield Haven; Wickham Common, 18.7 and 12.8.98, tenanted mines (RJD); Lordswood, mines on *Malus* spp.; Royal Victoria Country Park, 23.8.00, mines (PAB); Alver Valley NR, Gosport, 22.9.97, one mine on *M. domestica* (JRL, IRT); Waterlooville, 15.4.00, resting on door (RJM).

■ vc12 Wildhern, 20.7.98, mines on *Malus* spp. (DGG); Pamber, 1994 (GJD); Bartley Heath NR, 24.10.94, mines common on *Malus* spp. moths bred, 22.5.99, two moths (AHD).

0327 Phyllonorycter cydoniella ([Denis & Schiffermüller], 1775)

There are several known localities in the mainland vice-counties for this local species, where the larva mines the leaves of crab apple *Malus sylvestris*. (Goater, 1983, 1992).

■ vc11 Roydon Woods, 3.10.98, mines (JRL), 6.10.99, mines (BE); Sparsholt College (AHD); Crab Wood, 20.9.97, mines (JRL, *et al.*); Catisfield (RJD).

■ vc12 Harewood Forest, 26.10.97, mines; Micheldever Spoil Heaps, 29.7.00, adult (DGG); Bartley Heath NR, 24.10.94, mines scarce, moths bred, 22.5.99, two moths (AHD).

0329 Phyllonorycter pomonella (Zeller, 1846)
= *spinicolella* (Zeller, 1846)
= *cerasicolella* (Herrich-Schäffer, 1855)

Although there are only a few records from the Isle of Wight (Goater, 1992), this species is otherwise widespread in all three vice-counties. All records of mines reported under *pomonella* have been on blackthorn. The following are of mines on cherry *Prunus cerasus* or *P. avium*, reported as *P. cerasicolella*.

■ vc10 Newtown, 18.9.97, a few mines on *Prunus cerasus* (AME, JRL); Mill Copse, Yarmouth, 1996, mines, conf. JRL; Brading, 16.10.95, mines on *P. avium*; Tolt, 1.6.96, imago (DTB).

■ vc11 Roydon Wood, 6.10.99, mines (BE); Mudeford Wood, 17.9.99, mines; Peartree Green and Bitterne Park, Southampton, October, 1999, mines; Botany Bay, Sholing, 5.10.99, mines; Royal Victoria Country Park, 23.8.00, mines (PAB); Wickham Common, 1998 (RJD); Hookheath Meadows NR, Southwick, 17.10.92, one mine on *P. avium*; Upper Hamble Country Park, 7.10.96, several mines; Botley Wood, 29.9.94, a few mines on *P. avium*; Sandy Point NR, Hayling Island, 17.10.96, a few mines (JRL *et al.*); Waterlooville, 1996–1999 (RJM).

■ vc12 Brighton Hill, Basingstoke, 25.10.95, mines common on cultivated *Prunus*, moths bred 1996 (AHD); Farnborough, 1994, mines in cherry, moths bred, 1.5.95 (five) (RWP).

0331 *Phyllonorycter lantanella* (Schrank, 1802)
Frequent on the chalk in all three vice-counties (Goater, 1974, 1992). The larva mines leaves of wayfaring-tree *Viburnum lantana*.
■ vc10 Osborne, 10.1.96, mines with larvae (DTB).
■ vc11 Crab Wood, 20.9.97, mines (JRL, *et al.*); Hen Wood, East Meon, 10.10.94, several mines (JRL).
■ vc12 Wildhern, nr Andover, 6.10.96, 29.9.97, mines; Tangley, 2.10.97, mines; Northington, 3.10.99, mines (PAB); Noar Hill, 13.10.96, mines (DGG).

0332 *Phyllonorycter corylifoliella* (Hübner, 1796)
Mines common to abundant on hawthorn, apple *Malus* spp., pear *Pyrus* spp. and *Sorbus* spp. in all three vice-counties (JRL).
■ vc8 Martin Down, 5.5.90 (S. Nash), 24.8.90 (MFVC and S. Nash).

0332a *Phyllonorycter leucographella* (Zeller, 1850)
This is another comparative newcomer to the British fauna which was first reported in Essex in 1989 (Emmet, 1989) and has since spread rapidly (Nash *et al.*, 1995). The larva mines the leaves of fire-thorn *Pyracantha coccinea*, and was first discovered in Hampshire in 1998, more or less simultaneously in both S and N Hants.
■ vc10 Gurnard, 146 mines, some with larvae, on one bush, 31.3.01, conf. JRL (DTB). **New vc record.**
■ vc11 Bournemouth University, 10.3.00, several mines (PHS); Otterbourne Hill, 4.1.99, mines; Southampton, 5.12.98, mines; Southampton Common, 14.9.99, mines; Peartree Green, 9.10.99, mines (PAB); Fareham Creek, 9.1.01, and Hoeford, same date, mines on *Pyracantha* (LM); Droxford; Park Gate, 30.1.98, mines; Portsdown; Portsmouth (RJD); Southsea, mines common on *Pyracantha* in neighbour's garden, 21.1.98, and moths at light during May and August/September (JRL), at light in garden, 17.8 and 28.9.98, and subsequently, det. JRL (IRT). **New vc record.**
■ vc12 Brighton Hill, Basingstoke, 17.1.98, mines locally common, det. JRL; first moths bred indoors, 10.2.98 (AHD); Fleet, 14.10.00, mines on *Pyracantha* in recorder's garden (RE). **New county record.**

0333 *Phyllonorycter salictella* (Zeller, 1846)
subsp. *viminiella* (Sircom, 1848)
Locally common in damp areas with sallow *Salix* spp. bushes in all three vice-counties, and bred also from aspen *Populus tremula*, a species not given as a foodplant in Emmet *et al.* in Heath and Emmet (1985).
■ vc8 Martin Down, 5.5.90 (S. Nash).
■ vc10 Newport, 12.6.95, imago emerged from mine taken there (DTB).
■ vc11 Soberton, 30.6.95, one at m.v. light; Havant Thicket, 11.10.92, many mines on aspen, moths bred (JRL), 23.6.98, two males (RJD).
■ vc12 Pamber, 1994 (GJD); Pamber Forest Farm, 18.10.00, mines fairly common on sallow *Salix cinerea*; Bartley Heath NR, 24.10.94, mines common on *S. cinerea*, moths bred (AHD); Fleet Pond LNR, 7.10.97,

mines on crack willow *S. fragilis* (DGG); Shortheath Common, 20.8.98, a few mines on *S. fragilis* (JRL).

0334 *Phyllonorycter viminetorum* (Stainton, 1854)
Recorded from all three vice-counties (Goater, 1974, 1992) but extremely local, the larva feeding apparently exclusively on osier *Salix viminalis*.

0335 *Phyllonorycter salicicolella* (Sircom, 1848)
The species is widespread and fairly common on sallow *Salix* spp. in the mainland vice-counties, and has also been bred from aspen (Goater, 1992).
■ vc10 Parkhurst Forest (RJD); St George's Down, 15.10.97 (DTB).
■ vc11 South Bentley Inclosure, New Forest, 1.6.99 (DGG); Titchfield Haven; Wickham Common, 18.7.98, tenanted mine on *Salix* spp. (RJD).
■ vc12 Pamber, 1994 (GJD); Greywell Moors NR, 15.10.94, mines fairly common on *S. caprea*, moths bred; Bramley Frith Wood, 3.12.94, mines fairly common; Bartley Heath NR, 24.10.94, mines scarce (AHD); Eelmoor Marsh, 5.7.98, tenanted mines on *Salix*, moths bred (DGG).

0336 *Phyllonorycter dubitella* (Herrich-Schäffer, 1855)
The first British record was made in 1969 by the late D.W.H. Ffennell, who found mines in the leaves of goat willow *Salix caprea* along the Winchester by-pass (Goater, 1974). It has since been found in several places in the two mainland vice-counties (Goater, 1992).
■ vc11 Botley Wood (RJD); Southsea, 22.7.96, one at m.v. light (JRL).
■ vc12 Greywell Moors NR, 15.10.94, mines fairly common on *Salix caprea*, moths bred; Bramley Frith Wood NR; Bartley Heath (AHD); Ashford Hangers NR, 18.10.93, a few mines (JRL).

0337 *Phyllonorycter hilarella* (Zetterstedt, 1839)
= *spinolella* (Duponchel, 1840)
Emmet *et al.* in Heath and Emmet, 1985 indicate the presence of this species on the Isle of Wight on their map, but the records given below are the first to have reached the authors. According to JRL, the mines are to be found only on goat willow *Salix caprea*.
■ vc10 Firestone Copse 20.11.95; Combley Great Wood, mines, 31.10.00 (DTB); Parkhurst Forest, several moths bred from mines on *S. caprea* coll. 8.1.77; nr Luccombe, 7.6.72, adult det. RJD (DMA). **New vc record.**
■ vc12 Micheldever Wood; Pamber Forest (RJD), 2000 (GJD); Bramley Frith Wood NR; Bartley Heath (AHD); Eelmoor Marsh, 24.7.98, at m.v. light (DGG).

0338 *Phyllonorycter cavella* (Zeller, 1846)
Recorded from several localities in S and N Hants (Goater, 1974, 1992), but not yet from the Isle of Wight. The larva mines the leaves of birch *Betula* spp.
■ vc11 Ashurst, 16.10.99, mines on birch seedlings; Emer Bog, October, 1999, mines common (BE).
■ vc12 Wildhern, nr Andover, 28.9.96, mines (DGG); Pamber, 1994 (GJD); Bartley Heath (AHD).

0339 *Phyllonorycter ulicicolella* (Stainton, 1851)
This local species is associated with gorse *Ulex europaeus*, in the green shoots of which the larva mines. All Hampshire records are of caught moths.
▪ vc11 Lions Hill, 14.6.99, one taken by day (PHS); Browndown, 18.6.93, two (JRL, RMP).
▪ vc12 Silchester Common, 19.6.96, common, beaten out of gorse (AHD). **New vc record.**

0340 *Phyllonorycter scopariella* (Zeller, 1846)
The first Hampshire records were given in Goater (1983) and repeated in Goater (1992). There have been no further reports. The larva feeds in the shoots of broom *Cytisus scoparius* and, like that of *P. ulicicolella*, is difficult to locate.

0341 *Phyllonorycter maestingella* (Müller, 1764)
Recorded from all three vice-counties, with "countless" records from S and N Hants (JRL, DHS). The larva mines the leaves of beech *Fagus* spp.
▪ vc10 Westover Plantation, 7.8.95, mines (DTB); Luccombe Chine (RJD).

0342 *Phyllonorycter coryli* (Nicelli, 1851)
Mines abundant wherever hazel occurs in all three vice-counties (JRL).

0343 *Phyllonorycter quinnata* (Geoffroy, 1785)
Locally common amongst the foodplant, hornbeam *Carpinus betulus*; records from all three vice-counties are given in Goater (1974, 1992).
▪ vc10 Osborne, 28.9.96, many mines with larvae on DTB, conf. JRL (Agassiz *et al.*,1998). **New vc record.**
▪ vc11 Roydon Woods, 3.10.98, many mines; Netley, 21.10.99, mines (PAB); Upper Hamble Country Park, 7.10.96, a few mines; Fareham, 10.10.97, several mines; Hilsea, 30.9.97, many mines, moths bred (JRL *et al.*).
▪ vc12 Tangley, 2.10.97, mines (DGG); Basingstoke, 20.10.94, mines fairly common, moths bred (AHD); Bentley Station Meadow, mines, 28.8.98 (DGG).

0344 *Phyllonorycter strigulatella* (Lienig & Zeller, 1846)
The larva of this species is monophagous on grey alder *Alnus incana*; where this plant occurs, the moth is often common, but there are few records outside Hampshire and the Isle of Wight (Emmet *et al.*, *in* Heath and Emmet, 1985).
▪ vc11 Funtley, mines (RJD); Milton Common, Southsea, 1994, mines (IRT); Portsmouth, 30.8.96, several mines, moths bred; Farlington Marshes NR, 6.9.93, a few mines (JRL).

0345 *Phyllonorycter rajella* (Linnaeus, 1758)
Mines common on alder *Alnus* spp. in the two mainland vice-counties (JRL). On the Isle of Wight, the moth has been bred from *A. cordata* (Goater, 1992).

0347 *Phyllonorycter anderidae* (Fletcher, 1885)
Recorded from several localities in the two mainland vice-counties (Goater, 1974, 1994). The larva mines the leaves of birch *Betula* spp.

▪ vc11 Roydon Woods, 3.10.98, several mines on *B. pubescens* on heathland (RJD, JRL); Matley Heath, 11.10.98, mines on *Betula* (DGG); Wickham Common, 7.10.98, mines very locally common (RJD).
▪ vc12 Eelmoor Marsh, 30.8.98, by day (DGG).

0348 *Phyllonorycter quinqueguttella* (Stainton, 1851)
Recorded hitherto only from S Hants, where the moth is locally common in boggy ground where the foodplant, creeping willow *Salix repens* occurs.
▪ vc11 Roydon Woods, 3.10.98, a few mines (RJD, JRL).
▪ vc12 Bartley Heath (AHD). **New vc record.**

0351 *Phyllonorycter lautella* (Zeller, 1846)
Widespread and locally common in all three vice-counties. The larva mines the leaves of oak *Quercus* spp., evidently preferring the foliage of saplings and stooled oaks (Emmet *et al.*, *in* Heath and Emmet, 1985).
▪ vc10 Osborne Estate, 12.3.94, pupa and mine on *Q. canariensis* (JMC).
▪ vc11 Roydon Woods, 3.10.98, many mines on *Quercus* seedling (RJD, JRL); Matley Heath, 11.10.98, mines on *Quercus* (DGG); Ashurst, 12.7.93, many mines; Crab Wood, 20.9.97, one adult; Hookheath Meadows NR, Southwick, 17.10.92, many mines; Upper Hamble Country Park, 7.10.96, one mine; Clanfield, 4.10.97, several mines; Alver Valley NR, Gosport, 22.9.97, several mines (JRL, *et al.*); Emer Bog and Ampfield Wood, October, 1999, mines common (BE); Wickham Common, 9.10.98, 20+ mines; Oxenbourne Down (RJD).
▪ vc12 Wildhern, 13.10.98, mines; St John's Copse, Oakley, 5.8.98, mines (DGG); Eelmoor Marsh SSSI, 19.10.97, mines; Fleet Pond LNR, 7.10.97, mines (DGG); Brighton Hill, Basingstoke, 1996 (AHD); Shortheath Common, 20.8.98, several mines (AMD, JRL, IRT).

0352 *Phyllonorycter schreberella* Fabricius, 1781
Widespread in all three vice-counties (Goater, 1974, 1992). The larva mines the leaves of elm *Ulmus* spp. The numerous new records are given below.
▪ vc10 Shalfleet, 10.9.97, mine with larva (DTB); Newtown, 18.9.97, a few mines on *U. procera* (AME, JRL).
▪ vc11 Mudeford Wood, 17.9.99, mines; Peartree Green, Southampton, 9.10.99, mines (PAB); Pennington, 8.11.93, a few mines; Lower Test Marshes NR, 1.10.96, a few mines (JRL); Catisfield (RJD); Fareham, 14.8.97, several mines; Hookheath Meadows NR, Southwick, 17.10.92, several mines on *U. procera*; Alver Valley NR, Gosport, 22.9.97, several mines; Hilsea, 16.8.92, mines common on *U. procera* and a few on *U. glabra*; Gutner Point NR, Hayling Island, 6.10.96, several mines (JRL *et al.*).
▪ vc12 Wildhern, nr Andover, 28.7.96, 17.8.97, mines on *U. procera* (DGG); Basingstoke, 20.10.94, mines scarce on *U. procera*, moths bred (AHD).

0353 *Phyllonorycter ulmifoliella* (Hübner, 1817)
Mines widespread and common on birch *Betula* spp. in all three vice-counties (JRL).

0354 *Phyllonorycter emberizaepennella* (Bouché, 1834)
Scattered records from all three vice-counties (Goater, 1974, 1992), to which may be added the following. The larva mines the foliage of honeysuckle *Lonicera* spp., snowberry *Symphoricarpos albus* and Himalayan honeysuckle *Leycesteria formosa*.
■ vc10 Seagrove Bay, 26.11.95, mines and pupae on *Leycesteria* (DTB).
■ vc11 Winchester, 26.11.90, mines on *L. formosa*, one moth bred 4.91; one at m.v.light 30.7.92 (RJBH); Upper Hamble Country Park, 7.10.96, a few mines on *Lonicera* (AMD, AME, JRL).
■ vc12 Wildhern, nr Andover, 26.9.97, mines on *Lonicera* (DGG); Basingstoke, 28.10.94, mines locally common on *Symphoricarpus*, moths bred (AHD). Second and third records for vc12.

0356 *Phyllonorycter tristrigella* (Haworth, 1828)
Mines widespread and common on elm *Ulmus* spp. in the two mainland vice-counties (JRL), and evidently widespread also on the Isle of Wight.
■ vc10 Tennyson Down, 18.5.92, one (JRL, DHS, PHS); Parkhurst Forest, Priory Woods, 1995, mines and larvae (DTB).

0357 *Phyllonorycter stettinensis* (Nicelli, 1852)
Widespread and frequent in the vicinity of the foodplant, alder *Alnus glutinosa*. It is considered likely to turn up in other places on the Isle of Wight.
■ vc10 Yafford, 16.10.96, mine, conf. JRL (DTB). **New vc record.**
■ vc11 Lower Test Marshes NR, 11.10.96, a few mines (JRL); Chessel Bay, Southampton, 6.10.99, mines; Weston Common, 5.10.99, mines; Stoke Park Wood, 19.10.99, mines (PAB); Hookheath Meadows NR, Southwick, 4.8.92, many mines; Lower Titchfield Haven NR, 21.10.96, a few mines; Farlington Marshes, 7.6.93, one, 6.9.93, many mines on *A. glutinosa* and *A. incana* (JRL).
■ vc12 Pamber, 1994 (GJD); Greywell Moors NR, 15.10.94, mines common, moths bred; Bramley Frith Wood NR (AHD); Fleet Pond LNR, 7.10.97, mines (DGG).

0358 *Phyllonorycter froelichiella* (Zeller, 1839)
This is another species the larva of which mines the leaves of alder *Alnus glutinosa*. Recorded from all three vice-counties (Goater, 1974, 1992).
■ vc10 Alverstone, 21.9.97, mines (RJD).
■ vc11 Matley Bog (RJD); Chessel Bay, Southampton, 6.10.99, mines; Weston Common, 5.10.99, mines (PAB); Lower Test Marshes NR, 1.10.96, several mines; Hookheath Meadows NR, Southwick, 4.8.92, mines; Upper Hamble Country Park, 7.10.96, many mines; Lower Titchfield Haven NR, 21.10.96, one mine (JRL *et al.*); Cherque (RJD).
■ vc12 Fleet Pond LNR, 7.10.97, mines (DGG).

0359 *Phyllonorycter nicellii* (Stainton, 1851)
Mines common on hazel in all three vice-counties (JRL).

0360 *Phyllonorycter kleemannella* (Fabricius, 1781)
Mines can be found on alder *Alnus* spp. in a number of localities in the mainland vice-counties, and further records may be expected from the Isle of Wight. The following are in addition to those given in Goater (1974, 1992).
■ vc10 north of Newport, 6.11.96, mines and pupae, conf. JRL (DTB). **New vc record.**
■ vc11 Sparsholt College (AHD); Funtley; Curbridge; Rowner Wild Grounds (RJD); Royal Victoria Country Park, 23.8.00, mines (PAB); Hookheath Meadows NR, Southwick, 12.6.92, a few; Upper Hamble Country Park, 7.10.96, a few mines; Lower Titchfield Haven NR, 20.8.93, one; Alver Valley NR, Gosport, 22.9.97, a few mines; Farlington Marshes NR, 6.9.93, a few mines on *A. glutinosa* (JRL *et al.*).
■ vc12 Pamber, 1994 (GJD); Basingstoke, 28.10.94, mines fairly common; Greywell Moors NR, 15.10.94, mines fairly common on *Alnus* spp., moths bred; Bramley Frith Wood NR (AHD); Farnborough, 12.8.95, two (RWP); Ashford Hangers NR, 18.10.93, a few mines (JRL).

0361 *Phyllonorycter trifasciella* (Haworth, 1828)
Common in all three vice-counties, mines on honeysuckle *Lonicera periclymenum* (JRL), sometimes on *Leycesteria formosa* and *Symphoricarpos* (PAB).
■ vc8 Martin Down, 29.4.90 (S. Nash).
■ vc10 Bouldnor; Godshill (RJD).

0362 *Phyllonorycter acerifoliella* (Zeller, 1839)
= *sylvella* (Haworth, 1828)
Mines common on field maple *Acer campestre* in all three vice-counties (JRL).

0363 *Phyllonorycter platanoidella* (de Joannis, 1920)
The larva is monophagous on Norway maple *Acer platanoides*. The first Hampshire records were given in Goater (1983), all from S Hants, and further ones, including the first for N Hants, in Goater (1992).
■ vc10 Bouldnor Forest, 14.10.00, many mines with larvae (DTB, conf. JRL). **New vc record.**
■ vc11 Holbury, 23.10.00, mines (JEC); Sparsholt College (AHD); Ampfield Wood, 25.9.99, mines; Lordswood and Riverside Park, Southampton, October, 1999, mines; Weston Common, 5.10.99, mines (PAB); Crab Wood, 20.9.97, one mine; West Walk, 6.11.92, many mines; Fareham, 14.8.97, several mines (JRL, *et al.*).
■ vc12 Isle of Wight Woods, Porton Down, 3.10.94, several mines (RJBH, JRL); Wildhern, nr Andover, 20.9.97, mines; Fleet Pond LNR, 7.10.97, mines (DGG); Itchen Wood, Micheldever, 10.11.98, mines (PAB); Brighton Hill, Basingstoke (AHD); Shortheath Common, 20.8.98, one mine (AMD, JRL, IRT).

0364 *Phyllonorycter geniculella* (Ragonot, 1874)
Mines widespread and common on sycamore *Acer pseudoplatanus* in all three vice-counties (JRL).

0367 *Phyllocnistis saligna* (Zeller, 1839)
Recorded from S Hants in Goater (1974) and from Leckford in N Hants in Goater (1992). The larva mines

the leaves of long-leaved willows *Salix* spp. especially *S. purpurea*.

■ vc12 Leckford, September, 1999, mines and cocoons abundant on *S. purpurea* (BE).

0368 *Phyllocnistis unipunctella* (Stephens, 1834)

Scattered records are given in Goater (1974, 1992), to which the following may be added. The larva mines the leaves of poplars *Populus* spp.

■ vc10 Bembridge, 6.9.98, mine with dead larva (DTB); Shanklin (JMC).

■ vc11 Purbrook, 28.9.98, many mines (JRL); Milton Common, Southsea, at light in garden, 1998 2000 (IRT); Sandy Point NR, Hayling Island, 30.7.96, a few mines on *Populus × canadensis* JRL, RMP).

Sesiidae (13 + [1])

The clearwings require special effort to find them. Traditionally, the early stages are sought during the winter months, but recently several synthetic pheromone lures have been used to attract males. So far, little use has been made of these in Hampshire and none in the Isle of Wight, and the whole family remains grievously neglected, even though traditionally they have been treated as Macrolepidoptera. All known records were included in Goater (1974, 1992).

0370 *Sesia apiformis* (Clerck, 1759)
Hornet Clearwing   **Notable/Nb**

There is still only one known locality for this species in Hampshire, where it persists to this day.

0371 *Sesia bembeciformis* (Hübner, 1806)
Lunar Hornet Clearwing

■ vc11 Brambridge, 29.3.96, workings in cut stumps; Titchfield Haven NR, 5.4.95, numerous workings in *Salix* stumps (BG); Browndown, common (DSW).

■ vc12 Anton Lakes, 19.8.98, larval workings in *Salix* spp. (DGG); Pamber, 1994 (GJD).

0372 *Paranthrene tabaniformis* (Rottemburg, 1775)
Dusky Clearwing

There have been no recent records of this species in Britain. There is one old record for Hampshire in 1909 (Goater, 1974).

0373 *Synanthedon tipuliformis* (Clerck, 1759)
Currant Clearwing   **Notable/Nb**

The larva feeds in the twigs of currant *Ribes* spp. and is sometimes common in gardens and allotments, and the moth flies in sunshine over the bushes, but because of its habits, it is not often seen by lepidopterists.

■ vc10 Hamstead, 10.6.95 (DTB).

■ vc11 Ganger Farm, Ampfield, 18.6.00, three attracted to pheromone lure (ARC, TJN); Alverstoke, from 1987, larvae common in currant bushes (DSW).

0374 *Synanthedon vespiformis* (Linnaeus, 1761)
Yellow-legged Clearwing   **Notable/Nb**

Larval workings of this species may sometimes be found in abundance between the bark and wood of one-year-old oak stumps, and the moth is occasionally seen in flight in woodland where trees have been felled.

■ vc10 Bonchurch Down, July 1996 and 1997, moths seen and photographed and pupal exuviae found protruding from stumps of holm oak *Quercus ilex*, sometimes 8–12 per stump; Luccombe Down, 15.7.94, female seen ovipositing in freshly cut sweet chestnut gatepost (A. Butler).

■ vc11 Hurn, 5.5.97, larvae in oak stump (PD); Westbourne, 27.7.92, (Miss M.M. Brooks, comm. PHS); Merrietown Heath, 30.4.97, larvae in cut oak stump (PHS).

■ vc12 Harewood Forest, 26.10.97, larval workings in stumps of *Quercus* (DGG); Pamber, 1994 (GJD); Bartley Heath NR, 11.9.95, larvae and mines in *Quercus* stumps (AHD); Odiham Common, 11.6.00, freshly emerged

The distribution maps show:

▲ 0370 *Sesia apiformis*
Hornet Clearwing

▲ 0371 *Sesia bembeciformis*
Lunar Hornet Clearwing

▲ 0373 *Synanthedon tipuliformis*
Currant Clearwing

▲ 0374 *Synanthedon vespiformis*
Yellow-legged Clearwing

▲ 0375 *Synanthedon spheciformis*
White-barred Clearwing

▲ 0377 *Synanthedon flaviventris*
Sallow Clearwing

female, male attracted to pheromone, and empty pupa-cases found (DGG, TJN); Yateley, 10.6.00, male attracted to pheromone (ARC, AMD, TJN); Farnborough, 23.7.94, one in conservatory (RWP).

0375 *Synanthedon spheciformis* ([Denis & Schiffermüller], 1775)
White-barred Clearwing   **Notable/Nb**

Very locally frequent amongst young alder *Alnus glutinosa* and birch *Betula* spp.

■ vc12 Bartley Heath NR (AHD), larvae in young birch, 22.10.95 (GJD); Fleet, Ancells Farm HWT NR, June 1994, larvae in young stems of birch (RWP); Fleet Pond, 21.4.98, workings in freshly cut alder stumps (DGG); Shortheath Common, 15.6.99, one seen by day (R.M. Fry, pers. comm.); Yateley, 10.6.00, male attracted to pheromone (AMD).

0377 *Synanthedon flaviventris* (Staudinger, 1883)
Sallow Clearwing   **Notable/Nb**

The galls made by the larva of this species on sallow *Salix cinerea* are sometimes locally common in the winters of "even" years, but the insect is often heavily parasitised.

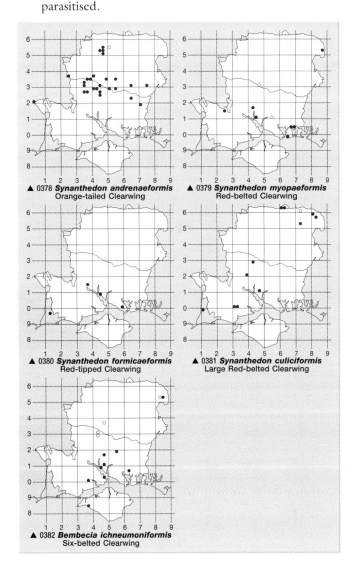

▲ 0378 *Synanthedon andrenaeformis*
Orange-tailed Clearwing

▲ 0379 *Synanthedon myopaeformis*
Red-belted Clearwing

▲ 0380 *Synanthedon formicaeformis*
Red-tipped Clearwing

▲ 0381 *Synanthedon culiciformis*
Large Red-belted Clearwing

▲ 0382 *Bembecia ichneumoniformis*
Six-belted Clearwing

0378 *Synanthedon andrenaeformis* (Laspeyres, 1801)
Orange-tailed Clearwing   **Notable/Nb**

Small colonies occur locally on the chalk downs, sometimes in open woodland on the chalk, the larva feeding in the stems and twigs of wayfaring-tree *Viburnum lantana* and less often in guelder-rose *V. opulus*. Old galls are conspicuous, but tenanted ones are difficult to see.

■ vc11 Kings Somborne, 15.1.95, old workings in stems of *V. opulus* along old railway N of village (PAB, BG, TJN).

■ vc12 Porton Down, Isle of Wight Woods, 1.7.00, galls in *V. lantana* (DGG); Itchen Abbas, winter, 1993–94, two occupied stems of *V. lantana* collected, one moth bred (BG); Ropley, Mount Pleasant, 17.2.95, larvae workings in *V. lantana*; Noar Hill, Selborne, 17.2.95, larval workings in *V. lantana* (DGG).

0379 *Synanthedon myopaeformis* (Borkhausen, 1789)
Red-belted Clearwing   **Notable/Nb**

This is another essentially garden or suburban species, colonies often affecting a single apple tree in an area. In the Southampton and Portsmouth areas, it has been attracted to pheromone bait in several localities.

■ vc11 Near Bramshaw, 29.5.94 (ARGM); Bassett, 2000, two moths seen and many empty pupa-cases protruding from a sick cordon apple *Malus* cultivar (J. and I. Baker); Sholing, a total of 17 attracted to pheromone lure between 16.7 and 7.8.00 (ARC); Fareham, 25.7.99, one in conservatory (RJD); Drayton, 8.6.95, eight; Farlington, 8.6.95, seven, Southsea, 7.6.95, five, all at pheromone lure (JRL).

■ vc12 Farnborough, 20.7.95, one (KW).

0380 *Synanthedon formicaeformis* (Esper, 1783)
Red-tipped Clearwing   **Notable/Nb**

■ vc11 Sopley, galls in sallow *Salix* spp., 4.4.96, two moths bred (PD); Lower Test NR, 1991 (M. Oates), 1992 (RAC, I. Hoare); Westwood Woodland Park, Netley, 19.6.98, one swept (PH); Browndown, single specimens bred from larvae found in 1987 and 1988 (DSW); Alver Valley, 10.6.00, moth bred (SS).

0381 *Synanthedon culiciformis* (Linnaeus, 1758)
Large Red-belted Clearwing   **Notable/Nb**

Locally common, the larva making characteristic tunnels under the bark of birch trees and stumps.

■ vc11 Merrietown Heath, 30.4.97, 14.6.99, vacated pupae in cut birch stumps (PHS); Roydon Woods, 20.5 and 28.5.98 (PAB); Netley Common, 27.5.91 (PAB).

■ vc12 Pamber, 1995, larvae (GJD); Bartley Heath NR, 22.5.99, five empty pupal cases and one containing imago, in birch stump (AHD); Yateley Common, 26.3.94, workings in birch stumps (TD, BG, JRL), 10.6.00, male attracted to pheromone (ARC, AMD, TJN).

0382 *Bembecia ichneumoniformis* ([Denis & Schiffermüller], 1775)
= *scopigera* auct.
Six-belted Clearwing   **Notable/Nb**

Local, mainly in downland localities, and most certainly overlooked.

■ vc10 Compton Chine, 2.6.91, freshly emerged (A and LB).

■ vc11 Allington, 1.7.98 (CA); Netley Common, 19.6.98, one swept; Westwood Woodland Park, Netley, 7.7.98, one swept; Claylands NR, Bishops Waltham, 25.7.98, 11.7.00, single specimens swept (PH); Portsdown Hill, 14.7.98, one swept (JRL, IRT).

■ vc12 Eelmoor Marsh, 5.7.98, one swept from *Lotus corniculatus* (DGG).

[0383 *Synansphecia muscaeformis* (Esper, 1783)
Thrift Clearwing   **Notable/Nb**
No record since that given in Goater (1974).]

0384 *Pyropteron chrysidiformis* (Esper, 1782)
Fiery Clearwing   **RDB1**
No record since that given in Goater (1974).

Choreutidae (4 + [1])

Recent research, hinted at by Pelham-Clinton in Heath and Emmet (1985), has resulted in the placement of these moths in a separate superfamily Choreutoidea, the systematic position of which follows the Tortricoidea (Karsholt and Razowski, 1996). For the purposes of easy reference to previous publications (Goater, 1974, 1992), they follow Sesiidae in this work.

0385 *Anthophila fabriciana* (Linnaeus, 1767)
Seen abundantly in daytime wherever stinging nettle *Urtica dioica* grows, in all three vice-counties.

[0386 *Tebenna micalis* (Mann, 1857)
= *bjerkandrella* auctt.
The old records from the Isle of Wight, given in Goater (1974) require confirmation.]

0387 *Prochoreutis sehestediana* (Fabricius, 1776)
Very local, and chiefly in the New Forest. There is a single record from N Hants (Goater, 1974) and none from the Isle of Wight.

■ vc11 Fletchwood Meadows NR, Ashurst, 12.7.93, several larvae on skullcap *Scutellaria* sp., moths bred (JRL).

0388 *Prochoreutis myllerana* (Fabricius, 1794)
The only confirmed records of this insect in Hampshire are those given in Goater (1983). It is probably overlooked or confused with the previous species.

0389 *Choreutis pariana* (Clerck, 1759)
Recorded from all three vice-counties, but only one since 1973 on the Isle of Wight, and hitherto only two records from N Hants.

■ vc10 Freshwater, 26.8.00 (SAK-J).

■ vc11 Winchester, Sarum Road, 15.8.91, several larvae on cultivated apple *Malus*, three moths bred (RJBH); Portsdown, 5.6.90, larva on hawthorn, moth bred (RJD); Fareham, 17.9.97, a few vacated spinnings on apple *M. domestica*; Browndown, 13.5.98, one (JRL *et al.*);

Southsea, 29.9.92, one at m.v. light, occasionally since (JRL); Milton Common, 1994, mines; 12.10.96, 25.7.00, at m.v. light, both conf. JRL (IRT); Sandy Point NR, Hayling Island, 14.7.92, one (JRL).

■ vc12 Newtown Common, 24.8 and 25.8.86, many larvae, moths bred (JRL, DHS) (Goater, 1992); Brighton Hill, Basingstoke, 10.6.99, larvae on whitebeam *Sorbus aria* (AHD).

Glyphipterigidae (7 + [1])

The genus *Glyphipterix* comprises small diurnal moths which are often encountered flying over their foodplants. Some of them can be mistaken for tortricids of the genus *Cydia*, having similar colouration and markings, but the palpi are more slender and upcurved and the hindwings are narrower (Pelham-Clinton *in* Heath and Emmet, 1985). The larvae are leaf-miners or feed in the seeds of herbaceous plants. The monotypic subfamily Orthoteliinae has been transferred from Yponomeutidae to Glyphipterigidae (Emmet, 1996; Karsholt and Razowski, 1996).

0391 *Glyphipterix simpliciella* (Stephens, 1834)
Common in the two mainland vice-counties (JRL). The larva feeds in seeds of cock's-foot, *Dactylis glomerata*, and other grasses.

■ vc8 Martin Down, 5.5.90 (S. Nash).

■ vc10 Totland; Yarmouth; Redcliff; Parkhurst Forest; Luccombe Chine (RJD).

■ vc11 Fareham (RJD); Milton Common, Southsea, at light in garden, 1998 (IRT); Waterlooville, 20.5.00, swept by day, conf. JRL (RJM).

■ vc12 Winnall Moors NR (DHS); Wildhern, nr Andover, 24.5.97, by day (DGG); Pamber, 1994 (GJD).

0392 *Glyphipterix schoenicolella* Boyd, 1858
There is a single old record from the Isle of Wight (Goater, 1974). The foodplant, black bog-rush *Schoenus nigricans*, occurs very locally in the New Forest, but the moth has yet to be found there.

[0393 *Glyphipterix equitella* (Scopoli, 1763)
■ vc10 Given as present on the Isle of Wight by Heath and Emmet, 1985, but the authors have been unable to trace the source.]

0394 *Glyphipterix forsterella* (Fabricius, 1781)
Local in S Hants. There is also an old record from the Isle of Wight (Goater, 1974) and a recently discovered one from N Hants, given below. The larva feeds on species of sedge *Carex*.

■ vc11 Emer Bog, June 1999, several; Flexford Meadows, June 1999, one – this species is suffering badly from the heavy grazing regime in this locality (BE); Marwell Zoological Park (RJD); Hookheath Meadows NR, Southwick, 15.5.92, one; Titchfield, 20.5.94, several (JRL).

■ vc12 Pamber Forest, one on 21.5.74 det. RJD (DMA). **New vc record.**

0395 *Glyphipterix haworthana* (Stephens, 1834)
Recorded only from S Hants, where it appears to be locally common in the bogs of the New Forest. The larva feeds on cottongrass *Eriophorum* spp.

0396 *Glyphipterix fuscoviridella* (Haworth, 1828)
Widespread in all three vice-counties. The larva feeds on field wood-rush *Luzula campestris*.
■ vc8 Martin Down, 8.6.92 (JRL, RMP).
■ vc10 Freshwater, 18.5.98, at m.v. light (SAK-J); Afton Down; Compton Bay; Brook Bay; Redcliff; Luccombe Chine (RJD).

0397 *Glyphipterix thrasonella* (Scopoli, 1763)
Although the species is considered to be abundant in rushy places, the identity of the foodplant is uncertain (Pelham-Clinton *in* Heath and Emmet, 1985). There are records from all three vice-counties, to which can be added the following.
■ vc10 Firestone Copse; Luccombe Chine (RJD).
■ vc11 Roydon Woods, 10.7.96 (PRD, JRL); Balmer Lawn (RJD); Matley Bog and Pig Bush, 16.10.99, imagines noted (BE); Hookheath Meadows NR, Southwick, 9.6.92, many (JRL); Fareham; Wickham Common (RJD); Havant Thicket, 28.6.95, 8.7.98 (JRL).
■ vc12 Greywell Moors NR (AHD); Pamber, 1995 (GJD); Fleet, Ancells Farm NR, 21.6.96, abundant (RWP).

0470 *Orthotaelia sparganella* (Thunberg, 1788)
Locally common in all three vice-counties, but especially in some of the bogs in the New Forest. The larva is associated mainly with bur-reed *Sparganium* spp.
■ vc11 Botley Wood, 12.7.94, one at m.v. light (JRL); Milton Common, Southsea, at light in garden, 1998 (IRT).

Yponomeutidae (68)

This is another group of smaller Lepidoptera, the status of which is still controversial. The appearance and habits of the moths included here, and of their larvae, show considerable variation. The genera *Argyresthia*, *Ypsolopha* and *Yponomeuta* are familiar to many, though the species may be difficult to distinguish, and the abundant migrant *Plutella xylostella* is now recognised confidently by a majority of the county's lepidopterists.

0401 *Argyresthia laevigatella* (Heydenreich, 1851)
Local amongst larch *Larix* spp. Numerous records for S Hants, a few for N Hants, but only one from the Isle of Wight (Goater, 1974, 1992).

[0402 *Argyresthia illuminatella* Zeller, 1839
According to Agassiz *in* Emmet (ed.), 1996, all British records of this species have been based on misidentifications. The records given in Goater (1974) must be deleted.]

0403 *Argyresthia glabratella* (Zeller, 1847)
Local amongst Norway spruce *Picea abies* in mainland

Hampshire, though no records have been received since 1992 (Goater, 1974, 1992).

0404 *Argyresthia praecocella* Zeller, 1839
The only Hampshire record is of one beaten from juniper *Juniperus communis* at Stockbridge vc12, in 1976 (Goater, 1983).

0405 *Argyresthia arceuthina* Zeller, 1839
Common amongst juniper *Juniperus communis* in the mainland vice-counties but unrecorded from the Isle of Wight. Records from Southsea suggest the species can live on cultivated *Juniperus* in gardens.

0406 *Argyresthia abdominalis* Zeller, 1839
A few records from sites of juniper *Juniperus communis* in the mainland vice-counties (Goater, 1974, 1992), but none more recently.

0407 *Argyresthia dilectella* Zeller, 1847
Recorded from amongst juniper at Farley Mount vc11 and in the Stockbridge area vc12 and also from Southsea where it could be associated with either juniper or cypress *Cupressus* spp. All records are given in Goater (1974, 1992).

0408 *Argyresthia aurulentella* Stainton, 1849
This is yet another *Juniperus*-feeding *Argyresthia*. The only Hampshire records are given in Goater (1974) from Southampton and Chilbolton.

0409 *Argyresthia ivella* (Haworth, 1828)
Locally fairly common amongst wild and cultivated apple *Malus* spp., whence the moth can be beaten, in the mainland vice-counties. All previous records are given in Goater (1974, 1992).
■ vc11 Hollands Wood; Rowner Wild Grounds (RJD).
■ vc12 Eelmoor Marsh SSSI, 23.8.97, at light (DGG); Pamber, 1994 (GJD).

0409a *Argyresthia trifasciata* Staudinger, 1871
An adventive species, probably imported from mainland Europe with cultivated conifers.
■ vc12 Farnborough, 20.5.98, one at light, det. conf. JRL (Parfitt, 1999). **New county record.**

0410 *Argyresthia brockeella* (Hübner, 1813)
Frequent in birch country in the mainland vice-counties.
■ vc10 Cranmore, 7.7 and 9.7.97 (Knill-Jones, 1998c). **New vc record.**

0411 *Argyresthia goedartella* (Linnaeus, 1758)
Common amongst birch *Betula* spp. and alder *Alnus glutinosa* in the mainland vice-counties, but still only once reported from the Isle of Wight (Goater, 1992).

0412 *Argyresthia pygmaeella* ([Denis & Schiffermüller], 1775)
Recorded from all three vice-counties, but not recently from the Isle of Wight. It is usually common amongst sallows and willows *Salix* spp.

0413 *Argyresthia sorbiella* (Treitschke, 1833)
Apparently extremely scarce in Hampshire. The only records, both in vc11, are given in Goater (1974, 1992). The moth is associated with rowan *Sorbus aucuparia* and whitebeam *S. aria*.

0414 *Argyresthia curvella* (Linnaeus, 1761)
= *arcella* (Fabricius, 1776)
Surprisingly uncommon, or overlooked (Goater 1974, 1992). According to Agassiz *in* Emmet (ed.) (1996), this species can be a pest in apple orchards.
■ vc11 Catisfield; Fareham (RJD).
■ vc12 Selborne, 1993, 1994 (AEA); Farnborough, two in 1994 (RWP).

0415 *Argyresthia retinella* Zeller, 1839
Common amongst birch in the two mainland vice-counties (JRL), but unrecorded from the Isle of Wight.
■ vc22 Benyon's Inclosure (RJD).

0416 *Argyresthia glaucinella* Zeller, 1839
Probably common in all three vice-counties, but only once reported (as common) in the Isle of Wight, and first given for N Hants as recently as 1980. The larva lives in bark of oak *Quercus* spp. and sweet chestnut *Castanea sativa*. All recent vc12 records are included below.
■ vc12 Leckford, 8.4.89, larval workings in oak, moths not bred (DHS, JRL) (see Agassiz, 1991); Micheldever, 7.4.97, larval workings; Monkwood, 2.4.97, larval workings; Selborne, 28.3.96, larval workings in bark of *Quercus* (JRL).

0417 *Argyresthia spinosella* Stainton, 1849
= *mendica* (Haworth, 1828)
Recorded from all three vice-counties (Goater 1974, 1992), but not recently from the Isle of Wight. The larva lives in flowering shoots of blackthorn *Prunus spinosa*.
■ vc10 Headon Warren, 8.6.78, one beaten from blackthorn (RJD).
■ vc11 Hook Valley NR, 2.6.98, several beaten from blackthorn (RJD); Milton Common, Southsea, 18.6.00, one at m.v. light (IRT).
■ vc12 Wildhern, 20.4.98, larvae; Fleet Pond, 21.4.98, larva beaten from *Prunus* blossom (DGG); Selborne, 26.6.96, specimen conf. JRL (AEA).

0418 *Argyresthia conjugella* Zeller, 1839
Uncommon or overlooked in the mainland vice-counties. The larva lives in the fruits of rowan *Sorbus aucuparia* and apple *Malus* spp., and the moth can be disturbed from the foodplant. The following records are to be added to those given in Goater (1974, 1992).
■ vc11 Wickham Common; Portsdown (RJD); Widley, Portsdown (PMP).
■ vc12 Wildhern, nr Andover, 18.7.97 (DGG); Pamber Forest (RJD).

0419 *Argyresthia semifusca* (Haworth, 1828)
The larva of this species inhabits young shoots of rowan *Sorbus aucuparia*. The moth appears to be rare or

overlooked, but there are records from all three vice-counties (Goater, 1974, 1992).
■ vc11 Sparsholt College (AHD); Catisfield; Fareham; Browndown; Farlington (RJD).
■ vc12 Farnborough, three from 26.7.94, two from 12.8.95 (RWP, comm. JRL). **New vc record.**

0420 *Argyresthia pruniella* (Clerck, 1759)
Recorded from all three vice-counties, and locally common (Goater, 1974, 1992). Larva in shoots and young fruits of wild cherry *Prunus cerasus*.

0421 *Argyresthia bonnetella* (Linnaeus, 1758)
= *curvella* auctt.
Frequent amongst hawthorn, especially in scrub on downland, in all three vice-counties.

0422 *Argyresthia albistria* (Haworth, 1828)
Widespread and common amongst blackthorn in all three vice-counties.

0423 *Argyresthia semitestacella* (Curtis, 1833)
The few records of this species in Hampshire and the Isle of Wight are given in Goater (1974, 1992). To these can be added the records given below.
■ vc10 Parkhurst Forest, 19.9.77, adult; Brighstone Down, 22.9.77, adult (AME *et al.*).
■ vc11 Botley Wood, 28.8.99, one beaten from beech (RJD); Catisfield, 28.8.71, one at m.v. light; Hazel Holt, 11.8.74 det. RJD (DMA).
■ vc12 Harewood Forest, 11.9.76, several beaten (AME *et al.*).

0424 *Yponomeuta evonymella* (Linnaeus, 1758)
There are a few records from all three vice-counties. The species seems to occur regularly but nowhere commonly. The foodplant, bird cherry *Prunus padus*, is not native in Hampshire and Agassiz *in* Emmet (ed.), 1996, suggests that most specimens taken in southern England are immigrants.
■ vc10 Luccombe Chine, 17.7.76, adult (RJD).
■ vc11 Burley New Inclosure, New Forest, 1.7.99; Frame Wood, 3.7.99 (DGG); Sparsholt College (AHD); Bitterne Park, 1.7.99 (PAB); Locks Heath, 24.7.00, conf. RJD (PCa); Fareham (RJD); Cosham (TJJ); Milton Common, Southsea, 3.7 and 20.7.99, singles at m.v. light (IRT).
■ vc12 Winnall Moors NR (DHS); Magdalen Hill Down, 8.7.99 (PAB); Abbotstone Down, 27.7.94, one at m.v. light (RJBH, JRL); Oakley; Bramley Frith Wood NR; Bartley Heath NR (AHD); Pamber Forest, 2000 (GJD); Selborne, 22.7.94, eight in 1995, at light (AEA); Wick Hill Hanger, 5.7.99 (PAB); Yateley Common, uncommon (AMD); Farnborough, three in 1995 from 9.7 (RWP).

0425 *Yponomeuta padella* (Linnaeus, 1758)
Widespread and sometimes common, especially as larvae, which feed communally in webs on blackthorn and hawthorn. Recorded occasionally from all three vice-counties.

■ vc10 Yarmouth, 18.5.92, larval nests on blackthorn (JRL, DHS, PHS).

■ vc11 North Solent NNR, Beaulieu, 2.5.1.92, larval nests on blackthorn (DJLA, AME, JRL); Old Winchester Hill NNR, 3.6.93, larvae on blackthorn (JRL); Titchfield Haven NR, 1996; Wickham Common (RJD); Waterlooville, 5.8.00, at m.v. light (RJM).

■ vc12 Bramley Frith Wood NR; Mapledurwell Fen, 25.7.99, one at m.v. light (AHD).

0426 *Yponomeuta malinellus* Zeller, 1838

This species is very similar to *Y. padella*, and has been regarded as merely a form of it. The larva, however, occurs on apple *Malus* spp. The identity of caught specimens should be regarded with some suspicion.

■ vc11 Sparsholt College (AHD); Milton Common, Southsea, four between 18.7 and 7.8.00, seen by JRL (IRT).

■ vc12 Rye Common, 5.8.96 (AMD); Farnborough, 22.7.97 (RWP).

0427 *Yponomeuta cagnagella* (Hübner, 1813)

Widespread and often common on calcareous soils where spindle *Euonymus europaeus* occurs; the larvae are sometimes found, too, on cultivated japonica *E. japonica*.

■ vc8 Martin Down, 5.5.90 (S. Nash), 24.8.90 (MFVC and S. Nash).

■ vc10 Westover Plantation, 15.11.95, mines; Dodnor, 12.10.96, mines (DTB).

■ vc11 Sparsholt College (AHD); Chandlers Ford, larvae sometimes destructive on *E. japonica* (BG); Swanwick NR, 20.8.96, one at m.v. light (JRL); Milton Common, Southsea, at light in garden, 1998 (IRT); Waterlooville, 1996–2000 (RJM).

■ vc12 Winnall Moors NR (DHS); Danebury, 27.5.99 (PAB); Wildhern, nr Andover, 29.7.97 (DGG); Overton; Oakley (AHD); Selborne, 1993, 1994 (AEA); Farnborough, 25.7.95 (RWP).

0428 *Yponomeuta rorrella* (Hübner, 1796)

Normally a very scarce presumed immigrant. There was a population explosion in southern England in 1989 when several specimens were reported for the mainland vice-counties (Goater, 1992).

■ vc11 Southsea, 19.7.00, one at m.v. light (JRL); Milton Common, Southsea, 28.7.96, at actinic trap, conf. JRL (IRT).

■ vc12 Winnall Moors NR (DHS); Bramley Frith Wood NR (AHD); Rye Common, 5.8.96 (AMD).

0429 *Yponomeuta irrorella* (Hübner, 1796)

Very local and occasional in N Hants (Goater, 1974), and recorded once from S Hants (Goater, 1992). No recent record. Larva on spindle *Euonymus europaeus*.

0430 *Yponomeuta plumbella* ([Denis & Schiffermüller], 1775)

Widespread in all three vice-counties where the foodplant, spindle *Euonymus europaeus* occurs, though, as usual, few records are available for the Isle of Wight.

■ vc8 Martin Down (RJD).

■ vc10 Freshwater, 11.8.98, at m.v. light (SAK-J).

0431 *Yponomeuta sedella* Treitschke, 1832
= *vigintipunctata* (Retzius, 1783)

Widespread but local, and no recent record from the Isle of Wight. The larva of this species feeds on orpine *Sedum telephium*, a local plant in Hampshire. The following may be added to the records given in Goater (1974, 1992).

■ vc11 Hollands Wood, 29.7.76 (RJD); Sparsholt College (AHD); Bitterne, 23.8.99 (PAB); Locks Heath, 24.7.00 (PCa); Rowner, 12.8.00, one at m.v. light (LM).

■ vc12 Farnborough, 23.7.95, two at light (RWP).

0435 *Zelleria hepariella* Stainton, 1849

There are a few records from all three vice-counties, to which may be added the following. The larva feeds on ash *Fraxinus excelsior*, and the moth overwinters in thick foliage such as yew *Taxus baccata*.

■ vc10 Freshwater, 14.7.87 (Knill-Jones, 1994c). **New vc record.**

■ vc12 Danebury Hillfort, 8.8.89, one beaten from *Juniperus* (RJBH); Wildhern, nr Andover, 8.3.97 (DGG).

0436 *Pseudoswammerdamia combinella* (Hübner, 1786)

Recorded from all three vice-counties, but apparently uncommon. The following can be added to the records given in Goater (1974, 1992).

■ vc8 Martin Down, 29.4.90 (S. Nash).

■ vc10 Freshwater, 13.6.94, 22.5.97 (SAK-J).

■ vc11 Sparsholt College (AHD), Sparsholt, 19.5.99, one disturbed by day (BE); Warsash shore, 17.6.98, one; Titchfield Haven, 1996; Wickham Common (RJD); Hookheath Meadows NR, Southwick, 24.5.92, one at m.v. light; Lower Titchfield Haven NR, 24.5.93, one; Browndown, 13.5.98, one; Great Salterns NR, Portsmouth (JRL); Waterlooville, 13.5.00, at m.v. light, conf. JRL (RJM).

■ vc12 Wildhern, nr Andover, 23.5.99, at m.v. light (DGG); Pamber, 1995 (GJD); Bramley Frith Wood NR (AHD); Selborne, 4.5.99, 6.6.00 (AEA); Yateley Common, 21.4.97 (AMD).

0437 *Swammerdamia caesiella* (Hübner, 1796)

Common in all three vice-counties wherever birch occurs (JRL).

0438 *Swammerdamia pyrella* (de Villers, 1789)

Widespread and usually common amongst the foodplants apple *Malus* spp. and hawthorn.

■ vc8 Martin Down, 5.5.90 (S. Nash).

■ vc10 Tennyson Down, 18.5.92, two larvae on hawthorn (JRL, DHS, PHS).

0439 *Swammerdamia compunctella* (Herrich-Schäffer, 1855)

The only record of this species is that reported in Goater (1983, repeated in 1992).

0440 *Paraswammerdamia albicapitella* (Scharfenberg, 1805)
= *spiniella* (Hübner, 1809)

Local or perhaps overlooked, in all three vice-counties (Goater 1974, 1992). Additional records are given below. The larva feeds on blackthorn *Prunus spinosa*.

■ vc8 Martin Down, 24.8.90 (MFVC and S. Nash).
■ vc11 Hook-with-Warsash; Fareham; Titchfield Haven, 1996; Brownwich; Chilling Copse; Browndown; Rowner Wild Grounds; Fort Widley, 7.7.98, one beaten; Great Salterns NR, Portsmouth (RJD); Botley Wood, 12.7.94, a few at m.v. light; Lower Titchfield Haven NR, 24.6.94, a few at m.v. light; Portsdown, 3.5.93, larvae, moth bred; Southsea, 24.7.92, one at m.v. light; Sandy Point NR, Hayling Island, 14.7.92, one at m.v. light, and regularly since (JRL); Milton Common, 1.8.99, 14.6.00, singletons at m.v. light, 27.7.00, two (IRT); Waterlooville, 8.7 and 19.7.00, at m.v. light (RJM).
■ vc12 Wildhern, 15.7.98 (DGG).

0441 *Paraswammerdamia lutarea* (Haworth, 1828)
Widespread, especially in S Hants, but recorded only once from the Isle of Wight (Goater, 1974, 1992).
■ vc12 Wildhern, 15.7.98 (DGG); Brighton Hill, Basingstoke; Bramley Frith Wood, 1.7.95, three at m.v.light (AHD); Farnborough, 18.6.94 (RWP).

0442 *Cedestis gysseleniella* Zeller, 1839
This species occurs in the Scots pine country of Hampshire, but is unrecorded from the Isle of Wight.
■ vc11 Botley Wood, 17.6.93, one (JRL, RMP); Catisfield (RJD).
■ vc12 Farnborough, 9.7.95, one at light (RWP); Whitmoor Vale (RJD).

0443 *Cedestis subfasciella* (Stephens, 1834)
This species is also widespread amongst Scots pine in the mainland vice-counties.
■ vc11 Hookheath Meadows NR, Southwick, 24.5.92, one at m.v. light (JRL); Catisfield; West Walk (RJD).
■ vc12 Farnborough, two in 1994 (RWP); Whitmoor Vale (RJD).

0444 *Ocnerostoma piniariella* Zeller, 1847
Easily confused with the next species and separable only by dissection. The few definite records are given in Goater (1974, 1992). Both species are associated with Scots pine *Pinus sylvestris.*
■ vc11 Frame Wood, 3.7.99 (DGG); Curbridge; Oxenbourne Down (RJD).
■ vc12 Conford Moor, 21.6.95, one (JRL, RMP).

0445 *Ocnerostoma friesei* Svensson, 1966
Like *O. piniariella*, recorded sparsely from pine woodland in mainland Hampshire.
■ vc11 Merrietown Heath, February, 1994, several tenanted mines in needles of Scots pine *Pinus sylvestris* (PHS); Denny Wood; Fareham, genit. checked (RJD); West Walk, Wickham, 25.8.95; Southsea, 19.5.92, one at m.v. light (JRL).
■ vc12 Farnborough, 5.8.94, det JRL (RWP).

0449 *Prays fraxinella* (Bjerkander, 1784)
Widespread and common in the vicinity of ash *Fraxinus excelsior* in all three vice-counties.
■ vc10 Freshwater, 17.6.97 (Knill-Jones, 1998b).

0450 *Scythropia crataegella* (Linnaeus, 1767)
Common amongst blackthorn and hawthorn, though there is no recent record from the Isle of Wight (Goater, 1974).

0451 *Ypsolopha mucronella* (Scopoli, 1763)
Local. No recent record from the Isle of Wight. The larva feeds on spindle *Euonymus europaeus.*
■ vc11 Sparsholt College (AHD); Chandlers Ford, 11.3.95, one at light (BG); Wickham Common, 17.4.71 (RJD); Waterlooville, 1996–2000 (RJM).
■ vc12 Wildhern, nr Andover, 22.4.97, 1.5.99 (DGG); Abbotstone Down, 30.7.92, larva found descending from a spindle bush, moth em. 25.8 (RJBH); Selborne, few every year from 1991, at light (AEA).

0452 *Ypsolopha nemorella* (Linnaeus, 1758)
Widespread but usually uncommon in woodland in the mainland vice-counties; no recent record from the Isle of Wight. Larva on honeysuckle *Lonicera periclymenum.*
■ vc11 The Moors NR, Bishops Waltham, 25.7.98, one; Havant Thicket, 8.7.97, one at m.v. light; Sandy Point NR, Hayling Island, 14.7.92, one at m.v. light (JRL, IRT, *et al.*).
■ vc12 Pamber, 1994 (GJD); Bramley Frith Wood NR (AHD).

0453 *Ypsolopha dentella* (Fabricius, 1775)
Widespread and rather common in woodland in all three vice-counties. Larva on honeysuckle *Lonicera periclymenum.*
■ vc8 Martin Down, 24.8.90 (MFVC and S. Nash).

0455 *Ypsolopha scabrella* (Linnaeus, 1761)
Widespread and often fairly common in open, wooded areas in all three vice-counties. The larva feeds on hawthorn and apple.
■ vc8 Martin Down, 24.8.90 (MFVC and S. Nash).

0456 *Ypsolopha horridella* (Treitschke, 1835)
Local and rather uncommon in the two mainland vice-counties. The larva feeds on blackthorn and apple. To the records given in Goater (1974, 1992) may be added the following.
■ vc8 Martin Down, 24.8.90 (MFVC and S. Nash).
■ vc11 The Moors NR, Bishop's Waltham; Rowner Wild Grounds (RJD); Portsdown, 7.7.1.92, one at m.v. light (JRL).
■ vc12 Wildhern, 11.8.98 (DGG).

0457 *Ypsolopha lucella* (Fabricius, 1775)
There are a few records from the mainland vice-counties, but this species is evidently scarce (Goater, 1974). The larva feeds on oak *Quercus* spp.
■ vc11 Botley Wood; Wickham Common; Rowner Wild Grounds (RJD).
■ vc12 Wildhern, nr Andover, 2.9.96 (DGG).

0458 *Ypsolopha alpella* ([Denis & Schiffermüller], 1775)
Agassiz *in* Emmet (ed.) (1996) gives this species as common in oak-woods in the south of England, but

although it has been recorded from all three vice-counties, it is evidently uncommon in Hampshire and the Isle of Wight. The larva feeds on oak *Quercus* spp.

■ vc11 Cadland Estate, Beaulieu, 12.7.97, one at m.v. light (BG, JRL); Sparsholt College (AHD); Swanwick NR, 20.8.96, a few at m.v. light (JRL); Rowner Wild Grounds (RJD); Milton Common, Southsea, 1.8.99, one at m.v. light, det. JRL (IRT).

0459 *Ypsolopha sylvella* (Linnaeus, 1767)
Evidently rare (Goater 1974, 1992). The larva feeds on oak *Quercus* spp.

■ vc11 Roydon Woods, 23.8.00, at light (PAB); Hamble Common, 19.6.95, larva on oak, moth bred 7.7.95 det. RJD (DMA); Curbridge, 3.7.95, moth bred from larva det. RJD (DMA); Southsea, 1.10.95, one at m.v. light (JRL).

■ vc12 Overton; Bartley Heath NR (AHD); Pamber, 1994 (GJD); Farnborough, two in September 1994, 10.10.95 (RWP).

0460 *Ypsolopha parenthesella* (Linnaeus, 1761)
Common and widespread in the mainland vice-counties, though Isle of Wight records remain sparse. The larva feeds on a variety of deciduous trees and shrubs, including oak *Quercus* spp., hazel and birch *Betula* spp.

■ vc10 Shalcombe Down, 9.8.95 (SAK-J); Parkhurst Forest (PJC, 1995).

0461 *Ypsolopha ustella* (Clerck, 1759)
Common amongst oak *Quercus* spp. in the mainland vice-counties (JRL).

■ vc10 Freshwater, 10.8.98, at m.v. light (SAK-J); Cranmore, 9.7.97 (Knill-Jones, 1998b).

0462 *Ypsolopha sequella* (Clerck, 1759)
Local in the vicinity of the foodplant, field maple *Acer campestre*, but no recent record from the Isle of Wight (Goater 1974, 1992).

■ vc11 Roydon Woods, 23.8.00, at light (PAB); Spearbed Copse, Exbury, 31.8.95, one at light (BG); Sparsholt College (AHD); Chandlers Ford, 18.8.95, one at light (BG); Botley Wood (RJD); Widley, Portsdown (PMP); Waterlooville, 1996–2000 (RJM).

■ vc12 Wildhern, nr Andover, 31.7.97 (DGG); Overton; Bramley Frith Wood NR (AHD); Pamber, 1994 (GJD); Odiham Common, 24.8.96, one; Rye Common, 26.7.96; (AMD); Selborne, 1993 onwards, few at light (AEA); Farnborough, two in September 1994 (RWP), one on 5.8.00 (KBW); Yateley Common, 8.8.94; Priors Lane, Yateley, 12.8.97 (AMD).

0463 *Ypsolopha vittella* (Linnaeus, 1758)
The only records received are given in Goater (1974, 1992). It has been recorded in all three vice-counties but not recently. The larva feeds on elm *Ulmus* spp.

The larvae of *Ochsenheimeria* mine the leaves and later the stems of grasses Poaceae (Gramineae). Only one species seems to be at all common in Hampshire.

0251 *Ochsenheimeria taurella* ([Denis & Schiffermüller], 1775)
= *mediopectinellus* (Haworth, 1828)
There are a few records from all three vice-counties, but found commonly only on Farlington Marshes NR (Goater, 1992).

■ vc8 Martin Down, 28.7.76 (RJD).

■ vc10 Steephill, 28.8.76 (RJD).

■ vc11 Botley Wood, 31.8.74, two; Galley Down, 11.8.74; Portsdown, 7.7.74, 30.8.75; Oxenbourne Down, 23.8.74 (RJD); Great Salterns NR, Portsmouth, 5.9.94, two (RJBH, JRL).

0252 *Ochsenheimeria urella* (Fischer von Röslerstamm, 1842)
No record since Goater (1974), the most recent being from Itchen Abbas in 1969.

0253 *Ochsenheimeria vacculella* (Fischer von Röslerstamm, 1842)
The one good record for the county is of several moths under the bark of larch *Larix decidua* on Teg Down in vc11. Goater (1992) gives one other credible record, also from vc11.

0464 *Plutella xylostella* (Linnaeus, 1758)
A common to abundant migrant species.

0465 *Plutella porrectella* (Linnaeus, 1758)
The foodplant, dame's violet *Hesperis matronalis*, is local in Hampshire and so therefore is the moth. One record for the Isle of Wight was given in Goater (1974).

■ vc8 Martin Down, 6.5.90 (S. Nash).

■ vc10 Cranmore, 28.4.97 (Knill-Jones, 1998b); Freshwater, 9.9.98, at m.v. light (SAK-J).

■ vc11 Milton Common, Southsea, 4.6.00, one at m.v. light in garden (IRT).

■ vc12 Selborne, recorded from 1993 onwards, with 90 specimens in 1995 and 216 between May and October 2000, at light in garden, conf. JRL (AEA); Farnborough, 9.10.98, at m.v. light (RWP).

[0467 *Rhigognostis annulatella* (Curtis, 1832)
The status of this species in Hampshire is discussed in Goater (1974). Its presence in the county remains unconfirmed.]

0469 *Eidophasia messingiella* (Fischer von Röslerstamm, 1840)
The first record for Hampshire (Goater, 1974) was from Martyr Worthy, vc12 in 1966. All further occurrences are detailed below. The foodplant, hoary cress *Lepidium draba*, is increasing, especially on and near the coast in the SE of S Hants, and further reports of this moth are to be expected.

■ vc11 Southsea, 14.6.92, one at m.v. light (JRL), Milton Common, 14.6.99, 17.6.00, at m.v. light, det. JRL (IRT). **New vc record.**

■ vc12 Wildhern, nr Andover, 2.9.96, (DGG); Selborne, 10.7.95, one at light; identified by JRL from a photograph, 2.7.96, two, conf. JRL; 19.6.98, one (AEA); Farnborough, 13.6.93 (RWP, comm. JRL).

0471 *Digitivalva perlepidella* (Stainton, 1849)
■ vc12 Ashford Hangers NR, 21.5.93, one by day (Langmaid, 1994b). **New county record.**

0472 *Digitivalva pulicariae* Klimesch, 1956

Locally common amongst fleabane *Pulicaria dysenterica* on the Isle of Wight and in S Hants, but so far there is only one record (below) from N Hants.

■ vc11 North Solent NNR, Beaulieu, 2.6.92, a few mines with larvae on *Pulicaria* (DJLA, AME, JRL); Swanwick 14.6.97, one tenanted mine (JRL); Milton Common, Southsea, 6.7, 11.8 and 20.8.00, at m.v. light (IRT).

■ vc12 Selborne, 27.9.96, one at light (Aston, 1998). **New vc record.**

0473 *Acrolepiopsis assectella* (Zeller, 1839)

The appearance of this species in S Hants and the Isle of Wight during the mid-1940s is detailed in Goater (1974), and it is still present in the Portsmouth area. However, the only post-1992 record received is from N Hants, given below. The larva feeds on onion, leeks and garlic *Allium* spp., and is a potential pest.

■ vc12 Farnborough, 8.8.93, 7.7 and 1.8.94, 19.6.95, 6.8.95 (RWP). **New vc record.**

0475 *Acrolepiopsis marcidella* (Curtis, 1850)

Since the discovery of this moth in S Hants in 1986 (Goater, 1992), searches for the early stages, led by JRL, have yielded the following results.

■ vc11 Ashurst, 17.7.97, a few tenanted mines in cladodes of butcher's broom *Ruscus aculeatus* (JRL); West Walk, Wickham, 13.6.92, eight beaten from *Ruscus* and old cocoons on cladodes and shoots (R.J. Heckford, JRL); Hoe Gate, larval workings, 28.9.99; Fareham, 14.8.97, many larval feeding signs with exit-holes in fruits of *Ruscus*; Alver Valley NR, Gosport, 22.9.97, one larva in fruit of *Ruscus*, moth bred; Hayling Island, 25.7.97, in two localities vacated mines in cladodes and shoots, and larvae in fruits of *Ruscus*, moths bred (JRL, IRT).

0476 *Acrolepia autumnitella* Curtis, 1838

Local amongst the foodplant, bittersweet *Solanum dulcamara* in all three vice-counties (Goater 1974, 1992).

■ vc10 Newtown, 18.9.97, a few vacated mines (AME, JRL); Dodnor, 12.6.95, mines and larvae (DTB); Parkhurst, Seaview, 4.7.99, mines (JMC).

■ vc11 Chandlers Ford, October 1999, fairly common (BE); Fareham; Hookheath Meadows; Hook Valley; Hook-with-Warsash; Titchfield Haven, 1996 (RJD); Botley Wood, 20.9.92, tenanted mines; Bursledon, 8.9.98, several tenanted mines; Lower Titchfield Haven NR, 24.5.94, a few tenanted mines; Fareham, 14.8.97, many tenanted mines (JRL *et al.*); Milton Common, Southsea, 1996 (IRT); Gutner Point NR, Hayling Island, 11.9.96, a few tenanted mines (AMD, JRL).

■ vc12 Ashford Hangers NR, 18.10.93, a few tenanted mines (JRL).

Lyonetiidae (7)

Emmet *in* Heath (1985) described the Lyonetiidae as a "large heterogenous family which has been variously interpreted". In Karsholt and Razowski (1996), everything has been moved out with the exception of three genera, two of which, *Leucoptera* and *Lyonetia*, are British. The larvae are leaf-miners and the adults are small, whitish moths with an attractively ornamented outer zone of the forewings.

0254 *Leucoptera laburnella* (Stainton, 1851)

Widespread and often abundant in gardens in the vicinity of *Laburnum* in the mainland vice-counties, and recorded also from the Isle of Wight, though not recently. The larva mines the leaves of *Laburnum* and has been reported also on dyer's greenweed *Genista tinctoria* in vc's 10 (see Goater, 1974) and 11.

■ vc11 North Solent NR, Beaulieu, 2.6.92, a few vacated mines on *G. tinctoria* (DJLA, AME, JRL).

f. *wailesella* Stainton, 1858

Mines, from which moths were bred, were found on Hayling Island vc11 on *G. tinctoria* in 1982 (see Goater, 1992). No other record.

0256 *Leucoptera spartifoliella* (Hübner, 1813)

Local in all three vice-counties. The moth comes to light and the larva mines the shoots of broom *Cytisus scoparius*. To the records given in Goater (1974, 1992, add:

■ vc11 Fareham; Browndown (RJD); Southsea, 19.6.98, one at m.v. light, first for garden (JRL).

■ vc12 Pamber, 1994 (GJD).

0258 *Leucoptera lathyrifoliella* Stainton, 1866

Best-known from Luccombe Chine, Isle of Wight, where it probably still exists. Old records from the New Forest are also given in Goater (1974). The larva mines the leaves of narrow-leaved everlasting-pea *Lathyrus sylvestris*.

0259 *Leucoptera lotella* (Stainton, 1858)

Local in the mainland vice-counties where it appears to be associated with greater bird's-foot-trefoil *Lotus pedunculatus* and not *L. corniculatus*.

■ vc11 Avon Heath Country Park, 23.8.93, mines common on *L. pedunculatus* (PHS); North Solent NR, Beaulieu, 2.6.92, early mines (DJLA, AME, JRL); Hookheath Meadows NR, Southwick, 2.6.92, early mines (JRL).

■ vc12 Fleet Pond, 17.7.93, mines common; one moth emerged 26.7.93 and two on 16.5.94 (RJBH); Eelmoor Marsh, 30.8.98, mines (DGG).

0260 *Leucoptera malifoliella* (Costa, 1836)

Widespread in all three vice-counties. The larva mines the leaves of a variety of Rosaceous trees and shrubs.

■ vc11 Farlington Marshes NR, 17.8.93, many tenanted mines on hawthorn (JRL).

■ vc12 Wildhern, nr Andover, 27.9.97, mines on apple *Malus* spp.; Harewood Forest, 26.10.97, mines on hawthorn and apple (DGG).

0263 *Lyonetia clerkella* (Linnaeus, 1758)

Abundant in all three vice-counties (JRL, DHS). The larva mines the leaves of Rosaceous trees and shrubs and also birch.

■ vc10 Osborne, 16.9.95, Brading, 16.10.95, Nettlestone, 26.11.95, mines (DTB).

0264 *Bedellia somnulentella* (Zeller, 1847)

Records have been received from all three vice-counties. The larva mines the leaves of bindweeds *Convolvulus* and *Calystegia*.

■ vc10 Gurnard, 24.8.96, mines and larvae (DTB).

■ vc11 Wickham Common, 1998; Hookheath Meadows, larvae; Fareham, 8.8.98, tenanted mine (RJD); Milton Common, Southsea, 1994, mines; 1998, at light in garden, (IRT); Bursledon, 8.9.98, several larval feedings on *Calystegia*; Lower Titchfield Haven NR, 20.8.93, larval feedings on *Convolvulus*; Great Salterns NR, Portsmouth (JRL); Milton Common, Southsea, 1999, 2000 (IRT); North Hayling Island (RJD).

■ vc12 Farnborough, 1.9.96 (RWP).

Coleophoridae (85 + [1])

This family includes the very large and difficult genus *Coleophora* Hübner, 1822. The British species have recently received comprehensive treatment by Emmet *et al.* (1996). Many of the imagines are virtually impossible to identify without recourse to dissection. The larvae live in cases of characteristic form and many are monophagous, a fact which facilitates identification. The genitalia and larval cases of the British species are illustrated most beautifully in the work of Emmet *et al.* (1996). Eighty-three species have been recorded in the county, out of a total of 107 in Britain. Most students of the family find it important to retain examples of the cases for future reference.

0486 *Augasma aeratella* (Zeller, 1839)

This species is possibly extinct in Britain, the last record being from Dorset in 1956 (Emmet *et al.*, 1996). There is a single record from the Isle of Wight, in 1907 (Goater, 1974).

0487 *Metriotes lutarea* (Haworth, 1828)

Now recorded from all three vice-counties, but very local and mainly in S Hants.

■ vc11 Tournebury Wood; Titchfield Haven; West Walk; Wickham Common (RJD).

■ vc12 Fleet Pond LNR, 22.4.98, three at m.v. light, genitalia det. (DGG). **New vc record.**

0488 *Goniodoma limoniella* (Stainton, 1884)

Common in the saltmarshes of the Isle of Wight and S Hants. The larva feeds on the flowers of sea-lavender *Limonium vulgare*, inside a case made from a calyx.

■ vc10 Newtown, 18.9.97, a few cases on *Limonium* (AME, JRL).

■ vc11 Milton Common, Southsea, 19.8.97, at light (IRT); Hayling Island, cases abundant on *Limonium vulgare* on all saltmarshes (JRL).

0490 *Coleophora lutipennella* (Zeller, 1838)

Adults separable from those of *C. flavipennella* (Dup.) only by dissection. The recent discovery of differences in feeding behaviour and construction of the cases (Emmet *et al.*, 1996) allows the early stages to be differentiated

with confidence. The larva feeds on the catkins and foliage of oak *Quercus* spp.

■ vc11 Frame Wood, 3.7.99 (DGG); Cadland Estate, Beaulieu, 12.7.97, several at m.v. light, genitalia det. (JRL); Chandlers Ford, 1999, very common, genitalia det. (BE); Hamble Common, 1996; Hook Valley NR; Catisfield; Fareham, genit. checked; Hook-with-Warsash, 1996 (RJD); The Moors NR, Bishops Waltham, 7.8.98, on at m.v. light, genitalia det.; Upper Hamble Country Park, 7.10.96, one case; Browndown, 7.11.94, a few small cases on *Q. robur*; Sandy Point NR, Hayling Island, 14.7.92, one at m.v. light, genitalia det. (JRL *et al.*).

■ vc12 Wildhern, 15.7.98, genitalia det.; Harewood Forest, 26.10.97, cases; Oakley, 18.6.99 (DGG); Winnall Moors NR (DHS); Abbotstone Down, 27.7.94, a few at m.v. light, genitalia det. (RJBH, JRL); Cow Down Copse, Oakley; Bartley Heath NR (AHD); Bramdean Common, 8.10.96, a few cases (AME, JRL, IRT); Farnborough, 19.7.94, two, det. JRL (RWP).

0491 *Coleophora gryphipennella* (Hübner, 1796)

Widespread in all three vice-counties, the cases on rose *Rosa* spp. (Goater, 1974, 1992).

■ vc10 Shamblers Copse, 21.9.98, one case (DTB); Newtown, 18.9.97, larval feedings; Parkhurst Forest, 18.9.97, larval feedings (AME, JRL).

■ vc11 Frame Wood, 3.7.99 (DGG); Ashurst, 12.7.93, larval feedings (JRL); Hilliers Arboretum, Ampfield, 1998 (TJN); Flexford Meadows NR, May 1999, very common (BE); Hookheath Meadows NR, Southwick, 17.10.92, larval feedings; Soberton, 30.6.95, one at m.v. light, genitalia det.; Old Winchester Hill NNR, 3.6.93, larval feedings; Upper Hamble Country Park, 7.10.96, larval feeding; Curbridge NR, 4.6.98, larval feedings; West Meon, 8.10.96, a few cases; Clanfield, 15.4.97, a few cases; Portsdown, 19.4.92, a few cases (JRL *et al.*); Hook-with-Warsash, 1996, cases; Hook shore, two cases; Titchfield Haven; Curbridge (RJD); Southsea, 20.7.95, one at m.v. light, genitalia det.; Sandy Point NR, Hayling Island, 12.5.97, larval feedings (JRL).

■ vc12 Chilbolton Down, 25.5.92, larval feedings (JRL, DHS); Wildhern, nr Andover, 12.10.97, cases on *Rosa* spp.; Oakley, 18.6.99, feeding damage on *Rosa* sp.; Fleet Pond, 21.4.98, cases; Eelmoor Marsh SSSI, 19.10.97, cases; Harewood Forest, 26.10.97, cases (DGG); Bramdean Common, 8.10.96, a few cases; Ashford Hangers NR, 18.10.93, larval feedings (JRL *et al.*).

0492 *Coleophora flavipennella* (Duponchel, 1843)

Separable from *C. lutipennella* on genitalia and on differences in the early stages (see above). Now recorded from many places in the mainland vice-counties and once on the Isle of Wight.

■ vc10 Whitefield Wood, 23.5.99 (JMC). **New vc record.**

■ vc11 Roydon Woods, 10.7.96, many at m.v. light, genitalia det.; Cadland Estate, Beaulieu, 12.7.97, several at m.v. light, genitalia det.; Chandlers Ford, 1999, very common, genitalia det. (BE); The Moors NR, Bishops Waltham, 25.7.98, one, genitalia det.; Soberton, 30.6.95, a few at m.v. light, genitalia det.; Swanwick NR, 20.8.96,

one at m.v. light, genitalia det.; Hookheath Meadows NR, Southwick, 17.10.92, small cases on *Quercus robur*; Upper Hamble Country Park, 7.10.96, one case; Titchfield, 20.5.94, one case, moth bred; West Meon, 8.10.96, a few cases; Great Salterns NR, Portsmouth; Havant Thicket, 28.6.95 (JRL *et al.*); Hamble Common, 1996; Chilling Copse; Wickham Common, 11.6.98, one bred from case found on 21.4.; Fareham; Shedfield Common; Hook-with-Warsash, 1996, all genitalia det. (RJD); Sandy Point NR, Hayling Island, 17.10.96, one case (JRL).
■ vc12 Pamber, 1995, bred from a case coll. 1.7.95 (GJD); Farnborough, 26.6.94, det. JRL (RWP).

0493 *Coleophora serratella* (Linnaeus, 1761)
Abundant throughout all three vice-counties, cases on birch *Betula* spp, alder *Alnus glutinosa*, elm *Ulmus* spp., hornbeam *Carpinus betulus* and whitebeam *Sorbus aria* (JRL).

0494 *Coleophora coracipennella* (Hübner, 1796)
Separable on genitalia from *C. prunifoliae* Doets and *C. spinella* (Schrank). The cases of all three species are found on blackthorn and no feature is known for distinguishing them: the moths must be bred and dissected. The distribution of all three species is therefore imperfectly known.
■ vc10 Tennyson Down, 18.5.92, one case, moth bred and genitalia det. (DHS, PHS, JRL). **New vc record.**
■ vc11 Park Gate; Hook; Warsash shore, 17.6.98; Fareham; Titchfield, 10.5.98, one case, female bred (RJD); Great Salterns NR, Portsmouth; Gutner Point NR, Hayling Island, 6.10.96, one case, moth bred and genitalia det. (JRL).

0494a *Coleophora prunifoliae* Doets, 1944
Cases of this species have also been found occasionally on apple *Malus* spp., as at Browndown in 1990 (Goater, 1992).
■ vc11 Titchfield Haven, 5.5.98, four cases on blackthorn, moths bred; Brownwich cliffs, 1996, a dozen cases on blackthorn, moths bred, genitalia det. (RJD); Hookheath Meadows NR, Southwick, 15.5.92, cases, one moth bred, genitalia det. (JRL).

0495 *Coleophora spinella* (Schrank, 1802)
= *cerasivorella* Packard, 1870
Common in all three vice-counties, cases mainly on hawthorn and apple *Malus* spp. (JRL). According to Emmet *et al.* (1996), cases on hawthorn are usually those of *C. spinella*, but this cannot be taken for granted: dissection of the adult is necessary, as with moths bred from cases on blackthorn.
■ vc8 Martin Down, 8.6.92, one case on privet amongst the foodplant, hawthorn (JRL, RMP).
■ vc10 Shanklin (RJD); Gurnard, 23.5.95, larvae, emerged July, det. JRL (DTB).

0496 *Coleophora milvipennis* Zeller, 1839
Known from amongst birch *Betula* spp. on the mainland, but not yet from the Isle of Wight. All records are included, but that given in Goater (1974) should be regarded as unconfirmed.

■ vc11 Merrietown Heath, 18.10.93, 9.10.99, several cases on *B. pendula* (PHS); Roydon Woods, 3.10.98, a few cases (RJD, JRL); Norleywood, 2.9.94, one case (JRL); Emer Bog, October 1999, cases common (BE); Wickham Common, 27.9.98, two cases (RJD).
■ vc12 Eelmoor Marsh SSSI, 19.10.97; Harewood Forest, 28.4.96, cases (DGG).

0496a *Coleophora adjectella* Herrich-Schäffer, 1855
Recorded from one locality on the Isle of Wight (Goater, 1992). In Britain, the larva is associated with blackthorn.

0497 *Coleophora badiipennella* (Duponchel, 1843)
There are a few records from the mainland vice-counties (Goater, 1974, 1992), to which may be added the following. The cases are found on elm *Ulmus* spp.
■ vc10 Freshwater, 23.6.97, case, conf. JRL (DTB). **New vc record.**
■ vc11 Upper Pennington, 12.10.99, one case (PAB); Hook-with-Warsash, 1996, genitalia det.; Hook Valley NR, 2.6.98, one fixed case (RJD); Fareham, 17.9.97, a few tenanted mines; Alver Valley NR, Gosport, 22.9.97, several mines with larvae; Great Salterns NR, Portsmouth (JRL, *et al.*).
■ vc12 Wildhern, nr Andover, 28.9.97, cases (DGG).

0498 *Coleophora alnifoliae* Barasch, 1934
The only records of this species in Hampshire given in Goater (1974), are from Pamber and Hook Common in N Hants. Cases occur on alder *Alnus glutinosa*, occasionally grey alder *A. incana*.
■ vc11 Hookheath Meadows NR, 5.6.99, 14 cases on *A. glutinosa*, moths bred (RJD, JRL, PHS). **New vc record.**

0499 *Coleophora limosipennella* (Duponchel, 1843)
There are a few confirmed records of this species given in Goater (1974, 1992), to which the following may be added. Cases on elm *Ulmus* spp., especially on young growth in hedgerows.
■ vc11 Botley Wood, 29.9.94, a few cases on *U. procera*; Bitterne, October 1999, nine cases on *Ulmus* sp. (BE); Fareham, 10.10.97, one case; Great Salterns NR, Portsmouth (JRL *et al.*); Milton Common, Southsea, 29.5.99, one at m.v. light, det. JRL (IRT).
■ vc12 Wildhern, nr Andover, 2.6.97, cases on *U. procera* (DGG).

0501 *Coleophora siccifolia* Stainton, 1856
There are sparse records from the mainland vice-counties given in Goater (1974, 1992), but nothing has been heard of this species since. Cases found in Hampshire have been on hawthorn or crab apple *Malus sylvestris*.

0502 *Coleophora trigeminella* Fuchs, 1881
There are two records of this species in Hampshire, both from S Hants (Goater, 1983, 1992). It is probably overlooked on account of the secretive habits of the larva (see Emmet *et al.*, 1996).

0503 *Coleophora fuscocuprella* Herrich-Schäffer, 1855
First recorded in the county from Havant Thicket in 1979 (Goater, 1983), and since from Crab Wood, Emer Bog and Botley Wood, all in S Hants (Goater, 1992, and below). Cases are found on hazel and birch *Betula* spp.
■ vc11 Crab Wood, 20.9.97, cases on hazel (JRL, *et al.*); Emer Bog, October 1999, cases common (BE); Botley Wood, 20.5.98, female at m.v. light, genitalia det. (RJD); Stoke Park Wood, 19.10.99, case with larva on hazel (PAB).

0504 *Coleophora lusciniaepennella* (Treitschke, 1833)
= *viminetella* Zeller, 1849
Recorded from all three vice-counties, but mainly from S and N Hants (Goater, 1974, 1992). In the New Forest, most records of cases are from bog-myrtle *Myrica gale*, elsewhere from sallows *Salix* spp.
■ vc10 Redcliff; Parkhurst Forest (RJD).
■ vc11 South Bentley Inclosure, New Forest, 1.6.99, case on *Salix* sp. (DGG); Roydon Woods, 3.10.98, a few larval feedings on *Myrica* (RJD, JRL); Pig Bush, 16.10.99, cases abundant on *Myrica* (BE); Swanwick NR; Titchfield Haven, 1996, cases; Shedfield Common (RJD); Soberton, 30.6.95, one at m.v. light, genitalia det.; Lower Titchfield Haven NR, 24.5.93, larval feedings on *Salix caprea*; Fareham, 17.9.97, one case on *S. cinerea*; Browndown, 18.6.93, larval feedings on *S. cinerea* (JRL); Milton Common, Southsea, at light in garden, 1998 (IRT).
■ vc12 Porton Down, 24.7.94, larval feedings on *S. caprea* (JRL); Wildhern, 24.5.98, cases on *Salix*; Fleet Pond LNR, 8.5.98, cases on *Salix* (DGG).

0509 *Coleophora violacea* (Ström, 1783)
Apparently rather scarce in the mainland vice-counties, typical finds being of single cases or single moths at light. The fact that the larva is highly polyphagous (see Emmet *et al.*, 1996) probably means that it is difficult to target.
■ vc11 Merrietown Heath, 18.10.93, one case on *Betula pendula* (PHS); Broughton Down, 16.5.00, one disturbed by day (AHD); Fareham, 5.6.98, female at m.v. light, genitalia det.; Havant Thicket, 23.6.98, male at m.v. light, genitalia det. (RJD).
■ vc12 Oakley, 18.6.99 (DGG); Yateley, 23.9.94, one case on *Sorbus aucuparia* (AMD, JRL).

0510 *Coleophora juncicolella* Stainton, 1851
A heathland species, the cases of which occur on ling *Calluna vulgaris* and bell heather *Erica cinerea*. It is recorded from heathy places in the mainland vice-counties (Goater 1974, 1992), but is stated to be difficult to breed.
■ vc11 Merrietown Heath, 21.7.93, by day (PHS); Matley Bog margins, 10.5.99, many cases swept off *Calluna* (BE); Browndown (RJD); Sandy Point NR, Hayling Island, 8.5.96, several cases swept from *Calluna* (JRL).
■ vc12 Fleet Pond, 21.4.98, cases swept from *Erica* (DGG).

0511 *Coleophora orbitella* Zeller, 1849
First recorded in the county in 1975, from Martyr Worthy vc12 (Goater, 1983), and subsequently from Newtown Common, also in N Hants and a few places in S Hants (Goater, 1992). In Hampshire, cases have been found on birch.
■ vc11 Merrietown Heath, 7.10.99, one case on *Betula pendula* (PHS); Havant Thicket, 28.6.95, one at m.v. light, genitalia det. (JRL).

0512 *Coleophora binderella* (Kollar, 1832)
The following records are additional to those few given in Goater (1974, 1992). Cases are found on birch *Betula* spp., alder *Alnus glutinosa* and *A. incana* and hazel.
■ vc10 Gatcombe, 14.6.96, mines with larvae, and case (DTB).
■ vc11 Ashurst, 12.7.93, one case on *Betula* (JRL); Hilliers Arboretum, Ampfield, 1998 (TJN); Fareham; Wickham Common (RJD); Upper Hamble Country Park, 7.10.96, one case on *Corylus* (AMD, AME, JRL).
■ vc12 Wildhern nr Andover, 20.7.98, at m.v. light, genitalia det., 30,vii,99; Abbotstone Down, 1.6.93, a few cases on *Corylus* (RJBH, JRL, DHS); Fleet Pond, 21.4.98, case on alder (DGG); Harewood Forest, 14.5.96, one case on hazel (JRL, D.O'Keefe); Yateley, 23.9.94, two cases on downy birch *Betula pubescens* (AMD, JRL). **New vc record.**

0513 *Coleophora potentillae* Elisha, 1885
A few records from all three vice-counties (Goater 1974, 1992). The larva is somewhat polyphagous, but the majority of cases are found on rosaceous herbs and shrubs.
■ vc10 Reeth Bay, 23.5.97, mines and cases (DTB).
■ vc11 Emer Bog, October 1999, four cases (BE); Hookheath Meadows NR, Southwick, 17.10.92, larval feedings on bramble *Rubus fruticosus* agg. (JRL).
■ vc12 Yateley Common, 26.3.94, larval feedings on *R. fruticosus* agg. nr Wyndhams Pool, 26.3.94 (AMD, BG, JRL).

0514 *Coleophora ahenella* Heinemann, 1876
Local in the mainland vice-counties (Goater 1974, 1992). In the New Forest, cases are on alder buckthorn *Frangula alnus,* and on the chalk the chosen foodplant is buckthorn *Rhamnus catharticus* .
■ vc11 Winchester, Sarum Road and Crab Wood, autumn 1989, cases on *Rhamnus* in lanes, several moths bred 1990 (RJBH).
■ vc12 Bramdean Common, 8.10.96, several cases on *Rhamnus* (AME, JRL, IRT).

0515 *Coleophora albitarsella* Zeller, 1849
Scattered records from all three vice-counties (Goater, 1974, 1992). In Hampshire, cases have been reported on marjoram *Origanum vulgare* and ground-ivy *Glechoma hederacea*.
■ vc10 Bouldnor, 9.12.95, mines (DTB).
■ vc11 Frame Wood, 3.7.99 (DGG); Parnholt Wood, 14.5.96, larval feedings on *Origanum*; Portsdown, 19.4.92, a few cases on *Origanum*, moths bred (JRL).
■ vc12 Wildhern, 25.5.98, genitalia det.; Harewood Forest, 26.10.97, cases on *Glechoma* (DGG); Bramdean Common, 8.10.96, a few larval feedings on *Glechoma* (AME, JRL, IRT).

0516 *Coleophora trifolii* (Curtis, 1832)
Local in all three vice-counties (Goater, 1974, 1992). The foodplants, melilot *Melilotus* spp. though frequent enough, are characteristic of wasteland and disturbed ground and tend to come and go; *C. trifolii* appears to be host-specific on this genus of plants, and species that have been confused with it in the past are associated with clovers *Trifolium* spp.
■ vc10 Luccombe Chine (RJD).
■ vc11 Locks Heath, 20.7.00, det. RJD (PCa); Funtley; Fareham; Titchfield Haven; Portsdown (RJD); Swanwick, 14.6.97, one; Great Salterns NR, Portsmouth (JRL); Milton Common, Southsea, at light in garden, 1998 (IRT).
■ vc12 Oakley (AHD); Yateley Common, 12.7.94, one (AMD).

[0517 *Coleophora frischella* (Linnaeus, 1758)
Agassiz (2000) pointed out the confusion that has arisen over the identity of this species and *C. alcyonipennella* (Kollar). The two species are superficially alike and can only be distinguished with certainty by examination of the genitalia, which are distinctive. Unfortunately, the captions of the genitalia figures given in Patzak (1974) were transposed and this has led to misidentification by subsequent authors. True *C. frischella* has yet to be found in Britain and the records given for Hampshire (Goater, 1983, 1992) are more likely to refer to *C. alcyonipennella*. The following records, received as *C. frischella*, most probably also refer to the next species.
■ vc11 Sparsholt College (AHD); West Walk, Wickham, 25.8.95; Swanwick NR, 20.8.96 (JRL); Catisfield; Fareham, 1.7.98, one; Titchfield Haven; Portsdown (RJD); Denmead, Creech Wood, 1997 (JRL, EAP).
■ vc12 Wildhern, nr Andover, 29.9.97, two, 25.7.98, two (DGG); Overton; Brighton Hill, Basingstoke; Bramley Frith Wood, 29.7.99, three at m.v. light (AHD); Basing Forest (RJD).]

0517a *Coleophora alcyonipennella* (Kollar, 1832)
■ vc11 Bishops Waltham, 18.8.93, one at m.v. light; Botley Wood, 4.7.95, one at m.v. light; Swanwick, 20.8.96, a few at m.v. light; Hookheath Meadows NR, Southwick, 24.5.92, one at m.v. light; West Walk, Wickham, 25.8.95, several at m.v. light; Creech Wood, Denmead, 22.8.97, two at m.v. light; Southsea, 12.8.96, cases on *Trifolium hybridum* and *T. repens*, moths bred; Sandy Point NR, Hayling Island, 18.8.95, 15.8.98, one at m.v. light (JRL); Milton Common, Southsea, at light in garden, 1998, 12 in 1999, between 12.7 and 29.8 (IRT).
■ vc12 Abbotstone Down, 27.7.94, one at m.v. light (RJBH, JRL).

0518 *Coleophora mayrella* (Hübner, 1813)
= *spissicornis* (Haworth, 1828)
Recorded from all three vice-counties (Goater, 1974 as *C. spissicornis*, 1992). The special technique for discovering the cases in heads of white clover *Trifolium repens* is described by Emmet *et al.*, 1996). Most Hampshire specimens have been taken at light.

■ vc11 Roydon Woods, 10.7.96, one at m.v. light (PRD, JRL); Catisfield; Fareham; Titchfield Haven (RJD); Botley Wood, 4.7.95, one at m.v. light; Great Salterns NR, Portsmouth (JRL); Milton Common, Southsea, 30.6.00, two at m.v. light, det. IRT (IRT).
■ vc12 Wildhern, nr Andover, 17.8.97, cases on white clover (DGG); Farnborough, 12.7.95 (RWP).

0519 *Coleophora deauratella* Lienig & Zeller, 1846
Records given in Goater (1992) and below are considered to be reliable, but earlier ones could refer to this species or *C. alcyonipennella*. Emmet *et al.* (1996) give red clover *Trifolium pratense* as the only foodplant, but JRL has recently bred the moth from white clover *Trifolium repens* and kidney vetch *Anthyllis vulneraria*.
■ vc11 Fareham, genitalia checked (RJD); Botley Wood, 4.6.93, a few; Portsdown, 25.8.92, cases on *Trifolium pratense*, 12.7.95, one case on kidney vetch, moth emerged 29.5.96, genitalia det. (JRL); Milton Common, Southsea, at light in garden, 1998 (IRT); Southsea, 4.6.93, one bred from seedheads of white clover *T. repens* collected 24.7.92; Havant Thicket, 28.6.95, a few at m.v. light; Sandy Point NR, Hayling Island, 22.7.95, one at m.v. light (JRL); Milton Common, Southsea, six at m.v. light in 1999, and again in 2000, det. JRL (IRT).
■ vc12 Farnborough, two in 1994, 26.8.95 (RWP).

0521 *Coleophora conyzae* Zeller, 1868
Recorded from all three vice-counties (Goater, 1974, 1992). Cases occur on fleabane *Pulicaria dysenterica* in damp places and on ploughman's spikenard *Inula conyza* on the downs.
■ vc10 Culver Cliff (RJD).
■ vc11 North Solent NNR, Beaulieu, 2.6.92, one case (DJLA, AME, JRL); Fareham, genit. checked (RJD); Hookheath Meadows NR, Southwick, 23.5.92, several cases on *Pulicaria*; Sandy Point NR, Hayling Island, 2.10.97, a few cases on *Pulicaria* (JRL).

0522 *Coleophora lineolea* (Haworth, 1828)
Recorded from all three vice-counties Goater (1974, 1992). In Hampshire, cases have been found mainly on hedge woundwort *Stachys sylvatica* but also on black horehound *Ballota nigra*.
■ vc10 Dodnor, 12.10.96, mines (DTB).
■ vc11 South Bentley Inclosure, New Forest, 1.6.99, cases on *S. sylvatica* (DGG); Crab Wood, 20.9.97, a few cases on *S. sylvatica* (JRL, *et al.*); Botley Wood; Fareham, 16.8.98, male; Portsdown, 1999, cases; Eastney (RJD).
■ vc12 Winnall Moors NR (DHS); Cheesefoot Head, 19.10.99, case on *S. sylvatica* (PAB); Wildhern, nr Andover, 20.9.97, cases on *S. sylvatica*; Tangley, 2.10.97, cases on *S. sylvatica*; Harewood Forest, 26.10.97, cases on *S. sylvatica* (DGG); Farnborough, 26.7.96, one (RWP).

0523 *Coleophora hemerobiella* (Scopoli, 1763)
There is but a single record in Hampshire, from Shroner Wood, vc12, in 1965 (Goater, 1974). Cases occur on a variety of rosaceous trees and shrubs.

0524 *Coleophora lithargyrinella* Zeller, 1849
The only Hampshire record is of cases on greater stitchwort *Stellaria holostea* on Odiham Common, vc12 in 1963 (Goater, 1974).

0526 *Coleophora laricella* (Hübner, 1817)
Recorded from all three vice-counties (Goater, 1974, 1992). Cases on larch *Larix decidua*.
■ vc11 Fareham, genit. checked; Staunton Country Park (RJD); Milton Common, Southsea, at light in garden, 1998 (IRT).

0530 *Coleophora lixella* Zeller, 1849

6 mm

Recorded from all three vice-counties in Goater (1974, 1992). It should still occur on the remaining areas of unspoilt chalk downland. The larva feeds at first on flower heads of wild thyme *Thymus polytrichus* then, after hibernation, on grasses (Poaceae) and glaucous sedge *Carex flacca*.
■ vc11 Broughton Down, 1.7.99, two by day (BE); Oxenbourne Down, 4.7.75 (RJD).
■ vc12 Porton Down, 1.7.00, many by day (DGG).

0531 *Coleophora ochrea* (Haworth, 1828)
A very local species of chalk and limestone in southern England. It was recorded on the Isle of Wight up to 1933, but has not been relocated despite searches (Goater, 1974). The larva feeds on rock-rose *Helianthemum nummularium*.

0532 *Coleophora albidella* ([Denis & Schiffermüller], 1775)
Present in the mainland vice-counties but seldom reported (Goater, 1974, 1992). The cases occur on species of sallows and willows *Salix* spp.
■ vc11 Roydon Woods, 10.7.96, one at m.v. light (PRD, JRL); Havant Thicket, 5.5.97, one case on *S. cinerea*, moth bred (JRL); Waterlooville, 1.7.00, at m.v. light, conf. JRL (RJM).
■ vc12 Oakley, 18.6.99 (DGG).

0533 *Coleophora anatipennella* (Hübner, 1796)
Locally frequent, mainly in blackthorn scrub on the coast and on downland, in the mainland vice-counties. An old record from the Isle of Wight remains unconfirmed.
■ vc10 Ashey, 21.6.98, one case, conf. JRL (DTB).
■ vc11 Pennington, 8.11.93, larval feedings on blackthorn; Hookheath Meadows NR, Southwick, 17.10.92, one case on blackthorn; Curbridge NR, 4.6.98, one case on *P. domestica*; Browndown, 7.11.94, larval feedings on blackthorn; Alver Valley NR, Gosport, 22.9.97, one old case on blackthorn; Portsdown, 3.5.93, one case on *P. spinosa* (JRL), 30.5.98, case on hawthorn, moth bred (RJD); Great Salterns NR, Portsmouth (JRL).
■ vc12 Wildhern, nr Andover, 12.10.97, cases on blackthorn (DGG); Farnborough, 2.7.94, det. JRL (RWP).

0534 *Coleophora currucipennella* Zeller, 1839
There are two old records from the Isle of Wight (Goater, 1974), but nothing has been heard of this species on the Island since 1934. It is rare and local in Britain and seems also to have decreased (Emmet *et al.*, 1996).

0535 *Coleophora ibipennella* Zeller, 1849
= *ardeaepennella* Scott, 1861
The records of *C. ardeaepennella* given in Goater (1974, 1992) are referable to this species, whereas those given under *C. ibipennella* are actually *C. betulella* Heinemann (see Emmet *et al.*, 1996).
■ vc11 Ocknell Inclosure, 26.5.99, cases on *Quercus* (DGG); Cadland Estate, Beaulieu, 12.7.97, a few at m.v. light (JRL); Fareham, genitalia checked; Hook-with-Warsash, 1996 (RJD); The Moors NR, Bishops Waltham, 25.7.98, one; Hookheath Meadows NR, Southwick, 17.10.92, one case on *Quercus robur*; Swanwick, 14.6.97, one case; West Meon, 8.10.96, one old case on *Quercus*; Havant Thicket, 8.7.97, a few at m.v. light; Sinah Common, Hayling Island, 29.5.95, several cases on *Q. robur* (JRL, IRT, *et al.*).
■ vc12 Abbotstone Down, 1.6.93, one case on *Quercus* (RJBH, JRL, DHS); Bartley Heath NR, 22.5.99, cases (AHD); Farnborough, 8.7.93, 7.7.94 det. JRL (RWP).

0536 *Coleophora betulella* Heinemann, 1876
The records given in Goater (1974, 1992) under *C. ibipennella* refer to this species. The cases of *C. betulella* are found on birch *Betula* spp. and those of *C. ibipennella* are on oak *Quercus* spp. and only doubtfully recorded on birch.
■ vc11 Havant Thicket, 8.7.97, at m.v. light (JRL, IRT, *et al.*).
■ vc12 Eelmoor Marsh, 4.7.98, at m.v. light (DGG). **New vc record.**

0537 *Coleophora palliatella* (Zincken, 1813)
Local in oak woodland and known in numbers only from Roydon Woods (see below) and Botley Wood (Goater, 1992).
■ vc10 Parkhurst Forest (RJD).
■ vc11 Burley New Inclosure, 1.7.99; Frame Wood, 3.7.99; Sloden Inclosure, 2.7.99 (DGG); Roydon Woods, 10.7.96, many at m.v. light, genitalia det. (PRD, JRL), 4.10.98, one old case on *Quercus* (RJD, JRL); Hook-with-Warsash, 1996, cases; Wickham Common, 21.4.98, two cases, moth bred (RJD); Havant Thicket, 8.7.97, one at m.v. light (JRL, IRT, *et al.*).
■ vc12 Wildhern, 15.7.98, genitalia det.; Oakley, 18.6.99 (DGG).

0538 *Coleophora vibicella* (Hübner, 1813)
The foodplant, dyer's greenweed *Genista tinctoria* has decreased of late, and in Botley Wood, where cases were common up to the mid-1980s, the site has been overgrown by conifers. The moth has been recorded from the Isle of Wight and S Hants (Goater, 1974, 1992), but never from N Hants.
■ vc10 Freshwater–Yarmouth railway line (RJD).

■ vc11 Titchfield Haven, 22.7.77, male at m.v. light (RJD); North Hayling Island, 10.6.97, one case on *G. tinctoria* (JRL, IRT).

0541 *Coleophora pyrrhulipennella* Zeller, 1839

Recorded from heathy places in all three vice-counties (Goater, 1974, 1992). The cases are found on ling *Calluna vulgaris* and bell heather *Erica cinerea*.

■ vc11 Sopley Common, 13.5.00, several cases on *E. cinerea* (PHS); Merrietown Heath, 18.6.99, one at m.v. light (PHS *et al.*); Shatterford and Matley Passage, 10.5.99, cases swept off *Calluna* (BE); Shedfield Common, 21.3.97, several cases swept from *Calluna* (JRL, IRT); Milton Common, Southsea, at light in garden, 1998 (IRT).

■ vc12 Eelmoor Marsh SSSI, 19.10.97, cases on *E. cinerea*; Fleet Pond LNR, 7.10.97, cases on *E. cinerea*, 12.4.98, cases swept from *Erica* (DGG); Farnborough, 11.7.94, det. JRL (RWP).

0544 *Coleophora albicosta* (Haworth, 1828)

Widespread amongst the foodplant, gorse *Ulex europaeus*, in all three vice-counties (Goater, 1974, 1992).

■ vc8 Martin Down, 5.5.90 (S. Nash).

■ vc10 Parkhurst Forest (RJD).

■ vc11 Sopley Common, 12.5.00, several at m.v. light (PHS *et al.*); Fritham Plain and Ocknell Inclosure, 26.5.99 (DGG); Matley Wood; Hamble Common, 1996; Fareham, genit. checked; Titchfield Haven; Browndown Wendleholme NR (RJD); Hookheath Meadows NR, Southwick, 24.5.92, one at m.v. light (JRL): Wickham Common; Sandy Point, Hayling Island, genitalia checked (RJD).

■ vc12 Pamber, at light 2.5.95 and two on 20.5.95, keyed out under microscope and compared with specimens in Reading Museum coll. (GJD); Silchester Common, 19.6.96, beaten from *Ulex europaeus* (AHD); Fleet Pond, 21.4.98, case in dead flower of *Ulex*; 8.5.98, one at m.v. light (DGG); Farnborough, 12.6.96 (RWP); Eelmoor Marsh, 4.7.98, at m.v. light (DGG).

0545 *Coleophora saturatella* Stainton, 1850

Recorded very occasionally from the Isle of Wight and S Hants (Goater, 1974, 1992). Cases have been found on dyer's greenweed *Genista tinctoria* but not from the alternative foodplant, broom *Cytisus scoparius*.

0546 *Coleophora genistae* Stainton, 1857

Recorded from all three vice-counties (Goater, 1974, 1992), and probably under-recorded for want of searching the local foodplant, petty whin *Genista anglica*.

■ vc11 Ocknell Plain, 6.5.99, cases (DGG); Matley, 26.5.91, cases, nine moths bred (RJBH).

■ vc12 Bartley Heath NR, 22.5.99, cases (AHD).

0547 *Coleophora discordella* Zeller, 1849

Recorded from all three vice-counties, though only once recently from the Isle of Wight (Goater, 1974, 1992). Cases on bird's-foot-trefoils *Lotus corniculatus* and *L. pedunculatus*.

■ vc10 Freshwater, 10.8.00 (SAK-J).

■ vc11 Hookheath Meadows, larva (RJD); Old Winchester Hill NNR, 3.6.93, larval feedings on *L. corniculatus*; Oxenbourne Down NR, 25.5.93, a few cases on *L. corniculatus* (JRL).

■ vc12 Winnall Moors NR (DHS); Bramley Frith Wood NR (AHD); Chawton Park Wood (RJD).

0548 *Coleophora niveicostella* Zeller, 1839

Recorded only from Broughton Down vc11 and Leckford and Martyr Worthy vc12 (Goater, 1983, 1992). Cases on wild thyme *Thymus* spp. on downland.

■ vc11 Oxenbourne Down, 4.7.75 (RJD).

0525 *Coleophora solitariella* Zeller, 1849

This is another species which feeds on greater stitchwort *Stellaria holostea*. There are a few records from the mainland vice-counties, the most recent in 1986 (Goater, 1974, 1992).

■ vc11 Botley Wood, 20.5.98, one male; Titchfield Haven, 5.5.98, cases very locally abundant, moths bred; Browndown (RJD).

0550 *Coleophora silenella* Herrich-Schäffer, 1855

Recorded occasionally in the mainland vice-counties, mainly as cases on bladder campion *Silene vulgaris*: Droxford and Portchester, vc11, and Leckford and Martyr Worthy, vc12 (Goater, 1974, 1992).

■ vc8 Martin Down, 6.5.90 (S. Nash).

0553 *Coleophora striatipennella* Nylander, 1848

Records from several places in the mainland vice-counties are given in Goater (1974, 1992), but it has yet to be discovered in the Isle of Wight.

■ vc8 Martin Down, 8.6.92 (JRL, RMP).

■ vc11 Merrietown Heath, 8.5.98, by day (PHS); Hamble Common, 1996; Wickham Common, abundant; Fareham, 19.6.98, male, genit. checked; Titchfield Haven; Portsdown (RJD); Hookheath Meadows NR, Southwick, 23.5.92, one, genitalia det., 24.5.92, one (JRL); Milton Common, Southsea, 19.5.99, one at m.v. light, det. JRL (IRT).

■ vc12 Winnall Moors NR (DHS); Farnborough, 10.6.97, det. JRL (RWP).

0554 *Coleophora inulae* Wocke, 1876

Emmet *et al.* (1996) state that the current headquarters of this species in Britain are on the Isle of Wight and in S Hants. Also recorded from Martyr Worthy and Shroner Wood in vc12 during the 1960s (Goater, 1974). Cases are found on fleabane *Pulicaria dysenterica* in damp places and on ploughman's spikenard *Inula conyza* in drier areas.

■ vc11 Sandy Point NR, Hayling Island, 2.9.97, one case on *Pulicaria* (JRL, IRT).

0555 *Coleophora follicularis* (Vallot, 1802)
= *troglodytella* (Duponchel, 1843)

Recorded from all three vice-counties since first reported from Itchen Valley vc12 in 1966 (Goater, 1974). More recent records are given in Goater (1992) and below. The larvae feed principally on two quite different plants, hemp-agrimony *Eupatorium cannabinum* and fleabane *Pulicaria dysenterica* and show differences both in behaviour and in the colour of the head, but studies of genitalia indicate that a single species is involved. Details are given in Emmet, *et al.*, 1996).

■ vc10 Tennyson Down, 18.5.92, larval feedings on *Eupatorium* (JRL, DHS, PHS); St Catherine's Point, 2.7.94, at m.v. light, det. JRL (SRC, PMP).

■ vc11 Hookheath Meadows NR, Southwick, 23.5.92, cases on *Pulicaria*; Swanwick, 14.6.97, larval feedings on *Pulicaria* (JRL); Fareham, 14.5.98, strong colony on *Pulicaria* in garden; Titchfield Haven; Portsdown, 30.5.98, mines and two cases on *Eupatorium* (RJD); Milton Common, Southsea, at light in garden, 1998 (IRT); Portsdown, 29.4.97, one case on *Eupatorium*; Oxenbourne Down NR, 25.5.93, larval feedings on *Eupatorium*; Sandy Point NR, Hayling Island, 29.5.95, a few cases on *Pulicaria* (JRL).

■ vc12 Leckford, 4.5.92, a few cases on *Eupatorium* (JRL, DHS); Winnall Moors NR (DHS).

0556 *Coleophora trochilella* Duponchel, 1843

Since the true identity of this species was sorted out, it has been recorded with certainty from all three vice-counties (Goater, 1974, 1992) and below. More work is needed into the range of foodplants, but in Hampshire, cases have been found on yarrow *Achillea millefolium*, sneezewort *A. ptarmica*, tansy *Tanacetum vulgare* and mugwort *Artemisia vulgaris*.

■ vc11 Curbridge NR (RJD); Milton Common, Southsea, 6.8.97, at light (IRT).

■ vc12 Eelmoor Marsh, 4.7.98, at m.v. light, genitalia det. (DGG).

0557 *Coleophora gardesanella* Toll, 1953

First recorded in Hampshire in 1977, from Botley Wood vc11, and since found in several localities in S Hants and two in N Hants (Goater, 1983, 1992). Cases have been found on sneezewort *Achillea ptarmica* and mugwort *Artemisia vulgaris*.

■ vc11 Hookheath Meadows NR, Southwick, 23.5.92, a few cases on *A. ptarmica*, moths bred (JRL); Milton Common, Southsea, 14.6.99, one at m.v. light, det. JRL (IRT).

0559 *Coleophora peribenanderi* Toll, 1943

This is another *Coleophora* that has been misunderstood in the past (Goater, 1974). Satisfactory records have now been received from all three vice-counties (Goater, 1992). Cases are reported most often from creeping thistle *Cirsium arvense*.

■ vc11 Catisfield; Fareham, genitalia checked; Hook-with-Warsash, 1996, genitalia; Chilling Copse; Titchfield Haven; Rowner Wild Grounds (RJD); The Moors NR, Bishops Waltham, 7.8.98, one, genitalia det.; Hookheath Meadows NR, Southwick, 23.5.92, one case on *C. arvense*; Upper Hamble Country Park, 7.10.96, one case on *C. arvense*; Great Salterns NR, Portsmouth (JRL *et al.*); Milton Common, Southsea, 18.7.96, at actinic trap, genitalia det. JRL, 1998, 3.7 and 26.7.00 (IRT); Havant

Thicket, October 1999, one case (BE); Sandy Point NR, Hayling Island, 10.6.94, one case on *C. vulgare* (JRL).

■ vc12 Winnall Moors NR (DHS); Wildhern, nr Andover, 20.9.97, cases on *C. arvense*; Eelmoor Marsh SSSI, 19.10.97, cases on *C. arvense*; Fleet Pond LNR, 7.10.97, cases on *C. arvense* (DGG); Bramdean Common, 8.10.96, larval feedings on *C. arvense* (AME, JRL, IRT).

0560 *Coleophora paripennella* Zeller, 1839

The records given in Goater (1974, 1992) and below are considered to be reliable. The cases are found most often on black knapweed *Centaurea nigra* and creeping thistle *Cirsium arvense*, but have also been seen in Hampshire on saw-wort *Serratula tinctoria*, greater knapweed *Centaurea scabiosa* and burdock *Arctium* spp.

■ vc10 Firestone Copse, 10.6.78, one case on *Serratula* (RJD). **New vc record.**

■ vc11 Parnholt Wood, 1.5.98, one case on *C. nigra*; Crab Wood, 20.9.97, one case on *C. nigra*; Botley Wood, 11.5.98, one case on *C. nigra*, others on *Serratula* (RJD); Hookheath Meadows NR, Southwick, 15.5.92, one case on *C. nigra*; Oxenbourne Down NR, 25.5.93, larval feedings on *C. nigra* (JRL, *et al.*).

■ vc12 Ashford Hangers NR, 18.10.93, one case on *C. nigra* and larval feedings on *Arctium lappa* (JRL).

0561 *Coleophora therinella* Tengström, 1848

The first cases ever to be found in Britain were discovered by DHS on Teg Down vc11 on black bindweed *Fallopia convolvulus* in August 1990, and at Southsea, where a few specimens were taken at m.v. light and genitalia det. in 1986, 1989 and 1991 (Goater, 1992).

■ vc11 Portsdown; Catisfield, genitalia det. (RJD); Milton Common, Southsea, 18.7.00, one at m.v. light, genitalia det. JRL (IRT).

0562 *Coleophora asteris* Mühlig, 1864

This species occurs along the coasts of South Hampshire and the Isle of Wight (Goater 1974, 1992). The larvae feed in cases on sea aster *Aster tripolium*.

■ vc11 St Denys, Southampton, 29.9.99, along bank of River Itchen; Hook Shore, 15.10.99, cases (PAB); Hamble Common, 14.8.95, one male, genitalia det. (RJD).

0563 *Coleophora argentula* (Stephens, 1834)

Cases common to abundant throughout S Hants on yarrow *Achillea millefolium*, especially near the coast (JRL). There are fewer records from N Hants and none since Goater (1974) from the Isle of Wight.

■ vc12 Winnall Moors NR (DHS); Itchen Wood, Micheldever, 10.11.98, cases (PAB); Wildhern, nr Andover, 4.10.97, cases; Eelmoor Marsh SSSI, 19.10.97, cases, 29.8.98, at m.v. light, genitalia det.; Harewood Forest, 26.10.97, cases (DGG); Yateley Common (AMD).

0564 *Coleophora obscenella* Herrich-Schäffer, 1855
= *virgaureae* Stainton, 1857

Cases are sometimes abundant in heads of goldenrod *Solidago virgaurea*. The moth is probably still in Nunny's

Wood vc10, and at Parnholt Wood, Botley Wood and Havant Thicket vc11 but, curiously, it does not seem to have been found in the New Forest since Minstead, 1968 (Goater 1974, 1992).

■ vc11 Parnholt Wood, 19.9.91, cases abundant., many bred 1992 (RJBH); Botley Wood, 12.10.92, cases (JRL); West Walk (RJD); Stoke Park Wood, 19.10.99, one case (PAB).

0565 *Coleophora saxicolella* Duponchel, 1843
= *benanderi* Kanerva, 1941
Recorded from all three vice-counties (Goater, 1974, as *C. annulatella*, 1992). Cases, on orache *Atriplex* spp., have only been reported from the coast of S Hants.
■ vc11 Hound shore; Fareham, 17.8.98, genit. checked (RJD); Milton Common, Southsea, 31.7 and 5.8.99, singles at m.v. light, det. JRL (IRT); Sinah Common, Hayling Island, 15.8.98, several at m.v. light, genitalia checked (JRL, IRT, *et al.*).
■ vc12 Winnall Moors NR (DHS).

0566 *Coleophora sternipennella* (Zetterstedt, 1839)
Locally very common on the coast of S Hants, the cases on fat-hen *Chenopodium album* and orache *Atriplex* spp., but not recorded from any of the other vice-counties.
■ vc11 Fareham, 9.8.98, two, genit. checked (RJD).

0567 *Coleophora adspersella* Benander, 1939
There are scattered records from all three vice-counties (Goater, 1974, 1992). The only foodplant specifically reported is grass-leaved orache *Atriplex littoralis*.
■ vc11 Cadland Estate, Beaulieu, 12.5.2.97, one at m.v. light, genitalia det.; Bursledon, 8.9.98, a few cases on *A. littoralis* (JRL); Fareham, 5.7.98, male at m.v. light, genitalia det.; Titchfield Haven (RJD); Gutner Point NR, Hayling Island, 7.9.98, two cases on *A. littoralis* (JRL).

0568 *Coleophora versurella* Zeller, 1849
Recorded from all three vice-counties (Goater, 1974, 1992). Cases have been located on fat-hen *Chenopodium album*, spear-leaved orache *Atriplex prostrata* and grass-leaved orache *A. littoralis*.
■ vc11 Catisfield; Fareham, 5.6.98, one male, 5.7.98, 8.8.98; Browndown, genit. checked (RJD); Milton Common, Southsea, at light in garden, 1998, 1999, 2000 (IRT); Sinah Common, Hayling Island, 15.8.98, a few at m.v. light, genitalia det. (JRL, IRT, *et al.*).
■ vc12 Eelmoor Marsh, 24.7.98, at m.v. light, genitalia det. (DGG).

0569 *Coleophora squamosella* Stainton, 1856
Very locally common in the mainland vice-counties. Records are detailed in Goater (1974, 1992). The foodplant is blue fleabane *Erigeron acer*, on which the cases should be sought.

[0572 *Coleophora vestianella* (Linnaeus, 1758)
Single records for S Hants and N Hants are given in Goater (1974) with the *caveat* that older records are unreliable. Emmet *et al.* (1996) exclude both vice-counties from their

distribution map, and state it is the most local and least common of the species which feed on Chenopodiaceae.]

0573 *Coleophora atriplicis* Meyrick, 1928
Local on the salterns of the Isle of Wight and S Hants (Goater, 1974, 1992). The larva feeds on coastal Chenopodiaceae, grass-leaved orache *Atriplex littoralis,* sea-purslane *A. portulacoides,* annual sea-blite *Suaeda maritima* and glassworts *Salicornia* spp.
■ vc11 Marchwood, 8.9.98, a few cases on *S. maritima*; Lower Test Marshes NR, 8.9.98, one case on *Salicornia* (JRL); Upper Hamble Country Park, 7.10.96, a few cases on *A. portulacoides* (AMD, AME, JRL), 24.9.99; Hook Shore, 15.10.99, on *A. portulacoides* (PAB); Fareham, 17.8.98, genit. checked (RJD); Milton Common, Southsea, at light in garden, 1998 (IRT).

0574 *Coleophora deviella* Zeller, 1847
= *suaedivora* Meyrick, 1928
■ vc11 Gutner Point, Hayling Island, 11.9.96, several cases on sea-blite *Suaeda maritima*, moths emerged 4.7.97 (Langmaid, 1997). **New county record.**

0574a *Coleophora aestuariella* Bradley, 1984
■ vc11 Gutner Point, Hayling Island, 11.9.96, 6.10.96, many cases on sea-blite *Suaeda maritima*, moths emerged from 14.7.97 (Langmaid, 1997). **New county record.**

0575 *Coleophora salinella* Stainton, 1859
Very local on the salterns of S Hants, and one old record from the Isle of Wight (Goater, 1974).
■ vc11 Hound shore, 2.8.74 (RJD); Milton Common, Southsea 1994, cases; 1998, at light in garden (IRT); Northney saltmarsh, Hayling Island, 22.9.92, cases on *Atriplex portulacoides*; 11.9.96, many cases on *A. littoralis* (JRL).

0577 *Coleophora artemisicolella* Bruand, 1855
The very few records for this species are given in Goater (1974, 1992) and below. The cases occur in the old seedheads of mugwort *Artemisia vulgaris* and perhaps have been overlooked.
■ vc11 Hookheath Meadows NR, Southwick, 6.3.92, old signs of larval feeding; Botley Wood, 20.9.92, one case; Hilsea, 17.1.92, larval feeding in old seedheads of *A. vulgaris* (JRL *et al.*); Milton Common, Southsea, 24.7.99, one at m.v. light, det. JRL (IRT).
■ vc12 Stockbridge Down, 6.9.91, few cases, one moth bred; Leckford, old railway line, 20.9.91, several cases, four bred (RJBH); Wildhern, nr Andover, 4.10.97, cases (DGG). **New vc record.**

0578 *Coleophora otidipennella* (Hübner, 1817)
= *murinipennella* (Duponchel, 1844)
Probably widespread on the mainland, but few records from the Isle of Wight. Cases on seed-heads of wood-rush *Luzula campestris* and *L. multiflora*.
■ vc12 Bramdean Common (RJD); Bramley Frith Wood, 22.4.98, two at m.v. light (AHD); Fleet Pond LNR, 8.5.98, one by day (DGG).

0552 *Coleophora lassella* Staudinger, 1859

The first English record was from Southampton in 1968 (Goater, 1974). Single adults, determined on genitalia, have since been discovered as follows. The larva feeds on toad rush *Juncus bufonius*, in damp places such as dune slacks.

■ vc10 Yarmouth, 19.5.92 (DHS, PHS). **New vc record.**

■ vc11 Fareham, 22.5.98, female netted at sunset, genitalia det.; Wickham Common, 31.5.99, female, genitalia det. (RJD); Southsea, 4.6.96, one at m.v. light, genitalia det. (JRL).

0581 *Coleophora taeniipennella* Herrich-Schäffer, 1855

Almost certainly overlooked through confusion with other *Juncus*-feeding species. Confirmed records, the majority from S Hants, are given in Goater (1983, 1992) and below.

■ vc11 Dockens Water, Ringwood, 18.4.92, one case on *Juncus inflexus* (JRL, DHS); Whitley Wood, New Forest; Fareham, 3.7.98, one male, 5.7.98; Wickham Common, 1999, genitalia checked (RJD); Emer Bog, October 1999, many cases on *J. articulatus* (BE); Hookheath Meadows NR, Southwick, 14.7.96, one, genitalia det.; Botley Wood, 29.9.94, a few cases on *J. acutiflorus*; Farlington Marshes NR, 6.9.93, one case on *J. articulatus* (JRL).

■ vc12 Eelmoor Marsh SSSI, 19.10.97, cases on *J. articulatus* (DGG); Old Alresford Pond (RJD); Pamber Forest, 18.10.00, cases common on *J. acutiflorus* (AHD); Yateley, 23.9.94, a few cases on *J. acutiflorus* (AMD, JRL). **New vc record.**

0582 *Coleophora glaucicolella* Wood, 1892

Widespread and common, perhaps replacing *C. alticolella* Zeller on the coast. Here, cases occur on the coastal rushes *Juncus gerardii* and *J. maritimus* which are not given as foodplants of *C. alticolella* by Emmet *et al.* (1996).

■ vc11 Cadland Estate, Beaulieu, 12.5.2.97, a few at m.v. light, genitalia det.; Lower Test Marshes NR, 3.5.96, a few cases with larvae on *J. effusus*; Southwick, 8.7.96, many, genitalia det.; Soberton, 30.6.95, a few at m.v. light, genitalia det. (JRL); Chessel Bay, Southampton, cases on *J. gerardii* (PAB); Swanwick NR; Fareham, genit. checked; Titchfield Haven; Portsdown (RJD); Lower Titchfield Haven NR, 24.6.94, a few at m.v. light, genitalia det.; Havant Thicket, 8.7.97, at m.v. light (JRL, IRT, *et al.*).

■ vc12 Winnall Moors NR (DHS); Eelmoor Marsh SSSI, 19.10.97, cases on *Juncus articulatus* and *J. inflexus* (DGG).

0583 *Coleophora tamesis* Waters, 1929
= *cratipennella* auctt.

Four records, one from N Hants, the rest from S Hants, all genitalia determined and the most recent in 1985, are given in Goater (1974, 1992). The early stages have not been reported in the county. The larva is stated by Emmet *et al.* (1996) to feed on jointed rush *Juncus articulatus*.

0584 *Coleophora alticolella* Zeller, 1849

Abundant in all three vice-counties (JRL). Cases, which are indistinguishable from those of *C. glaucicolella*, are

recorded from soft rush *Juncus effusus* and heath rush *J. squarrosus*, and less often from hard rush *J. inflexus* and jointed rush *J. articulatus*.

■ vc8 Martin Down, 8.6.92 (JRL, RMP).

0585 *Coleophora maritimella* Newman, 1873

A coastal species, the cases of which occur on sea rush *Juncus maritimus* on the Isle of Wight and S Hants.

■ vc11 Hengistbury Head, 1998, five, det. PHS (MJ); Cadland Estate, Beaulieu, 12.5.2.97, one at m.v. light, genitalia det.; Bursledon, 8.9.98, one case (JRL); Fareham, genit. checked; Titchfield Haven (RJD); Hilsea, 16.8.92, cases abundant on *J. maritimus*; Sandy Point NR, Hayling Island, 14.7.92, two at m.v. light, genitalia det. (JRL).

0586 *Coleophora adjunctella* Hodgkinson, 1882

This species occurs in the upper reaches of saltmarshes on the coasts of S Hants and the Isle of Wight, the cases on saltmarsh rush *Juncus gerardii*. The cases are very procryptic amongst the seed-heads; holes made in the seedheads may be the work of this species or of *C. glaucicolella* (Emmet *et al.*, 1996).

■ vc11 Lower Titchfield Haven NR, 24.6.94, one at m.v. light, genitalia det.; Hilsea, 16.8.92, cases on *Juncus gerardii* (JRL).

0587 *Coleophora caespititiella* Zeller, 1839

This is yet another *Juncus*-feeding species. It is recorded from many localities in all three vice-counties, and evidently shows a preference for open wooded areas rather than heaths, marshes and the sea-coast.

0588 *Coleophora salicorniae* Heinemann & Wocke, 1876

Local on the coasts of S Hants and the Isle of Wight (Goater 1974, 1992), the larva feeding on glasswort *Salicornia* spp.

■ vc11 Titchfield Haven; Rowner Wild Grounds (RJD); Portsmouth, 22.9.92, many cases on *Salicornia*, moths bred (JRL); Southsea, 22.9.92, several cases found with JRL, six moths emerged late August 1993 (RJBH), Milton Common, 5.8.96 (three), 17.8, 18.8 and 19.8.96, at actinic trap, conf. JRL, again in August, 1997, 1998 and 1999 (IRT); Gutner Point NR, Hayling Island, 6.10.96, many larval feeding signs on *Salicornia* (JRL, IRT).

0527 *Coleophora wockeella* Zeller, 1849

There has been no record since Freshwater, Isle of Wight (Morey, 1909) quoted in Goater (1974). The foodplant, betony *Stachys officinalis*, is still common on the east-facing slope of Tennyson Down and the moth should be sought there.

Elachistidae (39 + [1])

The genus *Elachista* itself is fairly easily recognised as a group of small, often strongly but simply marked moths, the forewings with rounded apices, but problems have always arisen in deciding what other genera should be included in the family. The arrangement given in Emmet *et al.* (1996) represents the current view.

0590 *Perittia obscurepunctella* (Stainton, 1848)
Recorded from the Isle of Wight and S Hants, but not commonly (Goater, 1974, 1992). The larva mines the leaves of honeysuckle *Lonicera periclymenum*.
■ vc10 Tennyson Down, 18.5.92, two (JRL, DHS, PHS).
■ vc11 Ashurst, 12.7.93, a few tenanted mines (JRL); Crab Wood, 14.6.92, several mines, three moths bred 1993 (RJBH); Hookheath Meadows NR; Botley Wood; West Walk (RJD).

0592 *Stephensia brunnichella* (Linnaeus, 1767)
This species occurs along the borders of woods on calcareous downland, where the larva mines the leaves of wild basil *Clinopodium vulgare*. Found recently in several localities in the mainland vice-counties, but not since 1938 on the Isle of Wight (Goater, 1974, 1992).
■ vc12 Ashford Hangers NR, 18.10.93, one (JRL).

Elachista Treitschke, 1833. The species in this rather difficult genus are also dealt with comprehensively by Emmet *et al.* (1996), with good illustrations and figures of all the critical genitalic characters of both sexes. The larvae mine in the leaves of grasses (Poaceae), sedges (Cyperaceae) and wood-rush *Luzula* spp. The presence of 25 of the 33 or so species known in Britain have been reported reliably from the area under review.

0593 *Elachista regificella* Sircom, 1849
The only confirmed records of this species in Hampshire are those given in Goater (1992) for Sparsholt and Havant Thicket, both in vc11. The larva mines the leaves of wood-rush *Luzula* spp.; those found in Hampshire were in hairy wood-rush *L. pilosa*.

0594 *Elachista gleichenella* (Fabricius, 1781)
The only records are those given in Goater (1974, 1992), from vc's 11 and 12, and the only foodplant reported is glaucous sedge *Carex flacca*. The larva also feeds on other species of sedge and on *Luzula* spp.
■ vc10 Firestone Copse, 10.6.78 (RJD). **New vc record.**

0596 *Elachista poae* Stainton, 1855
This is a waterside species, the larva of which lives in reed sweet-grass *Glyceria maxima*. It has been recorded from all three vice-counties (Goater, 1974, 1992), but not since 1985, probably through want of searching.

0597 *Elachista atricomella* Stainton, 1849
Recorded from all three vice-counties (Goater, 1974, 1992). The larva mines the leaves of cock's-foot *Dactylis glomerata*.
■ vc10 Firestone Copse (RJD).
■ vc11 Botley Wood; Catisfield; Browndown; Portsdown (RJD).
■ vc12 Pamber, 1995 (GJD); Noar Hill (RJD).

[0598 *Elachista kilmunella* Stainton, 1849]
Goater (1974) gives a record from Freshwater, Isle of Wight, in 1951, stating that confirmation is required. Emmet *et al.* (1996) discount all records from southern England as being highly improbable, and the vc10 record should be deleted.

0599 *Elachista alpinella* Stainton, 1854)
There are old records for S Hants in 1935 and 1936 (Goater 1974) and more recent ones from Leckford, N Hants in Goater (1992). This species occurs in marshy places where the larva mines leaves of some of the more robust sedges *Carex* spp. such as lesser pond-sedge *C. acutiformis*.

0600 *Elachista luticomella* Zeller, 1839
Hitherto, records have reached the authors only from the mainland vice-counties. The larva mines the leaves of cock's-foot *Dactylis glomerata* and is almost certainly overlooked.
■ vc10 Luccombe Farm, 7.7.99, one imago, conf. JRL (DTB). **New vc record.**

0601 *Elachista albifrontella* (Hübner, 1817)
Recorded in all three vice-counties (Goater, 1974, 1992), and probably widespread and common. The larva mines the leaves of several species of grass (Poaceae).
■ vc11 Hookheath Meadows NR, Southwick, 10.6.92, two (JRL); Titchfield Haven; West Walk (RJD).
■ vc12 Wildhern, 19.7.98, at dusk; Eelmoor Marsh, 4.7.98, at m.v. light (DGG); Pamber, 1995 (GJD).

0602 *Elachista apicipunctella* Stainton, 1849
There is a single record given in Goater (1974) from "Southampton", 13.6.37. Fassnidge was always vague about his localities, and the precise place where he took this specimen is uncertain. The larva mines the leaves of numerous species of Poaceae in open, wooded areas.

0603 *Elachista subnigrella* Douglas, 1853
This is a moth of chalk grassland, the larva of which feeds on robust grasses such as upright brome *Bromopsis erecta* and downy oat-grass *Helictotrichon pubescens*. It has been reported from all three vice-counties (Goater, 1974, 1992) but, like others of the genus, is probably under-recorded.
■ vc8 Martin Down, 6.5.90 (S. Nash), 8.6.92 (JRL, RMP).
■ vc10 High Down, Freshwater (RJD).
■ vc11 Fareham; Portsdown (RJD); Oxenbourne Down NR, 18.5.93, one (JRL).

0606 *Elachista humilis* Zeller, 1850
Now recorded from all three vice-counties (Goater, 1974, 1992) and below. The larva is found in various species of grass, particularly tufted hair-grass *Deschampsia flexuosa*. In 1986, DHS recorded it from a new foodplant, greater tussock-sedge *Carex paniculata*, from which he bred a moth (Goater, 1992).
■ vc11 Botley Wood, 20.5.98, one male (RJD); Funtley, 1999 (MLO, comm. RJD); Hookheath Meadows NR, Southwick, 6.3.92, tenanted mines on *Deschampsia cespitosa*; Clanfield, 1.4.97, one vacated mine (JRL).

■ vc12 Leckford, 4.5.92, one tenanted mine on *D. cespitosa* (JRL, DHS). **New vc record.**

0607 *Elachista canapennella* (Hübner, 1813)
Widespread and common in all three vice-counties. The larva feeds in the leaves of several species of grass (Poaceae), but all the Hampshire records appear to refer to caught specimens.

0608 *Elachista rufocinerea* (Haworth, 1828)
Common in the mainland vice-counties (JRL), and also recorded from the Isle of Wight (Goater, 1974, 1992). The species occurs over a wide range of grassland habitats.
■ vc8 Martin Down, 6.5.90 (S. Nash).
■ vc10 Tennyson Down, 18.5.92, one (JRL, DHS, PHS).

0609 *Elachista maculicerusella* Bruand, 1859
= *cerusella* (Hübner, 1796)
= *monosemiella* Rössler, 1881
Widespread and common in marshy places in the mainland vice-counties (Goater, 1974, 1992). No record has reached the authors from the Isle of Wight, although Emmet *et al.* (1996) include vc10 on their distribution map. The larva feeds mainly in the foliage of reed canary-grass *Phalaris arundinacea* and common reed *Phragmites australis*.

0610 *Elachista argentella* (Clerck, 1759)
Recorded in all three vice-counties (Goater, 1974, 1992), but perhaps particularly common in S Hants, especially near the coast (JRL). The larva feeds in the leaves of numerous species of grass, but most Hampshire records are of moths found flying in the evening or taken at light.
■ vc8 Martin Down, 8.6.92 (JRL, RMP).
■ vc10 Yarmouth, 18.5.92, many (JRL, DHS, PHS); High Down, Freshwater; Totland Bay; Afton Down; Compton Bay; Knowles Farm; Redcliff; St Catherine's Point; Luccombe Chine; Culver Cliff (RJD).

0611 *Elachista triatomea* (Haworth, 1828)
Recorded from all three vice-counties (Goater, 1974, 1992) but only one recent record. The larva feeds in the narrow leaves of fescue-grasses *Festuca ovina*, *F. rubra*.
■ vc12 Noar Hill, 27.7.97, one by day (DGG).

0613 *Elachista subocellea* (Stephens, 1834)
Single records from all three vice-counties have been received (Goater, 1974, 1992), but none since 1981. The larva feeds in false brome *Brachypodium sylvaticum*.

0614 *Elachista triseriatella* Stainton, 1854
Emmet *et al.* (1996) include S Hants and N Hants on their distribution map, but the authors have been unable to locate any specific records.

[0615 *Elachista dispunctella* (Duponchel, [1843])
This taxon has recently been recognised as a species-complex (Emmet *et al.*, 1996), and *E. dispunctella* itself appears to be absent from Britain. The records given in Goater (1974) may refer to *E. triseriatella* or to *E. cahorsensis* Traugott-Olsen, 1992.]

0616 *Elachista bedellella* (Sircom, 1848)
Recorded from all three vice-counties (Goater, 1974, 1992). A species of dry grassland. In Britain, the larva is associated with meadow oat-grass *Helictotrichon pratense*, and in Hampshire and the Isle of Wight, all records are from downland sites where this grass grows.
■ vc8 Martin Down, 8.6.92 (JRL, RMP).
■ vc10 Tennyson Down, 18.5.92, one (JRL, DHS, PHS).
■ vc11 Oxenbourne Down NR, 13.8.93, two (JRL).

0616a *Elachista littoricola* le Marchand, 1938
This is a special Hampshire moth. It was discovered at Hurst Castle vc11 in 1982 by EHW (Goater, 1983, 1992), and this remains its only known British locality.

0617 *Elachista megerlella* (Hübner, 1810)
Recorded from all three vice-counties (Goater, 1974, 1992). The larva mines the leaves of several species of grass (Poaceae); in Hampshire, it has been bred from false brome *Brachypodium sylvaticum* and creeping soft-grass *Holcus mollis*.
■ vc8 Martin Down, 8.6.92, vacated mine on *B. sylvaticum* (JRL, RMP).
■ vc10 Tennyson Down, 18.5.92, one mine on *B. sylvaticum* (JRL, DHS, PHS).
■ vc11 Southwick, 15.5.92, mine on *B. sylvaticum*; Meonstoke, 22.5.93, one, genitalia det.; Portsdown, 19.4.92, mines on *H. mollis* and *B. sylvaticum*, moths bred (JRL).
■ vc12 Cholderton, 21.5.95, one mine on *B. sylvaticum* (JRL); Wildhern, 20.6.98, genitalia det. (DGG).

0619 *Elachista unifasciella* (Haworth, 1828)
This is a local species occurring in southern England. In Hampshire, it is known only from Leckford vc12, whence it has been bred from larvae in cock's-foot *Dactylis glomerata* (Goater 1992).

0620 *Elachista gangabella* Zeller, 1850
There are records from all three vice-counties (Goater, 1974, 1992), and several recent ones, given below. In Hampshire, mines containing larvae are found in false brome *Brachypodium sylvaticum*.
■ vc10 Newtown, 18.9.97, a few tenanted mines (AME, JRL).
■ vc11 Roydon Woods, 3.10.98, mines locally common, many larvae (RJD, JRL); Crab Wood, 20.9.97, tenanted mines; Hookheath Meadows NR, Southwick, 17.10.92, larvae in mines; Hen Wood, East Meon, 10.10.94, a few larvae (JRL, *et al.*).
■ vc12 Isle of Wight Woods, Porton Down, 3.10.94, a few tenanted mines (RJBH, JRL); Wildhern, nr Andover, 20.9.97, mines; Harewood Forest, 26.10.97, mines (DGG); Ashford Hangers NR, 18.10.93, a few tenanted mines (JRL).

0621 *Elachista subalbidella* Schläger, 1847
This is a species of damp heaths and as such, its strongholds in Hampshire are in the New Forest, vc11. There is one record from Woolmer Forest, vc12 (Goater, 1992) and

the moth is likely to occur more widely in that area, too. The larva mines in purple moor-grass *Molinia caerulea*.
■ vc11 Avon Heath Country Park, 23.8.93, one tenanted mine on *Molinia* (PHS); Frame Wood, 3.7.99; Fritham Plain and Ocknell Inclosure, 26.5.99; Sloden Inclosure, 2.7.99 (DGG); Bishops Dyke, 2.6.92, one by day (RJBH).

0622 *Elachista adscitella* Stainton, 1851
= *revinctella* Zeller, 1850
So far, there have been three Hampshire records of this species, all in S Hants. The record below represents the second from Southsea, and one was taken at Winchester in 1984 (Goater, 1983, 1992). The moth is widespread in sheltered woodland glades in England, north Wales and southern Ireland and is likely to turn up in other parts of Hampshire.
■ vc11 Southsea, 4.7.95, one at m.v. light, genitalia det. (JRL).

0623 *Elachista bisulcella* (Duponchel, 1843)
Present in all three vice-counties (Goater, 1974, 1992), but clearly overlooked. Most records are comparatively recent.
■ vc11 Crab Wood, 28.7.92, mines on *Deschampsia cespitosa*, six moths bred (RJBH); Hookheath Meadows NR, Southwick, 9.6.92, a few tenanted mines on *D. cespitosa*, moths bred (JRL).

0624 *Biselachista trapeziella* (Stainton, 1849)
The larva of this moth feeds in the leaves of great woodrush *Luzula sylvatica*, a very local plant in Hampshire. The only known locality for *B. trapeziella* in the county is at Sandy Balls, near Godshill vc11, where it was discovered in 1991 (Goater, 1992).

0625 *Biselachista cinereopunctella* (Haworth, 1828)
There are several records from the two mainland vice-counties (Goater, 1983, 1992) and Emmet *et al.* (1996) include the Isle of Wight on their distribution map, but the authors have been unable to locate any records.
■ vc11 Oxenbourne Down, 25.5.74 (RJD).

0626 *Biselachista serricornis* (Stainton, 1854)
Reported from Matley Bog vc11 in 1979 and 1981 by JRL (Goater, 1983). There have been no further records. According to Emmet *et al.* (1996) the usual foodplant is wood sedge *Carex sylvatica*, but in this locality the larvae must feed on some other species of sedge.

0595 *Biselachista (Elachista) biatomella* (Stainton, 1848)
Recorded from all three vice-counties. The larva mines in glaucous sedge *Carex flacca* and on Hayling Island long ago it was reported from sand sedge *C. arenaria* (Victoria History, 1900). The moth is still there, and it would be interesting to rediscover the mines on this plant.
■ vc8 Martin Down, 5.5.90 (S. Nash), 24.8.90 (MFVC and S. Nash).
■ vc10 High Down, Freshwater (RJD).
■ vc11 Botley Wood; Queen Elizabeth Country Park, 1999; Portsdown Hill 2000 (RJD); Sinah Common,

Hayling Island, 15.8.98, many at m.v. light (JRL, IRT, *et al.*).
■ vc12 Bramdean Common (RJD); Micheldever, 7.4.97, one; Ashford Hangers NR, 21.5.93, a few (JRL).

0627 *Biselachista scirpi* (Stainton, 1887)
Recorded in the past from the salt marshes at Yarmouth, Isle of Wight (Goater, 1974) and more recently from some of the salterns on the coast of S Hants (Goater, 1992). The larva mines in sea club-rush *Bulboschoenus maritimus*, which is locally abundant along the coast, and perhaps also in saltmarsh rush *Juncus gerardii*.
■ vc11 Hook-with-Warsash, 1996; Browndown; Fareham, 2000 (RJD).

0628 *Biselachista eleochariella* (Stainton, 1851)
The only record for Hampshire, given in Goater (1974), is from "Southampton", 6.8.38.

0629 *Biselachista utonella* (Frey, 1856)
Recorded from all three vice-counties (Goater, 1974, 1992). In Hampshire and the Isle of Wight, larvae have been reported mining the sedges *Carex acutiformis* and *C. paniculata*.

0630 *Biselachista albidella* (Nylander, 1847)
Found mainly in the boggy areas of the New Forest vc11 and north-east Hampshire, and unrecorded from the Isle of Wight (Goater, 1974, 1992). The foodplant is cottongrass *Eriophorum angustifolium* and, in areas where this does not grow, probably spike-rush *Eleocharis palustris*.
■ vc12 Eelmoor Marsh, 4.7.98, at m.v. light (DGG).

0631 *Cosmiotes freyerella* (Hübner, 1825)
Recorded very occasionally from all three vice-counties (Goater, 1974, 1983, 1992). It is necessary to examine the genitalia in order to be certain of the specific identity of this and the next two species.
■ vc10 Redcliff area, 18.5.73, one male after dusk, genitalia det. RJD (DMA).
■ vc12 Wildhern, 20.6.98, at dusk; Fleet Pond, 21.4.98, one at m.v. light; Eelmoor Marsh, 4.7.98, at m.v. light (DGG).

0632 *Cosmiotes consortella* (Stainton, 1851)
Recorded from the two mainland vice-counties, but probably overlooked in other localities (Goater, 1983, 1992).
■ vc11 Merrietown Heath, 3.5.00, two by day (PHS); Milton Common, Southsea, at light in garden, 1998 (IRT).
■ vc12 Abbotstone Down, 1.6.93, one (RJBH, JRL, DHS).

0633 *Cosmiotes stabilella* (Stainton, 1858)
Recorded in the past from Freshwater and Ventnor, Isle of Wight (Goater, 1974) and from all the vice-counties surrounding mainland Hampshire, but not until now from this county. The larva feeds in the leaves of various grasses (Poaceae) and is easily overlooked.

vc11 Milton Common, Southsea, 5.8.00, one at m.v. light, conf. JRL (IRT). The specimen is in coll. JRL. **New vc record.**

Oecophoridae (66 + [4])

There has been a major regrouping of the genera hitherto included in the Family Oecophoridae (see Karsholt and Razowski, 1996), which plays havoc with the sequence in the Bradley and Fletcher Checklist. In the present work, it has been deemed sensible to adhere to the latter sequence so as to cross-reference more easily with previous works (1974, 1983, 1992).

0634 *Schiffermuellerina grandis* (Desvignes, 1842)
Recorded in the mid-1930s from Bolderwood and Holmsley (Goater, 1974) but not since. The larva feeds in rotten beech *Fagus sylvatica* and oak *Quercus* spp. stumps.

[0638 *Denisia augustella* (Hübner, 1796)
A definite record of this species in Hampshire has yet to be received (see Goater, 1992).]

0638a *Denisia albimaculea* (Haworth, 1828)
The only records of this species, recently differentiated from *D. augustella*, are from Southsea vc11, four specimens taken at light by JRL between 1979 and 1988 (Goater, 1992).

0637 *Crassa (Schiffermuelleria) tinctella* (Hübner, 1796)
Recorded from all three vice-counties, but very sparsely (Goater, 1974, 1992).
vc11 Matley Wood, 25.8.72 (RJD).
vc12 Bartley Heath NR, 1996 (AHD).

0640 *Batia lunaris* (Haworth, 1828)
Present in all three vice-counties and sometimes common in woods and parkland, even in towns. The larva feeds on rotten wood under bark and in old fence posts, but no records have been received of the moth having been bred in Hampshire.
vc10 Freshwater, 13.7.98, at m.v. light (SAK-J).

0641 *Batia lambdella* (Donovan, 1793)
According to Jacobs (1948), the strongholds of this species in Britain are in the New Forest and the Isle of Wight. However, no report of it from the Island has been received since those given in Goater (1974). It is still present in the New Forest whence it has been bred from old, dead stems of gorse *Ulex europaeus*, and has been recorded from other sites near the coast of S Hants (Goater, 1974, 1992), but never, as far as is known, from the heathlands of N Hants.
vc10 Freshwater, 1.9.98, at m.v. light (SAK-J).
vc11 Hamble Common, 1996; Fareham, 6.8.98; Browndown (RJD); Milton Common, Southsea, 7.8.97, at light (IRT); Sinah Common, Hayling Island, 15.8.98, one at m.v. light (JRL); Sandy Point (RJD).

0642 *Batia unitella* (Hübner, 1796)
Recorded from all three vice-counties, widespread and common in vc's 11 and 12 (JRL). The larva of this species also lives in dead wood.
vc10 Freshwater, 14.7.98, at m.v. light (SAK-J); Shanklin (JMC).

0644 *Borkhausenia fuscescens* (Haworth, 1828)
Recorded from all three vice-counties (Goater, 1974, 1992). The following are additional records. All those received refer to caught specimens, or moths taken at light. The larva feeds amongst decaying vegetation or in old birds'-nests.
vc11 Chandlers Ford, 19.8.95, det. JRL (BG); Titchfield Haven, 1996; Fareham; Brownwich; Catisfield; Sarisbury; Farlington (RJD); Milton Common, Southsea, at light in garden, 1998–2000 (IRT); Waterlooville, 1996–1999 (RJM); Sinah Common, Hayling Island, 15.8.98, a few at m.v. light (JRL, IRT, *et al.*).
vc12 Wildhern, nr Andover, 10.7.99, at m.v. light (DGG); Selborne, 1993, 1994, 1996, conf. JRL (AEA); Farnborough, 3.7.94, det. JRL (RWP).

[0645 *Borkhausenia minutella* (Linnaeus, 1758)
The old records given in Goater (1974) are considered to require confirmation. The larva feeds on decaying vegetable matter.]

0646 *Telechrysis tripuncta* (Haworth, 1828)
Now recorded from all three vice-counties, but not recently from the Isle of Wight in Goater (1974, 1992) and below.
vc11 Roydon Woods, 20.6.93, one beaten from holly *Ilex aquifolium* (RJBH); Catisfield, 10.6.73, at dusk; Wickham Common, at dusk, 28.6.93; Hook Lake, 17.6.94, at dusk; Hook Valley NR, 2.6.98, one disturbed from ivy; Chilling Copse, 19.6.96 (RJD).
vc12 Selborne, 10.6.92, one at light (AEA); Yateley Common, 11.6.94, one (AMD). **New vc record.**

0647 *Hofmannophila pseudospretella* (Stainton, 1849)
Abundant throughout the area. The commonest house moth, which also comes frequently to light.

0648 *Endrosis sarcitrella* (Linnaeus, 1758)
Common and widespread, indoors and out, in all three vice-counties. Second only to *H. pseudospretella* as a house pest.

0649 *Esperia sulphurella* (Fabricius, 1775)
Common and widespread in the mainland vice-counties (JRL), and probably also on the Isle of Wight, though fewer records are to hand.
vc8 Martin Down, 29.4.90 (S. Nash).
vc10 Tennyson Down, 18.5.92, one (JRL, DHS, PHS); Gurnard (JMC), 13.6.96; Fattingpark Copse, 17.4.95 (DTB).

0650 *Esperia oliviella* (Fabricius, 1794)
The occurrence of this species in Hampshire was confirmed in 1977 by PHS who took a specimen by day near Winchester vc11. It was subsequently found to be

breeding under the bark of small, decaying oak trees in Harewood Forest vc12, where it still occurs. (Goater, 1983, 1992).

0651 *Oecophora bractella* (Linnaeus, 1758)

10 mm

Larvae of this species were discovered in the spring of 1983 by JRL, DHS and PHS, in habitat similar to that of *E. oliviella*, in Harewood Forest, vc12 (Goater, 1992). It remains the only known locality in Hampshire for this very rare and local species.

0652 *Alabonia geoffrella* (Linnaeus, 1767)

Found, usually singly, in deciduous woodland in all three vice-counties (Goater 1974, 1992). The moth is frequently encountered by day, but also comes occasionally to light.
■ vc10 Grammars Common, 4.6.95, Hamstead, 10.6.95 (DTB); Osborne; Apse Heath; Borthwood, 28.5.95; Whitefield Wood, 23.5.99, three seen (JMC); Totland Bay; Afton Down; Brighstone Forest; Chale; Parkhurst Forest; Firestone Copse (RJD).
■ vc11 Keyhaven, 2.6.92, one (DJLA, AME, JRL); Sims Wood, Exbury, 1.6.95, one at light (BG); Redbridge, 3.6.86; Botley Wood, 30.5.84 (PAB); Titchfield Haven, 1996 (IRT); Hook Valley NR, 2.6.98, several by day; Wickham Common, 1999 (RJD); Warsash, 20.5.94, one; Curbridge NR, 4.5.1.98, many; Beacon Hill NNR, Warnford, 11.6.94, two; Lower Titchfield Haven NR, 24.5.93, a few (JRL *et al.*); Waterlooville, 31.5.00, netted by day (RJM).
■ vc12 Wildhern, nr Andover, 23.5.97, at dusk (DGG); Overton; Bramley Frith Wood NR; Bartley Heath NR (AHD); Selborne, 1993; Priory Wood, by day, 6.6.96 (AEA); Noar Hill, 20.6.96 (AMJ); lane nr Farnborough Station, 22.6.96, two seen by day (RWP); Yateley Common, 8.6.96 (AMD).

0656 *Tachystola (Parocystola) acroxantha* (Meyrick, 1885)

The following records represent another interesting addition to the Hampshire fauna. Known in Britain until recently only in S Devon, the species appears to be extending its range dramatically.
■ vc11 Drayton, 1.7.94, one at m.v. light by Dr M.T.M. Roberts, in coll. JRL. (Langmaid, 1995). **New county record.**
■ vc12 Fleet, five specimens at a Heath trap between 24.9 and 29.9.97; 4.5, 23.9, 24.9, 25.9 and 28.9 and 13.10.98 (Edmunds, 1998, 1999). **New vc record.**

0653 *Aplota palpella* (Haworth, 1828)

A few ancient records for S Hants are given in Goater (1974). There have been no reported occurrences since. The larva lives amongst moss on the trunks of trees.

0654 *Pleurota bicostella* (Clerck, 1759)

Common on heathland in the two mainland vice-counties, wandering occasionally. The two records from the Isle of

Wight (Goater, 1992, and below) surely do not represent its true status in such localities as Headon Warren.
■ vc10 Freshwater, 24.5.98, at m.v. light (SAK-J).
■ vc11 Sopley Common, 13.5.97, swept from heather (PD); Browndown (RJD).
■ vc12 Selborne, 1993 (AEA); Yateley Common (AMD); Farnborough, 29.5.98 (RWP).

0658 *Carcina quercana* (Fabricius, 1775)

Very common in oak woodland in all three vice-counties.

0659 *Amphisbatis incongruella* (Stainton, 1849)

Recorded in Hampshire only from vc11 (Goater 1974, 1992), where it is local on heaths, flying by day in springtime, in mid-morning sunshine.
■ vc11 Merrietown Heath, 12.4.94, one by day (PHS); Shedfield Common, 21.3.97, two swept from ling *Calluna vulgaris* (JRL, IRT).
■ vc22 Benyon's Inclosure (RJD).

0660 *Pseudatemelia josephinae* (Toll, 1956)

The few verified records of this species, from vc's 11 and 12, are given in Goater (1974, 1992) and below. Pre-1966 records of *Pseudatemelia* are not to be relied upon.
■ vc11 Cadland Estate, Beaulieu, 12.5.2.97, one at m.v. light (JRL); Chandlers Ford, 30.6 and 27.7.99 (BE); Wickham Common; Fareham, genitalia checked; Oxenbourne Down, genitalia checked (RJD).

0661 *Pseudatemelia flavifrontella* ([Denis & Schiffermüller], 1775)

Records given in Goater (1974, 1992) were verified by dissection. One further report of the species in Hampshire that has come to hand is given below.
■ vc11 Catisfield, 15.6.73 (RJD).

0662 *Pseudatemelia subochreella* (Doubleday, 1859)

One good record of this species at Newtown on the Isle of Wight is given in Goater (1974). All other reports are from S Hants, where it is evidently widespread, but it has yet to be recorded from vc12.

0663 *Diurnea fagella* ([Denis & Schiffermüller], 1775)

Very common in oak woodland and amongst large oaks in parkland in all three vice-counties. Males come freely to light in March and April, and may also be found commonly by day, resting on the oak trunks. The brachypterous female is seen far less often.

0664 *Diurnea phryganella* (Hübner, 1796)

This species, by contrast, flies in late autumn, in similar habitat to that of *D. fagella*. It is, however, far less common, and seems to have decreased in recent years. All records received are given in Goater (1974, 1992) and below.
■ vc11 Brockenhurst (JEC); nr Crab Wood, 1.11.90, one male by day (RJBH); Crock Hill, 1.11.97, two by day; Islands Thorns Inclosure, 1.11.97, two by day (DGG); Denny Wood; Lower Bursledon; Hamble Common (RJD).

0665 *Dasystoma salicella* (Hübner, 1796)

Formerly locally fairly frequent in the New Forest (Goater,

1974), where the larva could be found in rolled leaves of bog-myrtle *Myrica gale*. A few further records from S Hants were added (Goater, 1992), together with only the second for the Isle of Wight, but nothing has been heard of the moth in Hampshire since 1983.

0666 *Semioscopis avellanella* (Hübner, 1793)
There are very few records of this species in Hampshire and none from the Isle of Wight. Most reports have been of single specimens, and it has been given as locally common only in the Itchen Valley, N Hants, pre-1974 (Goater, 1974).
■ vc12 Selborne, 25.3.97, 14.3.99, singles at light, photograph, conf. BG (AEA); Yateley Common, 12 to 16.3.94, three (AMD).

0667 *Semioscopis steinkellneriana* ([Denis & Schiffermüller], 1775)
This species has been recorded from all three vice-counties, but only in small numbers except in Botley Wood, S Hants, where JRL reported it flying freely before sunrise in early April (Goater, 1992). If we rose earlier, perhaps we would see it more often!
■ vc8 Martin Down, 29.4.90 (S. Nash).
■ vc10 Freshwater, 12.4.90 (SAK-J).
■ vc12 Noar Hill NR, 11.4.95 (AMJ); Broxhead Common LNR, 19.4.96; Yateley Common, 19.4 and 21.4.94 (two) (AMD).

0668 *Luquetia (Enicostoma) lobella* ([Denis & Schiffermüller], 1775)
Recorded from all three vice-counties, but mostly in small numbers (Goater 1974, 1992), either as single specimens taken at light or as single larvae on blackthorn *Prunus spinosa*.
■ vc10 Freshwater, 15.6.97 (Knill-Jones, 1998b).
■ vc11 Chandlers Ford, 25.6.99, one at m.v. light (BE); Botley Wood; Browndown (RJD); Waterlooville, several at m.v. light during 1999–2000, between 12 and 26 June, conf. JRL (RJM).
■ vc12 Overton (AHD).

The genera *Depressaria* and *Agonopterix* form a distinctive group of similar-looking species for which, along with a few others, Heslop (1947) coined the not inappropriate English name "Flat-body". The larvae of the majority of species feed in the inflorescences of Apiaceae (Umbelliferae); others are associated with Asteraceae (Compositae), especially species of thistle *Cirsium, Carduus, Carlina*, and a few select other foodplants including St John's-wort *Hypericum* spp. and the foliage of sallows and willows *Salix* spp. Identification of the foodplant is often helpful in naming the species, though in a number of cases, genitalic examination of adults taken at large is necessary. In Hampshire, we are fortunate in having one of the acknowledged authorities, Dr Langmaid, resident in the county.

[0669 *Depressaria discipunctella* (Herrich-Schäffer, 1854)
The records given in Goater (1974) must be regarded as in need of confirmation. It is a local species, the larva of which feeds in the flowering and fruiting heads of Apiaceae (Umbelliferae), hogweed *Heracleum sphondylium* and angelica *Angelica sylvestris*.]

0670 *Depressaria daucella* ([Denis & Schiffermüller], 1775)
Common and widespread in all three vice-counties in marshes and ditches where the foodplant occurs. Moths overwinter, and are often recorded hibernating in thatch. Larvae are found mainly in the umbels of hemlock water-dropwort *Oenanthe crocata*, but also in those of other species of *Oenanthe*.

0671 *Depressaria ultimella* Stainton, 1849
The few records of this species in Hampshire are given in Goater (1983), and below. It has been bred from fool's water-cress *Apium nodiflorum*, in the stems of which the larvae pupate.
■ vc12 Selborne, 24.10.96, one at light, genitalia det. JRL (Aston, 1998b). **New vc record.**

0672 *Depressaria pastinacella* (Duponchel, 1838)
Common throughout the three vice-counties, larvae in umbels of hogweed *Heracleum sphondylium* and wild parsnip *Pastinaca sativa* (JRL *et al.*). The imago overwinters, and may be found in thatch, stables, outhouses, etc.

0673 *Depressaria pimpinellae* Zeller, 1839
Local on the chalk of S and N Hants around Winchester (Goater 1974, 1992), the larvae feeding in the umbels of burnet saxifrage *Pimpinella saxifraga*.
■ vc11 Sparsholt College (AHD); Winchester, West Hill Cemetery, 27.7.92, larvae, three moths bred (RJBH).

0674 *Depressaria badiella* (Hübner, 1796)
Although recorded from all three vice-counties, this appears to be an uncommon species in the county (Goater, 1974, 1992). The larva feeds among inflorescences and spun foliage of certain Asteraceae (Compositae), including sow-thistle *Sonchus* spp., dandelion *Taraxacum* spp. and cat's ear *Hypochaeris radicata*, but appears not to have been found in Hampshire or the Isle of Wight.
■ vc8 Martin Down, 24.8.90 (MFVC and S. Nash).

0676 *Depressaria pulcherrimella* Stainton, 1849
There are sparse records from all three vice-counties, though no recent ones from the Isle of Wight (Goater, 1974, 1992). The moth has been bred from larvae on burnet-saxifrage *Pimpinella saxifraga* and wild carrot *Daucus carota*, on the chalk downs.
■ vc8 Martin Down, 24.8.90 (MFVC and S. Nash).

0677 *Depressaria douglasella* Stainton, 1849
Recorded from all three vice-counties (Goater, 1974, 1992). The larvae have been found in some abundance locally, feeding on wild carrot *Daucus carota*, but also on wild parsnip *Pastinaca sativa* (Goater, 1974).
■ vc8 Martin Down, 24.8.90 (MFVC and S. Nash).

0678 *Depressaria sordidatella* Tengström, 1848
= *weirella* Stainton, 1849
The few records for this species are given in Goater (1974, 1992). Moths have been bred from hemlock *Conium*

maculatum inflorescences, and also from cow parsley *Anthriscus sylvestris*.

0680 *Depressaria albipunctella* ([Denis & Schiffermüller], 1775)
Apparently very rare. All records received, from vc's 10 and 11, are in Goater (1974).

0681 *Depressaria olerella* Zeller, 1854
Apart from two old records given in Goater (1974), the only recent ones are from Longmoor vc12, where larvae were found fairly commonly in inflorescences of yarrow *Achillea millefolium* (Goater, 1992), and below.
■ vc12 Selborne, 1993, 1994 (AEA).

0682 *Depressaria chaerophylli* Zeller, 1839
The presence of this species in Hampshire was confirmed in the late 1970s (Goater, 1992), when a few specimens were taken at light and larvae were located on rough chervil *Chaerophyllum temulentum* in the Winchester area of S and N Hants.
■ vc8 Martin Down, 21.8.90 (MFVC and S. Nash).
■ vc11 Braishfield, 15.7.98, a few larvae on *Chaerophyllum* (JRL, D. O'Keefe) and a few in June 1999 (BE).

[0683 *Depressaria depressana* (Fabricius, 1775)
= *depressella* (Fabricius, 1798)
There has been no recent record to confirm the one given in Goater (1974).]

0688 *Agonopterix heracliana* (Linnaeus, 1758)
Common to abundant in all three vice-counties (JRL), the larvae in inflorescences of hogweed *Heracleum sphondylium* and cow parsley *Anthriscus sylvestris*, the moth also comes to light quite often.
■ vc8 Martin Down, 24.8.90 (MFVC and S. Nash), 8.6.92, larvae on *Anthriscus* (JRL, RMP).

0689 *Agonopterix ciliella* (Stainton, 1849)
Recorded from all three vice-counties, though not recently from the Isle of Wight, and not on the mainland since 1974 (Goater, 1974, 1992). The moth has been bred from pepper-saxifrage *Silaum silaus*.
■ vc12 Wildhern, nr Andover, 25.2.99, at m.v. light (DGG).

0690 *Agonopterix cnicella* (Treitschke, 1832)
Extremely local on the coast of S Hants, where the larva feeds on sea holly *Eryngium maritimum*, an increasingly rare plant there. Last reported from Sandy Point, Hayling Island, 1986 (Goater, 1992), but perhaps not sought since.

0691 *Agonopterix purpurea* (Haworth, 1811)
Reported from all three vice-counties in Goater (1974, 1992), but evidently local and uncommon. The moth has been bred in the county from wild carrot *Daucus carota* and rough chervil *Chaerophyllum temulentum*.
■ vc8 Martin Down, 24.8.90 (MFVC and S. Nash).
■ vc11 Milton Common, Southsea, frequent at light in garden,1998–2000 (IRT).

0692 *Agonopterix subpropinquella* (Stainton, 1849)
Recorded from all three vice-counties (Goater, 1974, 1992), but recently only from S Hants. The larva feeds on thistles *Cirsium* and *Carduus* and knapweed *Centaurea* spp.
■ vc11 Milton Common, Southsea, fairly common at light in garden, 1996–2000 (IRT); Sandy Point NR, Hayling Island, 22.7.95, one at m.v. light (JRL).

0694 *Agonopterix nanatella* (Stainton, 1849)
Old records for the Isle of Wight are given in Goater (1974). The larva feeds on carline thistle *Carlina vulgaris*.

0695 *Agonopterix alstroemeriana* (Clerck, 1759)
Local in all three vice-counties, but seldom seen in numbers (Goater 1974, 1992). One of the easier species to identify. The larva feeds on hemlock *Conium maculatum*.
■ vc10 Binstead, 7.3.97 (Knill-Jones, 1998b).
■ vc11 Lower Test Marshes, 1995 (JP); Sparsholt College (AHD); Fareham; Portsdown (RJD); Great Salterns NR, Portsmouth (JRL *et al.*); Milton Common, Southsea, 1994–2000, at light (IRT); Waterlooville, 10.8.00, in garden shed (RJM); North Hayling Island, 10.6.97, larvae on *Conium* (JRL, IRT).
■ vc12 Wildhern, nr Andover, 16.8.97 (DGG); Overton; Oakley; Basingstoke; Bramley Frith Wood, 5.4.94, one at m.v. light (AHD); Selborne, 20.8.89, at light (AEA); Farnborough, 8.4 and 21.4.96 (RWP).

0696 *Agonopterix propinquella* (Treitschke, 1835)
There have been very few recent records of this species, and all are given in Goater (1974, 1992) and below. The larva feeds on thistles *Carduus* spp., but all specimens taken in Hampshire and the Isle of Wight have been caught as adults.
■ vc11 Fareham, 29.4.93, genit. checked (RJD).
■ vc12 Wildhern, nr Andover, 27.10.96, in stables (DGG).

0697 *Agonopterix arenella* ([Denis & Schiffermüller], 1775)
Widespread and rather common in all three vice-counties. It has been bred from thistles *Cirsium arvense* and *C. vulgare*, from greater knapweed *Centaurea scabiosa* and burdock *Arctium* sp.

0698 *Agonopterix kaekeritziana* (Linnaeus, 1767)
= *liturella* ([Denis & Schiffermüller], 1775)
Widespread and frequent amongst knapweed *Centaurea scabiosa* and *C. nigra* from which plants the moth has often been bred.
■ vc8 Martin Down, 8.6.92, a few larvae on *C. scabiosa* (JRL, RMP).

0699 *Agonopterix bipunctosa* (Curtis, 1850)
Very locally frequent amongst saw-wort *Serratula tinctoria* in the two mainland vice-counties (Goater, 1983, 1992).
■ vc12 Eelmoor Marsh SSSI, 23.8.97, one at light amongst saw-wort; specimen retained and identity confirmed at BENHS (DGG).

0700 *Agonopterix pallorella* (Zeller, 1839)
The few old records of this species are given in
Goater (1974, 1992). The larva feeds on knapweeds
Centaurea spp.
■ vc12 Porton Down, 24.7.94, two larvae on *C. scabiosa*,
moths bred (JRL). First recent Hampshire record.

0701 *Agonopterix ocellana* (Fabricius, 1775)
Widespread but not particularly common (Goater 1974,
1992) in damp places where sallows and willows *Salix*
spp. occur. The larva feeds in spun leaves of these plants.
■ vc11 Botley Wood; Warsash shore; Titchfield Haven,
17.3.98, one flying; Cherque; Browndown (RJD); Creech
Wood, Denmead, 22.8.97, one at m.v. light (JRL, IRT).
■ vc12 Bramley Frith Wood, 22.5.95, one at m.v. light;
Greywell Moors NR, 1996 (AHD); Rye Common,
24.3.96; Hazeley Heath, 13.8.96, two; Yateley Common,
9.4.94; Yateley, 24.3.96 (AMD); Farnborough, 7.5.95,
one at light (RWP).

0702 *Agonopterix assimilella* (Treitschke, 1832)
Widespread amongst broom *Cytisus scoparius* in all three
vice-counties (Goater 1974, 1992).

0703 *Agonopterix atomella* ([Denis & Schiffermüller], 1775)
The foodplant of this species, dyer's greenweed *Genista
tinctoria* is local and decreasing in the area. The moth is
correspondingly extremely local, and no recent occurrence
has been reported since the records given in Goater (1974,
1992).

0704 *Agonopterix scopariella* (Heinemann, 1870)
The only records of this species in Hampshire hitherto
are those given in Goater (1974, 1992).
■ vc11 Botley Wood, 20.5.98, one larva, moth emerged
21.6.98 (RJD).

0705 *Agonopterix umbellana* (Fabricius, 1794)
= *ulicetella* (Stainton, 1849)
Widespread amongst gorse *Ulex europaeus* in all three vice-
counties.

0706 *Agonopterix nervosa* (Haworth, 1811)
Common in all three vice-counties, wherever gorse, broom
or *Genista* spp. grow.
■ vc8 Martin Down, 24.8.90 (MFVC and S. Nash).

0708 *Agonopterix carduella* (Hübner, 1817)
There is one ancient record from Brockenhurst, cited in
Goater (1983).
■ vc10 Steephill, 28.8.76 (RJD). **New vc record.**

0709 *Agonopterix liturosa* (Haworth, 1811)
Local in the mainland vice-counties (Goater 1974, 1992).,
the larva feeding on St John's-wort *Hypericum* spp., but
unrecorded from the Isle of Wight.
■ vc8 Martin Down, 24.8.90 (MFVC and S. Nash).
■ vc11 Sparsholt College (AHD); Swanwick; Hamble
Common; Titchfield Haven (RJD); East Meon, 26.5.97,
one larva on *H. pulchrum*; Sandy Point NR, Hayling

Island, 10.6.94, a few larvae (JRL); Waterlooville, 10.8.97,
at m.v. light (RJM).
■ vc12 Winnall Moors NR (DHS); Abbotstone Down,
1.6.93, a few larvae on *Hypericum* spp. (RJBH, JRL, DHS);
Overton; Oakley (AHD); Selborne, 1993, 1994, 1995 and
1999 det. JRL (AEA); Noar Hill, 9.9.96 (AMJ); Rye
Common, 5.8.96 (AMD); Farnborough, 22.8.94, det. JRL
(RWP).

0710 *Agonopterix conterminella* (Zeller, 1839)
Recorded from all three vice-counties (Goater 1974,
1992), in damp places where sallows *Salix* spp. occur.
The larva lives amongst spun shoots of these plants.
■ vc10 Shanklin (JMC).
■ vc11 Hamble Common, 1996 (RJD); Botley Wood,
19.5.95, larva on *S. cinerea*, moth bred (JRL).

0711 *Agonopterix curvipunctosa* (Haworth, 1811)
The three specimens in the Wm Fassnidge collection,
1929–1930, from "Southampton" (Goater, 1974) are the
only Hampshire records.

0712 *Agonopterix astrantiae* (Heinemann, 1870)
Larvae of this species were discovered in a wood near East
Meon in 1982, on sanicle *Sanicula europaea* (Goater,
1983). They are difficult to locate, but continue to thrive
in this one locality.

0713 *Agonopterix angelicella* (Hübner, 1813)
Recorded from all three vice-counties, and locally
common. The larva feeds in bunched leaves of *Angelica*,
often gregariously (JRL).

0714 *Agonopterix yeatiana* (Fabricius, 1781)
Local in all three vice-counties (Goater 1974, 1992). The
larva is associated mainly with wild carrot *Daucus carota*.
■ vc11 Chandlers Ford, 7.5.95, one at light, det. JRL
(BG); Widley, Portsdown (PMP); Fareham, genitalia
checked (RJD); Lower Titchfield Haven NR, 24.5.93, a
few larvae on hemlock water-dropwort *Oenanthe crocata*,
moths bred (JRL); Milton Common, Southsea, 1.8.97,
det. JRL, 23.7.98, 31.5.99, at m.v. light in garden,
(IRT); Waterlooville, 14.5.00, at m.v. light, conf. JRL
(RJM).
■ vc12 Wildhern, nr Andover, 7.3.97, in stables, identity
confirmed (DGG); Mapledurwell Fen, 8.5.98, one at m.v.
light (AHD); Noar Hill, 25.4.93 (AMJ).

0715 *Agonopterix capreolella* (Zeller, 1839)
Recorded from Ventnor, Isle of Wight in 1928 (Goater,
1974) and relocated there in 1987, larvae in folded radical
leaves of burnet-saxifrage *Pimpinella saxifraga* (Goater,
1992). The only other record is from Minstead vc11,
1969.

0716 *Agonopterix rotundella* (Douglas, 1846)
Very rare on the Isle of Wight; the records given below
are the first since 1951 (Goater, 1974).
■ vc10 Freshwater, 16.3.98, at m.v. light, det. R.J.
Heckford (SAK-J); Ventnor, 19.4.77 (RJD).

Ethmiidae (3 + [1])

A small family, poorly represented in the area under review. The larvae feed on Boraginaceae, in a web beneath the leaves or amongst the flowers.

0718 *Ethmia dodecea* (Haworth, 1828)

There are a few records for S and N Hants (1974, 1992), to which the following may be added. The larva feeds on gromwell *Lithospermum officinale.*
■ vc11 Sparsholt College (AHD).
■ vc12 Wildhern, 28.6 and 25.7.00, singletons at m.v. light; Oakley, 18.6.99 (DGG).

[0719 *Ethmia funerella* (Fabricius, 1787)

The presence of this species in Hampshire has not been confirmed. A vague and doubtful record was included by Goater (1974).]

0720 *Ethmia bipunctella* (Fabricius, 1775)

This is a very scarce species on the coast of S Hants. There is only one inland record, at Winchester, 1990 (Goater, 1992). The larva feeds on viper's bugloss *Echium vulgare.*
■ vc10 Freshwater, 21.8.96, one at m.v. light (SAK-J). **New vc record.**
■ vc11 Southsea, 31.7.94, one at m.v. light (JRL).

0721 *Ethmia pusiella* (Linnaeus, 1758)

The old record given in Goater (1974) is thought to be reliable, but it would be very satisfactory to rediscover this species amongst lungwort *Pulmonaria* spp. either in the Isle of Wight or the New Forest.

Gelechiidae (108 + [3]

The Gelechiidae is one of the least well-known families of Lepidoptera; most of the species are small, inconspicuous and secretive, and until recently there has been a dearth of available literature to assist identification. In Hampshire, energetic studies are being undertaken by JRL and colleagues, and in vc12, many useful contributions have been made by AHD. However, much remains to be discovered about this group of moths.

0723 *Metzneria littorella* (Douglas, 1850)

Recorded only from the Isle of Wight, where it is locally common; the larva feeds on the seedheads of buck's-horn plantain *Plantago coronopus.* (See Goater, 1974, 1992).

0724 *Metzneria lappella* (Linnaeus, 1758)

Local, in all three vice-counties; the larva in seedheads of burdock *Arctium* spp.
■ vc10 Tennyson Down (JMC).
■ vc11 Sparsholt College (AHD); Hamble Common, 1996 (RJD); Hookheath Meadows NR, Southwick, 29.1.97, a few larvae in seedheads of *Arctium minus* (JRL,

IRT); Milton Common, Southsea, five between 17.7 and 25.7.00, at light in garden (IRT); Waterlooville, 19.6 to 26.7.00, total of four at m.v. light, conf. JRL (RJM).
■ vc12 Wildhern, 20.6.98 (DGG); Bramley Frith Wood, 3.6.97, one at m.v. light (AHD).

0725 *Metzneria aestivella* (Zeller, 1839)

= *carlinella* Stainton, 1851
Very locally frequent on chalk downs and on the coast, but unrecorded from vc12. The larva feeds in the seedheads of carline thistle *Carlina vulgaris.* (See Goater, 1974, 1992.)

0726 *Metzneria metzneriella* (Stainton, 1851)

Local in all three vice-counties; larva in seedheads of knapweed *Centaurea nigra* and possibly saw-wort *Serratula tinctoria* (See Goater, 1974).
■ vc10 West High Down, 1995, bred (DTB).
■ vc11 Wickham Common; Fareham (RJD); Hookheath Meadows NR, Southwick, 9.6.92, two; Great Salterns NR, Portsmouth (JRL); Milton Common, Southsea, at light in garden, 1998, 2000 (IRT).
■ vc12 Wildhern, 25.7.98; Eelmoor Marsh, 4.7.98, at m.v. light (DGG); Selborne, 1996, det. JRL (AEA).

0727a *Metzneria aprilella* (Herrich-Schäffer, 1854)

All accepted records are of this species and not *M. neuropterella* (Zeller, 1839) (See Goater, 1992). It has been found in both the mainland vice-counties but not on the Isle of Wight. Larvae have been found in seedheads of greater knapweed *Centaurea scabiosa.*
■ vc11 Sparsholt College (AHD).

0729 *Isophrictis striatella* ([Denis & Schiffermüller], 1775)

Locally fairly common amongst sneezewort *Achillea ptarmica* and tansy *Tanacetum vulgare* in the mainland vice-counties.
■ vc11 Fareham, 23.7.98, one at house lights (RJD); Milton Common, Southsea, 5.8.96, two in actinic trap, conf. JRL, 19.8.97, again in 1998 and 2000 (IRT).
■ vc12 Farnborough, 5.8.96 (RWP).

0730 *Apodia bifractella* (Duponchel, 1843)

Recorded from all three vice-counties. The larva is found in seedheads of fleabane *Pulicaria dysenterica* and ploughman's spikenard *Inula conyzae.*
■ vc11 Hamble Common, 1996 (RJD); Swanwick NR, 20.8.96, a few at m.v. light; Hilsea, 16.8.92, a few; Sandy Point NR, Hayling Island, 18.8.95, one at m.v. light (JRL).
■ vc12 Winnall Moors NR (DHS).

0731 *Eulamprotes atrella* ([Denis & Schiffermüller], 1775)

The larva feeds in the stems of perforate St John's-wort *Hypericum perforatum*; there are sparse records from both mainland vice-counties, but surprisingly, there is still no confirmed record from the Isle of Wight. (See Goater, 1974.)
■ vc11 Waterlooville, 25.7 and 4.8.00, at m.v. light, conf. JRL (RJM).

■ vc12 Winnall Moors NR (DHS); Selborne, 1996, det. JRL (AEA).

0732 *Eulamprotes unicolorella* (Duponchel, 1843)

There are a few records from the two mainland vice-counties; apparently the life history is still unknown.

■ vc11 Botley Wood, 9.6.92, (JRL, RMP); Hookheath Meadows NR, Southwick, 9.6.92, one (JRL, RMP, DHS).

■ vc12 Abbotstone Down, 1.6.93, a few (RJBH, JRL, DHS).

0733 *Eulamprotes wilkella* (Linnaeus, 1758)

Very locally frequent at St Helens, Isle of Wight (Goater, 1974), but only recently recorded from the mainland (see Goater, 1992, and below). The larva feeds on common mouse-ear *Cerastium fontanum*, in a silken tube below ground level.

■ vc11 Southsea, 4.8.96, one at m.v. light (JRL); Sinah Common, Hayling Island, 15.8.98, several at m.v. light (JRL, IRT, *et al.*).

0734 *Argolamprotes micella* ([Denis & Schiffermüller], 1775)

The only Hampshire record of this species is of one taken at light at Winchester, 14.7.87 by Col. D.H. Sterling (see Goater, 1992). The larva feeds on dewberry *Rubus caesius* and the moth might be expected to occur in the chalk country around Winchester.

0728 *Monochroa (Paltodora) cytisella* (Curtis, 1837)

This is one of the few species to be associated with bracken *Pteridium aquilinum*, in the rhachises of which the larva feeds. Recorded from all three vice-counties.

■ vc11 Sopley Common, 13.5.00, one larva in *Pteridium* (PHS); Cadland Estate, Beaulieu, 12.7.97, one at m.v. light; Southwick, 29.7.96, one at m.v. light; Sandy Point NR, Hayling Island, 22.7.95, several at m.v. light (JRL).

■ vc12 Bramshott Common, 23.5.98, several larvae on bracken, moths bred (JRL, IRT).

0735 *Monochroa tenebrella* (Hübner, 1817)

To the very few records given in Goater (1974, 1992) may be added the following. The larva feeds in the rootstocks of sheep's sorrel *Rumex acetosella*.

■ vc11 Hookheath Meadows NR, Southwick, 14.7.96, several (JRL).

■ vc12 Wildhern, 3.7.98, by day (DGG).

0736 *Monochroa lucidella* (Stephens, 1834)

The larva of this marsh-inhabiting species lives in the stems of common spike-rush *Eleocharis palustris*, and the moth may be found resting on the flower-heads during the afternoon. There are a few records from the mainland vice-counties.

■ vc11 Fareham, 3.7.98, one at m.v. light (RJD); Milton Common, Southsea, at light in garden, 9.7.98, 17.6 and 2.7.00, singles at m.v. light (IRT).

0737 *Monochroa palustrella* (Douglas, 1850)

There are three confirmed records of this species in the area, one in each of the vice-counties. The larva is stated

to live in the rootstocks of curled dock *Rumex crispus* (Emmet, 1979).

■ vc10 Cranmore, 10.6.97 (Knill-Jones, 1998b). **New vc record.**

■ vc11 Lower Test Marshes NR, 1992, at m.v. light (J. Pain, comm. and conf. DHS). **Presence in county confirmed.**

■ vc12 Bramley Frith Wood, 29.7.99, at m.v. light, conf. JRL (AHD). **New vc record.**

0740 *Monochroa hornigi* (Staudinger, 1883)

There have been just two records of this species in the area to date.

■ vc11 Great Salterns NR, Portsmouth, 8.7.94, one m.v. light; Southsea, 30.6.00, one at m.v. light (JRL). **New county record.**

0741 *Monochroa suffusella* (Douglas, 1850)

Recorded only from Matley Bog in the New Forest, where it has been described as common (Goater, 1974, 1992).

[0743 *Monochroa elongella* (Heinemann, 1870)

The presence of this species in the county still requires confirmation (see Goater, 1983).]

0744a *Monochroa moyses* Uffen, 1991

■ vc11 Sandy Point NR, Hayling Island, many tenanted mines on sea club-rush *Bulboschoenus maritimus*, moths bred (JRL, IRT). We are informed by JRL (pers. comm.) that this population is unusual in that pupation occurs within the larval mine, perhaps because the foodplant here is in standing water in ditches.

0746 *Chrysoesthia drurella* (Fabricius, 1775)

There are few records of this species in Hampshire, the only recent ones being from Emer Bog and Southsea in vc11 and Leckford in vc12 (Goater, 1992), in which localities the larvae have been found in some quantity on goosefoot *Chenopodium* spp.

■ vc11 Little Somborne, 8.89, mines common on red goosefoot *C. rubrum* in a farmyard, seven moths bred, May 1990 (RJBH); Chandlers Ford, August 1999, larvae locally very common (BE).

0747 *Chrysoesthia sexguttella* (Thunberg, 1794)

■ vc11 Upper Hamble Country Park, 7.10.96, a few tenanted mines on spear-leaved orache *Atriplex prostrata* (AMD, AME, JRL); Botley Wood, 20.9.92, tenanted mines on fat-hen *Chenopodium album* (JRL, PHS); Fareham, 29.9.97, very many mines, some with larvae, on *A. prostrata* (JRL, IRT); Portsmouth, 30.8.96, tenanted mines on *C. rubrum*; Great Salterns NR, Portsmouth (JRL); Milton Common, Southsea, 1994, mine with larva (IRT).

■ vc12 Wildhern, 31.8.98, by day (DGG).

0748 *Ptocheuusa paupella* (Zeller, 1847)

Fairly widespread in all three vice-counties, though most recent records have come from South Hants. The larva

feeds in the seed-heads of Asteraceae (Compositae) such as fleabane *Pulicaria dysenterica*, and mint *Mentha* spp.
- vc8 Martin Down, 24.8.90 (MFVC and S. Nash).
- vc11 Soberton, 30.6.95, one at m.v. light; Swanwick NR, 20.8.96, many at m.v. light; Bishops Waltham, 18.8.93, many at m.v. light (JRL); Hamble Common, 1996; Fareham (RJD); Hookheath Meadows NR, Southwick, 13.6.92, one; Creech Wood, Denmead, 22.8.97, one at m.v. light (JRL, IRT); Milton Common, Southsea, 15.6.97, one caught on fleabane *Pulicaria dysenterica*; 19.8.00, one at m.v. light (IRT); Havant Thicket, 8.7.97, one at m.v. light; Sandy Point NR, Hayling Island, 18.8.95, one at m.v. light (JRL, IRT, *et al.*).
- vc12 Winnall Moors NR (DHS).

0750a *Psamathocrita argentella* Pierce & Metcalfe, 1942
This species is now known from several localities along the Hampshire coast and has also been recorded from Newtown marshes on the Isle of Wight (See Goater, 1976, 1992).

0752 *Aristotelia ericinella* (Zeller, 1839)
- vc8 Martin Down, 24.8.90 (MFVC and S. Nash).
- vc11 Merrietown Heath, 21.7.93, 18.6.99; Avon Heath Country Park, 23.8.93; Town Common, Christchurch, 20.6.95, several larvae (PHS), 2.8.96, five at m.v. light (PD); Southsea, 4.9.96, 12.8.98, singletons at m.v. light; Sandy Point NR, Hayling Island, 22.7.95, one at m.v. light (JRL).
- vc12 Pamber, 1995 (GJD); Silchester Common, 19.8.95, one at m.v. light (MCH); Farnborough, two in 1994, 11.8.95 (RWP).

0753 *Aristotelia brizella* (Treitschke, 1833)
- vc11 Hurst Castle, 2.6.92, one by day (DJLA, AME, JRL).

[0777 *Bryotropha basaltinella* (Zeller, 1839)
Stated in the Victoria County History (1900) to occur in Hampshire, but never recorded since. Its presence in the county must be considered to require confirmation.]

0778 *Bryotropha umbrosella* (Zeller, 1839)
A few old records from S Hants are given in Goater (1974). There has been only one recent record, below.
- vc11 Merrietown Heath, 21.7.93, two by day (PHS).

0779 *Bryotropha affinis* (Haworth, 1828)
- vc11 Chandlers Ford, 19.8.95, one at light, det. JRL (BG); Locks Heath, 20.7.00, det. RJD (PCa); Fareham (RJD); Swanwick NR, 20.8.96, a few at m.v. light (JRL); Milton Common, Southsea, at light in garden, 1998, 2000 (IRT).
- vc12 Pamber, 1995 (GJD); Selborne, June, 1996, at light, det. JRL (AEA); Farnborough, 2.6.93, det. JRL, two in 1995 (RWP).

0780 *Bryotropha similis* (Stainton, 1854)
- vc11 Titchfield Haven, 1996; Fareham (RJD).
- vc12 Brighton Hill, Basingstoke (AHD); Farnborough, 26.7.96, two (RWP).

0781 *Bryotropha mundella* (Douglas, 1850)
There is an old record from St Helens, Isle of Wight (Goater, 1974) and a more recent one from Hayling Island (Goater, 1992). The moth is an inhabitant of coastal sandhills.

0782 *Bryotropha senectella* (Zeller, 1839)
- vc12 Winnall Moors NR (DHS); Selborne, July 96, det. JRL (AEA); Farnborough, 30.6.94, two, det. JRL, 11.6 and 25.6.95 (RWP).

0786 *Bryotropha desertella* (Douglas, 1850)
There are old records from the Isle of Wight and from S Hants, the most recent being Hayling Island, 1978, by Col. D.H. Sterling (See Goater, 1974, 1992).

0787 *Bryotropha terrella* ([Denis & Schiffermüller], 1775)
- vc11 Merrietown Heath, 21.7.93, by day; Bournemouth International Airport, 30.1.00, larva on the moss *Rhytidiadelphus squarrosus* (PHS); Sparsholt College (AHD); Chandlers Ford, 18.6.95, one at light, det. JRL (BG); Locks Heath, 21.7.00, det. RJD (PCa); Hamble Common, 1996; Chilling Copse; Titchfield Haven, 1996; Fareham (RJD); Great Salterns 2.6.00, at m.v. light (RJM); Havant Thicket, 8.7.97, at m.v. light (JRL, IRT, *et al.*).
- vc12 Oakley; Brighton Hill, Basingstoke; Bramley Frith Wood NR; Mapledurwell Fen (AHD); Farnborough, 19.6.95, 9.7.95 (RWP).

0788 *Bryotropha politella* (Stainton, 1851)
The only Hampshire record is of one taken by day at Leckford vc12, in 1985 by Col. D.H. Sterling (Goater, 1992).

0789 *Bryotropha domestica* (Haworth, 1828)
- vc11 Fareham (RJD); Milton Common, Southsea, 1996–2000, occasional at light in garden (IRT); Waterlooville, 2.7.00, at house light, conf. JRL (RJM).
- vc12 Selborne, 27.7.96, det. JRL from photograph (AEA); Farnborough, two in 1994, three in 1995 (RWP).

0755 *Stenolechia gemmella* (Linnaeus, 1758)
This species has been recorded, mostly as single specimens, in a few localities in vc's 11 and 12 (Goater, 1976, 1992). In August 1999, it was found very commonly at Chandlers Ford by BE.
- vc11 Hengistbury Head, higher saltmarsh, 9.9.00, one at m.v. light (PHS); Matley Passage, 28.7.99, one in flight by day (BE); Chandlers Ford, 1999 (see above); Winchester, Sarum Road, 25.8.91, one at m.v. light (RJBH).
- vc12 Farnborough, 1.9.96 (RWP).

0756 *Parachronistis albiceps* (Zeller, 1839)
- vc11 Soberton, 30.6.95, one at m.v. light (JRL); Fareham (RJD).
- vc12 Bramley Frith Wood NR (AHD); Farnborough, 26.6.96 (RWP).

0757 *Recurvaria nanella* ([Denis & Schiffermüller], 1775)
■ vc11 Milton Common, Southsea, 23.7 and 2.8.98, 30.7, 11.8 and 13.8.00, at light in garden (IRT).
■ vc12 Farnborough, three in 1993 from 3 July (RWP, comm. JRL). **New vc record.**

0758 *Recurvaria leucatella* (Clerck, 1759)
Recorded from several places in the mainland vice-counties (Goater, 1974, 1992).
■ vc12 Selborne, 1996, det. JRL (AEA).

0759 *Coleotechnites piceaella* (Kearfott, 1903)
The two specimens taken at Winchester by Col. D.H. Sterling in 1983 and 1984 remain the only ones known in the county.

0760 *Exoteleia dodecella* (Linnaeus, 1758)
■ vc11 Merrietown Heath, 18.6.99, one at m.v. light (PHS); Cadland Estate, Beaulieu, 12.7.97, one at m.v. light (JRL); Chandlers Ford, 19.8.95, one at light, det. JRL (BG); Fareham, genitalia checked (RJD); Milton Common, Southsea, at light in garden, 1998 (IRT); Havant Thicket, 28.6.95 (JRL).
■ vc12 Farnborough, 8.7.94, two, det. JRL (RWP).

0761 *Athrips tetrapunctella* (Thunberg, 1794)
There is a single record from Southampton, made by Dr D.J.L. Agassiz (Goater, 1976).

0762 *Athrips mouffetella* (Linnaeus, 1758)
■ vc11 Cadland Estate, Beaulieu, 12.7.97, a few at m.v. light (JRL); Fareham (RJD); Southsea, 5.8.96, one at m.v. light; Havant Thicket, 8.7.97, a few at m.v. light; Sandy Point NR, Hayling Island, 14.7.92, a few at m.v. light (JRL, IRT, *et al.*).
■ vc12 Pamber, 1994 (GJD); Selborne, 14.7.97, 21.7.00, singletons at light, det. from old specimen (AEA).

0763 *Xenolechia aethiops* (Humphreys & Westwood, 1845)
Recorded only from S Hants, the most recent record being of one at Beaulieu Road Station in 1973, by Rev. R.J. Dickson (Goater, 1992).

0764 *Pseudotelphusa scalella* (Scopoli, 1763)
■ vc11 Havant Thicket, 2.6.91, one on an oak trunk (RJBH).
■ vc12 Pamber, 7.5.95, at light in garden of AS (GJD).

0766 *Altenia (Teleiodes) scriptella* (Hübner, 1796)
■ vc11 Fareham, 26.6 and 30.6.93, one male at m.v. light each night (RJD). The only previous record for the county was one taken at Catisfield by RJD in 1971.

0765 *Teleiodes (Pseudotelphusa) vulgella* ([Denis & Schiffermüller], 1775)
■ vc10 Freshwater, 2.7.97 (Knill-Jones, 1998b).
■ vc11 Sparsholt College (AHD); Locks Heath, 20.7.00, det. RJD (PCa); Wickham Common; Fareham (RJD); Old Winchester Hill NNR, 23.7.97, one at m.v. light (RJD, JRL); Milton Common, Southsea, 1996–2000,

occasional at light in garden (IRT); Sandy Point NR, Hayling Island, 4.8.95, a few at m.v. light (JRL).
■ vc12 Farnborough, two in 1994 (RWP).

0767 *Teleiodes decorella* (Haworth, 1812)
■ vc11 Bratley, 13.3.91, one flying by day; Pig Bush, 17.7.92, one on an oak trunk; Woodfidley, 19.7.92, one on an oak trunk; Holmsley, 18.8.91, one on an oak trunk (RJBH); Sparsholt College (AHD); Waterlooville, 16.2.00, at house light, conf. JRL (RJM).
■ vc12 Farnborough, 10.3.95, one at light (RWP).

0768 *Teleiodes notatella* (Hübner, 1813)
■ vc12 Bartley Heath NR (AHD).

0769 *Teleiodes wagae* (Nowicki, 1860)
The only Hampshire records to hand are those given in Goater (1983, 1992) from Sparsholt and Botley Wood, both in S Hants. The latter was the first record for England in 1976.

0770 *Teleiodes proximella* (Hübner, 1796)
■ vc11 Havant Thicket, 28.6.95, 8.7.97, a few at m.v. light (JRL).
■ vc12 Pamber, 1995 (GJD); Bramley Frith Wood NR (AHD); Yateley Common, 6.6.96 (AMD).

0771 *Teleiodes alburnella* (Zeller, 1839)
■ vc11 Chandlers Ford, 4.7.95, one at light, det. JRL (BG), 25.8 to 28.8.99, three at m.v. light (BE); Havant Thicket, 8.7.97, one at m.v. light (JRL, IRT, *et al.*).
■ vc12 Farnborough, 5.8.95, one at light (RWP); Eelmoor Marsh, 4.7.98, at m.v. light (DGG).

0772 *Teleiodes fugitivella* (Zeller, 1839)
■ vc11 Brockenhurst, 23.7.98, one at rest on a birch trunk; Great Salterns NR, Portsmouth (JRL); Havant Thicket, 8.7.97, one at m.v. light (JRL, IRT, *et al.*).

0773 *Teleiodes paripunctella* (Thunberg, 1794)
■ vc12 Pamber, 1995 (GJD); Yateley Common, 30.5.94, one (AMD).

0774 *Teleiodes luculella* (Hübner, 1813)
■ vc11 Roydon Woods, 10.7.96, a few at m.v. light (PRD, JRL); Sparsholt College (AHD); Soberton, 30.6.95, one at m.v. light; Hookheath Meadows NR, Southwick, 24.5.92, one at m.v. light (JRL); Havant Thicket, 8.7.97, at m.v. light (JRL, IRT, *et al.*).
■ vc12 Oakley; Bramley Frith Wood NR; Bartley Heath NR, 12.5.96, one at m.v. light (AHD); Pamber, 1995 (GJD); Silchester Common, 30.5.93, one (JRL); Selborne, 30.6.95, one at light (AEA); Farnborough, 24.7.94 (RWP); Yateley Common (AMD).

0775 *Teleiodes sequax* (Haworth, 1828)
■ vc10 Freshwater, 2.9.97 (Knill-Jones, 1998b).
■ vc12 Stockbridge Down, 29.5.91, larvae on rock-rose *Helianthemum nummularium*, six moths bred (RJBH);

Porton Down, 24.7.94, many; Ashford Hangers NR, 18.10.93, a few larvae on rock-rose (JRL).

0776 *Teleiopsis diffinis* (Haworth, 1828)
■ vc11 Hurn, 5.5.97, one on path (PD); Merrietown Heath, 18.6.99, common at m.v. light (PHS); Roydon Woods, 3.10.98, one in flight (RJD, JRL); Matley, 29.9.91, one by day (RJBH); Sparsholt College (AHD); Hamble Common, 1996; (RJD); Browndown, 5.7.97, a few at m.v. light (JRL, IRT, *et al.*); Sinah Common, Hayling Island, 15.8.98, at m.v. light (JRL, IRT, *et al.*).
■ vc12 Castle Bottom NR, 30.8.98, det. JRL (AMD); Selborne, 2.5.96, at light, det. JRL (AEA).

0790 *Chionodes fumatella* (Douglas, 1850)
This is a species of coastal sandhills, and there are old records from Hayling Island There are also two inland records, from N Hants, far from its typical habitat (Goater, 1974, 1992).

0791 *Chionodes distinctella* (Zeller, 1839)
There has been no record since those given in Goater (1974, 1992). Emmet (1979) gives the foodplant as field wormwood *Artemisia campestris*, but in Britain it must surely be something different, probably mugwort *A. vulgaris*.

0792 *Mirificarma mulinella* (Zeller, 1839)
■ vc8 Martin Down, 24.8.90 (MFVC and S. Nash).
■ vc11 Hengistbury Head, 9.9.00, trapped in two different localities on the same night (PHS); Swanwick NR, 20.8.96, one at m.v. light (JRL); Milton Common, Southsea, 16.8 and 22.8.97, at light, again in 1998 and 2000 (IRT).
■ vc12 Farnborough, two from 21.8.93, 1.8.94 (RWP).

0793 *Mirificarma lentiginosella* (Zeller, 1839)
The larva of this moth feeds on dyer's greenweed *Genista tinctoria*. This is a local plant in this area, but the larva or moth has been found in several localities in all three vice-counties (Goater, 1974, 1992).

0796 *Aroga velocella* (Zeller, 1839)
■ vc10 Freshwater, 14.8.97 (Knill-Jones, 1998b).
■ vc11 Merrietown Heath, 21.7.93, by day (PHS); Cadland Estate, Beaulieu, 12.7.97, several at m.v. light; Old Winchester Hill NNR, 23.7.97, one at m.v. light (JRL *et al.*); Browndown, 5.7.97, a few at m.v. light (JRL, IRT, *et al.*); Milton Common, Southsea, 8.7 and 17.8.97, at light (IRT); Sinah Common, Hayling Island, 15.8.98 a few at m.v. light (JRL, IRT, *et al.*).
■ vc12 Leckford, 22.7.89 (DHS) (see Agassiz, 1991, *Ent. Rec.* **103**: 149); Farnborough, 14.8.93, 21.8.95, both det. JRL (RWP). **New vc record.**

0799 *Neofriseria singula* (Staudinger, 1876)
There are very few records of this species in mainland Hampshire, and none recently (See Goater, 1974, 1992).

0800 *Gelechia rhombella* ([Denis & Schiffermüller], 1775)
Several records are given for S Hants in Goater, 1974, 1992) and one from N Hants in 1896 (*ibid.* 1992). Unrecorded from the Isle of Wight.

0801a *Gelechia senticetella* (Staudinger, 1859)
■ vc11 Southsea, 3.8.93, one at m.v. light (Langmaid, Ent. Gaz. **45**: 36). Third British Record. **New county record.**

0802a *Gelechia sororculella* (Hübner, 1817)
■ vc11 Havant Thicket, 8.7.97, at m.v. light (JRL, IRT, *et al.*).

0806 *Gelechia nigra* (Haworth, 1828)
A few records are given from Isle of Wight and S Hants, mostly of larvae found on poplar *Populus* spp. and aspen *Populus tremula* (Goater, 1974, 1992), but as yet there are none from N Hants.
■ vc11 Lower Test Marshes NR, 13.5.00, spinnings on grey poplar *Populus canescens*, one moth em. 4 June; Southsea, 15.7.00, one male at m.v. light (JRL).

0807 *Gelechia turpella* ([Denis & Schiffermüller], 1775)
One specimen taken at light in 1969 beside the River Itchen near Martyr Worthy by the late D.W.H. Ffennell (Goater, 1974) remains the only record for the county.

0810 *Scrobipalpa suaedella* (Richardson, 1893)
There are old records from St Helens, Isle of Wight and Cracknore Hard, S Hants (Goater, 1974). None since 1937.

0811 *Scrobipalpa samadensis* (Pfaffenzeller, 1870)
Recorded in the past from the Isle of Wight and the Hampshire coast, most recently from Southsea in 1984 by Dr J.R. Langmaid (See Goater, 1974, 1992). The larva feeds on buck's-horn plantain *Plantago coronopus*.

0811a *Scrobipalpa stangei* (Hering, 1889)
The only known British specimens were taken at Yarmouth, Isle of Wight, in 1882, detected many years later by Dr. K. Sattler in the Brit. Mus. (Nat. Hist.) Collection (See Goater, 1992).

0812 *Scrobipalpa instabilella* (Douglas, 1846)
■ vc11 Cadland Estate, Beaulieu, 12.7.97, a few at m.v. light, genitalia det. (BG, JRL); Gutner Point NR, Hayling Island, 27.4.96, larvae on sea-purslane *Atriplex portulacoides*, moths bred (JRL, M.S. Parsons); Northney saltmarsh, 3.4.95, one pupa, moth bred (JRL).

0813 *Scrobipalpa salinella* (Zeller, 1847)
■ vc11 Milton Common, Southsea, 12.8.97, at light (IRT).

0814 *Scrobipalpa ocellatella* (Boyd, 1858)
■ vc11 Hurst Castle, 13.4.95, a few larvae (JRL, PHS); Browndown, 13.5.98, vacated spinnings (JRL); Milton Common, Southsea, 1996, 2000, at light, det. JRL (IRT); Sinah Common, Hayling Island, 15.8.98, at m.v. light;

Sandy Point NR, 6.5.94, several larvae on sea beet *Beta maritima* (JRL, IRT, *et al.*).

0815 *Scrobipalpa nitentella* (Fuchs, 1902)
■ vc10 Newtown, 18.9.97, several larvae on sea-purslane *Atriplex portulacoides* and annual sea-blite *Suaeda maritima* (AME, JRL).
■ vc11 Cadland Estate, Beaulieu, 12.7.97, one at m.v. light, genitalia det.; Marchwood, 8.9.98, many larvae on sea purslane; Lower Test Marshes NR, 8.9.98, many larvae on spear-leaved orache *A. prostrata*; Bursledon, 8.9.98, very many larvae on *Atriplex* sp. and annual sea-blite (JRL); Swanwick NR, 20.8.96, one at m.v. light, genitalia det.; Upper Hamble Country Park, 7.10.96, a few larvae on sea purslane (AMD, AME, JRL); Sandy Point NR, Hayling Island, 18.8.95, one at m.v. light; Gutner Point NR, 11.9.96, many larvae on spear-leaved orache and annual sea-blite (JRL).

0816 *Scrobipalpa obsoletella* (Fischer von Röslerstamm, 1841)
■ vc11 Sinah Common, Hayling Island, 15.8.98, a few at m.v. light, genitalia det.; Sandy Point NR, 4.8.95, one at m.v. light (JRL, IRT, *et al.*).

0818 *Scrobipalpa atriplicella* (Fischer von Röslerstamm, 1841)
■ vc10 Newtown, 18.9.97, one larva on spear-leaved orache *Atriplex prostrata* (AME, JRL).
■ vc11 Sparsholt College (AHD).
■ vc12 Selborne, 1994 (AEA).

0819 *Scrobipalpa costella* (Humphreys & Westwood, 1845)
■ vc8 Martin Down, 24.8.90 (MFVC and S. Nash).
■ vc11 Pennington, 8.11.95, one at m.v. light (BG, JRL); Nutburn, North Baddesley, 11.11.95, one at m.v. light; Sparsholt College (AHD); Fareham; Hook-with-Warsash, 1996; Titchfield Haven (RJD); Milton Common, Southsea, 1996–2000, at light in garden (IRT); Sinah Common, Hayling Island, 15.8.98, at m.v. light (JRL, IRT, *et al.*).
■ vc12 Winnall Moors NR (DHS); Brighton Hill, Basingstoke; Bramley Frith Wood NR; Bartley Heath NR, 1996; Greywell Moor; Mapledurwell Fen (AHD); Selborne, 1993 onwards, occasional (AEA); Farnborough, 19.10.94, det. JRL, 30.8.95 (RWP).

0822 *Scrobipalpa acuminatella* (Sircom, 1850)
■ vc8 Martin Down, 5.5.90 (S. Nash).
■ vc11 Lower Test Marshes NR, 1.10.96, a few tenanted mines on spear thistle *Cirsium vulgare*; Swanwick NR, 20.8.96, one at m.v. light; Upper Hamble Country Park, 7.10.96, several tenanted mines on *C. vulgare* (JRL *et al.*); Milton Common, Southsea, 29.5.96, at actinic trap, det. JRL, 19.8.97, at light, again in 1998 and 2000 (IRT); Sandy Point NR, Hayling Island, 22.7 and 18.8.95, a few at m.v. light (JRL).
■ vc12 Ashford Hangers NR, 18.10.93, a few tenanted mines on *C. vulgare* (JRL).

0823 *Scrobipalpula tussilaginis* (Stainton, 1867)
In 1987, larvae of this species were found at Milford-on-

Sea in leaves of coltsfoot *Tussilago farfara* by JLR and DHS (Goater, 1992).

0826 *Caryocolum vicinella* (Douglas, 1851)
■ vc11 Hurst Castle, 13.4.95, a few larvae on sea-campion *Silene maritima* (JRL, PHS).

0827 *Caryocolum alsinella* (Zeller, 1868)
■ vc11 Sinah Common, Hayling Island, 15.8.98, at m.v. light (JRL, IRT, *et al.*).

0829 *Caryocolum marmoreum* (Haworth, 1828)
Recorded from the coastal sandhills of St Helens, Isle of Wight, and Hayling Island, with occasional single specimens elsewhere on the coast (Goater, 1974, 1992).
■ vc11 Hengistbury Head, the new dunes, 9.9.00, one at m.v. light (PHS).

0830 *Caryocolum fraternella* (Douglas, 1851)
■ vc11 Bishops Waltham, 19.4.93, larvae on lesser stitchwort *Stellaria graminea*; Southsea, 31.7.92, one at m.v. light (JRL); Milton Common, 30.7, 6.8 (two) and 8.8.00 at m.v. light (IRT).
■ vc12 Abbotstone Down, 27.7.94, one at m.v. light (RJBH, JRL); Farnborough, 28.7.96 (RWP).

0831 *Caryocolum proximum* (Haworth, 1828)
■ vc12 Farnborough, 19.8.96, one at m.v. light, genitalia det. JRL (RWP). **New county record.**

0832 *Caryocolum blandella* (Douglas, 1852)
■ vc10 Freshwater, 17.6.97 (Knill-Jones, 1998b), 26.7.00 (SAK-J). First recent records for the Isle of Wight.
■ vc12 Selborne, 13.6.93, at light, det. JRL from photograph (AEA); Priors Lane, Yateley, 2.7.97 (AMD).

0834 *Caryocolum tricolorella* (Haworth, 1812)
■ vc11 Clanfield, 1.4.97, a few larvae; Browndown, 2.4.95, a few vacated spinnings; Hayling Island, 19.3.93, many larvae on greater stitchwort *Stellaria holostea*, moths bred (JRL).

[0835 *Caryocolum blandulella* (Tutt, 1887)
The old record for Hayling Island given in Goater (1974) has never been confirmed.]

[0837 *Caryocolum huebneri* (Haworth, 1827)
The only record is of one taken at Rhinefields, New Forest, in 1958 by the late R.M. Mere, and this is considered to require confirmation (see Goater, 1974, 1992).]

0840 *Thiotricha (Reuttia) subocellea* (Stephens, 1834)
■ vc11 Botley Wood, a few cases on mint *Mentha* spp. (RJBH, JRL); Waterlooville, 16.7.00, at m.v. light, conf. JRL (RJM).
■ vc12 Stockbridge Down, 11.9.92, cases on seedheads of marjoram *Origanum vulgare*, five moths bred June 1993 (RJBH). **New vc record.**

0841 *Sophronia semicostella* (Hübner, 1813)
■ vc11 Havant Thicket, 8.7.97, one at m.v. light; Sandy Point NR, Hayling Island, 22.7.95, a few at m.v. light (JRL, IRT, *et al.*).
■ vc12 Porton Down, 1.7.00 (DGG); Warren Heath, 24.7.96, two in Heath trap; Yateley Common, 1997 (AMD); Selborne, 6.7.00, one at m.v. light, det. JRL (AEA); Farnborough, 29.6.95, one at light (RWP).

0843 *Aproaerema anthyllidella* (Hübner, 1813)
There are several records from the Isle of Wight and S Hants (Goater, 1974, 1992) but none as yet from N Hants.
■ vc11 Milton Common, Southsea, at light in garden, 1998, 2000 (IRT); Swanwick, 20.8.96, a few at m.v. light; Portsdown, 19.4.92, mines and spinnings on kidney vetch *Anthyllis vulneraria*; Sandy Point NR, Hayling Island, 22.7.95, one at m.v. light (JRL).

0844 *Syncopacma larseniella* (Gozmány, 1957)
First recorded from Wickham in 1975, and subsequently from Ashurst, Ampfield and Botley Wood (Goater, 1992), all in S Hants, this species has since been located in a few other localities in vc11 and one in vc12. The larva is found on bird's-foot-trefoils *Lotus* spp., particularly on *L. pedunculatus*, and the imago is occasionally recorded at light.
■ vc11 Roydon Woods, 10.7.96, one at m.v. light (PRD, JRL); North Solent NR, Beaulieu, 2.6.92, larvae on marsh bird's-foot-trefoil *L. pedunculatus*; Soberton, 30.6.95, one at m.v. light; Hookheath Meadows NR, Southwick, 15.5.92, larvae on *L. pedunculatus*; Havant Thicket, 28.6.95 (JRL).
■ vc12 Selborne, July 96, at light, genitalia det. JRL (AEA). **New vc record.**

0847 *Syncopacma taeniolella* (Zeller, 1839)
Recorded in all three vice-counties, sometimes commonly. However, though it almost certainly still occurs there, no record has been received from the Isle of Wight since those given in Goater (1974).
■ vc11 Broughton Down, 1.7.99, very common (BE); Hookheath Meadows NR, Southwick, 14.7.96, two; Sandy Point NR, Hayling Island, 22.7.95, a few at m.v. light (JRL).
■ vc12 Bartley Heath NR; Bramley Frith Wood, 30.6.95, one at m.v. light (AHD); Selborne, 10.7.95, one at light (AEA).

0848 *Syncopacma albipalpella* (Herrich-Schäffer, 1854)
Recorded in the past from Southampton in 1928 and 1929 and in the north of the county from Hook Common in 1965 and Silchester in 1973 (Goater, 1974). There has been no more recent report. The larva feeds on petty whin *Genista anglica*.

0853 *Anacampsis populella* (Clerck, 1759)
Common throughout vc's 11 and 12 (JRL), and probably so on the Isle of Wight, although the most recent record to hand is from 1975 (Goater, 1992). The larva lives in rolled leaves of aspen *Populus tremula* and sallows *Salix* spp.

0854 *Anacampsis blattariella* (Hübner, 1796)
Locally fairly common in the mainland vice-counties, amongst the foodplant, birch *Betula* spp.
■ vc10 Freshwater, 22.7.95 (SAK-J). **New vc record.**
■ vc11 Brockenhurst, 23.7.98, one (JRL); Hamble Common, 1996; Titchfield Haven, 1996 (RJD); Botley Wood, 19.4.95, larva on birch, moth bred; Creech Wood, Denmead, 22.8.97 (JRL, IRT); Havant Thicket, 5.5.97, a few larvae on downy birch *Betula pubescens* (JRL, IRT, *et al.*).

0797 *Neofaculta ericetella* (Geyer, 1832)
Common to abundant on heathy ground, but the only records received from the Isle of Wight are those given in Goater (1974). The larva lives in spinnings in the shoots of heathers *Calluna* and *Erica* spp.
■ vc11 Sopley Common, 12.5.00, several at m.v. light; Town Common, Christchurch, 20.6.95, by day in two areas (PHS); Matley Bog and Shatterford, 10.6.99, abundant (BE); Hamble Common, 1996 (RJD); Havant Thicket, 28.6.95 (JRL).
■ vc12 Pamber, 1995 (GJD); Farnborough, 29.6.95 (RWP); Bricksbury Hill, 29.4.97 (AMD).

0856 *Anarsia spartiella* (Schrank, 1802)
Locally common amongst the foodplants gorse *Ulex europaeus*, Dyer's Greenweed *Genista tinctoria* and broom *Cytisus scoparius*. The most recent record from the Isle of Wight is Tennyson Down, 1975 (Goater, 1992).
■ vc11 Cadland Estate, Beaulieu, 12.7.97, one at m.v. light (JRL); Hook-with-Warsash, 1996 (RJD); Browndown, 5.7.97, a few at m.v. light (JRL, IRT, *et al.*); Milton Common, Southsea, at light in garden, 1998, 2000 (IRT); Havant Thicket, 28.6.95, 8.7.98, at m.v. light (JRL).
■ vc12 Farnborough, 2.7.94 (RWP); Yateley, 17.6.97, one (AMD).

0857 *Anarsia lineatella* Zeller, 1839
This adventive species was bred from an imported Spanish plum *Prunus domestica* in 1971 by the late D.W.H. Ffennell (Goater, 1974). This is the only record.

0858 *Hypatima rhomboidella* (Linnaeus, 1758)
Recorded in small numbers from localities in all three vice-counties, but not since 1975 on the Isle of Wight (Goater, 1992).
■ vc11 Wickham Common, 1996 (RJD); West Walk, Wickham, 25.8.95, one at m.v. light; The Moors NR, Bishops Waltham, 7.8.98, one at m.v. light (JRL *et al.*).
■ vc12 Wildhern, 14.7.98 (DGG); Bartley Heath NR (AHD); Selborne, 8.8.97 (AEA); Farnborough, 11.8.95, one at light, det BR Baker (RWP).

0859 *Psoricoptera gibbosella* (Zeller, 1839)
Recorded from all three vice-counties (Goater, 1974, 1992) and below. The larva feed on oak *Quercus* spp.
■ vc11 Hengistbury Head, higher salt marsh, 9.9.00, one at m.v. light (PHS); Chandlers Ford, 25.8.99, one at m.v. light (BE); Winchester, Sarum Road, 1.8.90, one at m.v. light; Crab Wood, 11.8.92, one disturbed by day (RJBH);

West Walk, Wickham, 25.8.95, one at m.v. light (JRL).
■ vc12 Odiham Common, 24.8.96, one (AMD);
Farnborough, 5.8.96 (RWP).

0855 *Acompsia cinerella* (Clerck, 1759)
Local in the two mainland vice-counties, especially on
the chalk. The larva is stated to feed on "moss" (Emmet,
1979).
■ vc12 Danebury Hillfort, 26.7.91, one beaten from
juniper *Juniperus communis*; Leckford, 18.7.92, one by
day; Abbotstone Down, 30.7.92, one in evening (RJBH);
Farnborough, 28.7.95, one at light (RWP).

0861 *Acompsia schmidtiellus* (Heyden, 1848)
This species is associated with marjoram *Origanum
vulgare*. So far it has been found on the Isle of Wight and
in S Hants, but not in N Hants.
■ vc10 Niton, 1939 and Brading Down, 1931 (Goater,
1974) but no more recent record.
■ vc11 Farley Mount, Warnford and Oxenbourne Down
(Goaster, 1974, 1992); East Meon, 26.5.97, a few larvae;
Portsdown, 29.4.97, one larva (JRL, IRT).

0862 *Dichomeris marginella* (Fabricius, 1781)
Associated with juniper *Juniperus communis* and now
occurring amongst cultivated junipers in several localities.
■ vc10 Freshwater, 8.7.89 (Knill-Jones, 1995, *Ent. Rec.*
10 7: 76); again on 12.7.95 and 3.8.96 (SAK-J). **New vc
record.**
■ vc11 Marwell, one at m.v. light, 13.6.97 (PAB, DGG);
Sparsholt College (AHD); Chandlers Ford, 3.7.99, two
at m.v. light (BE); Locks Heath, seven in 2000, first on
15.7.00 (PCa); Fareham, 30.6.98, one at m.v. light (RJD);
Widley, Portsdown (PMP).
■ vc12 Yateley Common, 12.7.94, one (AMD);
Farnborough, five in 1995 (RWP).

0865 *Dichomeris derasella* ([Denis & Schiffermüller], 1775)
= *fasciella* (Hübner, 1796)
There is a very ancient record from the New Forest given
in the Victoria County History (1900) and quoted by
Goater (1974). The larva feeds on blackthorn *Prunus spinosa*.

0851 *Acanthophila alacella* (Zeller, 1839)
The only known occurrences of this species in Hampshire,
from the New Forest and Southampton, are given in
Goater (1974, 1992).

0866 *Brachmia blandella* (Fabricius, 1798)
A widespread and often common species on the mainland,
but so far recorded only between Freshwater and
Yarmouth on the Isle of Wight (Goater, 1974, 1992).
■ vc10 Freshwater, 26.7.00, one (SAK-J).
■ vc11 Sparsholt College (AHD); Locks Heath, six in 2000,
first on 20.7.00, det. RJD (PCa); Milton Common,
Southsea, 18.7 and 20.7 and 8.8.00, singletons at m.v.
light (IRT); Waterlooville, 25.7.00, at m.v. light, conf.
JRL (RJM); Botley Wood, 4.7.95, one at m.v. light; Havant
Thicket, 8.7.97, one at m.v. light; Sandy Point NR, Hayling
Island, 22.7.95, a few at m.v. light (JRL, IRT, *et al.*).

■ vc12 Winnall Moors NR (DHS); Pamber, 1994 (GJD);
Bramley Frith Wood NR (AHD); Selborne, 27.6.96, det.
JRL from photograph; five during late July, 2000 (AEA);
Farnborough, 12.7.96 (RWP).

0868 *Helcystogramma (Brachmia) rufescens* (Haworth, 1828)
Widespread and often common in the mainland vice-
counties but not reported from the Isle of Wight since
1969. The larva feeds on broad-leaved species of grass
Poaceae (Gramineae).
■ vc11 Keyhaven, 2.6.92, larvae on tall fescue *Festuca
arundinacea* (DJLA, AME, JRL); Sparsholt College
(AHD); Wickham Common; Fareham (RJD); Portsdown,
19.4.92, one larva on false brome *Brachypodium sylvaticum*;
Great Salterns NR, Portsmouth (JRL); Milton Common,
Southsea, 1996–2000, at light in garden (IRT);
Waterlooville, 8.7, 19.7 and 9.8.00, at m.v. light, conf.
JRL (RJM).
■ vc12 Winnall Moors NR (DHS); Abbotstone Down,
27.7.94, one at m.v. light (RJBH, JRL); Oakley; Bramley
Frith Wood NR; Bartley Heath NR, 1996 (AHD);
Pamber, 1994 (GJD); Selborne, recorded most years from
1993, conf. JRL (AEA); Noar Hill NR, 18.7.95 (AMJ);
Farnborough, 11.7.94 (RWP).

0749 *Sitotroga cerealella* (Olivier, 1789)
■ vc11 Southsea, 28.7.95, one at m.v. light, genitalia det.
(JRL). **New county record.**

0808 *Platyedra subcinerea* (Haworth, 1828)
■ vc11 Great Salterns NR, Portsmouth (JRL); Milton
Common, Southsea, 1994–2000, at light in garden (IRT).

0809 *Pexicopia malvella* (Hübner, 1805)
■ vc11 Kings Somborne, 30.6.98, one at m.v. light, det
JRL from photograph (TJN); Milton Common, Southsea,
14.7, 18.7, 20.7 and 28.7.96, singletons at actinic trap,
det. JRL, 12.6 and 22.8.97, at light, again in 1998 and
2000 (IRT).
■ vc12 Leckford, 19.6.92 (DHS); Selborne, 30.7.00, one
at light, conf. JRL from photograph (AEA). **New vc
record.**

Autostichidae (2)

Species of *Oegoconia* can only be identified with certainty
by examination of the genitalia. Nearly all of those which
have been dissected have turned out to be *O. quadripuncta*,
and there is at present only one confirmed record of *O.
deauratella* from the county.

0870 *Oegoconia quadripuncta* (Haworth, 1828)
■ vc11 Sparsholt College (AHD); Chandlers Ford, 1.7.95,
one at light, det. JRL (BG); Locks Heath, 1.8.00, det.
RJD (PCa); Fareham (RJD); Bishops Waltham, 18.8.93,
one at m.v. light (JRL); Milton Common, Southsea, 1996–
2000, at light in garden, det. JRL (IRT); Waterlooville,
1996–2000 (RJM); Sinah Common, Hayling Island,
15.8.98, at m.v. light (JRL, IRT, *et al.*).

■ vc12 Oakley; Brighton Hill, Basingstoke, 3.8.96, one at m.v. light (AHD); Selborne, 20 between July and September 2000 (AEA); Noar Hill,17.6.93 (AMJ).

0871 *Oegoconia deauratella* (Herrich-Schäffer, 1854)
■ vc12 Farnborough, 10.6.93, det. JRL (RWP). **New vc record**, and first confirmed record for the county (see Goater, 1992).

Blastobasidae (3)

Meyrick [1927], in his introduction to the family, says, "It is decidedly the least attractive family of the *Microlepidoptera*, the imagos being usually extremely similar, obscure and dull-coloured, whilst the larvae are also very similar in habit, feeding on dry refuse, seeds, etc."

0873 *Blastobasis lignea* Walsingham, 1894
Widespread and often common in the mainland vice-counties. The moths come freely to light but the larva, which feeds on plant debris, bird droppings and probably other material, does not seem to have been reported.
■ vc8 Martin Down, 24.8.90 (MFVC and S. Nash).
■ vc10 Freshwater, 8.8.97 (Knill-Jones, 1998b). First recent record for the Isle of Wight.
■ vc11 Sparsholt College (AHD); Hilliers Arboretum, Ampfield, 21.7.98 (NB, TJN); Chandlers Ford, common at light in August, det. JRL (BG); Locks Heath, five in 2000, first on 20.7.00, det. RJD (PCa); Denmead, Creech Wood, 1997 (JRL, EAP); West Walk, Wickham, 25.8.95; Swanwick NR, 20.8.96; Great Salterns NR, Portsmouth (JRL); Hamble Common, 1996; Fareham (RJD); Milton Common, Southsea, 1996–2000, at light in garden (IRT); Waterlooville, 25.7.00, at m.v. light (RJM); Sinah Common, Hayling Island, 15.8.98, at m.v. light (JRL, IRT, *et al.*).
■ vc12 Wildhern, nr Andover, 11.8.97; St John's Copse, Oakley, 5.8.98; Eelmoor Marsh SSSI, 23.8.97, at light (DGG); Pamber, 1994 (GJD); Selborne, 1993, 1994 (AEA); Farnborough, common (RWP); Priors Lane, Yateley, 12.8.97; Castle Bottom NR, 30.8.98, det. JRL (AMD).

0874 *Blastobasis decolorella* (Wollaston, 1858)
This is a recent arrival in the county, the first record being from Portsmouth in 1994. This and all subsequent records are detailed below. The larva feeds on a variety of dead and decaying plant material.
■ vc10 Freshwater, 14.11 and 26.11.99, single specimens at m.v. light. (Knill-Jones, 2000). **New vc record.**
■ vc11 Merrietown Heath, 18.6.99, a few at m.v. light (PHS); Nutburn, North Baddesley, 9.6.95, one at light (AHD); Great Salterns NR, Portsmouth, 8.7.94, several at portable m.v. light, (JRL); Milton Common, Southsea, 28.7.96, at actinic trap, det. JRL, 6.7.97, 1998 and six between 19.6 and 18.7.00, at light (IRT); Waterlooville, 23.9.00, at m.v. light (RJM). **New county record.**
■ vc12 Brighton Hill, Basingstoke, 15.7.94, 20.7.96, now spreading through gardens; Pamber Forest, 19.7.97, one at m.v. light (MCH); Silchester Common, 19.6.96, locally

common amongst broom *Cytisus scoparius* (AHD); Selborne, 7.8.97, 21.8.98 (AEA); Farnborough, 8.7.93, 16.7.94, three between 16.6 and 10.7.95, at m.v. light (RWP); Rye Common, 26.7.96; Yateley, 4.6.93, 28.6.94, at m.v. light; Yateley Common, 18.6.97, six (AMD) (see Davis, 1998). **New vc record.**

0875 *Blastobasis phycidella* (Zeller, 1839)
The four specimens taken in Southampton in 1930 (Goater, 1974) remain the only British records.

Blastobasis sp.
■ vc11 The Moors NR, Bishop's Waltham, 17.7.98. As yet unidentified. **New to Britain**; possibly non-European in origin (RJD).

Batrachedridae (2)

A small family of small, narrow-winged moths, superficially rather similar to coleophorids.

0878 *Batrachedra praeangusta* (Haworth, 1828)
Widespread and locally common on the mainland, but unrecorded from the Isle of Wight (Goater, 1974, 1992). The larva lives in the catkins of sallows *Salix* spp. and poplars *Populus* spp.
■ vc11 Catisfield; Titchfield Haven; West Walk (RJD); Swanwick NR, 20.8.96, one at m.v. light; Lower Titchfield Haven NR, 24.5.93, one larva on goat willow *Salix caprea* (JRL); Milton Common, Southsea, 1996, det. JRL (IRT); Havant Thicket, 8.7.97, at m.v. light (JRL, IRT, *et al.*).
■ vc12 Winnall Moors NR (DHS); Old Alresford Pond (RJD); Farnborough, 19.8.96 (RWP).

0879 *Batrachedra pinicolella* (Zeller, 1839)
There are a few records from the mainland vice-counties, but this moth has been reported as common only at Botley Wood. It is likely to have been overlooked and examination of genitalia is needed for certain determination. The larva feeds on the needles of spruce *Picea abies* and Scots pine *Pinus sylvestris*.
■ vc11 Botley Wood, 12.7.94, many at m.v. light (JRL); Havant Thicket, 23.6.98, three at m.v. light (RJD).

Momphidae (14)

Moths of the genus *Mompha* are mostly associated with species of Onagraceae *Circaea*, *Epilobium* and *Chamerion*. *M. miscella* is an exception, living on common rock-rose *Helianthemum nummularium*. Larvae of many *Mompha* species make blotch mines, others live in spun shoots and others make a gall in the stem of the foodplant. Some species hibernate as adults, hiding in thatch or coming indoors.

0880 *Mompha langiella* (Hübner, 1796)
The mines of this species are often locally abundant in the leaves of enchanter's nightshade *Circaea lutetiana* and species of willowherb *Epilobium* spp. and of rosebay

Chamerion angustifolium, but so far, they have only been found in S Hants (Goater, 1974, 1992).

■ vc11 Near Ashurst, 12.7.93, mines abundant, leaving foliage of *Circaea* withered and white, with mines also on willowherbs *Epilobium montanum*, *E. parviflorum* and rosebay (Langmaid, 1993c); Fareham; Hook-with-Warsash, 1996; Hamble Common, 1996; Titchfield Haven, 1996 (RJD); Hookheath Meadows NR, Southwick, 4.8.92, a few vacated mines on *Circaea* (JRL).

0881 *Mompha terminella* (Humphreys & Westwood, 1845)
Mines with larvae of this species have been located in all three vice-counties, on enchanter's nightshade *Circaea lutetiana*, but the moth appears to be local (Goater, 1974, 1992).

■ vc10 Osborne, 22.8.98, mines with larvae (DTB).
■ vc11 Hookheath Meadows NR, 21.8.99 (RJD, JRL).

0882 *Mompha locupletella* ([Denis & Schiffermüller], 1775)
This species has also been recorded from all three vice-counties (Goater, 1974, 1992), but appears to be local. The larva makes blotches in the leaves of willowherbs *Epilobium* spp.

■ vc10 Apes Down (RJD); Wolverton Marsh, 5.8.00, one adult, det. JRL (DTB).
■ vc11 The Moors NR, Bishop's Waltham; Marwell Zoological Park; Catisfield; Park Gate (RJD).

0883 *Mompha raschkiella* (Zeller, 1839)
Many records from the mainland vice-counties (Goater 1974, 1992) and, judging from the recent records given below, widespread also on the Isle of Wight. The larva makes a mine in the leaves of rosebay *Chamerion angustifolium*.

■ vc8 Martin Down, 24.8.90 (MFVC and S. Nash).
■ vc10 Tennyson Down, 6.8.87, mines (JRL); Brighstone Forest (RJD); Parkhurst Forest, 18.9.97, a few vacated mines (AME, JRL); Alverstone (JMC); Shalcombe, 17.8.94, 6.7.96, mines; Rowridge Valley, 5.9.94, vacated mines; Shide 3.7.95, mines; Lake Common, 4.9.94, vacated mines; Osborne, 10.9.94, vacated mines; Bonchurch Landslip, 25.8.96, all conf. JRL (DTB). **New vc record.**

0884 *Mompha miscella* ([Denis & Schiffermüller], 1775)
Locally common on the chalk amongst the foodplant, common rock-rose *Helianthemum nummularium*, in the leaves of which the larva makes a blotch mine. Recorded from all three vice-counties (Goater, 1974, 1992).

■ vc10 Tennyson Down, 26.5.73 (RJD), 18.5.92, tenanted mines (JRL, DHS, PHS).
■ vc11 Beacon Hill NNR, Warnford, 11.6.94, two (JRL).
■ vc12 Abbotstone Down, 27.7.94, a few at m.v. light; Micheldever, 7.4.97, one tenanted mine; Ashford Hangers NR, 18.10.93, several mines with larvae (JRL *et al.*).

0885 *Mompha conturbatella* (Hübner, 1819)
Very local, perhaps overlooked, in the two mainland vice-counties (Goater, 1974, 1992). The larva lives in the crown of young plants of willowherbs *Epilobium* spp.

■ vc11 Crab Wood, 12.6.76; Botley Wood, 7.7.74 (RJD).

0886 *Mompha ochraceella* (Curtis, 1839)
Recorded from all three vice-counties, though only once from the Isle of Wight (Goater, 1974, 1992). The larva lives in the roots and stems of great willowherb *Epilobium hirsutum*, mining upwards into the petioles.

■ vc11 Botley Wood; Fareham, 20.6.98, one (RJD); Hilsea, 5.6.92, cocoon under leaf of *E. hirsutum*, moth bred; Great Salterns NR, Portsmouth (JRL).
■ vc12 Selborne, 1993, 13.7.99, (AEA).

0887 *Mompha lacteella* (Stephens, 1834)
There are occasional records from the two mainland vice-counties. Fassnidge, in his Diary, quoted by Goater (1974), gives an illuminating account of his discovery of this moth at Farley Mount. It is associated with rosebay *Chamerion angustifolium*, but we have no record of its having been bred in Hampshire.

■ vc11 Hookheath Meadows NR, Swanwick, 26.7.97 (RJD).

0888 *Mompha propinquella* (Stainton, 1851)
Recorded from all three vice-counties, the majority of localities being in S Hants (Goater, 1974, 1992). The larva makes blotch-mines in the leaves of *Epilobium* spp.

■ vc11 Oxenbourne Down, 2.8.75 (RJD).
■ vc12 Selborne, 15.8 and 27.8.95, 14.8.96, det. JRL, and 1997 onwards(AEA).

0889 *Mompha divisella* Herrich-Schäffer, 1854
Old records are given by Goater (1974) for the Isle of Wight and Bournemouth and Southampton. In the mainland localities, galls were found on the stems of broad-leaved willowherb *Epilobium montanum*.

0890 *Mompha subdivisella* Bradley, 1951
■ vc11 Fareham, 12.3.95, one male flying in early morning sunshine, det. JRL (Dickson, 1995b); Cams Bay, 21.8.99, larvae found on great willowherb *Epilobium hirsutum* (JRL). **New county record.**

0891 *Mompha sturnipennella* (Treitschke, 1833)
= *nodicolella* Fuchs, 1902
■ vc10 Bouldnor Forest, 26.8.98, one larva in a galled seedpod of rosebay *Chamerion angustifolium*, em. 11.9.98, det. JRL (DTB) (Knill-Jones, 1999). **New vc record.**
■ vc12 Farnborough, 15.8.95, det JRL (RWP). **New county record.**

0892 *Mompha subbistrigella* (Haworth, 1828)
Widespread and locally abundant on the mainland (Goater, 1974, 1992). The larva lives in the capsules of broad-leaved willowherb *Epilobium montanum*.

■ vc10 Shanklin, 6.5.95 (JMC). **New vc record.**
■ vc11 Chandlers Ford, 3.4.95, one at light, det. JRL (BG); Soberton, 10.6 and 30.6.94, at m.v. light (JRL); Park Gate; Catisfield; Fareham, 5.6 and 12.6.98, single males; Titchfield Haven (RJD); Milton Common, Southsea, 1996–2000, at light in garden, det. JRL (IRT); Waterlooville, 1996–2000 (RJM).

■ vc12 Winnall Moors NR (DHS); Selborne, 9.11 and 18.11.97, indoors (AEA); Farnborough, 19.6.95 (RWP).

0893 *Mompha epilobiella* ([Denis & Schiffermüller], 1775)
Recorded from all three vice-counties (Goater, 1974, 1992) and locally common. The larvae live in shoots of great willowherb *Epilobium hirsutum*.
■ vc10 Westover Farm, W of Calbourne, 31.7.99, in spun shoots (DTB); Knowles Farm area (RJD).
■ vc11 Hookheath Meadows NR, 1999; Hook area; Hamble Common; Titchfield Haven; Paulsgrove (RJD); Swanwick, 14.6.97, a few larvae; Fareham, 1.7.94, several larvae, 5.6.98, 7.8.98, singles at light; Lower Titchfield Haven NR, 20.8.93, many larval spinnings and pupae (JRL); Great Salterns NR, Portsmouth (JRL); Milton Common, Southsea, 1996–2000, at light in garden, det. JRL (IRT); Sandy Point NR, Hayling Island, 14.7.92, a few at m.v. light (JRL).
■ vc12 Winnall Moors NR (DHS).

Cosmopterigidae (14 + [2])

Small, narrow-winged moths, often brightly coloured and having metallic markings. The larvae mine leaves, stems or the bark of trees.

[0894 *Cosmopterix zieglerella* (Hübner, 1810)
The record given in the Victoria County History, quoted by Goater (1974) remains unconfirmed. The larva feeds on hop *Humulus lupulus*.]

0896 *Cosmopterix orichalcea* Stainton, 1861
Two old records are given in Goater (1974), but the only detailed one (Goater, 1992) is from Leckford, N Hants, where larvae have been found in some quantity in galleries in the leaves of reed canary-grass *Phalaris arundinacea*.

0896a *Cosmopterix scribaiella* Zeller, 1850
The mines of this species can be overlooked for those of *C. lienigiella*, being very similar. First recorded in Britain (Dorset) in 1997 (Sterling, 1998).
■ vc11 Hilsea Lines, Portsmouth, 14.9.97, mines in common reed *Phragmites australis*, from one of which a larva was dissected; mines subsequently found at Alver Valley NR, Gosport on 22.9 and 29.9.97 and in four localities within the Portsmouth City boundary, (Langmaid, 1998), moths subsequently bred (JRL); Milton Common, Southsea, one mine with larva, moth em. 18.5.98 (IRT). **New county record.**

0897 *Cosmopterix lienigiella* Lienig & Zeller, 1846
Browndown, vc11, is now a well-known locality for this species, and in 1988 it was discovered at Leckford, vc12 (Goater, 1974, 1992). It has since been discovered in a few other places in S Hants, near the coast. The larva makes a characteristic blotch-mine in common reed *Phragmites australis*.
■ vc11 Hengistbury Head, Rushy Peat, 10.9.00, a few tenanted mines on *Phragmites* (PHS); Marchwood, 8.9.98,

one mine with larva; Lower Titchfield Haven NR, 21.10.96, a few mines with larvae; Sandy Point NR, Hayling Island, 17.10.96, many tenanted mines, moths bred (JRL, IRT).

0898 *Limnaecia phragmitella* Stainton, 1851
Common to abundant amongst reed-mace *Typha latifolia* in all three vice-counties, although there have been no specific records from the Isle of Wight in recent years.
■ vc11 Sparsholt College (AHD); Swanwick NR; Botley Wood; Fareham; Titchfield Haven (RJD).
■ vc12 Winnall Moors NR (DHS); Mapledurwell Fen, 25.7.99, one at m.v. light (AHD); Fleet Pond, 21.4.98, larval workings in reed-mace *Typha latifolia* (DGG); Farnborough, 10.7.95, one at light (RWP).

0899 *Pancalia leuwenhoekella* (Linnaeus, 1761)
Locally common on downland in all three vice-counties (Goater, 1974, 1992), the larvae living in the rootstocks and leaf petioles of hairy violet *Viola hirta*.
■ vc8 Martin Down, 29.4 and 5.5.90 (S. Nash).
■ vc10 High Down, Freshwater; Apes Down (RJD).
■ vc11 Portsdown, 14.7.98, a few, all in good condition, swept from *Viola* sp., indicating possible second brood (JRL, IRT).
■ vc12 Chilbolton Down, 25.5.92, one (JRL, DHS); Bramdean Common; Noar Hill (RJD); Ashford Hangers NR, 21.5.93, a few (JRL).

[0900 *Pancalia schwarzella* (Fabricius, 1798)
= *latreillella* Curtis, 1830
Given in the Victoria County History as occurring on the sand-hills of Hayling Island (Goater, 1974), the record needs confirmation. Like the preceding species, the larva feeds on *Viola* spp.]

0902 *Chrysoclista (Glyphipteryx) lathamella* Fletcher, 1936
There is a single record of this species, from Woodmill near Southampton by Fassnidge (Goater, 1974). The larva lives in the bark of white willow *Salix alba*.

0903 *Chrysoclista (Glyphipteryx) linneella* (Clerck, 1759)
There are very few records of this species, from Southampton and Southsea in S Hants and from Northington in N Hants (Goater, 1974, 1992), though in two of those localities the moth was said to be common or fairly common. It clearly needs looking for. The larva lives in the bark of lime *Tilia* spp. PHS has recently located it in the Bournemouth area, see below.
■ vc11 Bournemouth, 17.5.97, Southbourne, 15.5.97, several larval feedings in bark of lime trees in both localities (PHS).

0904 *Spuleria flavicaput* (Haworth, 1828)
Local but evidently rather uncommon in all three vice-counties (Goater, 1974, 1992). The larva lives in twigs of hawthorn *Crataegus* spp.
■ vc10 Firestone Copse (RJD).
■ vc11 Milton Common, Southsea, at light in garden, 1998 (IRT).
■ vc12 Overton (AHD).

0905 *Blastodacna hellerella* (Duponchel, 1838)
Recorded locally in all three vice-counties, mostly as specimens taken at light. The larvae are found in the fruits of hawthorn *Crataegus* spp.
■ vc11 Botley Wood, 12.7.94, several at m.v. light; Great Salterns NR, Portsmouth (JRL); Milton Common, Southsea, 30.6.00, one at m.v. light (IRT); Waterlooville, 19.6.00, at m.v. light (RJM).
■ vc12 Selborne, 10.7 and 18.7.95, singletons at light (AEA); Farnborough, 12.6.94, two in 1995 (RWP).

0906 *Blastodacna atra* (Haworth, 1828)
The only records received up to 1992 were from Southampton, Farley Mount, Winchester and Southsea, all in S Hants (Goater, 1974, 1992). The larva feeds in the shoots of apple *Malus* spp.
■ vc11 Sparsholt College (AHD); Botley Wood; Fareham, 1998, several singletons at light during the summer (RJD); Swanwick NR, 20.8.96, one at m.v. light (JRL).
■ vc12 Bramley Frith Wood NR; Mapledurwell Fen, 25.7.99, one at m.v. light (AHD); Farnborough, 21.7.96, 4.8.96 by RWP, conf. JRL. **New vc record.**

0907 *Dystebenna stephensi* (Stainton, 1849)
This an ancient woodland species, the larva of which lives in the bark of old oaks *Quercus* spp. Old records from the New Forest are given in Goater (1974). There have been two recent records, these are given below.
■ vc11 Burley New Inclosure, 1.7.99 (DGG); Roydon Woods, 25.7.92, one flying near old oaks in evening (RJBH).

The genus *Sorhagenia* has been shown to be a complex of three species, separable only by examination of the genitalia. All three have been positively identified in Hampshire, but the records given in Goater (1974) could refer to any of them. The larvae of all three species feed on buckthorn *Rhamnus cathartica* or alder buckthorn *Frangula alnus*.

0908 *Sorhagenia rhamniella* (Zeller, 1839)
The only two confirmed records of this species are from Winchester, S Hants, on 2.8.91 (Goater, 1992) and that given below.
■ vc12 Abbotstone Down, 27.7.94, a few at m.v. light, genitalia det. and redetermined as this species (RJBH, JRL). **New vc record.**

0909 *Sorhagenia lophyrella* (Douglas, 1846)
A few records from S Hants and one from N Hants are given in Goater (1992). However, moths resulting from larvae found on Wickham Common have been redetermined as *S. janiszewskae* Riedl (JRL, pers. comm.). Hence, *S. lophyrella* is known hitherto only from Winchester and Droxford in S Hants, where the foodplant is buckthorn *Rhamnus cathartica*.
■ vc11 Portsdown, 3.5.93, many larvae, moths bred (JRL).
■ vc12 Leckford, 30.7.77 (RJD); Stockbridge Down, 22.7.99, imagines fairly common (BE).

0910 *Sorhagenia janiszewskae* Riedl, 1962
Recorded from a few localities in S Hants (Goater, 1992). This species is associated with alder buckthorn *Frangula alnus* only and therefore to be found only in places like the New Forest, Emer Bog and the Botley and Wickham areas.
■ vc11 Balmer Lawn; Botley Wood; Wickham Common, 1996 (RJD).

Scythrididae (4)

Often unicolorous bronzy moths which are easily overlooked. They fly by day, reluctantly, often content to hop short distances in the vicinity of their foodplants.

0911 *Scythris grandipennis* (Haworth, 1828)
The larva of this species makes silken webs on dwarf gorse *Ulex minor*. Records are mainly from the New Forest, also from Southampton Common, Baddesley Common and Browndown in S Hants, and from Bartley Heath NR in N Hants. There are two old records from the Isle of Wight. (Goater, 1974, 1992).
■ vc10 Bouldnor coast, pupa in spinning on gorse 5.6.78, moth bred 8.6.78 (RJD).
■ vc11 Merrietown Heath, 5.7.93, one by day (PHS).

0914 *Scythris crassiuscula* (Herrich-Schäffer, 1855)
Recorded from an area between Micheldever and the Test Valley, and from Oxenbourne Down, these being the only S Hants records (Goater, 1974, 1992). Accepted records of this and the next species are all of dissected specimens.
■ vc11 Broughton Down, 1.7.99, very common, genitalia det. (BE); Beacon Hill, Exton, 20.7.00 (BE, JRL, IRT).

0915 *Scythris picaepennis* (Haworth, 1828)
This species is local in the mainland vice-counties, on the chalk between Winchester, Micheldever and Broughton Down, but has not been reported recently. The old record from the Isle of Wight, given in Goater (1974) requires confirmation. All previous records were listed in Goater (1974, 1992). The only further addition is given below.
■ vc11 Old Winchester Hill, one on 23.7.97 genitalia det. JRL and S Coster (RJD).

0917 *Scythris empetrella* Karsholt & Nielsen, 1976
The first British record was from near Lyndhurst, June 1834 (Goater, 1992). This remained the only Hampshire occurrence until it was rediscovered in 1999.
■ vc11 Sopley Common, 13.5.00, many larvae on ling *Calluna* and bell heather *Erica cinerea*; Hengistbury Head, 5.5.99, larval feedings on *Calluna* (PHS); Lyndhurst area, 9.5.00, larvae very locally common on sandy heathland (DGG, MSP).

Cochylidae (36 + [2])

Species of this group of tortricoid moths tend to live inconspicuously, and with the exception of a few such as

Trachysmia inopiana (Haworth), they come infrequently to light. Some, such as *Falseuncaria ruficiliana* (Haworth) fly at dusk over their foodplant. Diligent search for larvae in fruits or inflorescences, or random collection of old, dead stems during the winter will often reveal the hitherto unsuspected presence of many species, though there is the added difficulty of getting the larvae, which hibernate full-fed, safely through to maturity. For those prepared to tackle and overcome these problems, the Cochylidae offer fruitful ground for research and discovery, witness the recent history of *Cochylis molliculana* Zeller in Hampshire. The modern view, expressed by Karsholt and Razowski (1996), is that this group of moths, far from constituting a family, are to be regarded as a tribe within the subfamily Tortricinae.

0921 *Phtheochroa (Hysterosia) inopiana* (Haworth, 1811)
Locally common in all three vice-counties amongst fleabane *Pulicaria dysenterica* in the roots of which the larva lives.

0923 *Phtheochroa sodaliana* (Haworth, 1811)
Very local on the chalk around Winchester between the Itchen and Test valleys, (vc's 11 and 12), and also recorded from Oxenbourne Down vc11 Goater (1974, 1992). The larva feeds in the berries of buckthorn *Rhamnus cathartica*.
- vc11 Sparsholt College (AHD); Yew Hill, 26.7.97 (DGG); Catisfield (RJD); Waterlooville, 11.6 and 26.6.00, singletons at m.v. light (RJM).
- vc12 South Wonston, 29.6.95, at m.v. light (PJSS).

0925 *Phtheochroa rugosana* (Hübner, 1799)

```
|————————————————————|
       10 mm
```

Local, especially on the chalk; now recorded from all three vice-counties (Goater 1974, 1992). The larva feeds in the berries of white bryony *Bryonia dioica*.
- vc10 Freshwater, 1.7.92, one at m.v. light (Knill-Jones, 1993). **Presence in vc10 confirmed.**
- vc11 Hengistbury Head, 1998, one, 1999, 12 (MJ); Sparsholt College (AHD); Chilling, nr Warsash; Titchfield Haven NR; Widley, Portsdown, 30.5.98, one at rest (PMP); Catisfield (RJD); Browndown, 5.7.97, one at m.v. light (JRL, IRT, *et al.*); Waterlooville, 1996–2000 (RJM).
- vc12 Magdalen Hill Down, 8.7.99 (PAB); South Wonston, 27.5.95, and subsequently, at m.v. light (PJSS); Overton (AHD); Selborne, 1993–2000, fairly common, 28 in 1995 (AEA); Noar Hill, 2.7.94 (AMJ).

0924 *Hysterophora maculosana* (Haworth, 1811)
Local and uncommon, or overlooked, in all three vice-counties. An inhabitant of bluebell *Hyacinthoides non-scripta* woods, the larva living in the seed-heads of that plant. All records are given in Goater (1974, 1992) and below.
- vc11 Botley Wood, 6.5.00, three in afternoon sunshine (BE, BG, JRL); Warsash, 20.5.94, one (JRL); Tournebury Wood (RJD).
- vc12 Bramley Frith Wood NR (AHD).

0926 *Phalonidia manniana* (Fischer von Röslerstamm, 1839)
Widespread but apparently uncommon, and no recent record from the Isle of Wight (Goater 1974, 1992). A marsh-inhabiting species, associated with water mint *Mentha aquatica* and gipsywort *Lycopus europaeus*.
- vc11 Botley Wood, 12.7.94, a few, 4.7.95, three at m.v. light; Southsea, 1.8.92, one at m.v. light (JRL).
- vc12 Winnall Moors NR (DHS); Bramley Frith Wood, 30.6.95, fairly common at m.v. light (AHD).

0932 *Phalonidia affinitana* (Douglas, 1846)
Locally common in saltmarshes, where the larva feeds on sea aster *Aster tripolium*. There are also some inland records Goater (1992).
- vc11 Hurst Castle, 2.6.92, one (DJLA, AME, JRL); Hound shore; Titchfield Haven, 1996 (RJD); West Walk, Wickham, 25.8.95, a few at m.v. light; Sandy Point NR, Hayling Island, 4.8.95, a few at m.v. light (JRL).

[0933 *Phalonidia gilvicomana* (Zeller, 1847) and
0934 *P. curvistrigana* (Stainton, 1859)
These two species have never been reported in Hampshire but might well occur. The former should be sought in woodland amongst wall lettuce *Mycelis muralis* or nipplewort *Lapsana communis* and the latter amongst wild goldenrod *Solidago virgaurea*.]

0929 *Gynnidomorpha (Phalonidia) vectisana* (Humphreys & Westwood, 1845)
This is a species of coastal saltmarshes, the larva feeding on sea arrowgrass *Triglochin maritima*. Thus it is local on the coasts of the Isle of Wight and S Hants (Goater 1974, 1992).
- vc10 Yarmouth, 18.5.92, a few (JRL, DHS, PHS).
- vc11 Hound shore; Curbridge NR (RJD).

0930 *Gynnidomorpha (Phalonidia) alismana* (Ragonot, 1883)
Nothing has been heard recently of this species in Hampshire, probably for want of searching for the larva, which lives in the stems of water-plantain *Alisma plantago-aquatica*. The late Wm Fassnidge reported it as fairly common to common in three localities in S Hants (Goater, 1974).
- vc11 Titchfield Haven, 1.6.78 (RJD).

0931 *Gynnidomorpha (Phalonidia) luridana* (Gregson, 1870)
A local and usually uncommon species, found mainly on the chalk around Winchester. There are a few records from S and N Hants (Goater, 1974, 1992). All known specimens have been caught, the majority at m.v. light.
- vc11 West Wood, Farley Mount, 25.7.77 (RJD).
- vc12 Abbotstone Down, 27.7.94, a few at m.v. light (RJBH, JRL).

0936 *Cochylimorpha (Stenodes) straminea* (Haworth, 1811)
Widespread and rather common in localities where the foodplant, black knapweed *Centaurea nigra* occurs, mainly on the chalk and along the coast. Recorded from all three vice-counties, but not recently from the Isle of Wight (Goater, 1974).

0937 *Agapeta hamana* (Linnaeus, 1758)
Widespread in all three vice-counties, and often very common in rough grassland, perhaps especially on the chalk, amongst thistles *Cirsium* spp. on which the larva feeds.

0938 *Agapeta zoegana* (Linnaeus, 1767)
Considerably more local and generally less common than the previous species, but nevertheless widespread in all three vice-counties. The larva feeds in the roots of black knapweed *Centaurea nigra* and small scabious *Scabiosa columbaria*.

0939 *Aethes tesserana* ([Denis & Schiffermüller], 1775)
Recorded from all three vice-counties, sometimes in abundance (Goater 1974, 1992). It seems to prefer xerothermic conditions such as dry, close-cropped chalk downland and coastal shingle. The larva feeds in the roots of Asteraceae (Compositae) which grow in such situations.
■ vc10 High Down, Freshwater; Brook Bay; Redcliff; Luccombe Chine (RJD).
■ vc11 Hurst Castle, 2.6.92, one (DJLA, AME, JRL); Hamble Common, 1996; Fareham; Wickham Common; Browndown; Portsdown (RJD).
■ vc12 Wildhern, nr Andover, 27.5.97, by day (DGG).

[0940 *Aethes rutilana* (Hübner, 1817)
Stated by Meyrick [1927] to occur in Hampshire (Goater, 1974) but there have been no confirmatory records, despite searches amongst the foodplant, juniper *Juniperus communis*.]

0941 *Aethes hartmanniana* (Clerck, 1759)
A rare and local species which has been recorded from all three vice-counties, mainly in localities on the chalk (Goater, 1974, 1992).
■ vc8 Martin Down, 8.6.92 (JRL, RMP).
■ vc11 Old Winchester Hill, 23.7.97, one at m.v. light (RJD); Portsdown, 28.5.96, adult disturbed by day det. RJD (DMA).
■ vc12 Noar Hill, adult, 6.7.74, det. RJD (G.C. Dickson); adult, 23.5.75 det. RJD (DMA).

0944 *Aethes williana* (Brahm, 1791)
Locally common on the Isle of Wight and in S Hants, on chalk and coastal shingle amongst wild carrot *Daucus carota* (Goater, 1974, 1992). Still unrecorded from N Hants.
■ vc10 Tennyson Cliffs, 12.6.90 (Knill-Jones, 1991b); High Down, Freshwater; Compton Bay; St Catherine's Point (RJD).

0945 *Aethes cnicana* (Westwood, 1854)
Recorded from all three vice-counties although, as so often, there are no recent records from the Isle of Wight (Goater, 1974). On the mainland, it is widespread and locally frequent on rough ground and in marshes, amongst thistles *Cirsium* spp.

0946 *Aethes rubigana* (Treitschke, 1830)
Locally common amongst burdock *Arctium* spp. in all three vice-counties, with the *proviso* that there have been no recent records from the Isle of Wight (Goater, 1974).

0947 *Aethes smeathmanniana* (Fabricius, 1781)
Widespread on waste ground, coastal shingle and chalk downland in all three vice-counties. The larva lives in the seed-heads of yarrow *Achillea millefolium* and black knapweed *Centaurea nigra*.

0948 *Aethes margaritana* (Haworth, 1811)
Nothing has been heard of this species in Hampshire since 1969. There are records prior to that date, all from S Hants save one unconfirmed report from the Isle of Wight (Goater, 1974, 1992).

0949 *Aethes dilucidana* (Stephens, 1852)
Recorded from all three vice-counties, mainly from chalk localities, where the larva feeds in stems of wild parsnip *Pastinaca sativa*.

0950 *Aethes francillana* (Fabricius, 1794)
Recorded from all three vice-counties (Goater 1974, 1992) but, like its near relatives, it does not come readily to light and is best collected as a larva during the winter months, in this case in old stems of wild carrot *Daucus carota*.
■ vc11 Sparsholt College (AHD); Fareham (RJD); Bishops Waltham, 18.8.93, one at m.v. light; Hilsea, 8.3.92, a few larvae in dead stems of wild carrot; Milton Common, Southsea, at light in garden, 1998–2000 (IRT); Sandy Point NR, Hayling Island (RJD).

0951 *Aethes beatricella* (Walsingham, 1898)
The larvae of this species can be collected during the winter in old stems of hemlock *Conium maculatum* and bred, sometimes in numbers. The moth itself is seen rather infrequently. Most records are from S Hants (Goater, 1974, 1992) and the species is unrecorded from the Isle of Wight.
■ vc11 Great Salterns NR, Portsmouth (JRL); Milton Common (RJD), 18.6.99, one, at light, conf. JRL (IRT).
■ vc12 Selborne, 12.7.96, one at m.v. light, conf. JRL (AEA). **New vc record.**

0952 *Commophila aeneana* (Hübner, 1800)
A very local and elusive species which is probably more widespread than the records suggest. It has been found in any number only in Botley Wood, though records exist from all three vice-counties (Goater, 1974, 1992).

0954 *Eupoecilia angustana* (Hübner, 1799)
Locally common, particularly on heaths, also on chalk downland, in all three vice-counties.
■ vc8 Martin Down, 24.8.90 (MFVC, S. Nash).
■ vc11 Hengistbury Head, one in 1999, det. PHS (MJ), 9.9.00, one at m.v. light (PHS).

0955 *Eupoecilia ambiguella* (Hübner, 1796)
Very local amongst alder buckthorn *Frangula alnus*, mainly in the New Forest, but discovered in 1987 on Newtown Common, N Hants (Goater, 1974, 1992).
■ vc10 Freshwater, 17.7.97 (Knill-Jones, 1998c). **New vc record.**
■ vc11 Emer Bog, late August 1992, larvae common in berries of *Frangula*, moths bred 1993 (RJBH).

0956 *Cochylidia implicitana* (Wocke, 1856)

Records exist from all three vice-counties (Goater, 1974, 1992), but on the whole this is an elusive and uncommon species. The larva lives in the stems, shoots and inflorescences of various Asteraceae (Compositae).

■ vc11 Sparsholt College (AHD); Botley Wood, 20.5.98, three at sunset; Hook Lake; Hamble Common, 1996; Titchfield Haven; Browndown; Brownwich; Rowner Wild Grounds (RJD); Milton Common, Southsea, 11.8.96, conf. JRL, 6.8 and 17.8.97, 1998, at light (IRT); Sandy Point NR, Hayling Island, 14.7.92, a few at m.v. light (JRL).

■ vc12 Wildhern, nr Andover, 16.8.97, identity confirmed (DGG); Bramley Frith Wood NR (AHD).

0957 *Cochylidia heydeniana* (Herrich-Schäffer, 1851)

Very local in Hampshire and associated mainly with blue fleabane *Erigeron acer*, but also probably with Canadian fleabane *Conyza canadensis*. Apart from the records given below, all known occurrences are given in Goater (1974).

■ vc11 Chandlers Ford, 9.8.92, one at m.v. light (BG). **New vc record.**

■ vc12 Noar Hill, 3.7.94 (AMJ).

[0958 *Cochylidia subroseana* (Haworth, 1811)

The record of Meyrick [1927] still requires confirmation (Goater, 1974).]

0959 *Cochylidia rupicola* (Curtis, 1834)

This is another species that needs looking for, otherwise it is not seen. The larva inhabits the inflorescences of hemp-agrimony *Eupatorium cannabinum*, preferring plants growing in drier localities. All records are given in Goater (1974, 1992) and below.

■ vc10 Ventnor; Firestone Copse (RJD).

■ vc11 Portsdown (RJD).

■ vc12 Winnall Moors NR (DHS); Selborne, 7.6.96, at light, det. K. Tuck (BMNH) (AEA).

0960 *Falsuncaria ruficiliana* (Haworth, 1811)

Very locally common in all three vice-counties, on downland among cowslips *Primula veris*. Records are given in Goater (1974, 1992) and below.

■ vc8 Martin Down, 5.5.90 (S. Nash), 24.8.90 (MFVC, S. Nash).

■ vc11 Yew Hill, 16.5.97 (DGG).

■ vc12 Selborne, 8.8 and 9.8.97 (AEA); Noar Hill, 24.5.76 (RJD), 6.7.93 (AMJ).

0962 *Cochylis roseana* (Haworth, 1811)

The moth is seldom seen, unless bred from old heads of teasel *Dipsacus fullonum* collected during the winter months. The larvae of this species feed inconspicuously in the seeds, often several in a head, whereas that of *Endothenia gentianeana* (Hübner) is found in the central pith. All records are given in Goater (1974, 1992) and below.

■ vc10 Freshwater, 30.7.97 (Knill-Jones, 1998b); Redcliff (RJD).

■ vc11 Hengistbury Head, 1998, bred from teasel (MJ); Kings Somborne, 4.8.98, one at m.v. light (TJN); Sparsholt College (AHD); Botley Wood; Fareham;

Titchfield Haven; Swanwick NR; Rowner Wild Grounds (RJD); Milton Common, Southsea, 6.8.00, one at m.v. light, teasel grows nearby (IRT).

■ vc12 Mapledurwell Fen, 10.8.98, one at m.v. light (AHD); Selborne, 1994 (AEA); Noar Hill 6.7.93 (AMJ).

0963 *Cochylis flaviciliana* (Westwood, 1854)

Single specimens have been taken at light from time to time in all three vice-counties. If the larva were sought more often in heads of field scabious *Knautia arvensis*, the species could turn out to be more common than the present records suggest (Goater, 1974, 1992).

■ vc11 Waterlooville, 1996–2000 (RJM).

0964 *Cochylis dubitana* (Hübner, 1799)

Widespread and locally quite common in the mainland vice-counties, but the record for the Isle of Wight given in Goater (1974) still requires confirmation.

0964a *Cochylis molliculana* Zeller, 1847

■ vc11 The occurrence of *Cochylis molliculana* in Britain is documented by Dr J.R. Langmaid (Langmaid, 1994c), following his discovery and subsequent dissection of a specimen taken in his light trap at Southsea on 21.8.93; another was recorded at Fareham on 25.8.93 (Dickson, 1994). It was later found that two earlier specimens had been taken in Dorset and remained unidentified until Dr Langmaid's revelation. In 1994, larvae were found in great abundance in heads of bristly ox-tongue *Picris echioides*, on waste ground at Southsea, Portsmouth and inland as far as Cosham (JRL); Fareham, 17.9.97, a few larvae (AME, JRL); Alver Valley NR, 22.9.97, one larva; Great Salterns NR, Portsmouth, 8.7.94, nine at m.v. light, larvae subsequently found in abundance (JRL *et al.*); Milton Common, Southsea, 19.7.96, and regularly afterwards, at actinic trap, records conf. JRL (IRT); Sinah Common, Hayling Island, 15.8.98, at m.v. light; Hayling Island, larvae common since 1994 (JRL *et al.*). **New to Britain.**

■ vc12 Selborne, 22.8.96, one at m.v. light, det. JRL (Aston, 1998c). **New vc record.**

0965 *Cochylis hybridella* (Hübner, 1813)

Taken occasionally at light in all three vice-counties (Goater 1974, 1992).

■ vc11 Hengistbury Head, one in 1999, det. PHS (MJ); Sparsholt College (AHD); Funtley, 25.7.99, genitalia det. (MLO, comm. RJD).

■ vc12 South Wonston, 18.7.94, 11.7.96, at m.v. light (PJSS); Oakley (AHD).

0966 *Cochylis atricapitana* (Stephens, 1852)

Widespread and fairly common amongst ragwort *Senecio jacobaea*, mainly on the chalk downs and along the coast.

■ vc8 Martin Down, 24.8.90 (MFVC, S. Nash).

■ vc10 Freshwater, 22.8.94 (Knill-Jones, 1998b).

■ vc11 Hengistbury Head, 1999, common, det. PHS (MJ).

0968 *Cochylis nana* (Haworth, 1811)

Frequent in birch country in the mainland vice-counties,

but only one old record from the Isle of Wight (Goater, 1974). The larva feeds in the catkins of birch.

- vc11 Sparsholt College (AHD); Chandlers Ford, 7.6.91 (BG); Wickham Common, 1996 (RJD); Southsea, 23.5.92, one at m.v. light (JRL).
- vc12 Conford Moor, 21.6.95, a few (JRL, RMP); Pamber, 1994 (GJD); Hook Common; Fleet Pond (RJD).

Tortricidae (260 + [3])

The modern view, expressed by Karsholt and Razowski (1996), is to continue to divide this family into two subfamilies, Tortricinae and Olethreutinae, but to include the cochylids, retained above as a family, as a tribe within Tortricinae. Among the most familiar of Tortricinae are the "bell moths" of the genera *Pandemis* and *Archips* and the "buttons", so-called because of the conspicuous scale tufts on the forewings, of the genus *Acleris*, species of which are often highly polymorphic. Many Olethreutinae are convincing bird-dropping mimics; others, like members of the large genus *Dichrorampha*, though small, are familiar because they fly in large numbers over their foodplants in the late afternoon sunshine; their larvae live in the roots of herbaceous plants, particularly yarrow *Achillea millefolium*, mugwort *Artemisia vulgaris* and ox-eye daisy *Leucanthemum vulgare*.

0969 *Pandemis corylana* (Fabricius, 1794)
Fairly common to common in deciduous woodland in all three vice-counties. The larva is polyphagous on a variety of deciduous trees and shrubs.
- vc11 Hengistbury Head, 1997 (MJ).

0970 *Pandemis cerasana* (Hübner, 1786)
Fairly common to common in deciduous woodland, orchards, hedgerows, *etc.* in all three vice-counties. The larva is polyphagous on a variety of deciduous trees and shrubs, including fruit trees.

0971 *Pandemis cinnamomeana* (Treitschke, 1830)
Widespread but local in the two mainland vice-counties, but unrecorded from the Isle of Wight (Goater, 1974, 1992). The larva is polyphagous on a variety of trees and shrubs, including conifers *Larix*, *Picea*.
- vc11 Brockenhurst (JEC); Marwell Zoological Park, 13.6.97 (PAB); Waterlooville, 1996–2000 (RJM).

0972 *Pandemis heparana* ([Denis & Schiffermüller], 1775)
Common in wooded habitats, hedgerows and scrub in all three vice-counties. The larva is polyphagous on a variety of deciduous trees and shrubs.
- vc8 Martin Down, 24.8.90 (MFVC, S. Nash).
- vc10 Shanklin (JMC).
- vc11 Hengistbury Head, 1997, 1999 (MJ).

0974 *Argyrotaenia ljungiana* Thunberg, 1797
= *pulchellana* (Haworth, 1811)
Common on heathland in the mainland vice-counties. No recent record from the Isle of Wight (Goater, 1976).

0976 *Archips oporana* (Linnaeus, 1758)
Formerly recorded from the New Forest (Goater, 1974). The following records are therefore of great interest: they are the first recent reports for the county, and the first outside its former stronghold. The larva feeds on Scots pine *Pinus sylvestris* and other conifers.
- vc11 Hurn, 21.7.98, female at m.v. light, det. BG; 30.6.00, another specimen (MJ).

0977 *Archips podana* (Scopoli, 1763)
Common in all three vice-counties. The larva is polyphagous on a wide variety of deciduous trees and shrubs, occasionally on conifers.
- vc10 Shanklin (JMC).
- vc11 Hengistbury Head, 1997, 1999 (MJ).

0979 *Archips crataegana* (Hübner, 1799)
Widespread in deciduous woodland, but rather local and less common than most of its congeners. Like them, the larva is polyphagous on trees and shrubs. Records are given in Goater (1974, 1992) and below.
- vc12 Bramley Frith NR (AHD).

0980 *Archips xylosteana* (Linnaeus, 1758)
Widespread and fairly common in all three vice-counties, in woodland. Another species with a highly polyphagous larval stage.
- vc11 Hengistbury Head, 1997 (MJ).

0981 *Archips rosana* (Linnaeus, 1758)
Recorded from all three vice-counties (Goater, 1974), but evidently local and rather uncommon. The larva is polyphagous on deciduous trees and shrubs, occasionally conifers, and is sometimes a pest in orchards.
- vc11 Chilling, nr Warsash (PMP); Southsea, 19.6.95, one at m.v. light (JRL).
- vc12 Wildhern, nr Andover, 9.6.97, by day (DGG); Selborne, 1995, 1996, 1997 at light, conf. JRL (AEA).

0982 *Choristoneura diversana* (Hübner, 1817)
This is apparently a very rare species in Hampshire. It has been recorded on single occasions from one locality in S Hants and two in N Hants, never from the Isle of Wight (Goater, 1974, 1992). The larva is polyphagous on trees, shrubs and herbaceous plants and may have been overlooked through having a local preference for an unsuspected pabulum.

0983 *Choristoneura hebenstreitella* (Müller, 1764)
This large, easily-identified species is characteristic of mature woodland, and is widely distributed in such localities in the two mainland vice-counties (Goater, 1974, 1992).
- vc10 Cranmore, 12.6.97 (Knill-Jones, 1998b).
- vc11 Roydon Woods, 10.7.96, one at m.v. light (PRD, JRL), Sloden Inclosure, 2.7.99; Dilton Meadows, 12.7.97, at m.v. light (DGG); Bitterne, 11.6.97 (PAB); Chilling Copse, 1996 (RJD).
- vc12 Wildhern, nr Andover, 13.6.97 (DGG); South Wonston, 27.7.97, at m.v. light (PJSS); Bartley Heath

NR, 1.6.95, larva on aspen *Populus tremula*, moth bred (AHD); Rye Common, 3.7.00, one, det. JRL (AMD).

0985 *Cacoecimorpha pronubana* (Hübner, 1799)

This species became established in southern England in the early part of the 20th century and has since spread. It is now widespread in Hampshire and the Isle of Wight, and is something of a suburban insect. The larva feeds on cultivated privet *Ligustrum ovalifolium* and cultivated *Euonymus*, besides a number of other plants, and the moths are often seen flying by day in the vicinity of privet hedges, and in gardens.

■ vc10 Shanklin (JMC); Bembridge Point, 25.9.96, larvae on sea buckthorn *Hippophae rhamnoides* (DTB).

0986 *Syndemis musculana* (Hübner, 1799)

10 mm

Common, mostly in wooded country, in the mainland vice-counties and probably also on the Isle of Wight.

■ vc8 Martin Down, 29.4.90 (S. Nash).

■ vc10 Headon Warren; Afton Down; Yarmouth; Bouldnor; Apes Down; Parkhurst Forest; Steephill; St Catherine's Point; Luccombe Chine; Firestone Copse (RJD).

■ vc11 Hengistbury Head, one in 1999, det. PHS (MJ).

0987 *Ptycholomoides aeriferanus* (Herrich-Schäffer, 1851)

This is another relatively recent arrival in Britain, having been first reported in 1951. The larva feeds on larch *Larix decidua*, and the moth is now fairly widespread in the two mainland vice-counties, in and near larch woods. So far, there has been only one record from the Isle of Wight (Goater, 1992).

■ vc11 Roydon Woods, 10.7.96 (PRD, JRL), Dilton Meadows, 12.7.97, at m.v. light (DGG); Chandlers Ford, 29.7.91, 27.7.93 (BG); St Cross, 8.7.99, two at m.v. light (TWa); Catisfield (RJD).

■ vc12 Abbotstone Down, 27.7.94, a few at m.v. light (RJBH, JRL); Oakley (AHD); Farnborough, 2.7.94 (RWP); Yateley Common, 2.7.94 (AMD); Selborne, 29.7.93, at light, conf. BG from photo (AEA); Bentley Station Meadow (PAB); Farnborough, 19.7.95, one (KW).

0988 *Aphelia viburnana* ([Denis & Schiffermüller], 1775)

Common in the New Forest bogs, and at Emer Bog, but we have no record from the north of the county. The larva is polyphagous, but in the New Forest, it appears to favour bog-myrtle *Myrica gale*.

■ vc10 Freshwater, 3.7 and 5.7.93 (Knill-Jones, 1995). **Presence in vc10 confirmed.**

0989 *Aphelia paleana* (Hübner, 1793)

A local and uncommon species in Hampshire (Goater, 1974, 1992). It affects open country, where the larva feeds on various grasses (Poaceae) and other herbaceous plants.

■ vc10 Freshwater, 9.7.94 (Knill-Jones, 1995). **Presence in vc10 confirmed.**

■ vc11 Hurn, one in 1999, det. PHS (MJ); Lower Test Marshes NR (DHS, 1992).

■ vc12 Overton (AHD); Selborne, 1994, 28.7.99 (AEA).

0991 *Clepsis senecionana* (Hübner, 1819)

Recorded from the New Forest bogs, but not recently (Goater, 1974). It is almost certainly still present, the larva feeding on bog-myrtle *Myrica gale*.

[0992 *Clepsis rurinana* (Linnaeus, 1758)

The unsatisfactory old record given in Goater (1974) has never been confirmed.]

0993 *Clepsis spectrana* (Treitschke, 1830)

Common in marshy places in all three vice-counties. The larva lives in spun shoots of willowherb *Epilobium* spp., meadowsweet *Filipendula ulmaria* and other herbaceous plants.

■ vc10 Shanklin (JMC).

0994 *Clepsis consimilana* (Hübner, 1817)

Common in all three vice-counties, in woodland and gardens, especially those with privet hedges. The larva feeds on cultivated privet *Ligustrum ovalifolium*, ivy *Hedera helix* and other shrubs.

■ vc10 Freshwater, 8.8.97 (Knill-Jones, 1998b); Shanklin, 8.7.97 (JMC).

■ vc11 Hengistbury Head, 1997 (MJ).

0997 *Epichoristodes acerbella* (Walker, 1864)

■ vc11 One bred, 5.5.90, from a larva found crawling on the outside of a bag of South African apples purchased at Sainsburys Supermarket, Badger Farm, Winchester. Identity confirmed by M. Schaffer (BMNH) (RJBH). **New county record.**

0998 *Epiphyas postvittana* (Walker, 1863)

Male

10 mm

This Australian species, first reported in Britain in 1936 in Cornwall, has spread rapidly along the south coast and is now so abundant in S Hants and the Isle of Wight as to be a nuisance. It was first seen at Chandlers Ford in 1991 and is now common; it has extended its range recently into N Hants, whence all records are given below. Moths have been seen in every month of the year. The larva is polyphagous, but shows a preference for japonica *Euonymus japonicus*.

■ vc10 Freshwater, 19.9.97 (Knill-Jones, 1998b); Shanklin, 6.5, 13.8, 2.11, 10.11.95, 8.8.97; Osborne, 29.5.92, one at light; Osborne Beach, 13.9.93, one at light (JMC); Gurnard, 23.12.96, imago, det. JRL (DTB).

■ vc11 Hengistbury Head, abundant, 210 in 1999 (MJ).

■ vc12 Wildhern, nr Andover, 30.9.96, to house lights, 25.5.99 (DGG); Magdalen Hill Down, 22.9.94 and subsequently (PAB); South Wonston, 13.10.95, at m.v. light (PJSS); Oakley, 18.6.99 (DGG); Basingstoke, 8.10.95, one at m.v. light (AHD); Selborne, 21.8.94, 6.9.97, several in 1999 (AEA); Greywell, first recorded 15.10.00 (PB); Farnborough, May–October, 1993, 1994,

1995 (RWP), 22.8.97, two; regular in 2000 from 4.5 to 8.12, up to six per night (KBW). **New vc record.**

0999 *Adoxophyes orana* (Fischer von Röslerstamm, 1834)
This is another recent arrival in the country. It is a potential pest of apple orchards. So far, it has been seen only at Southsea (Goater, 1992).

1000 *Ptycholoma lecheana* (Linnaeus, 1758)
Widespread and fairly common in woodlands in the mainland vice-counties, and probably also in the Isle of Wight, though there are few records to support this contention.

▪ vc10 Freshwater, 30.5.95 (SAK-J); Yarmouth; Bouldnor; Parkhurst Forest (RJD).

1001 *Lozotaenioides formosanus* (Geyer, 1830)

First recorded in NW Surrey in 1945, near the border with Hampshire, this species is now widespread in pinewoods in the mainland vice-counties, and there are a few records from the Isle of Wight (Goater, 1974, 1992).

▪ vc10 St Catherine's Point, 30.6 and 1.7.95, at m.v. light (SRC, PC, PMP).

▪ vc11 Hurn, three in 1999 (MJ); St Ives, Ringwood, 1987 at m.v. light (JHC); Pennington, 21.7.95 (RC); Brockenhurst, few each year (JEC); Roydon Woods, 10.7.96, one at m.v. light (PRD, JRL); Burley New Inclosure, 1.7.99; Set Thorns Inclosure, 22.6.99; Dilton Meadows, 12.7.97, at m.v. light (DGG); Cadlands Estate, Beaulieu, 12.7.97, several at m.v. light (BG, JRL); Sparsholt College (AHD); Hilliers Arboretum, Ampfield, 21.7.98, one at m.v. light (TJN *et al.*); Chandlers Ford, few each year (BG); Bitterne, 17.6.97 (PAB); Locks Heath, two in 2000, first on 19.7.00 (PCa); Catisfield; Fareham; Titchfield Haven; West Walk (RJD); Widley, Portsdown (PMP); Milton Common, Southsea, 1998, at light in garden (IRT); Havant Thicket, 8.7.97, at m.v. light (JRL, IRT, *et al.*).

▪ vc12 Porton Down, Isle of Wight Woods, 15.7.95, at m.v. light (DGG); Magdalen Hill Down (PAB); South Wonston, 15.8.93, and subsequently, at m.v. light (PJSS); Wildhern, 20.7.98, at m.v. light (DGG); Overton; Oakley (AHD); Basing House, 19.7.96 (AMD); Pamber, 1994 (GJD); Selborne, 12.7 and 13.7.94, 14.7 and 19.7.96, 4.7.97, at light, conf. BG from photographs (AEA); Farnborough, ten in 1993, between June and August; eight in 1994, four in 1995 (RWP); Frith End, 13.7.96 (KW); Bentley Station Meadow, 1995 (PAB); Yateley Common, 30.6 and 2.7.94; Yateley, 21.7.96, three; Zebon Copse, 9.7.97 (AMD).

1002 *Lozotaenia forsterana* (Fabricius, 1781)
Widespread but not very common, in wooded gardens, hedgerows and the edges of woodland in the mainland vice-counties, with a few Isle of Wight records (Goater, 1974, 1992).

▪ vc11 Hengistbury Head, one in 1999, det. PHS (MJ); Brockenhurst, common (JEC); Roydon Woods, 10.7.96, one at m.v. light (PRD, JRL); Nutburn, North Baddesley,

1996; Sparsholt College (AHD); Chandlers Ford, annually in small numbers (BG); Allbrook, 1994 (ML); Bitterne, 1.6.94 and subsequently; Marwell Zoological Park, 24.6.94 (PAB); Soberton, 30.6.95, one at m.v. light; Southwick, 8.7.96, a few at m.v. light; Botley Wood, 4.7.95, a few at m.v. light (JRL); Hamble Common, 1996; Chilling Copse, 1999; Catisfield; Fareham, few at m.v. light in 1998; Creech Wood, Denmead; Wendleholme NR (RJD); Titchfield Haven NR; Widley, Portsdown (PMP).

▪ vc12 Magdalen Hill Down (PAB); South Wonston, 1993 and subsequently, at m.v. light (PJSS); Overton; Oakley; Mapledurwell Fen; Bramley Frith NR; Bartley Heath NR (AHD); Pamber, 1994 (GJD); Selborne, 1993, 1994 (AEA); Yateley Common, 26.3.93, larvae on ivy (AMD, JRL); Farnborough, 16.6.95, two at light (RWP), 18.6.00, one (KBW).

1006 *Epagoge grotiana* (Fabricius, 1781)
Widespread in woodland in the mainland vice-counties; probably under-recorded on the Isle of Wight.

▪ vc10 Cranmore, 10.7.97 (Knill-Jones, 1998b). First recent record for the Isle of Wight.

1007 *Capua vulgana* (Frölich, 1828)
A widely distributed but not particularly common species in woodland in the three vice-counties (Goater, 1974, 1992).

▪ vc10 Tennyson Down, 18.5.92, one (JRL, DHS, PHS); Brighstone Forest; Apes Down (RJD).

▪ vc11 Lower Test Marshes NR (DHS, 1993); Chandlers Ford, occasional at light, first on 23.5.93 (BG); Fareham; Creech Wood, Denmead; Portsdown; Oxenbourne Down (RJD); Creech Wood, Denmead, 16.5.97, one at m.v. light (JRL).

1010 *Ditula angustiorana* (Haworth, 1811)
Common to very common in all three vice-counties. The larva is polyphagous on many plants, including yew and rhododendron, and sometimes does superficial damage to ripening fruits in orchards.

1011 *Pseudargyrotoza conwagana* (Fabricius, 1775)
Common amongst ash and privet in all three vice-counties. The larva feeds in the fruits of these plants.

▪ vc8 Martin Down, 24.8.90 (MFVC, S. Nash).

1012 *Sparganothis pilleriana* ([Denis & Schiffermüller], 1775)
Very local in bogs in the New Forest and in coastal marshes (Goater, 1974, 1992). There is no record from N Hants.

▪ vc10 Freshwater, 13.8.96, one at m.v. light (SAK-J).

▪ vc11 Hincheslea Bog, 27.7.96, c.18 during afternoon; Cranes Moor, 27.7.96, c.20 at light in bog (AHD); Strodgemoor Bottom, 23.7.97; Vales Moor, 23.7.97; Brockenhurst (JEC).

1015 *Eulia ministrana* (Linnaeus, 1758)
Common and widespread in the mainland vice-counties, especially in wooded areas (JRL).

▪ vc8 Martin Down, 29.4.90 (S. Nash).

▪ vc10 Apes Down (RJD).

Species of *Cnephasia* are difficult to determine with certainty unless dissected, and are hence under-recorded in the county. Three species, *C. stephensiana* (Doubleday), *C. asseclana* ([Denis & Schiffermüller]) and *C. incertana* (Treitschke) are undoubtedly common and widespread, but others may have been overlooked amongst them.

1016 *Cnephasia longana* (Haworth, 1811)
Confined to coastal areas and to the chalk downs, where it is locally common (Goater, 1974, 1992).
■ vc11 Hengistbury Head, one in 1999, det. PHS (MJ); Sparsholt College (AHD); Portsdown (RJD); Great Salterns NR, Portsmouth (JRL); Milton Common, Southsea, 3.7.00, one at m.v. light (IRT); Waterlooville, 1996–2000 (RJM).
■ vc12 Brighton Hill, Basingstoke; Bramley Frith NR (AHD); Selborne, three during August 2000 (AEA).

1018 *Cnephasia communana* (Herrich-Schäffer, 1851)
Recorded from all three vice-counties (Goater, 1974, 1992), but uncommon or overlooked.
■ vc11 Soberton, 30.6.95, three at m.v. light (JRL); Botley Wood; Fareham; Swanwick NR; Curbridge NR (RJD).
■ vc12 Bartley Heath NR, 5.96, one at m.v. light (AHD); Selborne, 20.6.94; eight in 1995 (AEA); Farnborough, 23.5 and 30.5.95, at m.v. light, det. JRL (RWP).

1019 *Cnephasia conspersana* Douglas, 1846
Found mainly on coastal cliffs and chalk downs. A scarce species in the county (Goater, 1974, 1992).
■ vc10 Culver Cliff, 16.8.78, genit det. (RJD).
■ vc11 Chilling Copse, 1996, genitalia det. (RJD).

1020 *Cnephasia stephensiana* (Doubleday, 1849)
Widespread and common in all three vice-counties.

1021 *Cnephasia asseclana* ([Denis & Schiffermüller], 1775)
= *interjectana* (Haworth, 1811)
Very common in the mainland vice-counties, and evidently widespread also on the Isle of Wight (Goater, 1974, 1992).
■ vc8 Martin Down, 8.6.92, bred from larva on ragwort *Senecio jacobaea* (JRL, RMP).
■ vc10 Bouldnor (RJD).

1022 *Cnephasia pasuiana* (Hübner, 1799)
Few records have been received recently. It has been recorded in the past from all three vice-counties, but chiefly from the mainland.
■ vc11 Hamble Common, 1996, genitalia det. (RJD).

1023 *Cnephasia genitalana* Pierce & Metcalfe, 1915
Almost certainly overlooked. Specimens can only be determined with certainty by dissection. Hitherto, the only other record for the county was from Southsea (Goater, 1992).
■ vc11 Winchester, 28.7.90, at m.v. light in garden; subsequent genitalic examination of locally-caught *Cnephasia* species showed this to be the second

commonest of the small species in the genus, recorded between 3 and 21 August (Sterling, 1994).

1024 *Cnephasia incertana* (Treitschke, 1835)
Common and widespread in the mainland vice-counties, and probably also on the Isle of Wight, though positive records are lacking.
■ vc10 Bouldnor; Ventnor (RJD).
■ vc11 Hengistbury Head, 1997, 1999, det PHS (MJ).

1025 *Tortricodes alternella* ([Denis & Schiffermüller], 1775)
Common in oak woodland in all three vice-counties. The moth is often seen flying by day in early spring sunshine, and also comes to light.
■ vc11 Hengistbury Head, 1998, common (MJ).

1027 *Neosphaleroptera nubilana* (Hübner, 1799)
The few records of this species in the area are given in Goater (1974, 1992).
■ vc11 Farlington Marshes NR, 29.4.97, larvae on hawthorn, moth bred (JRL, IRT).

1029 *Eana osseana* (Scopoli, 1763)
Occasional on heaths and downs in all three vice-counties (Goater, 1974, 1992).
■ vc11 Chandlers Ford, 4.8.94, specimen in coll. (BG); Locks Heath, 8.7.00 (PCa).
■ vc12 South Wonston, 19.7.94, at m.v. light (PJSS); Oakley (AHD); Selborne, 1993 (AEA).

1030 *Eana incanana* (Stephens, 1852)
Recorded from all three vice-counties, but not recently from the Isle of Wight (Goater, 1974, 1992). The larva lives in the flowers and ripening fruits of bluebell *Hyacinthoides non-scripta* and also ox-eye daisy *Leucanthemum vulgare*.
■ vc11 Chandlers Ford, from 11.7.97, several at m.v. light (BG).
■ vc12 Wildhern, 25.7.98 (DGG); Bramley Frith NR (AHD); Selborne, 1996, at light, det. K. Tuck (BMNH) (AEA).

1032 *Aleimma loeflingiana* (Linnaeus, 1758)
Very common in oak woodland, or amongst field maple *Acer campestre* in the mainland vice-counties, and almost certainly under-recorded from the Isle of Wight (Goater, 1974, 1992).

1033 *Tortrix viridana* (Linnaeus, 1758)
Formerly abundant in oakwoods throughout the three vice-counties, though numbers used to fluctuate from year to year. At times, the larvae would assume pest proportions and then form a staple diet of insectivorous birds feeding their young, but this phenomenon has rarely been noticed in recent years.
■ vc11 Hengistbury Head, 1997 (MJ).

1034 *Spatalistis bifasciana* (Hübner, 1787)
A rare or overlooked species, reported only from the mainland vice-counties (Goater, 1974, 1992). The larva

lives in the fruits of buckthorn *Rhamnus cathartica*, alder buckthorn *Frangula alnus* and dogwood *Cornus sanguinea*.
- vc10 Parkhurst Forest, 6.7.72 (RJD). **New vc record.**
- vc11 Chandlers Ford, 12.6.00, one at m.v. light (BE).
- vc12 Bramley Frith Wood, 30.6 and 2.7.95, three at m.v. light (AHD).

1035 *Acleris (Croesia) bergmanniana* (Linnaeus, 1758)
Locally frequent in all three vice-counties (Goater, 1974, 1992), along hedgerows and in scrub with roses *Rosa* spp.
- vc11 Lower Test Marshes NR (DHS, 1994); Sparsholt College (AHD); Meonstoke, 22.5.93, one (JRL); Titchfield Haven; Havant Thicket (RJD).
- vc12 Chilbolton, hedgerow by old airfield, 17.6.97, several netted late evening (BG); Magdalen Hill Down (PAB); Oakley (AHD); Selborne, 1994 and 1995 (AEA); Bentley Station Meadow (PAB).

1036 *Acleris (Croesia) forsskaleana* (Linnaeus, 1758)
Common to abundant amongst sycamore and field maple. Recent records from the Isle of Wight are given below.
- vc10 St Catherine's Point, 30.6 and 1.7.95, at m.v. light (SRC, PC, PMP); Ventnor; Priory Bay (RJD); Bembridge, 1.8.97 (Knill-Jones, 1998b).

1037 *Acleris (Croesia) holmiana* (Linnaeus, 1758)

10 mm

Recorded in all three vice-counties (Goater, 1974, 1992), but usually as single specimens or in very small numbers. The larva feeds in spun leaves of various Rosaceae, especially hawthorn and blackthorn.
- vc11 Lepe Country Park, 14.8.96 (PMP); Sparsholt College (AHD); Chandlers Ford, 26.7.91, specimen in coll. (BG); St Cross, 10.9.00, one at m.v. light, conf. BG (TWa); Catisfield; Titchfield Haven (RJD); Waterlooville, 1996–2000 (RJM); Sandy Point NR, Hayling Island, 14.7.92, two at m.v. light (JRL).
- vc12 Magdalen Hill Down (PAB); South Wonston, 15.7.97, at m.v. light (PJSS); Oakley; Mapledurwell Fen (AHD); Bramley Depot, Pamber, 1994 (GJD); Selborne, 1993, 8.7.94, 6.7.97 (AEA); Rye Common, 26.7.96 (AMD); Frith End, 17.8.96 (KW).

1038 *Acleris laterana* (Fabricius, 1794)
Widespread and fairly common in all three vice-counties.
- vc8 Martin Down, 24.8.90 (MFVC, S. Nash).
- vc10 Freshwater, 18.7.97 (Knill-Jones, 1998b).

1039 *Acleris comariana* (Lienig & Zeller, 1846)
Very local, but often abundant where it occurs, as at Emer Bog (Goater, 1974, 1992). The main foodplant, marsh cinquefoil *Potentilla palustris* is also local; the moth should be sought where it is common, e.g. Shortheath Common, N Hants. Elsewhere, when the larva is on strawberry *Fragaria* spp., the locality is more easily overlooked.

- vc10 Freshwater, 15.7.97 (Knill-Jones, 1998b), 1.7.00 (SAK-J).
- vc11 Sparsholt College (AHD); Catisfield; Gosport; Rowner Wild Grounds; Oxenbourne Down (RJD).

1041 *Acleris sparsana* ([Denis & Schiffermüller], 1775)
Common in beech woodland in all three vice-counties.
- vc10 Freshwater, 30.9 and 22.11.94, 25.9.97 (SAK-J).
- vc11 Hilsea, 5.6.92, one larva on sycamore (DJLA, AME, JRL).

1042 *Acleris rhombana* ([Denis & Schiffermüller], 1775)
Widespread and common in all three vice-counties.
- vc8 Martin Down, 24.8.90 (MFVC, S. Nash).
- vc10 Tennyson Down, 18.5.92, larvae on cultivated apple *Malus domestica*, moth bred (JRL, DHS, PHS).

1043 *Acleris aspersana* (Hübner, 1817)
Mainly associated with chalk downland in the south of England, but also found in other habitats such as marshes. Recorded from all three vice-counties (Goater, 1974, 1992).
- vc8 Martin Down, 24.8.90 (MFVC, S. Nash), 8.6.92, larva on salad burnet *Poterium sanguisorba* (JRL, RMP).
- vc10 Freshwater Bay Downs, 21.7.97 (Knill-Jones, 1998b).
- vc11 Merrietown Heath, 2.6.95, larvae on meadowsweet *Filipendula ulmaria* (PHS); Sparsholt College (AHD); Chandlers Ford, 12.8.91, 6.7.94 (BG); Oxenbourne Down (RJD).
- vc12 Porton Down, 24.7.94, many (BG, JRL); Winnall Moors NR (DHS); Mapledurwell Fen (AHD); Selborne, 12.7.96, at light, conf. JRL (AEA); Noar Hill (RJD); Yateley Common, 8.8.94, one (AMD).

1044 *Acleris ferrugana* ([Denis & Schiffermüller], 1775)
This and the next species are difficult to distinguish without recourse to dissection, and both are therefore under-recorded. The present species is associated with deciduous oaks, while the larva of *A. notana* (Donovan) feeds on birch. The records given in Goater (1992) and below are considered to be trustworthy, while those in Goater (1974) should be treated with a little suspicion.
- vc11 Denny Wood (RJD); Nutburn, North Baddesley, 11.11.95, two at m.v. light; Sparsholt College (AHD); Locks Heath, five in 2000, first on 8.3.00, genitalia det. (PCa); Botley Wood; Segensworth; Hook-with-Warsash, 1996; Fareham, all genitalia det.; Wickham Common; The Moors NR, Bishop's Waltham; Rowner Wild Grounds (RJD); Sandy Point NR, Hayling Island, 14.7.92, several at m.v. light, genitalia det. (JRL).
- vc12 Wildhern, nr Andover, 18.9.97, genitalia det. (DGG); Bramley Frith NR (AHD); Pamber, 1994, genitalia det. (GJD).

1045 *Acleris notana* (Donovan, 1806)
Probably common wherever birch is established.
- vc10 Freshwater, 7.11 and 25.11.97, 6.10.98 (SAK-J). **Presence in vc10 confirmed.**

■ vc11 Hurn, eight in 1999, det. PHS (MJ); Merrietown Heath, 20.10.98, several at m.v. light; 9.10.99, larvae on *Betula pendula*; Hengistbury Head, 9.9.00, two at m.v. light (PHS); Roydon Woods, 4.10.98, a few vacated spinnings on birch Denny Wood (RJD, JRL); Chandlers Ford, common (BG); Hamble Common; Wickham Common, 1998, genitalia det. (RJD).

■ vc12 Wildhern, nr Andover, 6.10.97, genitalia det.; Fleet Pond, 7.10.97, one at m.v. light, genitalia det. (DGG); Fleet, Ancells Farm NR, larvae on birch, two bred; Farnborough, 3.11.94, two in 1995 (RWP).

1046 *Acleris shepherdana* (Stephens, 1852)

Very local in marshes and water meadows; recorded from all three vice-counties in such habitat (Goater, 1974, 1992).

■ vc11 Titchfield Haven, 17.8.71 (RJD).

■ vc12 Winnall Moors NR (DHS), bred from meadowsweet *Filipendula ulmaria* (BG).

1047 *Acleris schalleriana* (Linnaeus, 1761)

Local (Goater, 1974, 1992). On the chalk, the larva is found mainly on wayfaring-tree *Viburnum lantana*, and in the New Forest and elsewhere, it is on guelder-rose *V. opulus.*

■ vc10 Newtown, 18.9.97, one spinning on guelder-rose *V. opulus* (AME, JRL).

■ vc11 Sparsholt College (AHD); Crab Wood, 20.9.97, vacated spinnings on wayfaring-tree *V. lantana*; Upper Hamble Country Park, 7.10.92, one vacated spinning on *V. opulus*; Hookheath Meadows NR, Southwick, 4.8.92, several larvae on *V. opulus* (JRL, *et al.*); Farcham (RJD), 14.8.97, a few larval spinnings on *V. lantana*; Clanfield, 4.10.97, a few spinnings on *V. lantana.*

■ vc12 Oakley (AHD); Bramdean Common, 8.10.96, one vacated spinning on *V. lantana* (AME, JRL, IRT); Selborne, 1993, 1994 (AEA); Farnborough, 21.11.95, det. JRL (RWP); Ashford Hangers NR, 21.5.93, larvae on *V. lantana* (JRL).

1048 *Acleris variegana* ([Denis & Schiffermüller], 1775)

10 mm

Very common in all three vice-counties. The larva is polyphagous, but is found most often on rose *Rosa* spp. and blackthorn *Prunus spinosa.*

■ vc8 Martin Down, 24.8.90 (MFVC, S. Nash).

■ vc10 Freshwater, 21.7.97 (Knill-Jones, 1998b); Shanklin (JMC); Redcliff (RJD).

■ vc11 Hengistbury Head, 1997, 1999, fairly common (MJ).

1050 *Acleris boscana* (Fabricius, 1794)

Very local on elm *Ulmus* spp. (Goater, 1974, 1992). Larvae of the summer brood are much commoner than those of the spring brood.

■ vc10 Newtown, 18.9.97, a few vacated spinnings on elm *U. procera* (AME, JRL).

■ vc11 Lower Test Marshes NR (DHS, 1992); Hook Valley NR, 2.6.98, deserted spinnings; Portchester Castle (RJD); Lower Titchfield Haven NR, 21.10.96, a few vacated spinnings; Fareham, 17.9.97, several vacated spinnings; Alver Valley NR, Gosport, 22.9.97, many vacated spinnings; Great Salterns NR, Portsmouth (JRL *et al.*).

■ vc12 Wildhern, nr Andover, 6.11.96, disturbed by day, 18.9.98 (DGG).

■ vc22 Mortimer West End, 2000, first record (GJD).

1051 *Acleris logiana* (Clerck, 1759)

The discovery of this species in Hampshire in 1992 (Langmaid, 1993b) was quite extraordinary. Elsewhere in Britain, it is known only from the Highlands of Scotland. It is unlikely to have been overlooked, and appears to be a new arrival which is beginning to spread.

■ vc10 Binstead, 1.97, one at m.v. light (Warne, 1998, Knill-Jones, 1998c). **New vc record.**

■ vc11 Hurn, 19.2.99, det. PHS, and another on 1.8.00 (MJ); Chandlers Ford, 6.3.96, one at m.v. light (BG); Botley Wood, 30.9.91, larvae collected from birch produced one specimen which was found dead in its container in March, 1992; two bred in October, 1992 from birch spinnings coll. 20.9.92 (Langmaid, *ibid.*), 17.9.94, one larva, moth bred (JRL); Havant Thicket, 2.4.95, one at rest on a tree trunk (JRL, M.S. Parsons). **New county record.**

1052 *Acleris umbrana* (Hübner, 1799)

In the past, this scarce and elusive species has been knocked out of old hawthorns in the New Forest (Goater, 1974), but nothing has been heard of it since the 1930s.

1053 *Acleris hastiana* (Linnaeus, 1758)

The larvae have been reported from many localities in the three vice-counties (Goater, 1974, 1992) on sallow *Salix cinerea*, especially small bushes; more occasionally the moth is taken at light.

■ vc11 Hengistbury Head, 1997, det. PHS (MJ); Hurn, three in 1999, det. PHS (MJ); Brockenhurst (JEC); Roydon Woods, 10.7.96, one at m.v. light (PRD, JRL); Lower Test Marshes NR (DHS, 1992); Sparsholt College (AHD); Chandlers Ford, 22.11.91, 4.2.92 (BG); Hook shore, 8.5.98, larva, moth bred; Botley Wood; Catisfield; Fareham, 5.6.98, one at m.v. light; Fort Fareham; Titchfield Haven (RJD); Milton Common, Southsea, 18.7.00, one at m.v. light (IRT); Havant Thicket, 8.7.97, at m.v. light (JRL, IRT, *et al.*); Sandy Point NR, Hayling Island (RJD).

■ vc12 Yateley Common, occasional (AMD).

1054 *Acleris cristana* ([Denis & Schiffermüller], 1775)

The classic way to obtain this species is to stumble, crouching, through thickets of blackthorn *Prunus spinosa* in autumn, net in one hand, heavy cudgel in the other, smiting the stems and netting the moths, or attempting to do so, as they fly off. The moth can still be found in this manner, but is more usually reported at light, in small numbers and mainly after hibernation. In the old days (Goater, 1974), the New Forest was a favourite locality which produced many interesting forms.

■ vc10 Freshwater, 30.1.93, 31.3.93, 29.7.97 (SAK-J); Yarmouth; Ventnor (RJD).

■ vc11 St Ives, Ringwood, 1987, at m.v. light (JHC); Lower Test Marshes NR (PHS, 1994); Sparsholt College (AHD); Kings Somborne, 3.2.95 (TJN); Chandlers Ford, occasional at m.v. light after hibernation (BG); Botley Wood; Catisfield; Fareham; West Walk; Cherque; Oxenbourne Down (RJD); Waterlooville, 1996–2000 (RJM); Catherington Down, 31.5.95, one larva on blackthorn, moth bred (JRL).

■ vc12 Wildhern, nr Andover, 29.9.97 (DGG); Harewood Forest (RJD); South Wonston, 30.4.95, 23.3.96, at m.v. light (PJSS); Bartley Heath NR (AHD); Pamber, 1994 (GJD); Selborne, 1993, 1997, fairly variable, occasional at light, but only once in autumn, 30.11.99, conf. JRL from photographs (AEA); Yateley Common, 7.2.94, one (AMD); Farnborough, 5.2.95, 26.8.95, at light (RWP).

1055 *Acleris hyemana* (Haworth, 1811)
This species is associated with heathers *Calluna*, *Erica* spp., and is most frequent in the New Forest. After hibernation, the moths are sometimes seen in numbers flying in the afternoon sunshine of early springtime. There is one record from the Isle of Wight (Goater, 1992) and a few, from outside the New Forest, which suggest the species may, on occasion, adapt to cultivated heathers (Goater, 1974).

■ vc12 Farnborough, 10.11.94 (RWP).

1057 *Acleris rufana* ([Denis & Schiffermüller], 1775)
This species, common in bogs in north Britain, is rare in the south, and the few Hampshire records are from the New Forest, where it is undoubtedly resident. There is one old record from the Isle of Wight (Goater, 1974).

■ vc11 Dockens Water, Ringwood, 18.4.92, one by day (JRL, DHS); Matley Bog, 14.10.89, one bred from a larva on bog-myrtle *Myrica gale* collected in September (RJBH).

1058 *Acleris lorquiniana* (Duponchel, 1835)
The outlying colony of this predominantly fenland species still exists at Browndown, where the larva may be found on purple-loosestrife *Lythrum salicaria*, and there is an old record from the Isle of Wight (Goater, 1974, 1992).

■ vc11 Titchfield Haven, 1978, two at m.v. light by J. Chadd, conf. RJD.

1061 *Acleris literana* (Linnaeus, 1758)
Two classic localities for this beautiful species have been Bouldnor on the Isle of Wight, worked extensively by the late L.T. Ford, and the New Forest, whence Sheldon named many new forms (Goater, 1974). Since those days, specimens have been taken in small numbers, mainly in S Hants and usually at light after hibernation. The larva feeds on oak.

■ vc10 Cranmore, 21.4.93, two (SAK-J); Binstead, 14.5.97, at m.v. light (Warne, 1998).

■ vc11 St Ives, Ringwood, 1987, at m.v. light (JHC); Holmsley Inclosure, 18.4.1987 (JHC); Holmsley, 8.8.92,

one beaten from oak (RJBH); Chandlers Ford, 4.4.74, 1.4.95, 23.8.97, 17.4.99, singles at m.v. light (BG); Fareham, 21.7.93, one at m.v. light (RJD).

■ vc12 Frith End, 20.4.96 (KW); Selborne, 8.4 and 9.4.99, 25.2.00, single specimens at m.v. light, conf. BG (AEA).

1062 *Acleris emargana* (Fabricius, 1775)
Widespread but apparently less common nowadays, in marshy places amongst sallows. The following may be added to the records given in Goater (1974, 1992).

■ vc10 Freshwater, 3.9.98; Fort Victoria, 3.8.95, common (SAK-J).

■ vc11 Hurn, four in 1999 (MJ); Brockenhurst (JEC); Beaulieu, 1995 (BI-J); Lower Test Marshes NR (DHS, 1992), 24.8.99; Testwood Park, 17.10.99; Hamble, 24.9.99 (PAB); Chandlers Ford, 18.9.94 (BG); Moorgreen Meadows, 22.9.85 (PAB); Curbridge NR, 10.10.98, one (JRL); Hamble Common, 1996; Botley Wood; Place Wood; Wickham Common, 1999; The Moors NR, Bishop's Waltham (RJD).

■ vc12 Bramley Frith NR; Bartley Heath NR (AHD); Fleet Pond LNR, 7.10.97, one at m.v. light (DGG); Selborne, 12.9.95, 8.9.96, singletons at light (AEA); Bentley Station Meadow, 1995 (PAB).

1013 *Olindia schumacherana* (Fabricius, 1787)
On the whole an uncommon and elusive species. There are a few mainland records (Goater, 1974, 1992) but none from the Isle of Wight. It seems to favour moist, shady woodland wherein the larva feeds on lesser celandine *Ranunculus ficaria*, sometimes on dog's mercury *Mercurialis perennis*.

■ vc11 Marwell Zoological Park, 13.6.97, at m.v. light (PAB); Soberton, 30.6.95, one at m.v. light; Botley Wood, 17.6.93, one (JRL); Waterlooville, 1996–2000, rather frequent (RJM).

■ vc12 Chilbolton, 22.6.92, one (JRL, DHS); Wildhern, nr Andover, 17.6.97, at dusk Harewood Forest, 23.6.00, at least eight seen flying by day (DGG); Pamber, 1995 (GJD); Pamber Forest, 19.7.97, one at m.v. light (MCH); Selborne, 22.6.92, male by day, and occasional subsequently at m.v. light in garden (AEA); Noar Hill NR, 11.7.95 (AMJ).

1014 *Isotrias rectifasciana* (Haworth, 1811)
A species of hedgerows and scrub, especially amongst hawthorn scrub on downland. It is reported from scattered localities in the mainland vice-counties, but not recently from the Isle of Wight (Goater, 1974, 1992).

■ vc11 Sparsholt College (AHD); Hook-with-Warsash, 1996; Portsdown (RJD); Waterlooville, 1996–2000 (RJM).

■ vc12 Harewood Forest (RJD); South Wonston, 1.7.94, at m.v. light (PJSS); Selborne, 2.7, 6.7 and 14.7.96, 10.6.97, at light, det. JRL from photographs (AEA); Noar Hill NR, 12.7.95 (AMJ).

1063 *Celypha striana* ([Denis & Schiffermüller], 1775)
Widespread and frequent in all three vice-counties (Goater, 1974, 1992). The larva lives in the roots of dandelion *Taraxacum* spp.

■ vc10 St Catherine's Point, 30.6 and 1.7.95, at m.v. light (SRC, PC, PMP); Queens Bower (JMC).
■ vc11 Hengistbury Head, 1997, det. PHS (MJ).

1064 *Celypha rosaceana* (Schläger, 1847)

Recorded from all three vice-counties (Goater, 1974, 1992) but local and by no means common. The larva lives in roots of dandelion and sow-thistle *Sonchus* spp.
■ vc10 Freshwater, 30.8.99 (SAK-J); Priory Bay (RJD).
■ vc11 Cadlands Estate, Beaulieu, 12.7.97, one at m.v. light (BG, JRL); Sparsholt College (AHD); Milton Common, Southsea, 1.8.00, one at m.v. light (IRT); Soberton, 30.6.95, one at m.v. light; Sandy Point NR, Hayling Island, 18.8.95, one at m.v. light (JRL); Sinah Common (RJD).
■ vc12 Overton; Oakley (AHD); Selborne, 1.7.1993 (AEA); Rye Common, 26.7.96 (AMD).

1067 *Celypha (Olethreutes) cespitana* (Hübner, 1817)

Local (Goater, 1974, 1992). The records indicate a preference for chalk downland and coastal areas. The authors have no report of the early stages having been found in the three vice-counties.
■ vc10 Shanklin (JMC).
■ vc11 Old Winchester Hill; Queen Elizabeth Country Park, 1999 (RJD).
■ vc12 Porton Down, 24.7.94, a few by day (BG, JRL).

1076 *Celypha (Olethreutes) lacunana* ([Denis & Schiffermüller], 1775)

Extremely abundant in all parts of the three vice-counties, and probably the commonest tortricid in Hampshire and the Isle of Wight. There are innumerable records.

1068 *Celypha (Olethreutes) rivulana* (Scopoli, 1763)

Very local, and found commonly only on the downland at Leckford (Goater, 1974, 1992). The larva is polyphagous on downland herbs.
■ vc12 Porton Down, 24.7.94, several by day (BG, JRL).

1069 *Celypha (Olethreutes) aurofasciana* (Haworth, 1811)

Old records of the scarce species are given in Goater (1974) from the Isle of Wight and S Hants. Nothing has been heard of it since. The larva is stated (Bradley *et al.*, 1979) to live in silken galleries amongst mosses growing on old, rotting bark of trees.

1080 *Olethreutes arcuella* (Clerck, 1759)

A local and uncommon woodland species which is perhaps overlooked. The moth is diurnal and difficult to follow in flight; occasionally it comes to light.
■ vc10 Osborne, 25.6.94; Brading Chalk Pit, 12.7.92 (JMC). **New vc record.**
■ vc11 Newlands Copse, 25.5.97, seen by day (PAB); Roydon Woods, 19.6.94, a number flying by day (RJBH); Studley Wood, Bramshaw, 8.7.98, one at m.v. light (NB).
■ vc12 Harewood Forest, Burnt Lodge Copse, 7.6.97, three flying around low bramble by day (DGG); Pamber Forest (RJD).

1073 *Olethreutes schulziana* (Fabricius, 1777)

Very local and usually uncommon on the heaths of the New Forest and NE Hampshire (Goater, 1974, 1992).
■ vc12 Shortheath Common, 13.8.97, two (AMD); 100+ there on 7.8.99 (RJH, JRL).

1075 *Olethreutes olivana* (Treitschke, 1830)

The only records of this species in the area are given in Goater (1974, 1983, 1992). Possibly, it is overlooked. According to Bradley *et al.* (1979), the moth is found in boggy places, and perhaps that is where it should be sought in Hampshire.

1079 *Piniphila (Olethreutes) bifasciana* (Haworth, 1811)

Locally common in pinewoods, especially in S Hants (Goater, 1974, 1992). The larva feeds among the flowers of pines *Pinus sylvestris* and also *P. pinaster*, a species that is locally common along the Hampshire coast.
■ vc11 Roydon Woods, 10.7.96, a few at m.v. light (PRD, JRL); Cadlands Estate, Beaulieu, 12.7.97, a few at m.v. light (BG, JRL); Soberton, 30.6.95, one at m.v. light (JRL); Catisfield; Fareham; West Walk (RJD).
■ vc12 Conford Moor, 21.6.95, one (JRL, RMP); Oakley (AHD); Selborne, occasional at m.v. light from 1993 (AEA); Farnborough, 20.6.94 (RWP).

1082 *Hedya pruniana* (Hübner, 1799)

Common amongst blackthorn in all three vice-counties. However, there are rather few published records from the Isle of Wight, and recent ones are listed below.
■ vc8 Martin Down, 8.6.92 (JRL, RMP).
■ vc10 Freshwater, 2.8.00, at m.v. light (SAK-J); Headon Warren; Totland Bay; Yarmouth; Apes Down; Chale; Steephill undercliff; Ventnor undercliff; Firestone Copse (RJD); Five Houses, Shanklin; Alverstone, (JMC); Watchingwell (DTB).

1083 *Hedya nubiferana* (Haworth, 1811)
= *dimidioalba* (Retzius, 1783)

Common and widespread in the two mainland vice-counties, though there seem to be few records from the Isle of Wight (Goater, 1974, 1992).
■ vc11 Hengistbury Head, 1999, det. PHS (MJ).

1084 *Hedya ochroleucana* (Frölich, 1828)

Widespread and fairly common amongst wild rose *Rosa* spp. in the mainland vice-counties. However, we can find no record from the Isle of Wight since Goater (1974).
■ vc11 Lower Test Marshes NR (DHS, 1993); Sparsholt College (AHD); Hilliers Arboretum, Ampfield, 1998 (NB, TJN); Chandlers Ford, 1.7.91, 2.7.92, 19.6.94 (BG); Old Winchester Hill NNR, 23.7.97, a few at m.v.

light (RJD, JRL); Titchfield Haven; West Walk; Creech Wood, Denmead; Oxenbourne Down (RJD); Soberton, 30.6.95, a few at m.v. light; Hookheath Meadows NR, Southwick, 9.6.92, one; Great Salterns NR, Portsmouth (JRL).
■ vc12 Chilbolton, 22.6.92, one (JRL, DHS); Wildhern, 15.7.98 (DGG); Bartley Heath NR, 1996 (AHD); Selborne, 1993, 1994 (AEA); Noar Hill, 25.6.93 (AMJ); Flats Road, Yateley, 17.6.97 (AMD).

1086 *Hedya salicella* (Linnaeus, 1758)
Local in damp areas where the foodplants, sallows and willows, occur. It is widespread in the mainland vice-counties, but there are few records from the Isle of Wight (Goater, 1974, 1992).
■ vc10 Cranmore, 1.7 and 2.7.93 (SAK-J).
■ vc11 Hurn, two in 1999 (MJ); Merrietown Heath, 18.6.99, a few at m.v. light (PHS); Cadlands Estate, Beaulieu, 12.7.97, one at m.v. light (BG, JRL); Lower Test Marshes NR, 1993 (DHS); Sparsholt College (AHD); Chandlers Ford, 11.7.94 (BG); Wickham Common, 1999 (RJD); Botley Wood, 12.7.94, a few at m.v. light; Browndown, 5.7.97, one at m.v. light; Southsea, 7.7.93, one at m.v. light (JRL *et al.*).
■ vc12 Oakley; Bramley Frith NR; Bartley Heath NR, 1996 (AHD); Pamber, 1995 (GJD); Selborne, 1993, 15.7.97 (AEA); Odiham Common, 11.7.97; Rye Common, 5.8.96, five; Hawley Meadows NR, 23.7.96, two; Hazeley Heath, 13.8.96, one; Yateley Common, 8.7.94, one, 3.8.96, two (AMD).

[1085 *Metendothenia (Hedya) atropunctana* (Zetterstedt, 1840)
The record given in Goater (1974) is still in need of confirmation.]

1087 *Orthotaenia undulana* ([Denis & Schiffermüller], 1775)
Widespread in the mainland vice-counties, though probably overlooked. There is no record from the Isle of Wight since Goater (1974).
■ vc8 Martin Down (RJD).
■ vc11 Hengistbury Head, 1997, det. PHS (MJ); Hurn, two in 1999 det. PHS (MJ); Brockenhurst (JEC); Roydon Woods, 10.7.96, a few at m.v. light (PRD, JRL); Hamble Common; Hook-with-Warsash, 1996; Chilling Copse; Titchfield Haven; Hill Head; Wickham Common, 1999; Curbridge NR (RJD); Browndown, 2.5.92, a few larvae on *Betula*, moths bred (JRL, IRT); Sandy Point, Hayling Island, 1999 (RJD).
■ vc12 Bramley Frith NR (AHD).

1088 *Pseudosciaphila branderiana* (Linnaeus, 1758)
Very locally frequent in the few aspen *Populus tremula* woods, seldom straying away from them (Goater, 1974, 1992).
■ vc12 Bartley Heath NR, 1.6.95, one larva, moth bred (AHD).

1089 *Apotomis semifasciana* (Haworth, 1811)
Very local (Goater, 1974, 1992) along damp woodland rides and similar localities where there is an abundance of sallow *Salix* spp. It has been found commonly only in one of the rides in Botley Wood.
■ vc10 Cranmore, 7.7.99 (Knill-Jones, 2000).
■ vc11 Botley Wood, 12.7.94, seen commonly (JRL), and again on 4.7.95 (BG, JRL).

1092 *Apotomis turbidana* (Hübner, 1825)
Common amongst birch *Betula* spp. in the two mainland vice-counties, but only one Isle of Wight record has been received since Goater (1974).
■ vc10 Cranmore, 30.6.93 (SAK-J).

1093 *Apotomis betuletana* (Haworth, 1811)
Common and widespread amongst birch *Betula* spp. in the two mainland vice-counties (JRL).
■ vc10 Cranmore, 13.8.97 (Knill-Jones, 1998b).

1094 *Apotomis capreana* (Hübner, 1817)
Local and rather uncommon in the mainland vice-counties; only one old record from the Isle of Wight (Goater, 1974). The larva feed on sallow *Salix* spp.
■ vc11 Merrietown Heath, 18.6.99, one at m.v. light (PHS); Wickham Common, 1996 (RJD); Bishops Waltham, 18.8.93, a few at m.v. light; Creech Wood, Denmead, 22.8.97, a few at m.v. light; Botley Wood, 12.7.94, a few at m.v. light; West Walk, Wickham, 25.8.95; Southsea, 26.6.95, one at m.v. light; Havant Thicket, 28.6.95, 8.7.98, at m.v. light (JRL).
■ vc12 Cow Down Copse, Oakley, 10.7.99; Bramley Frith NR (AHD); Selborne, 24.7.94, 4.7.95, two, at m.v. light, 19.8 and 1.9.96, 5.8, 6.8 and 7.8.97 (AEA); Rye Common, 5.8.96, three; Yateley Common, fairly common; Hazeley Heath, 5.7.97 (AMD).

1095 *Apotomis sororculana* (Zetterstedt, 1839)
There have been a very few records of this species in the two mainland vice-counties, and none from the Isle of Wight (Goater, 1974, 1992). It is a scarce insect in southern England. The larva feeds on birch *Betula* spp.
■ vc12 Cow Down Copse, Oakley, 1999 (AHD).

1096 *Apotomis sauciana* (Frölich, 1828)
In southern England, this moth is found in open woodland with bilberry *Vaccinium myrtillus*. In Hampshire, it is recorded occasionally in the New Forest and from one or two places in N Hants. There is one record from the Isle of Wight at Newtown on 4.8.75 (Goater, 1992).
■ vc12 Pamber, 1994 (GJD); Yateley Common, 4.6.94, one (AMD).

1097 *Endothenia gentianeana* (Hübner, 1799)
This species probably occurs wherever teasel *Dipsacus fullonum* is established: opening the old heads in winter seldom fails to produce evidence of a larva in the central pith.

1098 *Endothenia oblongana* (Haworth, 1811)
The occurrence of this moth in Hampshire was confirmed (Goater, 1983). It has since been reported from a few other localities on the mainland (Goater, 1992). It is a

chalk-downland species, the larva of which is thought to feed on black knapweed *Centaurea nigra* (Bradley *et al.*, 1979).
■ vc11 Old Winchester Hill NNR, 3.6.93, one (JRL), Milton Common, Southsea, 18.7.99, det. JRL, 30.7 and 31.7.99 (IRT).
■ vc12 Ashford Hangers NR, 21.5.93, one (JRL).

1099 *Endothenia marginana* (Haworth, 1811)
Widespread in the mainland vice-counties, but only one record from the Isle of Wight since Goater (1974).
■ vc8 Martin Down, 5.5.90 (S. Nash).
■ vc10 Freshwater, 6.8.00, one at m.v. light (SAK-J).
■ vc11 Hengistbury Head, 1997, det. PHS (MJ); Hamble Common, 1996; Park Gate; Fareham; Browndown; Wallington; Kite's Croft; Milton Common, Southsea; Oxenbourne Down (RJD), Hookheath Meadows NR, Southwick, 24.5.92, one; Bishops Waltham, 18.8.93, several at m.v. light; Portsdown, 7.8.92, a few at m.v. light; Sinah Common, Hayling Island, 15.8.98, a few at m.v. light (JRL *et al.*).
■ vc12 Wildhern, nr Andover, 19.7.97 (DGG); Abbotstone Down, 27.7.94, a few at m.v. light (RJBH, JRL); Selborne, 30.7.92, 7.7 and 12.7.99, singles at m.v. light (AEA); Hawley Meadows NR, 23.7.96 (AMD).

1100 *Endothenia pullana* (Haworth, 1811)
This elusive and apparently very scarce moth has been reported in the past from Brockenhurst (Goater, 1974) and Leckford (Goater, 1992). The larva lives in the stems and rootstocks of marsh woundwort *Stachys palustris*.
■ vc11 Lower Titchfield Haven NR, 24.6.94, one at m.v. light (JRL).

1101 *Endothenia ustulana* (Haworth, 1811)
This is another insect which is very seldom encountered. There are sparse records from all three vice-counties (Goater, 1974, 1992). It is apparently very sluggish and the larva, which inhabits the rootstocks and leaf-bases of bugle *Ajuga reptans*, shows little evidence of its presence.
■ vc11 Chandlers Ford, 7.6.96, one amongst bugle in garden (BG); Winchester, Sarum Road, 4.6.90, one female at rest; 8.8.92, pair *in cop.*, both near a flower bed where much *A. reptans* grows (RJBH); Botley Wood (RJD).

1102 *Endothenia nigricostana* (Haworth, 1811)
An inconspicuous and sluggish insect, the presence of which is often revealed by collecting dry old stems of hedge woundwort *Stachys sylvatica* during the winter. In the author's experience, most well-established patches of foodplant hold the moth. There has been no recent record from the Isle of Wight (Goater, 1974).
■ vc11 Crab Wood; Botley Wood; Oxenbourne Down (RJD).
■ vc12 Wildhern, 27.6.98 (DGG); Pamber, 1995 (GJD); Selborne, 24.6.94, one at m.v. light (AEA).

1103 *Endothenia ericetana* (Humphreys & Westwood, 1845)
This is another rather sluggish and inconspicuous species, though it is sometimes encountered on the wing at dusk,

and also comes to light. It appears to be rather rare in Hampshire, and there is no recent record from the Isle of Wight (Goater, 1974).
■ vc11 Lower Test Marshes, 1995 (JP); Sparsholt College (AHD); Hookheath Meadows NR, Southwick, 13.6.92, one by day (JRL); Catisfield; Rowner Wild Grounds; Queen Elizabeth Country Park, 1999 (RJD).
■ vc12 South Wonston, 1.8.94, at m.v. light (PJSS); Selborne, 25.7.95, at light, conf. JRL from photograph, 14.8 and 19.8.97 (AEA).

1104 *Endothenia quadrimaculana* (Haworth, 1811)
Local in water meadows and marshes (Goater, 1974, 1992). The larva is stated to feed in the roots and rhizomes of marsh woundwort *Stachys palustris*, possibly comfrey *Symphytum* spp. (Bradley *et al.*, 1979).
■ vc10 Freshwater, 6.8.94 (SAK-J).
■ vc11 Hurn, one in 1999, another on 8.9.00 (MJ); Lower Test Marshes, 1995 (JP); Sparsholt College (AHD); Swanwick NR, 20.8.96, one at m.v. light (JRL); Milton Common, Southsea, 2000, at m.v. light (IRT).
■ vc12 South Wonston, 18.7.94, at m.v. light (PJSS); Bramley Frith NR (AHD); Selborne, 1994, 13.8.96, conf. JRL (AEA); Rye Common, 5.8.96 (AMD).

1105 *Lobesia occidentis* Falkovitsch, 1970
Very local in open, sunny woodland amongst wood spurge *Euphorbia amygdaloides*. The moth is seldom seen, but larvae have been found in some number, when sought. So far, it has been reported only from the Farley Mount and Crab Wood area of S Hants, and from Micheldever Wood in N Hants (Goater, 1974, 1992).

1106 *Lobesia reliquana* (Hübner, 1825)
Widespread and locally common in the mainland vice-counties but unrecorded from the Isle of Wight (Goater, 1974, 1992).
■ vc11 Mallard Wood; Hook Valley NR, 2.6.98, several; Wickham Common, 1999 (RJD).
■ vc12 Pamber, 1995 (GJD).

1107 *Lobesia botrana* ([Denis & Schiffermüller], 1775)
This pest of vines in southern Europe first appeared in England in 1977. There is one record from Winchester on 8.8.89 (Goater, 1992).

1108 *Lobesia abscisana* (Doubleday, 1849)
Widespread and common in many localities in all three vice-counties.
■ vc10 Freshwater, 19.7.97 (Knill-Jones, 1998b).
■ vc11 Hengistbury Head, 1997, det. PHS (MJ).

1109 *Lobesia littoralis* (Humphreys & Westwood, 1845)
This species is common on the coast amongst thrift *Armeria maritima*, but has also become well-established in gardens where this plant is grown.
■ vc10 Compton Bay (RJD).
■ vc11 Sparsholt College (AHD); Chandlers Ford, 20.8.91 and subsequently (BG); Catisfield; Fareham, 1996; Titchfield Haven; Browndown (RJD).

■ vc12 Oakley (AHD); Selborne, 1993, 1994, 1995 and 1997 (AEA); Farnborough, six in 1994, three in 1995 (RWP).

1110 *Bactra furfurana* (Haworth, 1811)
There have been very few records of this species from the mainland vice-counties, and one old, doubtful one from the Isle of Wight (Goater, 1974, 1992). The larva is stated to live in the stems of bulrush *Scirpus lacustris* and compact rush *Juncus conglomeratus* (Bradley *et al.*, 1979).
■ vc11 Hengistbury Head, one in 1999, det. PHS (MJ); Lower Titchfield Haven NR, 24.6.94, one at m.v. light (JRL); Fareham, 26.6.93, 10.8 to 16.8.98, four at m.v. light (RJD).
■ vc12 Abbotstone Down, 27.7.94, one at m.v. light (RJBH, JRL).

1111 *Bactra lancealana* (Hübner, 1799)
Abundant amongst rushes *Juncus* spp. in all three vice-counties, in bogs, marshes and water-meadows.
■ vc10 River Yar marshes (JMC).
■ vc11 Hengistbury Head, 1997, det. PHS (MJ).

1112 *Bactra robustana* (Christoph, 1872)
Local in coastal saltmarshes on the Isle of Wight and S Hants, amongst sea club-rush *Bolboschoenus maritimus* in the stems of which the larva feeds.
■ vc10 Bembridge, 1.8.97 (Knill-Jones, 1998b).
■ vc11 Lower Test Marshes NR (DHS, 1993); Hook Park; Browndown (RJD); Lower Titchfield Haven NR, 24.6.94, many at m.v. light (JRL); Milton Common, Southsea, 5.8 and 11.8.96, at actinic trap, conf. JRL, 7.8, 9.8, 11.8 and 22.8.97, 1998, three between 8.7 and 1.8.99, det. JRL, and again in 2000 (IRT); Sinah Common, Hayling Island (RJD).

1113 *Eudemis profundana* ([Denis & Schiffermüller], 1775)

10 mm

Widespread and fairly common to common in oak woodland in all three vice-counties (Goater, 1974, 1992).
■ vc10 Freshwater, 9.7.97 (Knill-Jones, 1998b).
■ vc11 Brockenhurst (JEC); Cadlands Estate, Beaulieu, 12.7.97, several at m.v. light (BG, JRL); Lower Test Marshes NR (DHS, 1992); Chandlers Ford, 14.8.91, 23.7.93 and subsequently (BG); Crab Wood; Hamble Common, 1996; Warsash shore, 17.6.98; Catisfield; Fareham; West Walk; Browndown; Rowner Wild Grounds (RJD); Swanwick NR, 20.8.96, many at m.v. light (JRL); Milton Common, Southsea, 1998, at light in garden (IRT).
■ vc12 Oakley; Bartley Heath NR; Mapledurwell Fen; Greywell Moors NR (AHD); Pamber Forest (RJD); Warren Heath, 24.7.96, in Heath trap; Bramshill Common, 1.8.96; Rye Common, 26.7.96, three (AMD); Selborne, 25.7.95, at light, det. JRL from photo (AEA); Farnborough, four in 1994 (RWP); Yateley Common, scarce (AMD).

1114 *Eudemis porphyrana* (Hübner, 1799)
Very local in the two mainland vice-counties (Goater, 1974, 1992), but probably overlooked. The larva feeds on crab apple *Malus sylvestris*, a plant which tends to occur as isolated bushes in woodlands.
■ vc11 Sparsholt College (AHD); Fareham, 29.6.93, 20.7.93, genitalia checked (RJD).

1115 *Ancylis achatana* ([Denis & Schiffermüller], 1775)
Widespread and fairly common in all three vice-counties (Goater, 1974, 1992), in thickets of blackthorn and hawthorn and in hedgerows. The moth comes freely to light.
■ vc10 Freshwater, 9.7.93, 17.6.99 (SAK-J), appear to be the only recent records from the Isle of Wight.

1116 *Ancylis comptana* (Frölich, 1828)
Locally common to abundant on chalk downland in all three vice-counties (Goater, 1974, 1992).
■ vc11 Broughton Down, 16.5 and 26.7.00, very common by day (AHD); Old Winchester Hill NNR, 23.7.97, many at m.v. light (RJD, JRL); Milton Common, Southsea, 1998, 2000, at light in garden, probably wanderers from Portsdown Hill (IRT).
■ vc12 Wildhern, nr Andover, 17.7.97, at dusk, 15.7.98, identity confirmed (DGG); Micheldever, 7.4.97, many (JRL, IRT); Selborne, 1994 (AEA).

1117 *Ancylis unguicella* (Linnaeus, 1758)
Locally common on heathland in S and N Hants, where the larva feeds on heathers *Calluna* and *Erica* spp., but unrecorded from the Isle of Wight. There is some evidence that it may be adapting to cultivated heathers in gardens, which would account for its appearance at Winchester, for instance (Goater, 1992).
■ vc12 Pamber, 1994 (GJD); Selborne, 1994 (AEA).

1118 *Ancylis uncella* ([Denis & Schiffermüller], 1775)
Local and rather uncommon, usually on damp heathland amongst young birches. It has been recorded from several localities on the mainland, but not from the Isle of Wight (Goater, 1974, 1992).
■ vc12 Harewood Forest (RJD); Pamber, 1995 (GJD); Bartley Heath NR (AHD).

The identities of the three following species have been mixed up in the past, and the old records given in Goater (1974) should be treated with some suspicion. Those given in Goater (1992) and below are considered to be sound.

1119 *Ancylis geminana* (Donovan, 1806)
Local but seldom recorded in the two mainland vice-counties (Goater, 1974, 1992). It seems to be associated with sallow *Salix cinerea* growing in rather dry places.
■ vc11 Battramsley; West Walk; Wickham Common, 1996 (RJD).
■ vc12 Conford Moor, 21.6.95, a few (JRL, RMP); Bartley Heath NR, 2.6.94, one at m.v. light (AHD); Basing Forest; Odiham Common (RJD).

1119a *Ancylis diminutana* (Haworth, 1811)
A few records, some probably untrustworthy, are given in Goater (1974, 1992). There is one recent record.
■ vc11 Merrietown Heath, 4.6.98, one at m.v. light (PHS).

1119b *Ancylis subarcuana* (Douglas, 1847)
Local in the bogs of the New Forest. Fassnidge's records (Goater, 1974) are acceptable, and those of JRL and DHS, of larvae on creeping willow *Salix repens* at Pig Bush and Emer Bog (Goater, 1992) are impeccable.

1120 *Ancylis mitterbacheriana* ([Denis & Schiffermüller], 1775)
Common amongst oak, beech and sweet chestnut in the mainland vice-counties (JRL), but only one old record from the Isle of Wight (Goater, 1974).
■ vc11 Many localities in the New Forest woodlands (BG *et al.*); Crab Wood, 20.9.97, spinnings on oak and beech (JRL, *et al.*); Havant Thicket, 23.6.98 (RJD).
■ vc12 Wildhern, nr Andover, 20.9.97, larvae; Harewood Forest, 26.10.97, spinnings on oak; Fleet Pond LNR, 7.10.97, larvae on oak; Tangley, 2.10.97, larvae on oak (DGG); Pamber, 1994 (GJD); Bartley Heath NR, 8.6.96, one at m.v. light (AHD); Selborne, at light (AEA); Yateley Common, 23.5 and 26.5.94 (AMD).

1121 *Ancylis upupana* (Treitschke, 1835)
Doubtless rare in the county, but also probably overlooked on account of its secretive habits. According to the late AME (pers. comm.), the moth can be dislodged from its resting-place high in young birch trees by kicking the trees early in the morning, when the moths flutter to the ground. This technique could lead to the discovery of more localities in Hampshire.
■ vc12 Castle Bottom NNR, 16.6.96, one (AMD). This is only the second record for vc12.

1122 *Ancylis obtusana* (Haworth, 1811)
Local in boggy places amongst alder buckthorn *Frangula alnus* and on the chalk amongst buckthorn *Rhamnus cathartica*. Records from all three vice-counties are given in Goater (1974, 1992).
■ vc10 Firestone Copse, 10.6.78, several flying late pm. (RJD).
■ vc11 Botley Wood, 29.5.98, one at m.v. light (RJD).
■ vc12 Abbotstone Down, 1.6.93, one (RJBH, JRL, DHS).

1123 *Ancylis laetana* (Fabricius, 1775)
Local amongst aspen *Populus tremula* in all three vice-counties (Goater, 1974, 1992).
■ vc11 Merrietown Heath, 18.10.93, larval feedings on *Populus tremula*; 4.6.98, 18.6.99, singletons at m.v. light (PHS); Botley Wood, 6.6.98 (RJD); Hilliers Arboretum, Ampfield, 20.6.98 (PAB, DGG, TJN).
■ vc12 Harewood Forest; Pamber Forest (RJD); Fugelmere Marsh, Fleet Pond NR, 17.6.94 (PAB).

1124 *Ancylis unculana* (Haworth, 1811)
Like *A. obtusana*, local in boggy places amongst alder buckthorn *Frangula alnus*, and on the chalk amongst buckthorn *Rhamnus cathartica*, but not recorded from the Isle of Wight (Goater 1974, 1992).
■ vc9 Martin Down (RJD).
■ vc11 Sparsholt College (AHD); Crab Wood, 20.9.97, spinning on buckthorn (JRL, *et al.*).

■ vc12 Isle of Wight Woods, Porton Down, 3.10.94, one larva on buckthorn (RJBH, JRL); Winnall Moors NR (DHS); Magdalen Hill Down, 16.5.97, det. DGG (PAB); Abbotstone Down, 27.7.94, a few at m.v. light (RJBH, JRL).

1125 *Ancylis badiana* ([Denis & Schiffermüller], 1775)
Locally common in grassy places amongst vetches *Vicia* spp. in all three vice-counties (Goater, 1974, 1992). The moth flies in the late afternoon sunshine and also comes to light.
■ vc8 Martin Down, 29.4.90 (S. Nash).
■ vc10 Totland Bay; Luccombe Chine (RJD).

1129 *Ancylis apicella* ([Denis & Schiffermüller], 1775)
Generally regarded as a very local and scarce species, there are numerous records from Hampshire (Goater, 1974, 1994) and it is locally common. It is another species associated with either alder buckthorn *Frangula alnus* or buckthorn *Rhamnus cathartica*.
■ vc11 Lower Test Marshes NR (DHS, 1992); Botley Wood, larvae on alder buckthorn; Wickham Common, 1999; Portsdown, larvae on buckthorn (RJD).
■ vc12 Conford Moor, 21.6.95, one (JRL, RMP); Pamber, 1995 (GJD).

1130 *Epinotia pygmaeana* (Hübner, 1799)
Locally common amongst spruce *Picea abies*, especially in young plantations. It is recorded from several localities in Hampshire, but not from the Isle of Wight (Goater, 1974, 1992).

1131 *Epinotia subsequana* (Haworth, 1811)
Known from two localities in S Hants (Goater, 1992), where it is common amongst giant fir *Abies grandis*. In one of these places, the trees are in poor condition and the future of the moth there seems uncertain. A new locality, found in 2000, gives extra hope for its survival in the county.
■ vc11 Avon Heath Country Park, 30.7.00, a few larvae on *A. grandis* (PHS).

1132 *Epinotia subocellana* (Donovan, 1806)
For some reason, there are rather few recent records of this species in Hampshire and the Isle of Wight. It was certainly widespread, and common in places, up to a decade ago (Goater, 1972, 1992).
■ vc10 Totland Bay, 8.6.78, two moths beaten from sallow (RJD). **New vc record.**
■ vc11 Hengistbury Head, 1997, det. PHS (MJ); Hound coast; Botley Wood, 20.5.98, one at m.v. light (RJD); Titchfield, 20.5.94, a few; Milton Common, Southsea, 2.6.94, one at m.v. light (JRL).
■ vc12 Rye Common, 6.5.95, one at m.v. light (AHD).

1133 *Epinotia bilunana* (Haworth, 1811)
Widespread and common in birch country in the mainland vice-counties, but unrecorded from the Isle of Wight (Goater, 1974, 1992). The larva feeds in the catkins.

1134 *Epinotia ramella* (Linnaeus, 1758)
This is another species that is common in birch-woods. It has been reported from all three vice-counties (Goater, 1974, 1992) but not recently from the Isle of Wight. It flies later in the year than *E. bilunana* and, like that species, comes freely to light.

1135 *Epinotia demarniana* (Fischer von Röslerstamm, 1840)
Widespread but rather uncommon in birch-woods in the mainland vice-counties, but unrecorded from the Isle of Wight (Goater, 1974, 1992).
▪ vc11 Roydon Woods, 10.7.96, a few at m.v. light (PRD, JRL), 28.5.98 (PAB); Chandlers Ford, 10.6.91 (BG), 8.6.00 (BE); Funtley, 1999, conf. RJD (MLO, comm. RJD); Havant Thicket, 28.6.95, at m.v. light (JRL).
▪ vc12 Bartley Heath NR (AHD); Pamber, 1994 (GJD); Silchester Common, 30.5.93, one (JRL); Selborne, 12.6.97, conf. BG from photograph (AEA); Hook Common (RJD); Yateley Common, singles on 11.6 and 26.6.94 (AMD).

1136 *Epinotia immundana* (Fischer von Röslerstamm, 1839)
Common amongst birch in the mainland vice-counties, but not reported recently from the Isle of Wight (Goater, 1974, 1992). The moth comes readily to light.
▪ vc11 Cadlands Estate, Beaulieu, 12.7.97, several at m.v. light (BG, JRL); Lower Test Marshes NR (DHS, 1993); Chandlers Ford, annually (BG); Fareham (RJD); Hookheath Meadows NR, Southwick, 24.5.92, one at m.v. light; Creech Wood, Denmead, 22.8.97, one at m.v. light (JRL *et al.*).
▪ vc12 Pamber, 1994 (GJD); Selborne, 1993 (AEA); Yateley Common, very common (AMD); Farnborough, 6.5.95, one at light (RWP).

1137 *Epinotia tetraquetrana* (Haworth, 1811)
Widespread amongst birch and alder in the mainland vice-counties, but no record from the Isle of Wight (Goater, 1974, 1992).
▪ vc11 Lower Test Marshes NR (DHS, 1993); Hamble Common; Park Gate; Titchfield Haven; Hazel Holt; Kite's Croft; Wickham Common, 1999 (RJD).
▪ vc12 Harewood Forest; Odiham Common (RJD); Bramley Frith NR (AHD); Farnborough, 1.6.95, one at light (RWP).

1138 *Epinotia nisella* (Clerck, 1759)
Common amongst sallow *Salix* spp. in all three vice-counties; the distribution of f. *cinereana* Haworth on aspen is dependent on that of the foodplant.

1139 *Epinotia tenerana* ([Denis & Schiffermüller], 1775)
Frequent in hazel woods and amongst alder on the mainland (Goater 1974, 1992). The larva lives in the catkins.
▪ vc10 Newtown, 18.9.97, one (AME, JRL). First recent record.
▪ vc11 Crab Wood, 20.9.97, adults seen by day; The Moors NR, Bishops Waltham, 25.8.98, two; Creech Wood, Denmead, 26.9.97, one at m.v. light (JRL *et al.*); Swanwick NR; Botley Wood; West Walk (RJD).

▪ vc12 Wildhern, nr Andover, 19.6.97, at dusk (DGG); Magdalen Hill Down (PAB); Selborne, 1993, 1997 (AEA).

[1140 *Epinotia nigricana* (Herrich-Schäffer, 1851)
An old, unconfirmed record of this species is given in Goater (1974). The larva lives in the buds of silver fir *Abies alba*.]

1142 *Epinotia tedella* (Clerck, 1759)
Locally common to abundant in spruce *Picea abies* woods and plantations, especially in S Hants (Goater, 1974, 1992).
▪ vc10 Firestone Copse (RJD). **First confirmed record for the Isle of Wight.**

1143 *Epinotia fraternana* (Haworth, 1811)
Known from the same two localities in S Hants as *E. subsequana* (Goater, 1992) amongst giant fir *Abies grandis*, but it is less common, and its future status appears to be even more precarious in one area.

1144 *Epinotia signatana* (Douglas, 1845)
A local and uncommon species, reported from a few mainland sites (Goater, 1974, 1992). Larvae have been found on blackthorn and plum, and moths bred.
▪ vc11 Botley Wood, 1.7.75 (RJD), 17.6.93, a few (JRL, RMP); Chilling Copse, 26.6.95; Curbridge NR, 13.7.73, two (RJD).

1145 *Epinotia nanana* (Treitschke, 1835)
The few records of this species, all from the mainland vice-counties, are in Goater (1974, 1992). The larva mines the needles, especially those of the side-shoots, of spruce *Picea abies*.
▪ vc11 West Walk, 26.5.94, two moths beaten (RJD).

1146 *Epinotia rubiginosana* (Herrich-Schäffer, 1851)
Reported from all three vice-counties (Goater, 1974, 1992), but far from common. The larva makes a spinning amongst the needles of Scots pine *Pinus sylvestris*, but all Hampshire specimens have apparently been taken at light, or beaten from foliage.
▪ vc11 Botley Wood, 23.5.95, a few at m.v. light (JRL).
▪ vc12 Bramshott Common, 23.5.98, one (JRL, IRT).

1147 *Epinotia cruciana* (Linnaeus, 1761)
Common amongst sallow *Salix* spp. whence the moth is easily bred from spinnings taken in the spring. Stated to have been abundant on the Isle of Wight at the time of the Victoria County History (Goater, 1974), the only other record received for vc10 is that given below.
▪ vc10 Priory Bay (RJD).

1150 *Epinotia abbreviana* (Fabricius, 1794)
Common to very common amongst elm *Ulmus* spp. in all three vice-counties.
▪ vc10 Tennyson Down, 18.5.92, one larva on elm *Ulmus procera*, moth bred (JRL, DHS, PHS).

1151 *Epinotia trigonella* (Linnaeus, 1758)
Fairly common amongst birch in the mainland vice-counties, but unrecorded from the Isle of Wight (Goater, 1974, 1992).
■ vc11 West Walk, Wickham, 25.8.95, a few at m.v. light (JRL); Browndown (RJD).
■ vc12 Eelmoor Marsh SSSI, 23.8.97 (DGG); Bramshill Plantation, 6.9.97, one (AMD).

1152 *Epinotia maculana* (Fabricius, 1775)
Extremely local in aspen *Populus tremula* groves. Recorded from all three vice-counties (Goater, 1974, 1992), but not since 1979.

1153 *Epinotia sordidana* (Hübner, 1824)
Very local and usually uncommon (Goater, 1974, 1992). The moth is sometimes found flying sluggishly towards evening among young alders growing in rather dry places, and the larva may be collected from podded leaves. The following is the only record recently received.
■ vc11 Botley Wood, 18.5.96, larva, form which a moth was bred on 10.9.96 (RJD).

1154 *Epinotia caprana* (Fabricius, 1798)
Local and generally rather uncommon. Reported in the past from the Isle of Wight, but best-known from a few localities in S Hants (Goater, 1974, 1992). In the New Forest, it has been bred from bog-myrtle *Myrica gale*; elsewhere, it is associated with sallow *Salix cinerea*.
■ vc11 Titchfield Haven, 1996, fairly common (RJD).
■ vc12 Eelmoor Marsh SSSI, 23.8.97 (DGG). **New vc record.**

1155 *Epinotia brunnichana* (Linnaeus, 1767)
This species and the next are both polymorphic and some of the forms are difficult to differentiate. On the whole, *E. brunnichana* appears to be the commoner species.
■ vc11 Brockenhurst (JEC); Roydon Woods, Dilton Meadows, 12.7.97, at m.v. light (DGG); Sparsholt College (AHD); West Meon, 8.10.96, one; Havant Thicket, 8.7.97, at m.v. light (JRL *et al.*); Waterlooville, 1996–2000 (RJM).
■ vc12 Wildhern, 20.7.98 (DGG); Abbotstone Down, 27.7.94, one at m.v. light (RJBH, JRL); Bramley Frith NR; Bartley Heath NR, 1996 (AHD); Pamber, 1994 (GJD); Rye Common, 5.8.96, eight; Yateley Common, occasional (AMD).

1156 *Epinotia solandriana* (Linnaeus, 1758)
■ vc11 Matley Wood; Crab Wood; Upper Hamble Country Park; Botley Wood; Catisfield; Fareham; Swanwick NR; Kite's Croft; Rowner Wild Grounds (RJD); Southwick, 29.7.96, one at m.v. light (JRL, EAP); Old Winchester Hill NNR, 23.7.97, one at m.v. light (RJD, JRL); Milton Common, Southsea, 28.7.00, one at m.v. light (IRT).
■ vc12 Basingstoke, 30.7.94, at m.v. light; Bartley Heath NR (AHD); Pamber, 1994 (GJD); Rye Common, 5.8.96 (AMD).

1157 *Crocidosema plebejana* (Zeller, 1847)
Since the first record of this species at Martyr Worthy in 1961 (Goater, 1974), it appears to have become established at low density along the coast of S Hants and on the Isle of Wight. The larva feeds in the leaf axils and ripening fruits of tree-mallow *Lavatera arborea*.
■ vc10 Freshwater, 27.9.83, 18.11.90, 1.12.91 (SAK-J); see also (Knill-Jones, 1994d); again on 23.10.95, 1.9.98 (SAK-J); Binstead, 1.11.99, one at m.v. light (BJW). **New vc record.**
■ vc11 Hengistbury Head, two in 1999, det. PHS (MJ); Fareham, 6.9.99, 31.10.99, at m.v. light (RJD); Milton Common, Southsea, 2.8.96, at actinic trap, conf. JRL, 18.10.97, again in 1998, 14 in 1999 between 29.7 and 7.11. (IRT).
■ vc12 Selborne, 24.8.96, at light, det. K. Tuck (BMNH) (AEA).

1159 *Rhopobota naevana* (Hübner, 1817)
Widespread and common on the mainland, but only one recent report from the Isle of Wight The larva is polyphagous, but is particularly addicted to holly *Ilex aquifolium*, and several of the Hampshire records refer to an association with this tree.
■ vc10 Freshwater, 13.7, 14.7 and 15.7.00, at m.v. light in garden (SAK-J).
■ vc11 Whiteley Wood; Rhinefields; Crab Wood; Locks Heath, 10.8.00, det. RJD (PCa); Upper Hamble Country Park; Catisfield; Fareham, 18.6.98; Fort Fareham; Titchfield Haven; Swanwick NR (RJD); Lower Test Marshes NR (DHS, 1993); Chilling Copse, 1999; Fareham (RJD); Great Salterns NR, Portsmouth (JRL).
■ vc12 Wildhern, 29.7.98 (DGG); Selborne, 1993, 1994 (AEA); Farnborough, seven in 1994, three in 1995 (RWP).

1161 *Rhopobota (Griselda) stagnana* ([Denis & Schiffermüller], 1775)
Recorded from the chalk downs of all three vice-counties (Goater, 1974, 1992). More recent records include those given below.
■ vc8 Martin Down, 5.5 and 6.5.90 (S. Nash).
■ vc11 Broughton Down, May 1995, at light (NB); Oxenbourne Down NR, 25.5.93, one (JRL).
■ vc22 Mortimer West End, 2000, first record (GJD).

1162 *Rhopobota (Griselda) myrtillana* (Humphreys & Westwood, 1845)
This insect is associated with bilberry *Vaccinium myrtillus* growing in open woodland. In the past, it has been reported from Mark Ash and Matley in the New Forest, Chilworth and Pamber Forest (Goater, 1974, 1992), but nothing has been heard of it recently.

1160 *Acroclita subsequana* (Herrich-Schäffer, 1851)
Following old records from S Hants given in Goater (1974), nothing more was heard of this moth until the following record.
■ vc11 Sandy Point, Hayling Island, June 1996, larvae common on sea spurge *Euphorbia paralias*, moths bred (DMA).

1163 *Zeiraphera ratzeburgiana* (Ratzeburg, 1840)
Apparently very local and rather rare in spruce *Picea abies* woodland on the Hampshire mainland (Goater, 1974, 1992).
■ vc12 Farnborough, 10.7.95, one at m.v. light (RWP).

1164 *Zeiraphera rufimitrana* (Herrich-Schäffer, 1851)
There has been no record of this moth in Hampshire since the 1930s (Goater, 1974, 1992).

1165 *Zeiraphera isertana* (Fabricius, 1794)
Common amongst oak in all three vice-counties.
■ vc10 Freshwater, 10.7.97 (Knill-Jones, 1998b); Bouldnor; Appley Park, Ryde (RJD).

1166 *Zeiraphera griseana* (Hübner, 1799)
= *diniana* (Guenée, 1854)
Apparently very local and scarce (Goater, 1974, 1992). It is found in larch woodland, specimens sometimes wandering away and turning up at light in unexpected places.
■ vc11 Southsea, 1.8.95, one at m.v. light (JRL).
■ vc12 Wildhern, nr Andover, 23.7.97, at dusk (DGG).

1167 *Gypsonoma aceriana* (Duponchel, 1843)
Locally common amongst large poplars *Populus* spp., and recorded from all three vice-counties (Goater, 1974, 1992).
■ vc10 Bembridge, 1.8.97 (Knill-Jones, 1998b).
■ vc11 Fareham (RJD); Great Salterns NR, Portsmouth; Sandy Point NR, Hayling Island, 14.7.92, one at m.v. light (JRL).
■ vc12 Wildhern, nr Andover, 24.7.99 (DGG); Pamber, 1995 (GJD); Selborne, 1993, 1994 (AEA).

1168 *Gypsonoma sociana* (Haworth, 1811)
Local amongst poplars *Populus* spp., including aspen *P. tremula*, but no recent record from the Isle of Wight (Goater, 1974, 1992).
■ vc11 Sparsholt College (AHD); Hilliers Arboretum, Ampfield, 1998 (TJN); Soberton, 30.6.95, one at m.v. light; Botley Wood, 12.7.94, a few at m.v. light; Havant Thicket, 8.7.97, at m.v. light (JRL *et al.*).
■ vc12 Chilbolton, 23.6.97, one on poplar trunks (BG); Winnall Moors NR (DHS); Pamber, 1995 (GJD); Selborne, 1993 (AEA); Castle Bottom NNR, 16.6.96 (AMD).

1169 *Gypsonoma dealbana* (Frölich, 1828)
Common in the two mainland vice-counties, and probably, too, on the Isle of Wight, although there are no recent records to support this view. The larva feeds mainly in the buds and spun shoots of poplars and sallows, but also on hawthorn, oak and hazel (Bradley *et al.*, 1979).

1170 *Gypsonoma oppressana* (Treitschke, 1835)
Very local on poplar *Populus* spp., but often common where it occurs, on just a few isolated large trees. Recorded from the two mainland vice-counties, but not from the Isle of Wight (Goater, 1974, 1992).
■ vc11 Soberton, 30.6.95, one at m.v. light (JRL).

■ vc12 Chilbolton, 23.6.97, common on poplar trunks (BG); Selborne, 18.6.93, det. JRL from photo, 17.7.97 (AEA).

1171 *Gypsonoma minutana* (Hübner, 1799)
There is a strong colony of this species on white poplar *Populus alba* near Portsmouth airport. Occasional specimens have been reported elsewhere in S Hants and there is a fairly recent record from the Isle of Wight (Goater, 1992).

1174 *Epiblema cynosbatella* (Linnaeus, 1758)
Widespread and common in all three vice-counties. The larva feeds on wild and cultivated roses *Rosa* spp.
■ vc10 Totland Bay; Yarmouth; Knowles Farm area; Apes Down; Firestone Copse (RJD).

1175 *Epiblema uddmanniana* (Linnaeus, 1758)
Widespread and common in all three vice-counties (JRL). The larva makes a ragged spinning in shoots of bramble *Rubus fruticosus* agg.
■ vc8 Martin Down, 8.6.92, spinnings. (JRL, RMP).
■ vc10 Compton Bay; St Catherine's Point; Chale (RJD).
■ vc11 Hengistbury Head, 1997, det. PHS (MJ).

1176 *Epiblema trimaculana* (Haworth, 1811)
Recorded from all three vice-counties (Goater, 1974, 1992) but nowhere common. The larva feeds mainly on hawthorn *Crataegus* spp. whence it has been bred, though most records have been of moths taken at light.
■ vc11 Botley Wood, 9.6.92, a few at m.v. light; Southwick, 8.7.96, one at m.v. light (JRL); Hamble Common; Fareham, 5.6.98, at m.v. light; Titchfield Haven, 1996; Brownwich; Portsdown (RJD); Catherington Down, 31.5.95, a few (JRL); Sandy Point, Hayling Island, 1999 (RJD).

1177 *Epiblema rosaecolana* (Doubleday, 1850)
Widespread and fairly common in all three vice-counties. The larva feeds on rose *Rosa* spp. including cultivars.
■ vc10 Cranmore, 13.8.97 (Knill-Jones, 1998b); Shanklin (JMC).

1178 *Epiblema roborana* ([Denis & Schiffermüller], 1775)
Like the previous species, widespread and fairly common in all three vice-counties. The larva also feeds on rose *Rosa* spp. including cultivars.
■ vc11 Hengistbury Head, 1997, det. PHS (MJ).

1179 *Epiblema incarnatana* (Hübner, 1800)
According to TGW, the record for Alice Holt given in Goater (1974) was an incorrect identification and should be deleted. The following, therefore, qualifies as the first and only record for the county. The species is associated mainly with burnet rose *Rosa pimpinellifolia* growing in coastal localities. Inland, it is rare, the larva feeding on other species of wild rose.
■ vc12 Stockbridge Down, 14.8.92, one flying in evening, 30.7.94, another in same spot (RJBH). **New county record.**

1180 *Epiblema tetragonana* (Stephens, 1834)
There has been no record of this species in Hampshire and the Isle of Wight since Goater (1974).

1182 *Epiblema turbidana* (Treitschke, 1835)
This moth is associated with butterbur *Petasites hybridus*. It is sluggish and inconspicuous, and probably occurs in other localities than those detailed in Goater (1974, 1992). The moth rests on the foliage of the foodplant on warm, sunny afternoons and the larva is not difficult to detect in the rootstocks.

1183 *Epiblema foenella* (Linnaeus, 1758)
Locally frequent on waste ground amongst the foodplant, mugwort *Artemisia vulgaris* in all three vice-counties.
- vc10 Cranmore, 2.8.95 (SAK-J); Shanklin (RJD).
- vc11 Hengistbury Head, 1997 (MJ).

1184 *Epiblema scutulana* ([Denis & Schiffermüller], 1775)
Recorded from all three vice-counties and probably fairly common, at least locally. However, its true status remains uncertain owing to confusion with the next species. In Goater (1974, 1992), the two were considered to be conspecific. The larva feeds in the stems of spear thistle *Cirsium vulgare* and musk thistle *Carduus nutans*.
- vc10 Chillerton (JMC); Knowles Farm area (RJD).
- vc11 Hookheath Meadows NR, Southwick, 9.6.92, one (JRL, DHS); Hamble Common; Titchfield Haven; Wickham Common, 1999; Swanwick NR; Wendleholme NR; Kite's Croft; Portsdown; Oxenbourne Down (RJD).
- vc12 Winnall Moors NR (DHS).

1184a *Epiblema cirsiana* (Zeller, 1843)
This species, considered in the past to be just a small form of *E. scutulana*, is also widespread in the three vice-counties and is the commoner of the two. The larva feeds in the stems of marsh thistle *Cirsium palustre* and black knapweed *Centaurea nigra*.
- vc11 Hookheath Meadows NR, Southwick, 15.5.92, one; Old Winchester Hill NNR, 3.6.93, one (JRL).
- vc12 Noar Hill, 24.5.76 (RJD); Ashford Hangers NR, 21.5.93, one (JRL).

1185 *Epiblema cnicicolana* (Zeller, 1847)
The record for Itchen Valley, N Hants given in Goater (1974) was later withdrawn by the recorder (Goater, 1992). It has been recorded with certainty only from two localities in S Hants, Botley Wood (Goater, 1992) and below.
- vc10 Firestone Copse, 10.6.78 (RJD). **New vc record.**
- vc11 Hookheath Meadows NR, Southwick, 9.6.92, a few by day (JRL, DHS).

1186 *Epiblema sticticana* (Fabricius, 1794)
= *farfarae* (Fletcher, 1938)
Locally abundant amongst coltsfoot *Tussilago farfara* growing on waste ground and along the open, sunny banks of rivers, in all three vice-counties. As so often, however, the authors have received no record from the Isle of Wight since Goater (1974).

- vc11 Hamble Common; Hook-with-Warsash, 1996; Hill Head, 13.5.96, several (RJD).
- vc12 Bartley Heath NR (AHD).

1187 *Epiblema costipunctana* (Haworth, 1811)
Locally frequent, mainly on chalk downland and coastal sandhills, where the larva inhabits the rootstock of ragwort *Senecio jacobaea*.
- vc8 Martin Down, 8.6.92 (JRL, RMP).
- vc10 Cranmore, 10.7.97 (Knill-Jones, 1998b); Ventnor Undercliff (RJD).
- vc11 Hengistbury Head, 1997 and 1998, det. PHS; Hurn, one in 1999 (MJ); Hamble Common; Old Winchester Hill NNR, 3.6.93, one; Portsdown; Queen Elizabeth Country Park, 1999 (RJD); Hookheath Meadows NR, Southwick, 9.6.92, one; Swanwick, 14.6.97, one; Sandy Point NR, Hayling Island, 22.7.95, one at m.v. light (JRL).
- vc12 Woolbury Ring, 12.6.97, one by day on downs (BG); Selborne, 25.7.95, one at light (AEA).

1188 *Pelochrista caecimaculana* (Hübner, 1799)
Apparently very rare. The few records are given in Goater (1974, 1992), and the only place where it might be regarded as established is on Portsdown Hill. The larva lives in the roots of black knapweed *Centaurea nigra*.

1189 *Eriopsela quadrana* (Hübner, 1813)
A very local species, recorded only from a few S Hants localities when the foodplant, wild goldenrod *Solidago virgaurea*, happened to be abundant *viz.* at Baddesley Great Covert in the 1930s and Botley Wood in the 1970s and 1980s (Goater, 1992).

1192 *Eucosma conterminana* (Guenée, 1845)
First recorded in Hampshire at Itchen Valley in 1976 (Goater, 1983), there have been several records recently from S Hants, possibly associated with the increase in the foodplant, prickly lettuce *Lactuca serriola*. It seems to be well-established in the Portsmouth and Southsea area.
- vc11 Winchester, 9.8.92 (DHS); Great Salterns NR, Portsmouth; Southsea, 5.8.95, one at m.v. light, and regularly in small numbers since (JRL); Milton Common, Southsea, 20.7.94, on prickly lettuce; 22.7 and 5.8.96, 1998, 13.7 and 17.7.99, all records conf. JRL (IRT); Sinah Common, Hayling Island, 19.8.98, one at actinic light (RJD). **New vc record.**
- vc12 Bramley Frith Wood, 29.7.99, one (AHD).

1193 *Eucosma tripoliana* (Barrett, 1880)
Common in saltmarshes along the coasts of the Isle of Wight and S Hants (Goater, 1974, 1992). The larva feeds on sea aster *Aster tripolium*.
- vc11 Curbridge NR, 14.8.74 (RJD); Milton Common, Southsea, 1998, at light in garden (IRT).

1194 *Eucosma aemulana* (Schläger, 1849)
There has been no record of this moth in the county since 1970 (Goater, 1974). Like *Eriopsela quadrana*, it requires

extensive patches of wild goldenrod *Solidago virgaurea* growing in open woodland.

1196 *Eucosma metzneriana* (Treitschke, 1830)
The second British specimen of this moth was taken at Southsea in 1982 (Goater, 1983).

1197 *Eucosma campoliliana* ([Denis & Schiffermüller], 1775)
Common amongst the foodplant, ragwort *Senecio jacobaea*, particularly on chalk downland and near the coast, in all three vice-counties (Goater, 1974, 1992). Many recent records from the mainland.
■ vc10 St Helens Duver (RJD).
■ vc11 Hengistbury Head, 1997, 1999, det. PHS (MJ).

1199 *Eucosma pupillana* (Clerck, 1759)
Recorded in the past from St Catherine's Down and Ventnor, amongst wormwood *Artemisia absinthium* (Goater, 1974), but not since. The plant is now very rare, but occurs around Southampton (Brewis *et al.*, 1996).

1200 *Eucosma hohenwartiana* ([Denis & Schiffermüller], 1775)
incl. **f. *fulvana*** Stephens, 1834
Widespread and common in all three vice-counties (Goater, 1974, 1992) in rough grassland, downland and coastal localities. The larva lives in the seedheads of knapweed *Centaurea scabiosa*, *C. nigra* and saw-wort *Serratula tinctoria*. Larvae in *C. scabiosa* are stated to produce the f. *fulvana* (Stephens) (Bradley and Bradley, 1998), while a characteristic dwarf form occurs amongst saw-wort (JRL, BG, pers. obs.).
■ vc10 Culver Cliff (RJD).
■ vc12 Leckford, dwarf form on chalk downland amongst saw-wort (JRL, BG).

1201 *Eucosma cana* (Haworth, 1811)
Common in the two mainland vice-counties, and probably also on the Isle of Wight (Goater, 1974, 1992). Many recent records from Hampshire. The larva lives in the seedheads of thistles *Carduus* and *Cirsium* spp. and black knapweed *Centaurea nigra*.
■ vc10 Freshwater, 21.7.97, 13.7.98, at m.v. light (SAK-J).
■ vc11 Hengistbury Head, 1997, 1999, det. PHS (MJ).

1202 *Eucosma obumbratana* (Lienig & Zeller, 1846)
There are scattered records from all three vice-counties (Goater, 1974, 1992), but this is an uncommon moth in the two counties. The larva lives in the seedheads of perennial sow-thistle *Sonchus arvensis*.
■ vc10 High Down, Freshwater (RJD).
■ vc11 Lower Test Marshes NR (DHS, 1993); Broughton Down, 29.8.00, one at a Heath trap (AHD); Sparsholt College (AHD); Fareham; Titchfield Haven; Browndown (RJD); Milton Common, Southsea, 7.8.96 (IRT), 30.7.92, one at m.v. light; Sandy Point NR, Hayling Island, 14.7.92, one at m.v. light (JRL).
■ vc12 Brighton Hill, Basingstoke, 21.8.96, one at house lights (AHD); Selborne, 5.7.96, 7.7.97, 27.7.00 (AEA); Farnborough, 7.7.97 (RWP).

1204 *Thiodia citrana* (Hübner, 1799)
Mainly coastal, in the Isle of Wight and S Hants, but recorded once in N Hants, Itchen Valley, 1968 (Goater, 1974). The foodplant here is probably always yarrow *Achillea millefolium*.
■ vc11 Hurn, one in 1999 (MJ); Browndown, 5.7.97, one at m.v. light (JRL, IRT); Hamble Common; Titchfield Haven (RJD); Great Salterns NR, Portsmouth (JRL); Milton Common, Southsea, 1998, at light in garden (IRT); Sandy Point NR, Hayling Island, 14.7.92, a few at m.v. light (JRL).

1205 *Spilonota ocellana* ([Denis & Schiffermüller], 1775)
Widespread and common in all three vice-counties. Many recent records from the mainland. The larva is polyphagous, but shows a preference for woody Rosaceae such as hawthorn.

1205a *Spilonota laricana* (Heinemann, 1863)
Recorded from larch woods in several places in the two mainland vice-counties (Goater, 1974, 1992), often commonly.
■ vc11 Roydon Woods, 10.7.96, a few at m.v. light (PRD, JRL).
■ vc12 Oakley (AHD); Selborne, 1993, 1994 (AEA).

1206 *Clavigesta sylvestrana* (Curtis, 1850)
Very local along the south coast of Hampshire (Goater, 1974, 1992). The larva feeds amongst the male inflorescences of maritime pine *Pinus pinaster* and Bournemouth, where this tree has been planted extensively, remains a stronghold of the moth. Weymouth pine *P. strobus* is also stated to be a foodplant.
■ vc11 Cadlands Estate, Beaulieu, 12.7.97, a few at m.v. light (BG, JRL), 17.7.99, three (BG), near well-grown *P. pinaster*.

1207 *Clavigesta purdeyi* (Durrant, 1911)
Reported in the past from all three vice-counties (Goater, 1974, 1992), but local and usually uncommon. Occasional specimens are taken at light. The larva bores in the needles of Scots pine *Pinus sylvestris*.
■ vc11 Catisfield; Fareham; Titchfield Haven; Rowner Wild Grounds (RJD); Milton Common, Southsea, 1998, at light in garden, 25.7 and 29.7.99, singles at m.v. light, det. JRL (IRT).
■ vc12 Selborne, 6.8.95, one at light (AEA); Farnborough, 4.8.96 (RWP).

1208 *Pseudococcyx (Blastesthia) posticana* (Zetterstedt, 1839)
Found mainly in the New Forest where, by dint of hard searching, hollowed-out, resinous buds on the lateral shoots of small Scots pine trees, which hold the larva, can be located. The insect evidently has a preference for the smaller trees and moves about the area as habitat becomes available. There are very few records in Hampshire outside the New Forest, and none from the Isle of Wight.
■ vc11 Sopley Common, 12.5.00, two at m.v. light (PHS); Sparsholt College (AHD; Fareham, 14.5.98, one

at m.v. light (RJD); Southsea, 14.5.98, two at m.v. light, first for garden (JRL).

■ vc12 Rye Common, 6.5.95, one at m.v. light (AHD).

1209 *Pseudococcyx (Blastesthia) turionella* (Linnaeus, 1758)

Like that of the preceding species, larva of *P. turionella* feeds in the shoots of Scots pine but causes more damage by selecting the central bud of a shoot, aborting it. Little resin is exuded from the area which has been attacked. The moth is rather more widespread than *P. posticana*, and has been reported from several areas outside the New Forest (Goater, 1974, 1992).

■ vc10 Freshwater, 25.5.91 (Knill-Jones, 1995). **New vc record.**

■ vc11 Sopley Common, 12.5.00, common at m.v. light (PHS).

■ vc12 Selborne, 1993 (AEA); Yateley Common, 18.5.94 (two), 14.5.94, one (AMD).

1210 *Rhyacionia buoliana* ([Denis & Schiffermüller], 1775)

Common in Scots pine woods, especially in young plantations, where the larva sometimes causes considerable and lasting damage to the shoots which it attacks.

■ vc11 Hengistbury Head, 1997, Sopley Marsh, det. PHS (MJ); Fareham; West Walk; Oxenbourne Down (RJD).

■ vc12 Selborne, 1993 and 1995 (AEA); Rye Common, 5.8.96; Yateley Common, 17.6.94, one (AMD).

1211 *Rhyacionia pinicolana* (Doubleday, 1849)

Locally common in Scots pine woodland, especially in the New Forest. It is more common than *R. buoliana* at Chandlers Ford (BG). Recorded from all three vice-counties, but RJD (pers. comm.) states that he himself has no authenticated record of the species in Hampshire and that his record from Oxenbourne Down (Goater, 1992) should therefore be withdrawn. The larva lives in the shoots of pine, usually causing less damage than the previous species, however.

■ vc10 Cranmore, 11.8.98 (SAK-J).

■ vc11 Brockenhurst (JEC); Chandlers Ford, occurs every year (BG); Locks Heath, 6.7.00 (PCa).

■ vc12 Wildhern, 25.7.98 (DGG); Pamber Forest, 19.7.97, four at m.v. light (MCH); Mapledurwell Fen (AHD); Selborne, 1993, 1994 (AEA); Farnborough, 19.7.94, 5.7.95 (RWP); Yateley Common, occasional (AMD).

1212 *Rhyacionia pinivorana* (Lienig & Zeller, 1846)

Widespread and common in Scots pine woodland, and recorded from all three vice-counties (Goater, 1974, 1992).

■ vc10 Freshwater, 24.6.85 (SAK-J).

1214 *Retinia resinella* (Linnaeus, 1758)

■ vc11 Southsea, 22.5.89, one at m.v. light (RJD). **New county record.**

1215 *Cryptophlebia leucotreta* (Meyrick, 1913)

This African pest species is occasionally imported into Britain, probably with oranges. There are five records from Hampshire and the Isle of Wight, one bred, the other four taken at large or indoors (Goater, 1983, 1992, and below).

■ vc10 Freshwater, 29.9.89, one resting on a curtain in the house (Knill-Jones, 1994). **New vc record.**

■ vc11 Southsea, 11.8.95, one at m.v. light (Langmaid, 1996).

1216 *Enarmonia formosana* (Scopoli, 1763)

Recorded from all three vice-counties (Goater, 1974, 1992) but overlooked unless sought. The larva lives in the bark of wild cherry and other species of *Prunus*, apple *Malus* spp. and pear *Pyrus* spp., especially, it seems, ornamental species planted in suburbia. Its presence is betrayed by an exudation of frass in the crevices of bark.

■ vc11 Holmsley railway line, 17.6.72; Locks Heath, 28.6.96 (RJD); Chandlers Ford, 5.7.91, 8.6.93 (BG); Bishops Waltham, 19.4.93, larval workings in bark of cherry (JRL).

■ vc12 Wildhern, nr Andover, 16.7.96, (DGG); Farnborough, 24.6.95, one (KW).

1217 *Eucosmomorpha albersana* (Hübner, 1813)

A local and rather rare species of open woodland and glades where the foodplant, honeysuckle *Lonicera periclymenum* occurs. Recorded from all three vice-counties (Goater, 1974, 1992) but not recently from the Isle of Wight.

■ vc11 Roydon Woods, 5.6.98, one (PAB); Brockenhurst (JEC); Kite's Croft, 1.6.96 (RJD).

■ vc12 Pamber, 1995 (GJD; Bartley Heath NR, 1996 (AHD); Odiham Common, 25.5.76 (RJD).

1219 *Lathronympha strigana* (Fabricius, 1775)

Common and widespread amongst St John's-wort *Hypericum* spp. in the two mainland vice-counties (Goater, 1974, 1992), but only recently reported from the Isle of Wight.

■ vc8 Martin Down, 24.8.90 (MFVC, S. Nash), 8.6.92 (JRL, RMP).

■ vc10 Freshwater, 23.6.92 (Knill-Jones, 1995); Apes Down, 6.6.78, one adult (RJD). **New vc record.**

■ vc11 Lower Test Marshes NR (DHS, 1992); Sparsholt College (AHD); Bitterne, 20.5.97 (PAB); Hamble Common, 1996; Fareham (RJD); Creech Wood, Denmead, 1997 (JRL, EAP); Swanwick NR, 20.8.96; Great Salterns NR, Portsmouth (JRL); Milton Common, Southsea, 1998, at light in garden (IRT); Waterlooville, 1996–2000 (RJM).

■ vc12 Winnall Moors NR (DHS); South Wonston, 31.5.95, and subsequently, at m.v. light (PJSS); Wildhern, 1.9.98 (DGG); Oakley; Basingstoke; Bramley Frith NR (AHD); Selborne, 1993, 1994 (AEA); Farnborough, two in 1994 (RWP).

1221 *Strophedra weirana* (Douglas, 1850)

Widespread in the beech woods of the mainland vice-counties (Goater, 1974, 1992), but so far unrecorded from the Isle of Wight.

■ vc11 Roydon Woods, 3.10.98, larval spinnings on beech; Balmer Lawn, Brockenhurst (RJD); Crab Wood,

20.9.97, spinnings on beech; West Meon, 8.10.96, a few spinnings on beech (JRL, *et al.*); Botley Wood, 1999; West Walk (RJD).

■ vc12 Wildhern, nr Andover, 28.9.97, larvae; Eelmoor Marsh SSSI, 19.10.97, larvae on beech; Fleet Pond LNR, 7.10.97, larvae on beech; Tangley, 2.10.97, larvae on beech (DGG); Pamber Forest (RJD); Farnborough, 3.7.95, det. JRL (RWP).

1222 *Strophedra nitidana* (Fabricius, 1794)

Recorded from both the mainland vice-counties (Goater, 1974, 1992), for some reason very little has been seen of this species in recent years. It is stated (Bradley *et al.*, 1979) to be locally common in oak woods in southern England.

■ vc11 Set Thorns Inclosure, 22.6.99, two at m.v. light (DGG, MSP); Havant Thicket, 23.6.98, one at m.v. light (RJD).

1223 *Pammene splendidulana* (Guenée, 1845)

There have been a few records from the two mainland vice-counties (Goater, 1974, 1992). The imago seems to be elusive, but has sometimes been bred from randomly-collected spongy oak galls, and occasionally taken at light.

■ vc11 Browndown, 6.4.72, one bred by DWHF from spongy oak galls collected on 27.2.72 (comm. RJD); Kite's Croft, 8.5.95 (RJD).

■ vc12 Upper Hyde Woods, 10.5.80 (RJD); Zebon Copse, 21.4.97, conf. JRL (AMD).

1225 *Pammene obscurana* (Stephens, 1834)

A rare and local species, the larva of which feeds in the catkins of birch *Betula* spp. (Bradley *et al.*, 1979). Single specimens have been recorded in the past from Emer Bog and Botley Wood vc11 and Woolmer Forest vc12 (Goater, 1983, 1992). The imago can only be distinguished from its nearest congeners by genitalic examination.

■ vc11 Havant Thicket, 30.4.93, one at m.v. light (JRL).

1227 *Pammene inquilina* Fletcher, 1938

Recorded in small numbers from all three vice-counties (Goater, 1974, 1992). The moth flies early in the year and is easily overlooked; it is occasionally seen flying by day in afternoon sunshine.

■ vc12 Harewood Forest; Tadley Common (RJD).

1228 *Pammene argyrana* (Hübner, 1799)

Recorded from both mainland vice-counties, where it is locally common in oak woods, and also recently on the Isle of Wight (Goater, 1974, 1992).

■ vc10 Parkhurst Forest, 5.6.78, one at m.v. light (RJD). **New vc record.**

■ vc11 Matley Wood; Fareham; Wickham Common, 1999; Wendleholme NR; Rowner Wild Grounds (RJD); Gutner Point NR, Hayling Island, 24.4.93, three at rest on oak trunks (JRL, IRT).

■ vc12 Harewood Forest; Pamber Forest; Upper Hyde Wood (RJD); Oakley (AHD); Castle Bottom NR, 30.8.98, det. JRL (AMD).

1229 *Pammene albuginana* (Guenée, 1845)

Recorded from both mainland vice-counties (Goater, 1974, 1992), but not from the Isle of Wight. The moth is seldom seen, but has been bred from time to time from spongy oak galls collected in winter.

■ vc11 Hurn, 8.6.00, one at m.v. light (MJ); Roydon Woods, 10.7.96, a few at m.v. light (PRD, JRL); Hamble Common, 1996, one bred from a spongy oak gall (RJD); Hookheath Meadows NR, Southwick, 24.5.92, one at m.v. light (JRL).

■ vc12 Oakley (AHD).

1231 *Pammene spiniana* (Duponchel, 1843)

Recorded only occasionally, from all three vice-counties (Goater, 1974, 1992), and not since 1977. The larva feeds on blackthorn and hawthorn, and the moth is sometimes seen in numbers flying high along blackthorn hedgerows in late afternoon.

1232 *Pammene populana* (Fabricius, 1787)

A few records from the mainland vice-counties, and old ones from the Isle of Wight. The moth is found in damp areas, and is occasionally bred from spinnings found on sallows and willows *Salix* spp.

1233 *Pammene aurita* Razowski, 1991
= *aurantiana* (Staudinger, 1871)

First reported in Hamshire in 1957, this species is now widespread but local in all three vice-counties (Goater, 1974, 1992). The larva feeds on the seeds of sycamore *Acer pseudoplatanus*, and the moth comes readily to light.

■ vc10 Freshwater, 27.7.92 (SAK-J); Ventnor Undercliff, 28.7.77 (RJD); Shanklin, 21.7.95, two (JMC).

■ vc11 Hengistbury Head, one in 1999, det. PHS (MJ); Cadlands Estate, Beaulieu, 12.7.97, two at m.v. light (BG, JRL); Lower Test Marshes NR (DHS, 1992); Alverstoke, 10.8.98, one flying in sunshine around sycamore (SS); Waterlooville, 1996–2000 (RJM); Milton Common, Southsea, 12.8.99, one at m.v. light, det. JRL (IRT).

■ vc12 Selborne, 27.7.94, 15.7.97 (AEA); Farnborough, two in both 1994 and 1995 (RWP).

1234 *Pammene regiana* (Zeller, 1849)

Widespread in all three vice-counties but seldom seen unless the cocoons are sought under the bark of old sycamores during the winter: they are often abundant.

■ vc10 Freshwater, 11.7.92, 8.6.97, 15.6.98 (SAK-J); Shanklin, 30.6.95, one (JMC); Gurnard, 5.8.96 (DTB).

■ vc11 Bitterne, 22.7.94 (PAB); West Meon, 8.3.92, a few cocoons under sycamore bark (JRL); Hamble Common; Park Gate; Fareham; Wendleholme NR; Kingston, Portsmouth (RJD); Widley, Portsdown (PMP).

■ vc12 Bentley Station Meadow (PAB); Farnborough, two in 1994, 16.6.95 (RWP), 19.7.95, one (KW).

1235 *Pammene trauniana* ([Denis & Schiffermüller], 1775)

This is apparently very rare in Hampshire, having been reported only from Winchester and Botley Wood, a total of four specimens in all (Goater, 1983, 1992), and from Hurn in 2000, below. The larva feeds on the seeds of field

maple *Acer campestre*, and probably pupates in a manner similar to that of the previous species. The bark being less amenable to lifting, however, the cocoon is not detected.
- vc11 Hurn, 17.7.00, one at m.v. light, det. PJS (MJ).

1236 *Pammene fasciana* (Linnaeus, 1761)
Locally common in oak and sweet chestnut woodland, and recorded from all three vice-counties, though with few records from the Isle of Wight (Goater, 1974, 1992). The larva lives in acorns and sweet chestnuts, and the moth is sometimes bred from spongy galls. It also comes freely to light.
- vc10 Freshwater, 1.7 and 5.7.98, at m.v. light (SAK-J).

1236a *Pammene herrichiana* (Heinemann, 1854)
Very occasionally captured in the mainland vice-counties (Goater, 1974, 1992) in the vicinity of beech. The larva feeds in beech mast, and the insect is regarded by some authorities as an ecological race of *P. fasciana*.
- vc11 Lanes near Crab Wood, 8.3.91, one bred from dead stems of *Clematis* amongst beech trees (RJBH); Milton Common, Southsea, 1998, at light in garden (IRT); Sinah Common, Hayling Island, 15.8.98, at m.v. light (JRL, IRT, *et al.*).
- vc12 Cholderton, 21.5.95, two by day on beeches in H. Edmunds' garden (BG, JRL); Rye Common, 6.5.95, one at m.v. light (AHD).

1237 *Pammene germmana* (Hübner, 1799)
Recorded in numbers only in Botley Wood vc11 and Pamber Forest vc12 (Goater, 1974, 1992). Otherwise an uncommon and obscure species.
- vc11 Hookheath Meadows NR, Southwick, 10.6.94, one (JRL); Havant Thicket, 2.7.91, one on a tree trunk (RJBH).
- vc12 Wildhern, 1.7.98, at dusk (DGG); Abbotstone Down, 1.6.93, one (RJBH, JRL, DHS).

1238 *Pammene ochsenheimeriana* (Lienig & Zeller, 1846)
Recorded very occasionally from the mainland vice-counties; bred from aborted buds of giant fir *Abies grandis* (Goater, 1974, 1992). Otherwise associated with spruce *Picea abies* woodland.
- vc11 Holmsley area, 17.5.72 (RJD).

1239 *Pammene rhediella* (Clerck, 1759)
Recorded from all three vice-counties, and locally common (Goater, 1974, 1992). The moth flies rather high along hawthorn hedges in late afternoon, sometimes over blackthorn.
- vc10 Tennyson Down, 18.5.92, one (JRL, DHS, PHS).
- vc11 Lower Test Marshes NR (DHS, 1992); Farley Mount; Titchfield Haven (RJD); Browndown, 13.5.98, a few (JRL, IRT); Milton Common, Southsea, 1994 (IRT).
- vc12 Selborne, 1993 (AEA); Farnborough, 1.5.97 (RWP).

1271 *Pammene (Cydia) gallicana* (Guenée, 1845)
Locally common amongst the foodplant wild carrot *Daucus carota.*

- vc10 Whitecliff Bay (RJD).
- vc11 Pennington Marshes, 8.11.93, spinnings common on wild carrot *Daucus carota* along sea wall (BG, JRL); Balmer Lawn, Brockenhurst (RJD); Lower Test Marshes NR (BG, 1993); Botley Wood; Portsdown; Oxenbourne Down (RJD); Hilsea, 11.4.94, a few larvae; Great Salterns NR, Portsmouth (JRL); Southsea, 31.7.99, one at m.v. light; Milton Common, 9.8.99, one by day, both det. JRL, 19.7.00, one at light (IRT); Sandy Point NR, Hayling Island (RJD).

1272 *Pammene (Cydia) aurana* (Fabricius, 1775)
Very local, sometimes common (Goater, 1974, 1992), usually found resting on flowers of hogweed *Heracleum sphondylium* on sunny afternoons.
- vc8 Martin Down, 16.6.95, one by day (MCH).
- vc11 Sparsholt College (AHD); St Cross, 17.7.99, one at m.v. light (TWa); Hookheath Meadows NR, Southwick, 14.7.96, one (JRL); Browndown; Oxenbourne Down (RJD).
- vc12 Woolbury Ring, Stockbridge, 17.6.97, common flying round hogweed during the afternoon (BG); Wildhern, nr Andover, 29.6.97, by day (DGG).

1241 *Cydia compositella* (Fabricius, 1775)
Recorded from all three vice-counties (Goater, 1974, 1992). The moth is found in open country amongst clovers *Trifolium* spp., usually in small numbers but sometimes commonly, flying late in the afternoon sunshine.
- vc10 Werrar, 22.6.96 (DTB); Totland Bay (RJD).
- vc11 Wickham Common, 1999; Swanwick NR; Kite's Croft; Portsdown, 30.5.98, several at rest (RJD); Hookheath Meadows NR, Southwick, 23.5.92, one; Beacon Hill NNR, Warnford, 11.6.94, one; Southsea, 31.7.94, one at m.v. light (JRL).
- vc12 Winnall Moors NR (DHS); Bramley Frith NR (AHD); Odiham Common, 11.6.00, one by day (DGG); Farnborough, 12.6.95, one at light (RWP).

1242 *Cydia internana* (Guenée, 1845)
Very locally common to abundant amongst gorse in the mainland vice-counties (Goater, 1974, 1992), and recently found also on the Isle of Wight, below.
- vc10 Tennyson Down, 18.5.92, several by day (JRL, DHS, PHS). **New vc record.**
- vc11 Hale Purlieu, 14.5.94, flying commonly by day round just one or two gorse bushes (RJBH); Blackwell Common, 30 April (JEC); Hamble Common; Catisfield; Wickham Common; Wendleholme NR; Kite's Croft (RJD); Browndown, 13.5.98, a few; Sandy Point NR, Hayling Island, 10.6.94, one (JRL *et al.*).

1244 *Cydia gemmiferana* (Treitschke, 1835)
The classic locality for this species is Luccombe Chine, on the Isle of Wight, where it still flourishes. The foodplant is narrow-leaved everlasting-pea *Lathyrus sylvestris*.

1245 *Cydia janthinana* (Duponchel, 1835)
Local amongst the foodplant, hawthorn *Crataegus* spp. It is recorded from all three vice-counties, but there is

only one recent report from the Isle of Wight. The larva lives in the fruits.

■ vc10 Freshwater, 20.7.00, one at m.v. light (SAK-J).

■ vc11 Warsash shore, 13.7.95, genitalia det.; Hook Lake NR (RJD); Great Salterns NR, Portsmouth (JRL); Sandy Point NR, Hayling Island (RJD).

■ vc12 Yateley, Priors Lane, 21.7.96, one (AMD); Farnborough, 8.8.97 (RWP).

1246 *Cydia tenebrosana* (Duponchel, 1843)

Recorded in small numbers from all three vice-counties, but not recently from the Isle of Wight (Goater, 1974, 1992); it appears to be very local. The moth is occasionally encountered in flight on sunny afternoons, and the larva may be found in the fruits of wild rose *Rosa* spp.

■ vc11 Botley Wood, 29.9.94, a few larvae in fruits of rose *Rosa* spp. (RJBH, JRL).

1247 *Cydia funebrana* (Treitschke, 1835)

There are very few records from all three vice-counties (Goater, 1974, 1992). The imago is seldom seen, and is difficult to rear from fruits of blackthorn *Prunus spinosa* and cultivated plums containing larvae.

■ vc10 Yarmouth, 26.7.80, adult genitalia det. RJD (DMA).

■ vc11 Warsash shore, 17.6.98; Fareham, genit. checked; Chilling Copse (RJD); Milton Common, Southsea, 24.7.00, one at m.v. light, det. and set JRL (IRT).

■ vc12 Wildhern, nr Andover, 1.9.96, larvae (DGG); Farnborough, 10.6.95, bred from a Victoria plum (RWP).

■ vc22 Mortimer West End, 2000, first record (GJD).

1248 *Cydia molesta* (Busck, 1916)

This Oriental species has spread to many places across the world, where it is a pest of peach *Prunus persica* and other species of cultivated *Prunus*. It is occasionally imported accidentally into Britain. In Hampshire, two specimens are known to have been bred from imported fruit (Goater, 1992).

[1250 *Cydia lathyrana* (Hübner, 1813)

One unconfirmed record from Basingstoke (Goater, 1974).]

1251 *Cydia jungiella* (Clerck, 1759)

Widespread and common in rough grassland and downs, in all three vice-counties (Goater, 1974, 1992). The larva feeds on vetches *Vicia sepium* and other spp.

■ vc8 Martin Down, 29.4.90 (S. Nash).

■ vc10 Tennyson Down, 18.5.92, several (JRL, DHS, PHS); Totland Bay; Bouldnor; St Catherine's Bay; Old Park area; Luccombe Chine (RJD).

1254 *Cydia strobilella* (Linnaeus, 1758)

Local amongst spruce *Picea abies* in the mainland vice-counties (Goater, 1974, 1992). The moth is not often seen, but may be bred in abundance from fallen cones, collected in early spring.

■ vc11 Southsea, 15.5.98, one at m.v. light, first for garden (JRL).

1255 *Cydia succedana* ([Denis & Schiffermüller], 1775)

Abundant amongst gorse *Ulex* spp. throughout the three vice-counties, becoming established even on isolated bushes in gardens.

1255a *Cydia medicaginis* (Kuznetsov, 1962)

This species was found in Essex in 1988, and subsequent research revealed hitherto undetected specimens in collections, including two taken in Southampton in 1970 (Agassiz and Karsholt, 1989, Goater, 1992). Since then, two further specimens have been taken in Hampshire.

■ vc11 Winchester, 11.6 and 17.6.92 (DHS).

1256 *Cydia servillana* (Duponchel, 1836)

The slender, fusiform galls made in young sallow *Salix* spp. shoots by the larva of this species are locally common in the mainland vice-counties (Goater, 1974, 1992). Occasionally, the moth is seen in flight during sunny afternoons.

■ vc10 Shide Chalk Pit LNR, 14.6.99, empty pupa in galled twig of sallow *S. cinerea* (DTB) (Knill-Jones, 2000). **New vc record**.

■ vc11 Botley Wood, 19.5.95, three flying in afternoon sunshine (BG, JRL); Southwick, 29.1.94, several galls in *Salix cinerea* and *S. caprea* (RJH, JRL).

■ vc12 Winnall Moors NR (DHS).

1257 *Cydia nigricana* (Fabricius, 1794)

The "pea maggot", until recently a familiar sight in garden peas *Pisum sativum*, is now quite rare. The larva feeds also on the seeds of wild species of vetch *Vicia* and pea *Lathyrus*, but the moth is seldom reported at large. There are records from all three vice-counties (Goater, 1974, 1992).

■ vc11 Broughton Down, 16.5.00, three by day; Nutburn, nr North Baddesley; Sparsholt College (AHD); Wickham Common, 1999 (RJD); Botley Wood, 17.6.93, one (JRL, RMP); Sandy Point NR, Hayling Island, 29.5.95, one (JRL).

■ vc12 Wildhern, nr Andover, 4.6.97, at dusk, conf. AHD (DGG); Basingstoke; Bartley Heath NR (AHD).

1259 *Cydia fagiglandana* (Zeller, 1841)

Common in and around beech woods in the mainland vice-counties, but still only a few records from the Isle of Wight (Goater, 1974, 1992). The larva feeds in beech mast.

■ vc11 Roydon Woods, 10.7.96, several at m.v. light (PRD, JRL); Lower Test Marshes NR (DHS, 1993); Sparsholt College (AHD); Chandlers Ford, 5.7.91, 17.7.94 (BG); Soberton, 30.6.95, a few at m.v. light; Botley Wood, 12.7.94, a few at m.v. light; Southwick, 8.7.96, one at m.v. light; Creech Wood, Denmead, 16.5.97, one at m.v. light (JRL).

■ vc12 Selborne, 1994 (AEA); Noar Hill, 1993 (AMJ); Farnborough, 13.7.94 (RWP).

1260 *Cydia splendana* (Hübner, 1799)

Common amongst oak in all three vice-counties. The larva lives in acorns.

■ vc8 Martin Down, 24.8.90 (MFVC, S. Nash).

■ vc10 Shanklin (JMC).

■ vc11 Hengistbury Head, 1997, det. PHS (MJ).

1261 *Cydia pomonella* (Linnaeus, 1758)

10 mm

Common in orchards and gardens throughout the three vice-counties (JRL). This is the common "apple maggot".
■ vc10 Shanklin, one indoors on 1.2.97, probably emerged from stored apples (JMC).

1262 *Cydia amplana* (Hübner, 1799)

This species is a presumed immigrant which is appearing in increasing numbers in the West Country, notably at Portland, Dorset, and may become established. The first authenticated record was from S Devon in 1990.
■ vc11 Fareham, 19.8.97, one at m.v. light, genitalia det. conf. JRL (RJD). **New county record.**

1262a *Cydia deshaisiana* (Lucas, 1858)
= *saltitans* (Westwood, 1858)
Mexican Jumping Bean Moth
The only specimen known to have been taken at large in this country came to m.v. light in Southsea on 8.9.90 (Goater, 1992).

1266 *Cydia pactolana* (Zeller, 1840)
The first British specimen was taken at Alice Holt, N Hants, on 12.6.65 (Goater, 1974). Since then, four specimens have been caught in Botley Wood, S Hants, on different dates between 1.6.76 and 2.5.1.85 (Goater, 1992).

1266a *Cydia illutana* (Herrich-Schäffer, 1851)
This species was first reported in Britain in 1984 (Bradley, 1985), but the first known British specimen was subsequently shown to have been taken at Southsea, S Hants, on 10.6.75 (Goater, 1992). The moth has since been found breeding in cones of larch *Larix decidua* but not, so far, in Hampshire.

1267 *Cydia cosmophorana* (Treitschke, 1835)
The first British specimens were taken in 1930 at Beaulieu Road, New Forest (Goater, 1974), along with *C. coniferana* and *C. conicolana*. It has since been taken in Woolmer Forest, N Hants (Goater, 1992). There have been hardly any recent records, probably for want of searching for the species.
■ vc12 Brighton Hill, Basingstoke, 20.6.98, one at m.v. light (AHD). Second vc12 record.

1268 *Cydia coniferana* (Ratzeburg, 1840)
Widespread in the New Forest and parts of NE Hampshire (Goater, 1974, 1992). The moth flies around pine trees late in the afternoon, or may be dislodged from branches in dull weather. The larva feeds in the bark, betraying its presence by exuding frass in the crevices. The fact that it has not been reported very recently is almost certainly because it has not been looked for.

1269 *Cydia conicolana* (Heylaerts, 1874)
Local but almost certainly overlooked, amongst Scots pine *Pinus sylvestris* in the New Forest and NE Hampshire

(Goater, 1974, 1992). The moth has been seen flying around pine trees in late afternoon, but its presence is usually detected by finding fallen cones with an exit hole at the tip of one of the scales; if second-year cones are collected from the overhanging branches, the emergence in due course of one or more moths can be anticipated with some confidence.
■ vc12 Yateley Common, 26.3.94, larval exit holes seen in fallen cones on Scots pine (TD, BG, JRL).

The larva of most species of the following genus, *Dichrorampha*, live in the rootstocks of Asteraceae (Compositae), favouring yarrow *Achillea millefolium*, ox-eye daisy *Leucanthemum vulgare*, tansy *Tanacetum vulgare* and mugwort *Artemisia vulgaris*, and the moths fly over these plants on sunny afternoons and evenings during the summer. At other times of day they are inconspicuous, though at night they occasionally come to light.

1273 *Dichrorampha petiverella* (Linnaeus, 1758)
Locally common amongst yarrow *Achillea millefolium* and ox-eye daisy *Leucanthemum vulgare* in all three vice-counties. The moth flies around the foodplants in the late afternoon and evening.
■ vc10 Tennyson Down, 18.6.99 (SAK-J); Yarmouth; Compton Bay; Seaview; Apes Down (RJD).

1274 *Dichrorampha alpinana* (Treitschke, 1830)
Apparently rare amongst the foodplant, ox-eye daisy *Leucanthemum vulgare* (Goater, 1974, 1992), but now recorded from all three vice-counties. The moth flies over the foodplant in late afternoon and evening.
■ vc10 Freshwater, 14.7.97 (Knill-Jones, 1998c); Gurnard (JMC). **New vc record.**
■ vc11 Chandlers Ford, 8.8.91, one at m.v. light (BG); Fareham; Wickham Common; Shedfield Common; genit. checked (RJD).
■ vc12 Oakley (AHD); Selborne, 12.7.91 (AEA).

1275 *Dichrorampha flavidorsana* Knaggs, 1867
Very local, possibly overlooked, amongst tansy *Tanacetum vulgare*. Fassnidge had a colony in the Southampton area in the 1930s (Goater, 1974), and more recently, it has been found breeding at Southsea (Goater, 1992). No record from the Isle of Wight or N Hants.

1276 *Dichrorampha plumbagana* (Treitschke, 1830)
Common and widespread amongst yarrow *Achillea millefolium* in all three mainland vice-counties, although recent records from the Isle of Wight doubtless fail to give a complete picture. The moth flies around the foodplant in late afternoon, and also comes to light.
■ vc8 Martin Down, 8.6.92 (JRL, RMP).
■ vc10 Compton Bay; Brighstone Forest; Redcliff; Apes Down (RJD).

1277 *Dichrorampha senectana* Guenée, 1845
Stated to be locally common along the foot of the downs at Ventnor, Isle of Wight in 1880 (Goater, 1974), this

species has not been reported since from anywhere on the Island nor in Hampshire.

1278 *Dichrorampha sequana* (Hübner, 1799)
Local amongst the foodplants, yarrow *Achillea millefolium* and tansy *Tanacetum vulgare*. Recorded from all three vice-counties, but not recently from the Isle of Wight. The moth flies over the foodplants on sunny afternoons.
■ vc11 Botley Wood, 29.5.76; Portsdown, 3.7.75, and several in 1996 (RJD); Milton Common, Southsea, 1994 (IRT).
■ vc12 Brighton Hill, Basingstoke, 26.6.96, common on rough land (AHD).

1279 *Dichrorampha acuminatana* (Lienig & Zeller, 1846)
Local in all three vice-counties (Goater, 1974, 1992), and probably overlooked amongst commoner species which fly with it over ox-eye daisy *Leucanthemum vulgare* and tansy *Tanacetum vulgare* on sunny afternoons during the summer.
■ vc10 Yarmouth, 18.5.92, one (JRL, DHS, PHS).
■ vc11 Hengistbury Head, two in 1999, det. PHS (MJ); Sparsholt College, 16.8.94, one at Rothamsted trap (AHD); Swanwick NR, 19.5.95, genit. prep. 3840, conf. JRL; Fareham, 17.8.98; Wickham Common, 1999, genit. checked (RJD), Soberton, 30.6.95, one at m.v. light; Swanwick NR, 20.8.96, a few at m.v. light (JRL); Milton Common, Southsea, 2.9.96 (IRT).
■ vc12 Brighton Hill, Basingstoke (AHD); Selborne, 1993, 1994, 19.8.96, conf. K. Tuck (BMNH) (AEA).

1280 *Dichrorampha consortana* (Stephens, 1852)
Recorded from all three vice-counties (Goater, 1974, 1992) but evidently rare or overlooked. The larva lives in the flower-stems of ox-eye daisy *Leucanthemum vulgare*, causing a slight swelling, but colonies of the plant are often searched in vain for this evidence (BG, pers. obs.).
■ vc12 Selborne, 1994, 10.8, 22.8 and 25.8.98 (AEA).

1281 *Dichrorampha simpliciana* (Haworth, 1811)
Local amongst mugwort *Artemisia vulgaris* in the mainland vice-counties, but not reported recently from the Isle of Wight (Goater, 1974, 1992).
■ vc11 Botley Wood, 1999 (RJD); Swanwick NR, 26.7.97 (RJD), 20.8.96, a few at m.v. light (JRL); Hilsea, 16.8.92, one; Milton Common, Southsea, 1998, at light in garden (IRT); Sinah Common, Hayling Island, 15.8.98, a few at m.v. light (JRL *et al.*).
■ vc12 Winnall Moors NR (DHS); Greywell Moors NR, 2.8.94, two at m.v. light (AHD); Selborne, 15.8.93, conf. JRL from photograph (AEA).

1282 *Dichrorampha sylvicolana* Heinemann, 1863
This sluggish and inconspicuous species lives as a larva in the rootstocks of sneezewort *Achillea ptarmica*. The moth climbs up the foodplant during sunny afternoons but is reluctant to fly and readily drops out of sight. Fassnidge, quoted in Goater (1974), made acute observations on its habits. It has been reported from "Isle of Wight", and

Chandlers Ford, Emer Bog and Ashurst, all in S Hants (Goater, *ibid.* and 1992).

1284 *Dichrorampha gueneeana* Obraztsov, 1953
Local in all three vice-counties (Goater, 1974, 1992), flying over the foodplants, yarrow *Achillea millefolium* and ox-eye daisy *Leucanthemum vulgare* during the afternoon and evening.
■ vc10 Compton Bay (RJD).
■ vc11 Hook area; Park Gate; Fareham; Portsdown (RJD); Hookheath Meadows NR, Southwick, 14.7.96, one (JRL).
■ vc12 Brighton Hill, Basingstoke, 19.7.96, one (AHD); Farnborough, 26.6.94, three on 3.7.95 (RWP).

1285 *Dichrorampha plumbana* (Scopoli, 1763)
Common and widespread amongst yarrow *Achillea millefolium* in the two mainland vice-counties (JRL); on the Isle of Wight, the status suggested in Goater (1974) probably still holds good, though there are few records to support it.
■ vc8 Martin Down, 8.6.92 (JRL, RMP).
■ vc10 Brook; Luccombe Chine (RJD).

1286 *Dichrorampha sedatana* Busck, 1906
Recorded in the past from all three vice-counties (Goater, 1974, 1994), but evidently extremely local amongst the foodplant, tansy *Tanacetum vulgare*.

1287 *Dichrorampha aeratana* (Pierce & Metcalfe, 1915)
This species is distinguished with difficulty from *D. plumbana*, and records can only be accepted following genitalic examination. The sparse records indicate that it is probably fairly widespread on the mainland, but there is only one old report from the Isle of Wight (Goater, 1974, 1992). The larva inhabits the rootstocks of ox-eye daisy *Leucanthemum vulgare*.
■ vc11 Botley Wood, 4.6.93, one (JRL); Swanwick NR; Wickham Common, 1999; Oxenbourne Down; genit. checked (RJD).
■ vc12 Chilbolton Down, 25.5.92, one, genitalia det. (JRL); Winnall Moors NR (DHS); Noar Hill (RJD); Ashford Hangers NR, 21.5.93, two, genitalia det. (JRL).

Epermeniidae (7)

0477 *Phaulernis dentella* (Zeller, 1839)
There is a single record of this species in 1936 from S Hants (Goater, 1983). It may have been overlooked. The larva feeds in spun fruits of species of Apiaceae (Umbelliferae), notably rough chervil *Chaerophyllum temulentum*, burnet-saxifrage *Pimpinella saxifraga* and ground-elder *Aegopodium podagraria* (Godfray and Sterling, 1996).

0478 *Phaulernis fulviguttella* (Zeller, 1839)
Given as common in several localities in S Hants (Goater, 1974) and at Leckford in N Hants (Goater, 1992), but nothing has been heard of this species recently. There are no records from the Isle of Wight. The larva feeds in seed-

heads of angelica *Angelica sylvestris* and hogweed *Heracleum sphondylium*.
- vc11 Oxenbourne Down, 18.8.72 (RJD).
- vc12 Pamber Forest, 14.8.76 (RJD).

0480 *Epermenia (Cataplectica) profugella* (Stainton, 1856)
The few records of this insect in the county are given by Goater (1974, 1992), and there are no recent ones. Nor have the authors received confirmation of the species' presence on the Isle of Wight.

0481 *Epermenia falciformis* (Haworth, 1828)
= *illigerella* auctt.
Local in damp woodland and marshes. Recorded from all three vice-counties, but given as common only at Ampfield and Emer Bog (Goater, 1974) and Botley Wood, fairly common (Goater, 1992). Larva on wild angelica *Angelica sylvestris*.

0482 *Epermenia insecurella* (Stainton, 1849)
Recorded in the past from Freshwater and Sandown on the Isle of Wight (Goater, 1974), but not since. The moth is associated with bastard-toadflax *Thesium humifusum*. This plant still flourishes on the cliff-top at Freshwater and might well repay diligent search there, but it is very local and rather rare on the mainland (Brewis, *et al.*, 1996).

0483 *Epermenia chaerophyllella* (Goeze, 1783)
Common in many places in all three vice-counties. The larva feeds on foliage of several species of Apiaceae (Umbelliferae), but in Hampshire it is most often reported from hogweed *Heracleum sphondylium*.

0484 *Epermenia aequidentellus* (Hofmann, 1867)
Rare or overlooked. There are plenty of old records from the Isle of Wight, and scattered ones from the mainland vice-counties (Goater 1974, 1992).
- vc11 Southsea, 9.8.98, one at m.v. light, first for garden (JRL).
- vc12 Bramley Frith Wood North, 19.6.00, one at m.v. light (AHD).

Schreckensteiniidae (1)

0485 *Schreckensteinia festaliella* (Hübner, 1819)
Given as widespread and locally common in Britain (Godfray and Sterling, 1996), but there are few Hampshire records and only two recent ones from the Isle of Wight. The larva feeds on raspberry and bramble *Rubus idaeus* and *R. fruticosus* agg.
- vc10 Freshwater, 23.8.00, one at m.v. light (SAK-J); Brighstone Down, 17.5.86 (JRL).
- vc11 Sandy Balls, Godshill, 20.4.94, one (RJBH, JRL); Bitterne, 23.8.00, one at light, new record for site (PAB); Hamble Common; Hook-with-Warsash, 1996; The Moors NR, Bishop's Waltham; Portsdown; Farlington Marshes (RJD); Clanfield, 15.4.97, one; Havant Thicket, 8.5.98, one (JRL, IRT).
- vc12 Wildhern, nr Andover, 27.5.97, by day (DGG).

Alucitidae (1)

There is only one species in Britain belonging to this family. *Alucita hexadactyla* Twenty-plume Moth or Many-plumed Moth is not in fact related to the other plume moths in the family Pterophoridae. It is somewhat like them however in having cleft wings. In this case though both fore and hind wings are divided into six lobes.

1288 *Alucita hexadactyla* Linnaeus, 1758
Twenty-plume Moth
The larva feeds on honeysuckle *Lonicera periclymenun*.
- vc10 Gurnard; Shanklin (JMC).
- vc11 Hollands Wood, 2.5.94, two at toilet lights at campsite (AHD); Cadlands Estate, Beaulieu, 12.7.97, one at m.v. light (BG, JRL); Chandlers Ford, still common (BG); Winchester, Sarum Road, in house, 31.7.90, and at m.v. light, 24.5 and 5.9.91 (RJBH); Locks Heath, six in 2000, first on 8.4.00, (PCa); Fareham (RJD); Warsash, 20.5.94, one; Great Salterns NR, Portsmouth; Southsea, common; Sandy Point NR, Hayling Island, 14.7.92, one at m.v. light, and several since (JRL).
- vc12 Oakley (AHD); Bramley Depot, Pamber, 1994 (GJD); Selborne, 1993–95, fairly common (AEA); Farnborough, two in 1995 (RWP); Yateley Common, rare (AMD).

Pyralidae (149 + 4† + [1])

1289 *Euchromius ocellea* (Haworth, 1811)
A very scarce immigrant. Eight old records are given in Goater (1974), one from the Isle of Wight, three from vc11 and four from vc12. Since 1980, it has been reported on the following 12 occasions – in March (two), April

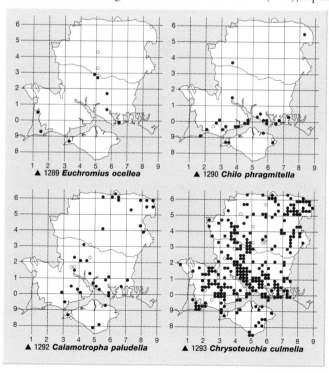

▲ 1289 *Euchromius ocellea*   ▲ 1290 *Chilo phragmitella*

▲ 1292 *Calamotropha paludella*   ▲ 1293 *Chrysoteuchia culmella*

(one), May (one), September (two), October (three) and November (three).

■ vc10 Freshwater, 23.9.85, 21.9, 20.10 and 12.11.88 and 8.3.97, singles at m.v. light (SAK-J).

■ vc11 Christchurch, 8.3.97, one at m.v. light (MJ); St Ives, nr Ringwood, 11.11.88 (JHC); Winchester, 5.4.85 (J. Wells), Morestead, 12.10.85 (DHS); Swanmore, 25.11.96, one found dead (Skinner and Parsons, 1999); Fareham, 14.5.98, one at m.v. light (Dickson, 1998); Southsea, 6.10.85 (JRL).

1290 *Chilo phragmitella* (Hübner, 1805)

Common in extensive reedbeds, an occasional wanderer elsewhere. That said, we have received only two records from vc12, from Leckford and Fleet Pond.

1292 *Calamotropha paludella* (Hübner, 1824)

Breeding colonies are extremely local but perhaps overlooked, and none have been reported since 1980 except at Freshwater vc10, Browndown vc11, Fleet Pond, and Alice Holt (Tilbury, 1993) vc12. Elsewhere, reported as an occasional wanderer.

1293 *Chrysoteuchia culmella* (Linnaeus, 1758)

Very common in grassy places throughout the three vice-counties.

1294 *Crambus pascuella* (Linnaeus, 1758)

Widespread and fairly common to common in grassy places. The dark-coloured ab. *obscurellus* has been reported from the New Forest and Chandlers Ford vc11.

1296 *Crambus silvella* (Hübner, 1813)

Locally common in bogs in the New Forest, very local and occasional elsewhere.

1297 *Crambus uliginosellus* Zeller, 1850

Locally common in the wetter bogs of the New Forest vc11, associated with deergrass *Trichophorum caespitosum*; not seen at Shedfield Common vc11 since 1973, and no recent record from Woolmer Forest vc12.

■ vc12 Bartley Heath, 14.7.87, conf. AMD (AHD).

1299 *Crambus hamella* (Thunberg, 1788)

Locally common on the drier moors of the New Forest; recently, there have been a number of records from North Hampshire, detailed below, but it is still unrecorded from the Isle of Wight.

■ vc11 Southsea, 28.8.00, one at m.v. light, first record for the area (JRL).

■ vc12 Eelmoor Marsh SSSI, 23.8.97, 30+ at m.v. light, identity confirmed (DGG); Farnborough, 15.8.95, two at m.v. light (RWP); Yateley Common, fairly common; Castle Bottom NNR, 16.8.97, one, 30.8.98, eight (AMD).

1300 *Crambus pratella* (Linnaeus, 1758)

Apparently very rare and local in the county, and the only recent record is from Highcliffe vc11, 5.7.89 (EHW). Possibly overlooked, but probably lost from localities such as Baddesley Great Covert (built over) and Farley Mount.

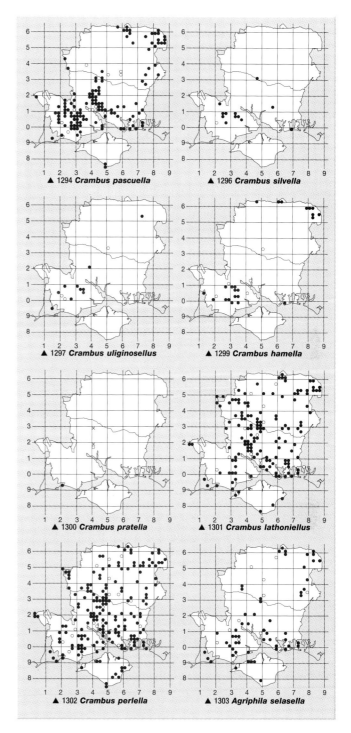

▲ 1294 *Crambus pascuella*   ▲ 1296 *Crambus silvella*

▲ 1297 *Crambus uliginosellus*   ▲ 1299 *Crambus hamella*

▲ 1300 *Crambus pratella*   ▲ 1301 *Crambus lathoniellus*

▲ 1302 *Crambus perlella*   ▲ 1303 *Agriphila selasella*

1301 *Crambus lathoniellus* (Zincken, 1817)

Common to very common throughout.

1302 *Crambus perlella* (Scopoli, 1763)

Common in boggy areas, where ab. *warringtonellus* Stainton predominates, and on chalk downland, more occasional elsewhere in the three vice-counties.

1303 *Agriphila selasella* (Hübner, 1813)

Local, chiefly coastal and in the New Forest, but also in other localities such as Selborne vc12, where it is fairly common (AEA). Other interesting records include those given below.

■ vc10 Chale Green, 16.7.95 (SRC).

■ vc11 Needs Ore, 14.8.96, common at light (BG); Chandlers Ford, 7.8.91, 23.7.96 (BG); N Hayling Island (PRD); Gutner Point, 16.8.96, two (AMD).

■ vc12 Winnall Moors NR (DHS); Selborne, 11 specimens from 25.7.95, at light (AEA); Bentley Station Meadow, 28.7.95 (PAB); Yateley Common, occasional; Rye Common, 26.7.96; Shortheath Common, 13.8.97, several; Castle Bottom NNR, 30.8.98 (AMD); Farnborough, 25.7.95, two at light (RWP).

1304 *Agriphila straminella* ([Denis & Schiffermüller], 1775)
Very common in grassy places throughout.

1305 *Agriphila tristella* ([Denis & Schiffermüller], 1775)
Generally common to very common in grassy places throughout the three vice-counties.

1306 *Agriphila inquinatella* ([Denis & Schiffermüller], 1775)
Common on coastal shingle and dunes, much less so inland.

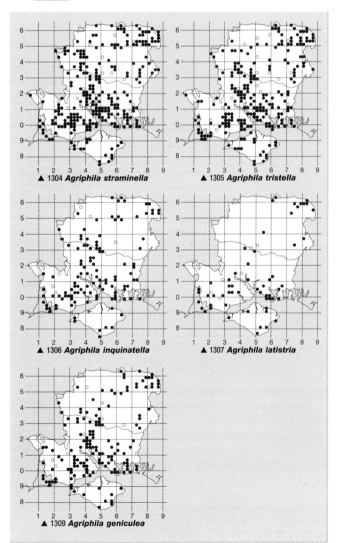

▲ 1304 *Agriphila straminella*

▲ 1305 *Agriphila tristella*

▲ 1306 *Agriphila inquinatella*

▲ 1307 *Agriphila latistria*

▲ 1309 *Agriphila geniculea*

1307 *Agriphila latistria* (Haworth)
Frequent in the New Forest, local to rare elsewhere. Recent records of interest are given below.

■ vc10 Shanklin, 16.7.97, one indoors (JMC).

■ vc11 Chandlers Ford, 15.8.91 (BG).

■ vc12 Pamber Forest, 2000, first record (GJD); Selborne, singletons at light during July and August in most years since 1995 (AEA); Yateley Common, occasional, 1991–1996; Castle Bottom NNR, 20.8.96, six, 30.8.98, two; Hazeley Heath, 13.8.96; Broxhead Common, 18.8.97, several (AMD); Farnborough, 19.7.95, one at light (RWP).

1309 *Agriphila geniculea* (Haworth, 1811)
The commonest autumn crambid throughout the three vice-counties.

1313 *Catoptria pinella* (Linnaeus, 1758)
Frequent in the New Forest, otherwise local and rather uncommon and chiefly in heathy localities.

■ vc10 Chale Green, 5.7 and 12.7.95 (SRC).

■ vc12 Selborne, fairly common at light (AEA); Bentley Station Meadow, 28.7.95 (PAB); Yateley Common, Bramshill Common, Shortheath Common, occasional (AMD).

1316 *Catoptria falsella* ([Denis & Schiffermüller], 1775)
A rather uncommon species which favours villages with old, thatched cottages. All recent records are given below.

■ vc11 Highcliffe, three between 3.7 and 5.8.94 (RAC); Beaulieu, 6.7.94 (BI-J); Cadlands House, 12.7.97, one at m.v. light (BG, JRL); Kings Somborne, several in July 1994, at m.v. light (TJN); Chandlers Ford, 4.8.91, 19.7.94 (BG); Moorgreen Meadows, 1.7 and 4.8.95; Marwell Zoological Park, 21.7.95 (PAB); N Hayling Island (PRD).

■ vc12 Cholderton, 1995, two at m.v. light (HE); Winnall Moors NR (DHS); East Stratton, 2.8.91 (BI-J); Alton, 24.7.95 (PAB); Greywell Moors, 1996 (AHD); Selborne, rather common at light, 31 specimens in 1995 (AEA); Yateley Common, occasional (AMD); Frith End, 22.7 to 27.8.95, four recorded (KW).

1317 *Catoptria verellus* (Zincken, 1817)
■ vc11 Southsea, 4.7.01, male at m.v. light (JRL, conf. BG). **First confirmed record for county.**

1321 *Thisanotia chrysonuchella* (Scopoli, 1763)
This species has virtually disappeared from Hampshire and the Isle of Wight. The only recent record to hand is given below.

■ vc10 Chale Green, 28.5.93 (SRC).

1323 *Pediasia contaminella* (Hübner, 1796)
Local but probably overlooked on account of its unprepossessing appearance. All recent records are given below.

■ vc10 St Helens Spit, 26.7.94 (SAK-J).

■ vc11 Hengistbury Head, first noted in 1994, very common in 1997 (MJ); Hincheslea Moor, 21.7.00, three at m.v. light (AHD); Beaulieu, 6.8.95 (BI-J); Southsea, 26.7.96, 5.7 and 8.9.97, at light (IRT); Sinah Common, Hayling Island, 15.8.98, at m.v. light (JRL, IRT, *et al.*); Gutner Point, 22.9.95 (AMD).

■ vc12 Basing House, 19.7.96, one; Warren Heath, 24.7.96, one in Heath trap (AMD); Selborne, 27.7.94, 16.7.95, 7.8.97, conf. BG from photo, singles at light (AEA); Yateley Common, rather common; Shortheath Common, 13.8.97 (AMD); Whitehill, 26.7.95 (S. Povey, det. AEA); Farnborough, 17.7.93 (RWP, comm. JRL), second record for vc12. Also seen in July 1994 and July–August 1995, fairly common (RWP).

1324 *Pediasia aridella* (Thunberg, 1788)

A very local coastal species, with one remarkable inland site discovered in 2000 by AHD. All recent records are given below.

■ vc11 Hengistbury Head, 1998, one, conf. BG (MJ); Hincheslea Moor, 21.7.00, two adults found amongst heather and grasses and another at m.v. light, conf. BG (AHD); Cosham, 19.8, 20.8, 21.8.95 (two), conf. JRL (TJJ); Southsea, 6.7.98 (IRT); N Hayling Island, occasional (PRD).

1325 *Platytes alpinella* (Hübner, 1813)

A rare coastal species which is very occasionally reported inland. Recent records are given below.

■ vc10 Freshwater, 12.7.94, 12.8.98, at m.v. light (SAK-J).

■ vc11 Highcliffe, 23.7.92 (EHW); Brick Kiln Inclosure 29.7.91 (AJP); Southsea, 20.8.97, one at light (IRT), 22.8.97, 10.8.99, singles at m.v. light (JRL); Hayling Island, Sinah Common, 15.8.98, several at m.v. light (TJN).

■ vc12 Farnborough, 23.7.94 (RWP). Second record for vc12.

1326 *Platytes cerussella* ([Denis & Schiffermüller], 1775)

Locally common on coastal shingle. Recent records include those given below.

■ vc10 Freshwater, 9.7.94 (SAK-J).

■ vc11 Cadlands House, 13.6.97, several at m.v. light (BG); Hurst Castle, 29.7.96 (JEC); Hook Shore, 11.7.96, two (RJD).

1328 *Schoenobius gigantella* ([Denis & Schiffermüller], 1775)

No breeding colony is known in Hampshire or the Isle of Wight, but very occasional wanderers appear at light. All recent records are given below.

■ vc10 Blackgang, one on 1.8.95 (DBW).

■ vc11 Winchester on 8.7.89 (DHS) and singles at Southsea on 19.6.98, 18.6.99, 30.6 and 5.7.00 (IRT), both in vc11.

1329 *Donacaula forficella* (Thunberg, 1794)

Local in marshes and bogs, especially those of the New Forest, and an occasional wanderer elsewhere.

■ vc10 Binstead, 1.8.97, first for garden (BJW).

■ vc11 Chandlers Ford, 21.6.00, a very dark male at m.v. light, identity checked with BG (BE).

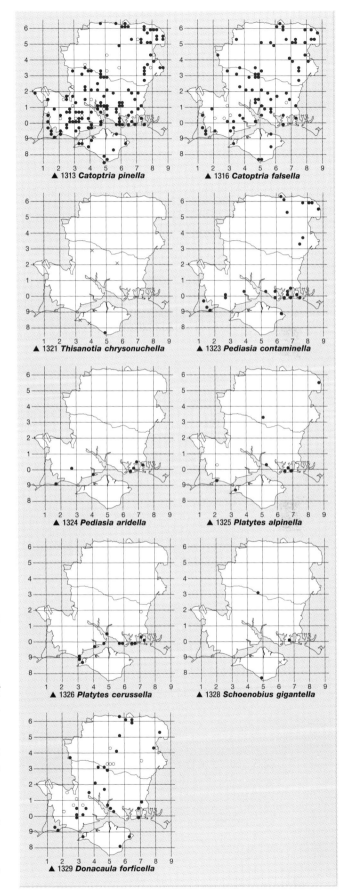

▲ 1313 **Catoptria pinella** ▲ 1316 **Catoptria falsella**

▲ 1321 **Thisanotia chrysonuchella** ▲ 1323 **Pediasia contaminella**

▲ 1324 **Pediasia aridella** ▲ 1325 **Platytes alpinella**

▲ 1326 **Platytes cerussella** ▲ 1328 **Schoenobius gigantella**

▲ 1329 **Donacaula forficella**

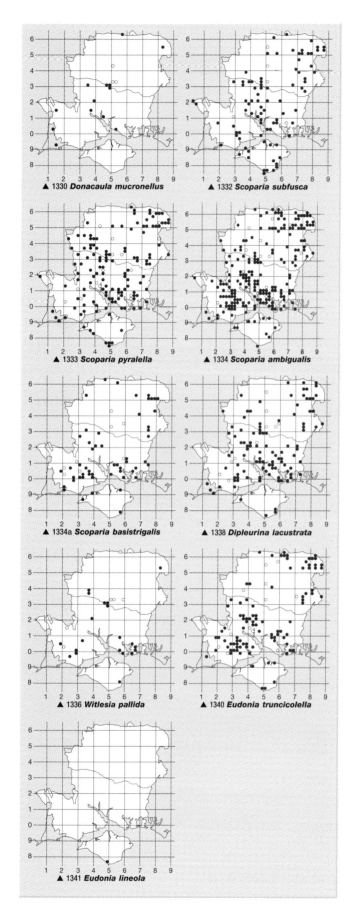

▲ 1330 *Donacaula mucronellus*

▲ 1332 *Scoparia subfusca*

▲ 1333 *Scoparia pyralella*

▲ 1334 *Scoparia ambigualis*

▲ 1334a *Scoparia basistrigalis*

▲ 1338 *Dipleurina lacustrata*

▲ 1336 *Witlesia pallida*

▲ 1340 *Eudonia truncicolella*

▲ 1341 *Eudonia lineola*

1330 *Donacaula mucronellus* ([Denis & Schiffermüller], 1775)
Another local and uncommon species; unlike the previous, associated more with fens and marshes than with bogs, and like it, an occasional wanderer.
■ vc10 Freshwater, 17.5.99 (SAK-J).
■ vc11 Woolston, 29.7.97, one at m.v. light (ARC); Titchfield Haven, 5.7.94 (PMP).

1332 *Scoparia subfusca* Haworth, 1811
Uncommon, but like its congeners probably either ignored or unidentified and so under-recorded.
■ vc11 Cadlands House, 13.6.97, one at m.v. light (BG), 13.7.97 (one) (BG, JRL); Whitenap, Romsey, 24.6.95 (MJB); Kings Somborne, 26.6.93 (TJN); Chandlers Ford, 4.8.91 (BG).
■ vc12 Basing House, 19.7.96, three; Castle Bottom NNR, 15.7.95; Rye Common, 5.8.96, five, 26.7.96, one (AMD); Bentley Station Meadow, 28.7.95 (PAB); Frith End, 22.7.95 (KW); Farnborough, 19.7.95, two at light, 5.6.96, two (RWP).

1333 *Scoparia pyralella* ([Denis & Schiffermüller], 1775)
Common on the coast and on what remains of the chalk downland; very occasional elsewhere.

1334 *Scoparia ambigualis* (Treitschke, 1829)
A common woodland species.

1334a *Scoparia basistrigalis* Knaggs, 1866
Uncommon, perhaps overlooked. Frequently misidentified. The following recent records are considered impeccable.
■ vc10 Freshwater, 26.7.98 (SAK-J).
■ vc11 Chandlers Ford, 7.7.92 (BG); Cosham, 11.8.94, det. JRL (TJJ); Milton Common, Southsea, 13.7.00, one, and 18.7.00, two, at m.v. light, conf. JRL (IRT); Havant Thicket, 28.6.95, at m.v. light (JRL).
■ vc12 Newtown Common, 5.7.95, two resting on oak boles (AHD); Basing House, 19.7.96, three; Hillside Common, 16.7.99, two; Odiham Common, 11.7.97, several; Rye Common, 5.8.96, three; Zebon Copse, 9.7.97, several (AMD); Selborne, 12 specimens from 28.6.95 to date, at light (AEA).

1335 *Scoparia ancipitella* (de la Harpe, 1855)
No recent record (Goater, 1992).

1338 *Dipleurina lacustrata* (Panzer, 1804)
Fairly common to common in many places throughout the three vice-counties.

1336 *Witlesia pallida* (Curtis, 1827)
Very local in bogs and marshes, wandering occasionally.
■ vc11 Vales Moor, 23.7.97; Brockenhurst, 1996, at m.v. light in garden (JEC); Emer Bog, 18.8.93 (NB), in coll. BG; Fareham, 23.6.00, at m.v. light conf. RJD (MLO); Southsea, 22.8.97, one at light (IRT).
■ vc12 Winnall Moors NR (DHS).

1340 *Eudonia truncicolella* (Stainton, 1849)
Common in woodlands throughout.

1341 *Eudonia lineola* (Curtis, 1827)

Extremely scarce or overlooked. Only one recent record, this is given below.
■ vc10 Chale Green, 1.9.93 (SRC).

1342 *Eudonia angustea* (Curtis, 1827)

Rather frequent on the coast, but very local inland except on the New Forest heaths.
■ vc11 Steamer Point Wood, 25.8.95; Yew Hill, 1.10.94 (PAB).
■ vc12 Hazeley Heath, 13.8.96; Rye Common, 6.5.95 (AMD); Selborne, common at light in autumn and also in spring, evidently having overwintered (AEA); Noar Hill NR, 13.10.95 (AMJ); Frith End, 10.6.95, one at light (KW).

1343 *Eudonia delunella* (Stainton, 1849)

The strongholds of this species in Hampshire appear to be Havant Thicket and parts of the New Forest, but recently several odd records have come in from elsewhere. No recent record from the Isle of Wight, and there remains but one record from vc12, from Whitehill in 1960 (DWHF in Goater, 1974).
■ vc11 Slodens Inclosure 2.7.99; Smoky Hole, 1.8.97 (JEC); Roydon Wood, 10.7.96 (PRD, JRL); Brockenhurst, 1996, at m.v. light in garden (JEC); Kings Somborne, 22.7.96, one at m.v. light, in coll. BG (TJN); Hursley, 23.7.97, one at light (DH); Chandlers Ford, 10.7.99, one at m.v. light (BG); Southsea, 22.7.96, one at m.v. light (JRL); Havant Thicket, 8.7.98, at m.v. light (JRL, IRT, *et al.*).

1344 *Eudonia mercurella* (Linnaeus, 1758)

Very common throughout.

1331 *Acentria ephemerella* ([Denis & Schiffermüller], 1775)
Water Veneer

Locally abundant in ponds, lakes and slow rivers. On certain nights, it has massive dispersal flights when it appears at light far from water.

1345 *Elophila nymphaeata* (Linnaeus, 1758)
Brown China-mark

Locally common in the New Forest bogs and in ponds and canals in all three vice-counties, with occasional wanderers reported elsewhere.

1348 *Parapoynx stratiotata* (Linnaeus, 1758)
Ringed China-mark

Evidently far less frequent than formerly. Like the previous species, it inhabits ponds and canals. Very few records from the Isle of Wight.
■ vc10 Freshwater, 4.8.94 (SAK-J).
■ vc12 Selborne, 10.7.99, male, 11.7.99, two females, at m.v. light, first for district (AEA).

1350 *Nymphula stagnata* (Donovan, 1806)
Beautiful China-mark

Very local and far less common than in Fassnidge's day (Goater, 1974).
■ vc11 Newlands Copse, Roydon Wood, 24.7.92 (PAB); Beaulieu, four between 30.6 and 28.7.95 (BI-J).

1353 *Oligostigma bilinealis* Snellen, 1876

No further record since the single dead moth found at an aquatic nursery. See Goater (1992). This is the only specimen taken in Hampshire of the group of adventive nymphulines associated with introduced tropical water plants.

1354 *Cataclysta lemnata* (Linnaeus, 1758)
Small China-mark

Local in ponds, ditches and canals from which it wanders occasionally. There are few recent records.

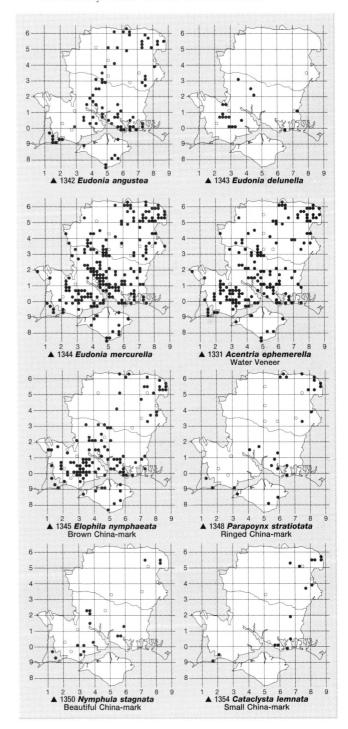

▲ 1342 *Eudonia angustea*

▲ 1343 *Eudonia delunella*

▲ 1344 *Eudonia mercurella*

▲ 1331 *Acentria ephemerella*
Water Veneer

▲ 1345 *Elophila nymphaeata*
Brown China-mark

▲ 1348 *Parapoynx stratiotata*
Ringed China-mark

▲ 1350 *Nymphula stagnata*
Beautiful China-mark

▲ 1354 *Cataclysta lemnata*
Small China-mark

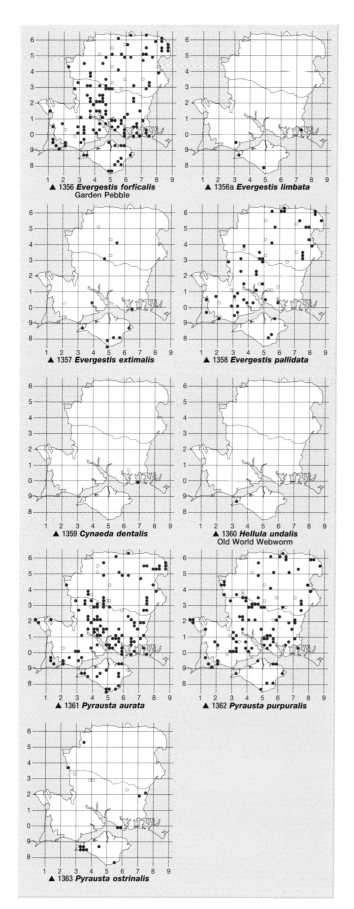

▲ 1356 *Evergestis forficalis* Garden Pebble

▲ 1356a *Evergestis limbata*

▲ 1357 *Evergestis extimalis*

▲ 1358 *Evergestis pallidata*

▲ 1359 *Cynaeda dentalis*

▲ 1360 *Hellula undalis* Old World Webworm

▲ 1361 *Pyrausta aurata*

▲ 1362 *Pyrausta purpuralis*

▲ 1363 *Pyrausta ostrinalis*

■ vc10 Freshwater, 8.8.00, one at m.v. light (SAK-J).

■ vc12 Frith End, 17.8.96, one (KW); Greywell, 29.7.00, one (PB); Fleet Pond, common between June and September (MAS); Shortheath Common, 29.7.95 (AMD); Farnborough, 2.8.96, one at light (RWP).

1356 *Evergestis forficalis* (Linnaeus, 1758)
Garden Pebble
Widespread but not very common nowadays.

1356a *Evergestis limbata* (Linnaeus, 1767)
Since the arrival of this species on the Isle of Wight in 1994, it has persisted at low density and also been discovered in Sussex. The foodplant, garlic mustard *Alliaria petiolata*, is common and the moth, once properly established, may be expected to spread.
■ vc10 Freshwater, 3.7 and 10.7.99 (SAK-J); Chale Green, 23.7 and 30.7.94, singletons at m.v. light (Colenutt, 1995); again on 14.7 and 21.7.95 (SRC). **New to Britain.**
■ vc11 Lymington, 8.8.00, female at m.v. light in garden (AJP); Northney, Hayling Island, 2.7.00, one at light (JWP). **New vc record.**

1357 *Evergestis extimalis* (Scopoli, 1763)
An uncommon migrant which may occasionally breed.
■ vc10 Freshwater, 18.7.90 (Knill-Jones, 1990), 13.9.91, 16.8.96 (SAK-J); St Catherine's Point, 27.6.96, by A. Steele (AMD); Chale Green, 30.7.94, one (SRC); Godshill, 4.8.94 (PJC *comm.* SAK-J).
■ vc11 Beaulieu, 7.8.94, 14.8.96 (BI-J); Hayling Island 21.8.85, one at m.v. light (JMW).
■ vc12 East Stratton, 7.8.88 (BI-J).

1358 *Evergestis pallidata* (Hufnagel, 1767)
Local and rather uncommon in damp woodland and marshy habitats.
■ vc10 Newchurch, 9.7.94 (BJW), 12.7.94 (Mr and Mrs D. Peach, *comm.* SAK-J); Godshill, 24.7.94 (PJC *comm.* SAK-J); Binstead, 9.8.96, first record for garden (BJW).
■ vc11 Beaulieu, 1994 (BI-J); Brockenhurst, 8.7.93 (JEC); Chandlers Ford, 22.7.91, 26.7.94 (BG): Moorgreen Meadows, 4.8.95 (PAB); Woolston, 28.7.96 (ARC).
■ vc12 Winnall Moors NR (DHS); East Stratton (BI-J); Fleet Pond, 17.7.93, one by day (RJBH); Rye Common, 20.7.98 (AMD); Selborne, fairly common at light (AEA); Noar Hill, 26.6.93 (AMJ); Farnborough, 19.8.96, one at light (RWP); Bentley Station Meadow, 28.7.95 (PAB); Yateley Common, occasional (AMD).

1358a *Eustixia pupula* (Hübner, 1823)
■ vc11 Bitterne, Southampton, 21.7.97, a male of this American species was taken at m.v. light by P.A. Budd and later identified by M. Shaffer of The Natural History Museum, London. (Budd and Goater, 1998). **New to Britain and Europe.**

1359 *Cynaeda dentalis* ([Denis & Schiffermüller], 1775)
Resident on South Hayling Island where viper's bugloss

Echium vulgare grows, and also possibly on Portsdown Hill (Goater, 1992).

■ vc11 Hayling Island, Sinah Common, 15.8.98, between two and six seen at m.v. light (PRD, JRL, IRT *et al.*).

1360 *Hellula undalis* (Fabricius, 1781)
Old World Webworm
A single record from Freshwater on 26.10.89 (SAK-J in Goater, 1992) is the only record of this migrant in the area.

1361 *Pyrausta aurata* (Scopoli, 1763)
Local on chalk downland, associated with marjoram *Origanum vulgare*, but sometimes abundant; also in gardens amongst cultivated mint.

1362 *Pyrausta purpuralis* (Linnaeus, 1758)

10 mm

Local on downland where the foodplant is wild thyme *Thymus polytrichus* and on heaths where it is probably associated with large thyme *T. pulegioides*.

1363 *Pyrausta ostrinalis* (Hübner, 1796)
Locally fairly common on surviving chalk downland, especially in West Wight.
■ vc10 Compton Down, 25.7.94, fairly common along a bank by footpath (BG, SAK-J).

1365 *Pyrausta despicata* (Scopoli, 1763)
Common on downland and on the coast, occasional elsewhere.
■ vc11 Chandlers Ford, 3.8.91, 23.6.94 (BG).

1366 *Pyrausta nigrata* (Scopoli, 1763)

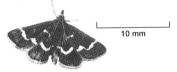

10 mm

Very locally frequent on chalk downs but surprisingly, only a single, old record from the Isle of Wight.
■ vc11 Kings Somborne, 27.7.95 (TJN); St Catherine's Hill, Winchester, 20.7.94 (RAC); Dean Hill, 21.5.95, by day (PAB).
■ vc12 Cholderton, 19.5.94, common in a stretch of downland by water works (HE, BG); Danebury, 18.7.97 (JHC), 10.7.99 (JEC); Stockbridge Down, 10.8.96 (AMD); Magdalen Hill Down, 30.6.95 (PAB); Beacon Hill, 10.8.96, one by day (AMD).

1367 *Pyrausta cingulata* (Linnaeus, 1758)
Recently recorded only from West Wight, but formerly, according to Fassnidge, on Farley Mount and Shawford Down, both in S Hants (Goater, 1974).
■ vc10 High Down, 25.7 and 31.7.95, common; Compton Down, one seen (SAK-J).

1368 *Loxostege (Margaritia) sticticalis* (Linnaeus, 1761)
A very occasional migrant. There was an influx of this species in 1995, when it was recorded in several places, mostly as single specimens.
■ vc10 Freshwater, 8.8.95 (SAK-J); Chale Green, 12.8 and 20.8.95 (SRC); Binstead, 7.8 and 21.8.95 (BJW).
■ vc11 Pennington, 22.8.95 (RC); Lymington, 17.8.96 (Davey, 1997); Beaulieu, 3.8.95, 6.8.95, two, 14.8.96, at m.v. light (BI-J); Stockbridge, 6.8.95, one netted by day (EA Sadler, comm. BFS); Chandlers Ford, 22.8.95, one at m.v. light (BG); Woolston, 5.8.95, one at m.v. light, specimens in coll. BG (ARC), Southsea, 9.8.97, one at light (IRT).

1369 *Uresiphita polygonalis* ([Denis & Schiffermüller], 1775)
= *gilvata* (Fabricius, 1794)
An extremely scarce immigrant. The only records since 1967 (Goater, 1974) are given below.
■ vc10 Freshwater, 31.10.99, one at m.v. light (SAK-J); Chale Green, 2.10.90, (SRC); Godshill, 29.7.90 by PC (Chalmers-Hunt and Skinner, 1992); Chale Green, 19.9.92 (SRC).
■ vc12 Crawley, 11.10.78, one at m.v. light (RAB).

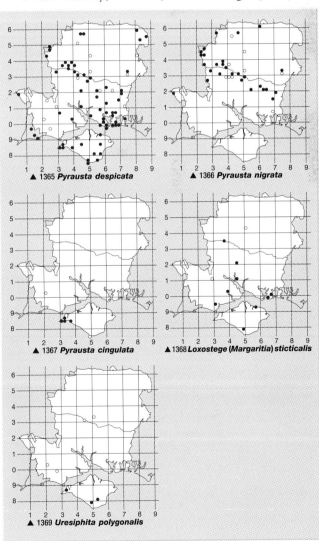

▲ 1365 *Pyrausta despicata* ▲ 1366 *Pyrausta nigrata* ▲ 1367 *Pyrausta cingulata* ▲ 1368 *Loxostege (Margaritia) sticticalis* ▲ 1369 *Uresiphita polygonalis*

1370 *Sitochroa palealis* ([Denis & Schiffermüller], 1775)

An immigrant which periodically becomes established. The larva feeds on the ripening fruits of wild carrot *Daucus carota*. Since 1990, single specimens have been seen regularly in different parts of the Isle of Wight and on the mainland, and breeding colonies are established, perhaps temporarily, in several localities mainly near the coast. It is apparently now breeding widely on all chalk downland sites in the home counties.

1371 *Sitochroa verticalis* (Linnaeus, 1758)

For some reason, this species seems to have virtually disappeared from Hampshire and the Isle of Wight. The only record since 1976 that has come to hand is :

■ vc11 Southsea, 20.5.81, one at m.v. light (JRL).

1373 *Paratalanta pandalis* (Hübner, 1825)

This is another species that has become very scarce. It remains unrecorded from the Isle of Wight, apart from the old reference in Morey (1909).

■ vc11 Broughton Down, 16.5 and 26.5.00, single specimens disturbed from chalk turf by day (AHD).

1374 *Paratalanta hyalinalis* (Hübner, 1796)

Nowadays evidently very rare except, perhaps, on Oxenbourne Down vc11 and Danebury vc12. It is associated with black knapweed *Centaurea nigra*. There is still only one record from the Isle of Wight (Goater, 1992).

■ vc12 Danebury, 20 on 10.7.99 (JEC); Selborne, 20.7.94 (AEA).

1374a *Sclerocona acutellus* (Eversmann, 1842)

No further record of this species in Hampshire since the one taken at Leckford in 1988 (Goater, 1992).

1375 *Ostrinia nubilalis* (Hübner, 1796)
European Corn-borer

A migrant, now evidently established on allotments and waste ground particularly near the coast in south-east Hampshire.

1376 *Eurrhypara hortulata* (Linnaeus, 1758)
Small Magpie

Very common, widespread and easily identified.

1377 *Perinephela lancealis* ([Denis & Schiffermüller], 1775)

Fairly frequent in damp woodland where the foodplant, hemp-agrimony *Eupatorium cannabinum* occurs.

1378 *Phlyctaenia coronata* (Hufnagel, 1767)

Common where elder flourishes; occasionally recorded away from the foodplant.

1380 *Phlyctaenia perlucidalis* (Hübner, 1809)

Apart from one in 1973, first recorded in the county in 1988, and now evidently established and spreading, though still at low density, on the mainland. It is found amongst thistles in meadows and on waste ground, and is easily disturbed by day.

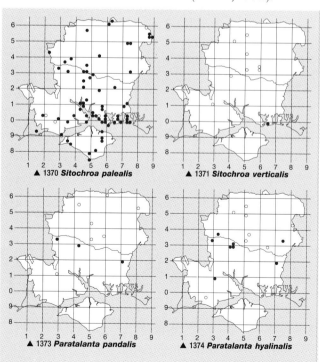

▲ 1370 *Sitochroa palealis*

▲ 1371 *Sitochroa verticalis*

▲ 1373 *Paratalanta pandalis*

▲ 1374 *Paratalanta hyalinalis*

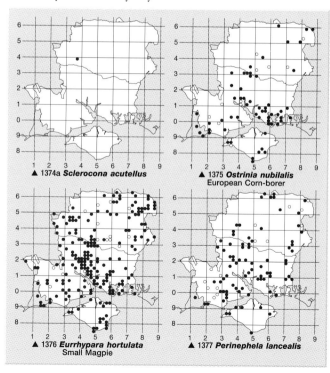

▲ 1374a *Sclerocona acutellus*

▲ 1375 *Ostrinia nubilalis*
European Corn-borer

▲ 1376 *Eurrhypara hortulata*
Small Magpie

▲ 1377 *Perinephela lancealis*

▣ vc10 Godshill, 27.7.95, one at light by P. Cramp (Knill-Jones, 1996). **New vc record.**

▣ vc11 Hengistbury Head, 1998, one, conf. BG; Hurn, 19.6.98 (MJ); Sack Copse, Sherfield English, 19.7.97, two; Kings Somborne, 3.7.93, 25.6.94, 1.7 and 11.7.97 (TJN); Sparsholt College, four between 21.6 and 8.7.92 (AHD); Titchfield Haven NNR, 26.7.96, first record (PMP).

▣ vc12 Leckford, 19.6.95, 19.5.97 (JHC), 7.6.98, one by day (BG); Brockley Warren, 11.6.97 (TJN); Magdalen Hill Down, 12.7.96, one (PAB); Abbots Worthy, 5.6.95, one disturbed in daytime from vegetation by River Itchen (AHD); East Stratton, 26.6 and 29.6.92 (BI-J); Farnborough, 30.6.98, at m.v. light (RWP).

▣ vc22 Mortimer West End, 2000, first record (GJD).

1384 *Phlyctaenia stachydalis* (Germar, 1821)

A scarce and elusive species. No confirmed records have been received since 1982 (Goater, 1974 and 1992).

1381 *Anania funebris* (Ström, 1768)

No recent record; presumed long extinct in Hampshire.

1382 *Anania verbascalis* ([Denis & Schiffermüller], 1775)

Local amongst wood sage *Teucrium scorodonia* in open country.

▣ vc11 Hurn, one in 1999 (MJ); St Ives, Ringwood, 10.7.89 (JHC); Brockenhurst, 4.7.98 (JEC); "East Hayling Island", 1984 by Dr R.M. Palmer (AMD).

▣ vc12 Selborne, 20.6.98, one at m.v. light, conf. BG from photograph (AEA).

1383 *Psammotis pulveralis* (Hübner, 1796)

A very scarce presumed migrant. Only one recent record.

▣ vc11 Matley Bog, 28.7.95, one by day by D. O'Keeffe (Agassiz *et al.*, 1995). **New vc record.**

1385 *Ebulea crocealis* (Hübner, 1796)

Local amongst the foodplant fleabane *Pulicaria dysenterica*.

1386 *Opsibotys fuscalis* ([Denis & Schiffermüller], 1775)

Locally common on downland amongst yellow rattle *Rhinanthus minor* and less so in acid woodland where the foodplant is cow-wheat *Melampyrum pratense*. Very occasional elsewhere.

▣ vc11 Chandlers Ford, 7.7.92 (BG).

1387 *Nascia cilialis* (Hübner, 1796)

There is a long-established and well-known small colony in the marsh at Browndown and another, discovered in 1987, at Titchfield Haven (Potts, 1990; Phillips 1991).

▣ vc11 wanderers have occurred at Crab Wood (Goater, 1992) and Southsea, 2.6.94, one at m.v. light (JRL).

1388 *Udea lutealis* (Hübner, 1809)

Locally common to abundant, but scarce or absent in many places, even though it is fairly polyphagous.

1389 *Udea fulvalis* (Hübner, 1809)

A casual immigrant which appears to have established itself in the last few years at Freshwater and around

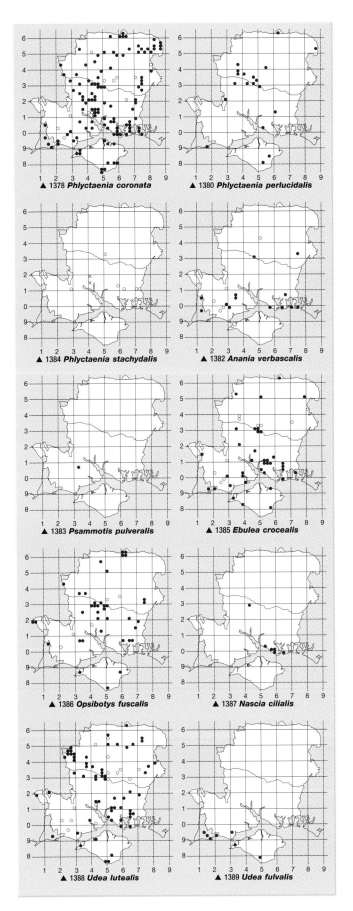

▲ 1378 *Phlyctaenia coronata*   ▲ 1380 *Phlyctaenia perlucidalis*

▲ 1384 *Phlyctaenia stachydalis*   ▲ 1382 *Anania verbascalis*

▲ 1383 *Psammotis pulveralis*   ▲ 1385 *Ebulea crocealis*

▲ 1386 *Opsibotys fuscalis*   ▲ 1387 *Nascia cilialis*

▲ 1388 *Udea lutealis*   ▲ 1389 *Udea fulvalis*

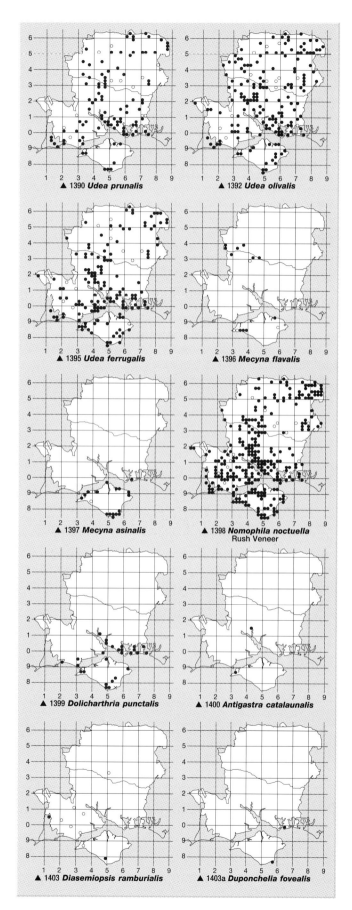

▲ 1390 *Udea prunalis*

▲ 1392 *Udea olivalis*

▲ 1395 *Udea ferrugalis*

▲ 1396 *Mecyna flavalis*

▲ 1397 *Mecyna asinalis*

▲ 1398 *Nomophila noctuella*
Rush Veneer

▲ 1399 *Dolicharthria punctalis*

▲ 1400 *Antigastra catalaunalis*

▲ 1403 *Diasemiopsis ramburialis*

▲ 1403a *Duponchelia fovealis*

Christchurch. In the second locality it is common at the time of writing, and moths can be found in some numbers at *Buddleia* flowers soon after dusk, in July. Atropos **10**, Pl.3 fig.14, bred specimen (RRC).

■ vc10 Freshwater, 8.8 and 11.8.93, first since 1959 (Knill-Jones, 1994); 17.8.94 (SAK-J); again on 11.7 and 17.7.95; seven taken during August, 1996, now temporarily established (SAK-J); Chale Green, 30.7.94 (SRC comm. SAK-J).

■ vc11 Hurn, two in 1999 (MJ); Christchurch, several in July 1993; late July 1994, several at light, on flowers of *Buddleia* at night, and tapped by day from bushes (MJ); 4.8.94, four tapped from a single bush (BG); frequent in 1995, moths seen regularly at *Buddleia* flowers at dusk (MJ); 20.7.97, two tapped from a patch of black horehound *Ballota nigra*, and eight netted as they flew around *Buddleia* from dusk, all very fresh (BG); Highcliffe, first recorded in 1991 (EHW in Goater, 1992); Lymington, 21.8.91, 8.8.00, single specimens (AJP).

1390 *Udea prunalis* ([Denis & Schiffermüller], 1775)

Common in hedgerows in many places in the three vice-counties, occasional elsewhere.

1392 *Udea olivalis* ([Denis & Schiffermüller], 1775)

Widespread and usually common.

1395 *Udea ferrugalis* (Hübner, 1796)

A common migrant, recorded every year in varying numbers.

1396 *Mecyna flavalis* ([Denis & Schiffermüller], 1775)

This very local species has two strongholds in the area where it is common, on Compton Down, vc10, and Porton Down, vc12. Occasional specimens encountered away from these localities suggest that there may be other, perhaps small, colonies still undetected. It was evidently common on Farley Mount vc11, in Fassnidge's day (Goater, 1974).

■ vc10 Compton Down, 19.7 and 21.7.90, series taken (SAK-J); 25.7.94, common (BG, SAK-J); Brook Down, 30.7.94, common; Binstead, July 1994, one at m.v. light (BJW).

■ vc11 Broughton Down, 26.7.00, three by day; 11.8.00, one (AHD).

■ vc12 Porton Down, 24.7.94, abdt. (BG, JRL); Cholderton, 8.94, one by day on set-aside (HE); Stockbridge Down, 30.7.94, one flying in evening (RJBH).

1397 *Mecyna asinalis* (Hübner, 1819)

Frequent on the coast of the Isle of Wight, associated with wild madder *Rubia peregrina*. The foodplant occurs occasionally on the mainland, but there is only one record of the moth (Goater, 1992).

1398 *Nomophila noctuella* ([Denis & Schiffermüller], 1775)
Rush Veneer

A migrant which is recorded every year, sometimes in immense numbers, as in 1996, when it is probably in every 2-km square in the county.

1399 *Dolicharthria punctalis* ([Denis & Schiffermüller], 1775)

Local and uncommon on the coasts of the Isle of Wight and mainland Hampshire.

■ vc10 Freshwater, three recorded during July, 1996, at m.v. light (SAK-J); Chale Green, 1995; St Helens Duver, 24.7.95, 55 seen (SRC).

■ vc11 Hurst Beach, 29.7.96 (JEC); Pennington, 13.7.96 (RC); Lepe Country Park, 14.8.96 (PMP); Woolston, 15.7.96, three at m.v. light (ARC); Hook Lake, 11.7.94, also in 1995 and 1996, common (RJD); Southsea, 1994 (JRL); N Hayling Island (PRD); Sandy Point, 22.7.95, by D. Young (AMD).

1400 *Antigastra catalaunalis* (Duponchel, 1833)

There are two records of this extremely scarce immigrant species.

■ vc10 One specimen taken at Freshwater in 1958 (Goater, 1974).

■ vc11 Portswood, Southampton, 1.9.00, one at light (A.and CD), in coll. Nat. Hist. Mus., London. **New vc record.**

1402 *Diasemia reticularis* (Linnaeus, 1761)

No record of this scarce migrant since 1958. The few Hampshire records up till then are given in Goater (1974).

1403 *Diasemiopsis ramburialis* (Duponchel, 1834)

A scarce migrant. Recent records are given below.

■ vc10 Chale Green, 12.8.90 by S. Colenutt (Chalmers-Hunt and Skinner, 1992).

■ vc11 St Ives, Ringwood, 3.11.87, one at m.v. light (JHC).

1403a *Duponchelia fovealis* Zeller, 1847

■ vc10 Ventnor, 23.6.00, one found indoors (PJC). **New vc record.**

■ vc11 Southsea, 3.9.99, one at m.v. light (JRL). **New county record.**

1405 *Pleuroptya ruralis* (Scopoli, 1763)

Mother of Pearl

10 mm

Abundant throughout, probably wherever nettles are established.

1405a *Herpetogramma licarsisalis* (Walker, 1859)

■ vc10 Freshwater, 9.11.98, male at m.v. light (Goater and Knill-Jones, 1999). **New to Britain and Europe.**

1408 *Palpita unionalis* (Hübner, 1796)

An uncommon migrant, recorded most years, chiefly on the Isle of Wight and near the Hampshire coast. Inland records include those given below.

■ vc11 St Ives, Ringwood, 20.10 to 22.10.87, eight at m.v. light (JHC); Beaulieu, 26.11.94 (BI-J); Brockenhurst, 21.7.90, 24.10.96 (JEC); Kings Somborne,

14.10.95 (TJN); Rownhams, 31.8.97 (KG); Woolston, 12.10.95, 8.6.97, singles at light; Sholing, 27.10.00 (ARC); Fareham, 26.9.98, male at m.v. light (RJD).

■ vc12 East Stratton (BI-J).

1410 *Agrotera nemoralis* (Scopoli, 1763)

One record only, Burley, 1946 (Goater, 1974).

1413 *Hypsopygia costalis* (Fabricius, 1775)

Gold Triangle

Very common throughout.

1414 *Synaphe punctalis* (Fabricius, 1775)

Common to very common on the coast, occasional inland where it has evidently decreased since the 1970s.

■ vc11 Hengistbury Head, 1997, very common (MJ); Brockenhurst, 29.6.93 (JEC); Cadlands House, 12.7.97, very common at m.v. light (BG, JRL); Kings Somborne, 20.7.96 (TJN); Woolston, 29.6.95, 23.6.97, singles at light (ARC); Gosport, 5.8.95, one at light, conf. JRL (DSW); Butser Hill, 13.7.97, several (AMD); Sinah Common, Hayling Island 15.8.98, at m.v. light (JRL, IRT, *et al.*).

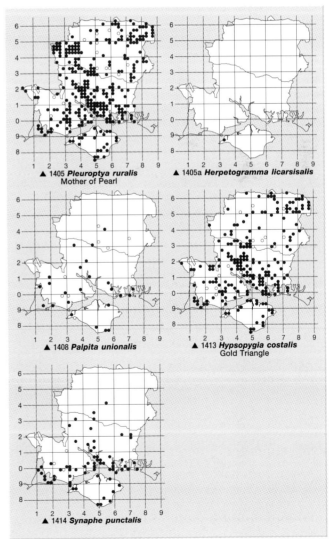

▲ 1405 *Pleuroptya ruralis*
Mother of Pearl

▲ 1405a *Herpetogramma licarsisalis*

▲ 1408 *Palpita unionalis*

▲ 1413 *Hypsopygia costalis*
Gold Triangle

▲ 1414 *Synaphe punctalis*

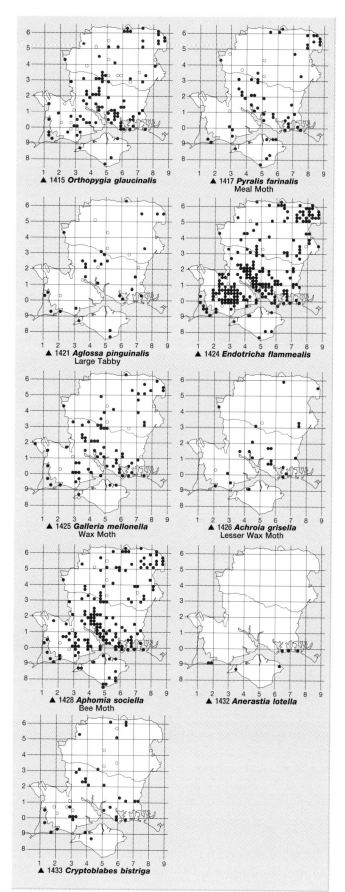

▲ 1415 *Orthopygia glaucinalis*

▲ 1417 *Pyralis farinalis*
Meal Moth

▲ 1421 *Aglossa pinguinalis*
Large Tabby

▲ 1424 *Endotricha flammealis*

▲ 1425 *Galleria mellonella*
Wax Moth

▲ 1426 *Achroia grisella*
Lesser Wax Moth

▲ 1428 *Aphomia sociella*
Bee Moth

▲ 1432 *Anerastia lotella*

▲ 1433 *Cryptoblabes bistriga*

1415 *Orthopygia glaucinalis* (Linnaeus, 1758)
Moderately frequent throughout the three vice-counties.

1417 *Pyralis farinalis* (Linnaeus, 1758)
Meal Moth
Predominantly an inhabitant of stables and grain stores. It is occasionally recorded at large.
■ vc11 Hengistbury Head, 1998, one at m.v. light (MJ); Pennington, 9.7.95 (RC); Brockenhurst, 24.7.95 (JEC); Whitenap, Romsey, 26.6.96 (MJB); Chandlers Ford, 10.8.91, 24.7.94 (BG); St Cross, 26.8.00, one at m.v. light (TWa); Bitterne, 22.7.97; Locks Heath, 17.7.00 (PCa); Durley Hall Lane, 10.7.91 (PAB); Woolston, 26.7.95, 22.7.96, singles at light; Sholing, 25.7.00 (ARC); Cosham, 13.7 and 3.8.96, singletons at m.v. light (TJJ); Gutner Point, Hayling Island, 22.9.95 (AMD).
■ vc12 Cholderton, 1995, two at m.v. light (HE); Pamber Forest, regularly (GJD); Yateley Common, occasional; Castle Bottom NNR, 20.8.96 (AMD); Selborne, 1993, 1994 and 1995, singletons, six in July, 1996, 11.7.97 (AEA); Farnborough, 19.6.94 (RWP).
■ vc22 Mortimer West End, 10.8.98, one seen at m.v. light (GJD).

1420 *Aglossa caprealis* (Hübner, 1809)
No record since the ancient and vague ones given in Goater (1974).

1421 *Aglossa pinguinalis* (Linnaeus, 1758)
Large Tabby
Very rarely recorded in the county, but perhaps overlooked on account of its association with farm buildings.
■ vc10 Freshwater, 5.8.96, one found in a greenhouse (SAK-J); Godshill, 7.7.96 (SRC).
■ vc11 Hurn, 1999, one; Avon Park, St Ives, Ringwood, 4.8.97, 2.8.99 (JHC); Christchurch, 5.6.97, one at m.v. light (MJ); Lymington, 16.6.94, "associated with pet guinea pigs" (AJP); Portswood, 9.8.98 (JPP); Sholing, 21.7.00, one at m.v. light (ARC); Romsey, July 2000 (NB); Timsbury, 1995 (DAT); Widley, Portsdown, 19.6.89 (PMP); Gosport, 8.8, 14.8 and 15.8.96 (DSW); N Hayling Island (PRD).
■ vc12 Cholderton, regular about the farm buildings (HE); Basingstoke, 11.8.97 (AHD); Hillside Common, 16.7.99; Yateley Common, 25.8.95 (AMD); Greywell, 25.8.84, one at m.v. light (PB); Selborne, 1.7.94 (AEA); Farnborough, 19.7.97 (RWP).
■ vc22 Mortimer West End, 29.5.98, one seen at m.v. light (GJD).

1424 *Endotricha flammealis* ([Denis & Schiffermüller], 1775)
Very common throughout the three vice-counties.

1425 *Galleria mellonella* (Linnaeus, 1758)
Wax Moth
Widespread but usually uncommon.
■ vc11 Beaulieu, 1994 (BI-J); Kings Somborne, 18.7.94 (TJN); Chandlers Ford, 28.8.91, 29.6.92, 7.8.93; 12.8.95 (BG).
■ vc12 Cholderton, fairly common (HE); East Stratton

(BI-J); Greywell Moors NR, 3.8.94, one at m.v. light (AHD); Selborne, 1994, several July–September 1997 (AEA); Noar Hill NR, 21.7.95 (AMJ); Farnborough, 19.7.94 (RWP).

1426 *Achroia grisella* (Fabricius, 1794)
Lesser Wax Moth
A pest of beehives, but seldom seen at large.

■ vc11 Brockenhurst, 25.9.98, 13.8.99, singles at m.v. light in garden (JEC); Chandlers Ford, 8.8.92, 8.6.93, singles at m.v. light (BG); Woolston, 7.8.97, one at m.v. light; Sholing, 27.6.00 (ARC); The Moors NR, Bishops Waltham, 1998; Fareham, 1997 (RJD); Cosham, 15.7 and 10.9.96, singletons at m.v. light (TJJ); Southsea, 1994 (JRL).

■ vc12 Cholderton, 1995, one (HE); Bramley Frith Wood, 17.3.94, larvae common in beehives (AHD); Selborne, 1993 onwards, several at light each year (AEA); Noar Hill NR, 22.8.95 (AMJ), Farnborough, 3.7.95 (RWP).

1428 *Aphomia sociella* (Linnaeus, 1758)
Bee Moth
Common in mainland Hampshire; scattered records from the Isle of Wight.

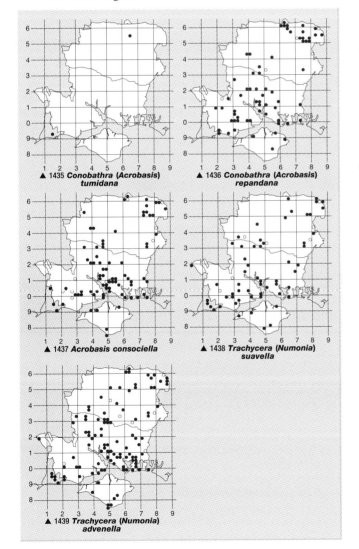

▲ 1435 *Conobathra (Acrobasis) tumidana*

▲ 1436 *Conobathra (Acrobasis) repandana*

▲ 1437 *Acrobasis consociella*

▲ 1438 *Trachycera (Numonia) suavella*

▲ 1439 *Trachycera (Numonia) advenella*

1429 *Melissoblaptes zelleri* de Joannis, 1932
Recorded in the past from St Helens, Isle of Wight, but not since 1909 (Goater, 1992).

1432 *Anerastia lotella* (Hübner, 1813)
Restricted to coastal sand dunes.

■ vc10 Freshwater, 5.7.97, one (SAK-J).

■ vc11 Hengistbury Head, 1997, on dunes (MJ); Hayling Island, Sinah Common, 15.8.98, several at m.v. light (TJN).

1433 *Cryptoblabes bistriga* (Haworth, 1811)
A species of oak woodland which is surprisingly uncommon in the county; there were only two records for the Isle of Wight given in Goater (1992).

■ vc10 Freshwater, 12.6.97; Cranmore, 11.8.98 (SAK-J).

■ vc11 Brockenhurst, 20.6.94 (JEC); Fareham, 1999 (RJD); Havant Thicket, 28.6.95, at m.v. light (JRL).

1434 *Cryptoblabes gnidiella* (Millière, 1867)
Occasionally bred from imported pomegranates which have not been frozen during storage.

■ vc11 Lymington, 9.1.93, one moth reared from pomegranate purchased at Sainsbury's (AJP); Winchester, Badger Farm, two em. February 1990 from pomegranates purchased at Sainsbury's (RJBH), one bred 1995 (BG).

1435 *Conobathra (Acrobasis) tumidana* ([Denis & Schiffermüller], 1775)
A very scarce immigrant.

■ vc11 Christchurch, 3.8.94, one at m.v. light (MJ), now in coll. BG; Cosham, 1.8.95, conf. JRL (TJJ); Southsea, 30.7.95, one at m.v. light (JRL). **Occurrence in county confirmed.**

1436 *Conobathra (Acrobasis) repandana* (Fabricius, 1798)
Fairly frequent in old oak woodland, scarce away from that biotope.

■ vc10 Binstead, 27.7.96, first record for garden (BJW).

■ vc11 Chandlers Ford, 29.7.91, 7.7.92, singles at m.v. light (BG); Gutner Point, Hayling Island, 24.7.94 (AMD).

■ vc12 Selborne, 25.7.94, 8.7 and 12.7.99 (AEA); Farnborough, 11.7.94 (RWP); Odiham Common, Hillside Common, Yateley Common, Bramshill Common, Rye Common, occasional at m.v. light (AMD).

1437 *Acrobasis consociella* (Hübner, 1813)
Fairly common though there are still very few records from the Isle of Wight.

■ vc10 St Catherine's Point, 1.7 and 10.7.95; Chale Green, 1993 and 1995 (SRC); Binstead, 14.7.97 (BJW).

1438 *Trachycera (Numonia) suavella* (Zincken, 1818)
Fairly common, though there are still few records from the Isle of Wight.

■ vc10 Chale Green, 1992, 1994 and 1995 (SRC); Binstead, 12.8.97 (BJW).

1439 *Trachycera (Numonia) advenella* (Zincken, 1818)
Fairly common, and identified with confidence by many recorders.

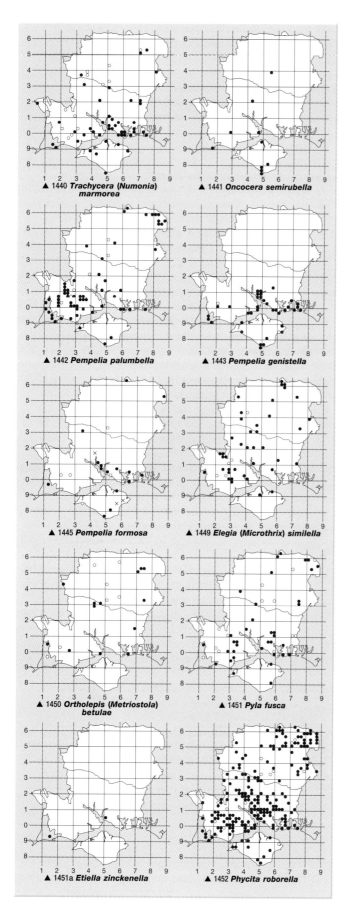

▲ 1440 *Trachycera (Numonia) marmorea*

▲ 1441 *Oncocera semirubella*

▲ 1442 *Pempelia palumbella*

▲ 1443 *Pempelia genistella*

▲ 1445 *Pempelia formosa*

▲ 1449 *Elegia (Microthrix) similella*

▲ 1450 *Ortholepis (Metriostola) betulae*

▲ 1451 *Pyla fusca*

▲ 1451a *Etiella zinckenella*

▲ 1452 *Phycita roborella*

1440 *Trachycera (Numonia) marmorea* (Haworth, 1811)

Local amongst blackthorn, especially stunted bushes on the coast.

■ vc11 Hengistbury Head, 23.7.97 (MJ); Chandlers Ford, 28.6.92, one at m.v. light (BG); Butser Hill, 13.7.93, three; Gutner Point, Hayling Island, 24.7.94 (AMD).

■ vc12 Magdalen Hill Down, 5.8.95 (PAB); Greywell Moors NR, 8.7.95, two at m.v. light (AHD); Odiham Common, 24.7.95 (AMD).

1441 *Oncocera semirubella* (Scopoli, 1763)

Occurs on the chalk downs of the Isle of Wight, but no records from the mainland until those detailed below.

■ vc10 St Catherine's Point, 20.7.95, 11 at m.v. light, 27.7.95, 45 at m.v. light (SRC, PC); Chale Green, 5.8.94, one (SRC); Godshill, 30.7.94 (PJC *comm.* SAK-J).

■ vc11 Hengistbury Head, 1998, one at m.v. light (MJ); Brockenhurst, 29.7.96, one at m.v. light in garden, another, 1.8.97 (JEC); Cadlands House, 12.7.97, one at m.v. light (BG, JRL); Chandlers Ford, summer 2000, one at m.v. light; specimen seen and confirmed by BG (ML). **New vc record.**

■ vc12 East Stratton, 16.6.89 (BI-J).

1442 *Pempelia palumbella* ([Denis & Schiffermüller], 1775)

Common on heaths; very occasional elsewhere.

■ vc10 Freshwater, 4.7.94; four during June–July, 1996, all at m.v. light (SAK-J).

■ vc11 Hengistbury Head, 5.7.97 (MJ); Cadlands House, 12.7.97, one at m.v. light (BG, JRL); Chandlers Ford, 29.6.92, one at m.v. light (BG); Southsea, 27.7.96, one at m.v. light (JRL).

■ vc12 Farnborough, 25.6.95, two at light (RWP).

1443 *Pempelia genistella* (Duponchel, 1836)

A speciality of the coastal areas of Hampshire and the Isle of Wight, amongst gorse *Ulex europaeus*, on which the larval webs are often abundant in spring.

■ vc10 Cranmore, 13.7.94 (SAK-J), 6.7.96, several (PJC, BJW); Chale Green, 5–10 per year (SRC).

■ vc11 Locally common along the coast between Hengistbury Head and Hayling Island.

1445 *Pempelia formosa* (Haworth)

Very few recent records: probably a casualty of Dutch elm disease; the larva feeds on elm *Ulmus* spp.

■ vc10 Chale Green, 2–4 per year (SRC).

■ vc11 Hurn, 13.7.00, one at m.v. light (MJ); Kings Somborne, 1–2 per year to light in garden (TJN); Woolston, 3.7.97, one at m.v. light (ARC); Chilling, July 1994, three (PMP; Fareham, 29.6.97 (RJD).

■ vc12 Yateley Common, 2.7.94, one (AMD).

■ vc22 Mortimer West End, 29.7.98, one seen at m.v. light (GJD).

1447a *Sciota adelphella* (Fischer von Röslerstamm, 1836)

A rare migrant and suspected colonist.

■ vc11 Southsea, 28.6.01, one at m.v. light (IRT, det. BG). **New county record.**

1449 *Elegia (Microthrix) similella* (Zincken, 1818)
Evidently widespread but rather scarce in oak woodland.
■ vc10 Parkhurst Forest, 9.7.96, by Peter Cramp *et al.* (Knill-Jones, 1997d), 8.5.2.99 (SAK-J); Binstead, 1.7.97, first for garden, 20.6.98 (BJW). **New vc record.**
■ vc11 Brockenhurst, 19.6.95 (JEC); Beaulieu, 1994, 8.7.00 (BI-J); Chandlers Ford, 5.7.91, 24.6.92, 6.6.96, at m.v. light (BG); Marwell Zoological Park, 13.6.97, seven seen at m.v. light (PAB); Woolston, 4.6.97, one at m.v. light (ARC); Fareham, 5.7.97, 17.6.98, at m.v. light (Dickson, 1998); Havant Thicket, 8.7.98, at m.v. light (JRL, IRT, *et al.*).
■ vc12 South Wonston, 25.6.97, at m.v. light (PJSS); East Stratton (BI-J); Selborne, 22.7.96, conf. BG from photo, 14.6.99 (AEA); Yateley Common, 11.6.93, 27.6.96 (AMD).
■ vc22 Mortimer West End, between 20.6 and 16.7.98, three seen at m.v. light (GJD).

1450 *Ortholepis (Metriostola) betulae* (Goeze, 1778)
A species of birch woodland, and evidently far less common in the county than might be expected. Scattered through the three vice-counties in suitable habitat.
■ vc12 Cholderton, 1995, two at m.v. light (HE); Selborne, 1993 (AEA).

1451 *Pyla fusca* (Haworth, 1811)
Common on heaths; there is evidence that is adapting to cultivated heathers *Erica* spp. and hence becoming more widespread in gardens on acid soils.
■ vc10 Binstead, 9.7.96 (BJW).
■ vc11 Chandlers Ford, 29.6.92, 7.6.93, at m.v. light (BG).
■ vc12 Selborne, 12.8.95, one at light (AEA); Farnborough, 12.6.94 (RWP).

1451a *Etiella zinckenella* (Treitschke, 1832)
■ vc11 Warsash, South Hants, 1.10.90, one at light by PMP det. JRL. (Potts, 1993); Christchurch, South Hants (Dorset), 11.8.95, one at m.v. light det. BG (Jeffes, 1995). Second and third British records.

1452 *Phycita roborella* ([Denis & Schiffermüller], 1775)
Possibly the commonest phycitine in the county, and, in Britain, one of the easier ones to identify. Larva on oak, but the moth is by no means confined to extensive oak woodland.

1454 *Dioryctria abietella* ([Denis & Schiffermüller], 1775)
This and the next species are hard to distinguish from one another, but the following records are considered reliable. Both species are evidently uncommon.
■ vc11 Chandlers Ford, 6.6.91, 17.7.94, 18.8.96, singles at m.v. light (BG); Woolston, 5.8.96, 3.8.97, singles at m.v. light (ARC); Fareham, 25.9.97 (MO); Cosham, 8.7.97, one at light, conf. BG (TJJ); Southsea, 2.8.99, one at m.v. light (IRT); North Hayling Island 30.7.96 (DSW).
■ vc12 Selborne, 3.7.98, 9.7.99, 3.7.00, singles at m.v.

light (AEA); Farnborough, 21.7.94 (RWP); Eelmoor Marsh, 5.7.97, one at m.v. light, identity confirmed (DGG).

1454a *Dioryctria schuetzeella* Fuchs, 1899
■ vc10 Freshwater, 16.7.85, one at m.v. light, det. BG (Knill-Jones, 1994). **New county record.**
■ vc11 New Forest, 25.7.92 (A.J. and C.T. Pickles,1993); Brockenhurst, 2.7.98, 16.7.99, at m.v. light in garden; Frame Wood, 3.7.99, one at m.v. light (JEC); Sims Wood, 12.7.97, two at m.v. light (JEC, JS). **New vc record.**
■ vc12 Selborne, 12.7.00, one at m.v. light (AEA), conf. BG. **New vc record.**

1455 *Dioryctria simplicella* Heinemann, 1863
= *mutatella* Fuchs, 1903
■ vc11 Hengistbury Head, 10.6.97, det. PHS (MJ); Brockenhurst, 13.7.99, one at m.v. light (JEC); Chandlers Ford, 31.7.91, 7.7.92, 27.7.93, singles at m.v. light (BG); Bitterne, 30.6.95 (PAB).
■ vc12 Farnborough, 6.6.96, one at light (RWP); Yateley Common, occasional Castle Bottom NNR, 16.6.96, 23.6.97, four (AMD).

1456 *Epischnia bankesiella* Richardson, 1888
No recent record. Goater (1974).

1457 *Hypochalcia ahenella* ([Denis & Schiffermüller], 1775)
Moderately frequent on what remains of the chalk downland.
■ vc10 Compton Down, 6.93, fairly common; Cranmore, 29.6.93 (SAK-J).
■ vc11 Farley Mount, 2.6.95, two by day (BG).
■ vc12 Magdalen Hill Down, 1995 (PAB); Selborne, 1994, 9.7.96, 26.5.97 (AEA).

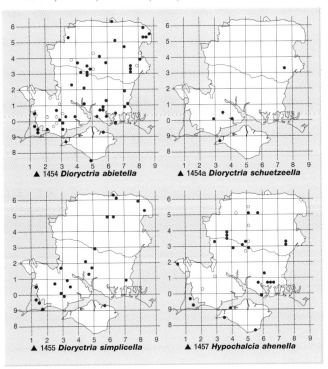

▲ 1454 *Dioryctria abietella*   ▲ 1454a *Dioryctria schuetzeella*

▲ 1455 *Dioryctria simplicella*   ▲ 1457 *Hypochalcia ahenella*

133

1458 *Myelois circumvoluta* (Fourcroy, 1785)
Thistle Ermine
Moderately frequent amongst thistles on field borders, waste ground, etc.

1459 *Eurhodope cirrigerella* (Zincken, 1818)
This species was known at Farley Mount vc11 from 1927 to 1946, and there was another small colony at Martyr Worthy vc12, where the last specimen was seen in 1960. Alas, it has not been refound.

1486 *Apomyelois bistriatella* (Hulst, 1887)
Associated with the fungus *Daldinia verrucosa* (Bond, 1998) growing on recently burnt gorse and birch, and as such, an opportunist, occurring in a suitable area for a few seasons before moving on. Found on the heaths of the New Forest and NE Hampshire and in Havant Thicket, an occasional wanderer elsewhere. No recent record from the Isle of Wight.
■ vc11 Beaulieu, 6.6, 8.6 and 9.6.93, 3.6.00, singletons at m.v. light (BI-J); Chandlers Ford, 15.6.93, one at m.v. light (BG); Woolston, 11.6.97, one at m.v. light, conf. BG (ARC); Fareham, 31.8.99, female at m.v. light, genit.

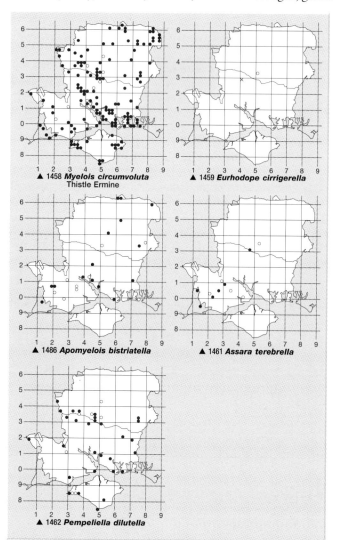

▲ 1458 *Myelois circumvoluta*
Thistle Ermine

▲ 1459 *Eurhodope cirrigerella*

▲ 1486 *Apomyelois bistriatella*

▲ 1461 *Assara terebrella*

▲ 1462 *Pempeliella dilutella*

checked (RJD); Browndown, fungus collected 8.97 from which four moths emerged between 22.6 and 8.7.98 (SS).
■ vc12 Brighton Hill, Basingstoke, 22.8.94, one at m.v. light (AHD, conf. PHS); Selborne, 3.7.94, 6.7.98 (AEA); Yateley, 30.4.93, pupa found in fungus on burnt birch, moth emerged 14.5.93 (RWP).

1460 *Ectomyelois ceratoniae* (Zeller, 1839)
Locust Bean Moth
This accidentally introduced species has been recorded only from Southampton (Goater, 1974) and Southsea (Goater, 1992).

1461 *Assara terebrella* (Zincken, 1818)
This rather elusive species occurs in stands of Norway spruce *Picea abies* in the New Forest area, and has been recorded occasionally elsewhere on the Hampshire mainland, but not since 1990 (Goater, 1992).

1462 *Pempeliella dilutella* ([Denis & Schiffermüller], 1775)
Common on chalk downland.
■ vc11 Locks Heath, 10.8.00, conf. RJD (PCa) is an interesting record off the chalk.

1463 *Pempeliella ornatella* ([Denis & Schiffermüller], 1775)
No recent record (Goater, 1974) of this chalk downland species.

1464 *Gymnancyla canella* ([Denis & Schiffermüller], 1775)
The foodplant, prickly saltwort *Salsola kali*, is a local and uncommon coastal plant, and very few localities are cited in Brewis, Bowman and Rose (1996). However, it is possible this moth is resident at St Helens, Hengistbury and perhaps Sandy Point, Hayling Island, where the plant is stated to be locally frequent. The larva is easy to find and should be sought.
■ vc10 St Helens Spit, 26.7.94 (Knill-Jones, 1995, *Ent. Rec.* **107**: 76); St Helens Duver, 24.7.95, three at m.v. light (PC, SRC). **New vc record.**
■ vc11 Hengistbury Head, 10.6.97; Christchurch, 18.8.96, one at m.v. light in garden (MJ). First Hampshire mainland records since Fassnidge (1923–24).

1465 *Nephopterix angustella* (Hübner, 1796)
Local, and far less widespread than the foodplant, spindle *Euonymus europaeus*.
■ vc10 Freshwater, 20.8.92, 1.9.98 (SAK-J); Chale Green, 21.9.92 (SRC).
■ vc11 Hengistbury Head, 1997, larvae common on spindle in wood; Christchurch, 23.8.97, one at m.v. light (MJ); Kings Somborne, 1–3 per year, 1994–99 (TJN); Chandlers Ford, 26.7.91, one at m.v. light (BG); Cosham, 28.8.95, conf. JRL (TJJ).
■ vc12 Selborne, 22.8.97, 9.7.98, at m.v. light (AEA).

1467 *Ancylosis oblitella* (Zeller, 1848)
A scarce and erratic migrant.
■ vc10 Freshwater, 21.8, 22.8 and 31.8.95 (SAK-J); St Catherine's Point, 20.7.95, one at m.v. light (SRC, PC); Chale Green, 23.6.92 (S. Colenutt, *BJENH* 6: 59);

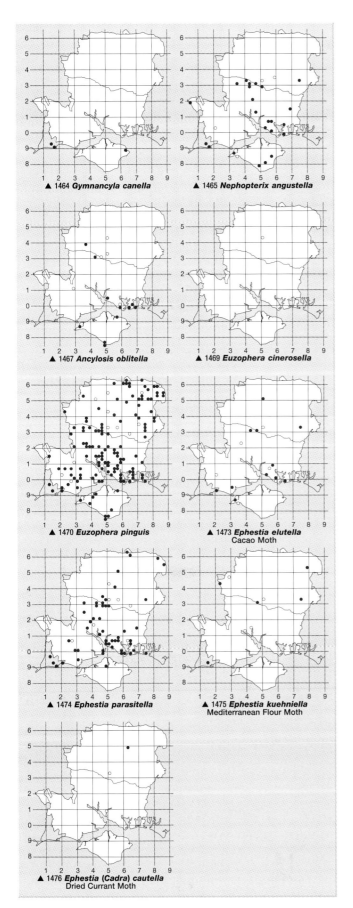

▲ 1464 *Gymnancyla canella*

▲ 1465 *Nephopterix angustella*

▲ 1467 *Ancylosis oblitella*

▲ 1469 *Euzophera cinerosella*

▲ 1470 *Euzophera pinguis*

▲ 1473 *Ephestia elutella*
Cacao Moth

▲ 1474 *Ephestia parasitella*

▲ 1475 *Ephestia kuehniella*
Mediterranean Flour Moth

▲ 1476 *Ephestia (Cadra) cautella*
Dried Currant Moth

13.7.92, 23.7.93, 17.8 (two), 19.8 and 22.8 and 22.9.95 (SRC); Binstead, 15.8.95 (BJW).

■ vc11 Sparsholt, 1.8.90 by A.H. Dobson (Chalmers-Hunt and Skinner, 1992); Warsash, 21.7 to 22.7.96 (PMP); Southsea, singletons at m.v. light on 10.8.95, 20.7 and 22.7, 7.8.96, and two on 18.8.96 and 2.8.99 (JRL), 18.8.96, one at actinic trap, conf. JRL (IRT); Sinah Common, Hayling Island, 15.8.98, at m.v. light (JRL, IRT, *et al.*).

■ vc12 Leckford, 21.7.92 (DHS).

1469 *Euzophera cinerosella* (Zeller, 1839)

No record since 1970 (Goater, 1974).

1470 *Euzophera pinguis* (Haworth, 1811)

Scattered records through the three vice-counties, but seldom of more than a few individuals. The larva feeds under the bark of ash, favouring particular trees.

1473 *Ephestia elutella* (Hübner, 1796)
Cacao Moth

Only two records of this species have been received since the commencement of the Mapping Project. Old records are given in Goater (1974, 1992). It is almost certainly common in barns and warehouses.

■ vc11 Titchfield Haven, 30.6.97, genitalia det. (RJD); Fareham, 6.5.00, female at m.v. light, det. RJD (MLO).

1474 *Ephestia parasitella* Staudinger, 1859

Locally common; an outdoor species, compared with the other British *Ephestia*. Almost certainly under-recorded; some of the more interesting records are detailed below.

■ vc10 Parkhurst Forest, 22.7.96 (SAK-J).

■ vc11 Hengistbury Head, 1997 (MJ); Chandlers Ford, common at m.v. light (BG); Woolston, 11.6.97, two at m.v. light, conf. BG (ARC).

■ vc12 Bramley Frith Wood, 5.5.94, one at m.v. light; Yateley Common, 8.6.96 (AHD); Selborne, 11.7.97 (AEA); Farnborough, 1994 (RWP).

1475 *Ephestia kuehniella* Zeller, 1879
Mediterranean Flour Moth

Seldom recorded, but then seldom sought, inside flour mills and warehouses.

■ vc11 Christchurch, 4.10 and 28.10.97, specimens found indoors (MJ).

■ vc12 Cholderton, 1995, breeding indoors (HE); Fleet, 27.9.98, one indoors and three dead *E. kuehniella* in a packet of porridge oats (RE).

1476 *Ephestia (Cadra) cautella* (Walker, 1863)
Dried Currant Moth

Imported occasionally with foreign food products. The only record since 1976 is given below.

■ vc12 Basingstoke, 22.10.90, larvae on garlic, adult reared 11.11.90 (AHD).

1477 *Ephestia (Cadra) figulella* (Gregson, 1871)
Raisin Moth

The only record since those given in Goater (1974) is given below.

■ vc10 Godshill, October 1991, P.J. Cramp, BENHS Exhibition, 1995 (Agassiz *et al.*, 1997). **New vc record.**

1479 *Plodia interpunctella* (Hübner, 1813)
Indian Meal Moth

There are few records of the moth at large; it is a pest of stored products.

■ vc10 Freshwater, 22.5.95, indoors (SAK-J).

■ vc11 Lymington, 11.7.92 (AJP); Gosport, 7.8.96, one at m.v. light (DSW); Southsea, 1993 (JRL).

■ vc12 Fleet, at light in garden between 17.1 and 5.11.98 (RDE), common in a pet shop in Fleet throughout the late 1990s (AMD).

■ vc22 Silchester, one in house, 2000 (PRB).

1480 *Homoeosoma nebulella* ([Denis & Schiffermüller], 1775)

There are two old and rather vague records from the Isle of Wight and two specimens from Micheldever vc12 (Goater, 1974), two records from vc11 (Goater, 1992), plus those given below.

■ vc10 Watershoot Bay, 24.6.96 (TS).

■ vc11 Broughton Down, 28.6.00, one at a Heath trap (AHD).

■ vc12 South Wonston, June, 1997, one at m.v. light, det. and coll. BG (PJSS).

1481 *Homoeosoma sinuella* (Fabricius, 1794)

Locally common, especially on coastal sand and shingle.

■ vc10 Binstead, 11.7.96, (BJW).

■ vc11 Cadlands House, 12.7.97, one at m.v. light (BG, JRL); Chandlers Ford, 16.7.94, one at m.v. light (BG); Bitterne, 24.6.95 (PAB); Woolston, 11.7.96, one at m.v. light (ARC); Portsdown, below Fort Nelson, 19.6.98, present in 1000s (RJD).

■ vc12 Magdalen Hill Down, 30.6.95 (PAB); Selborne, 28.6 and 10.7.95, 9.7 and 10.7.96, three in 1997, singletons at light (AEA); Frith End, 13.7.96 (KW); Danebury, 2.7.99; Old Basing, 19.7.96; Hazeley Heath, 5.7.97; Yateley Common, 11 on 27.6.96; Castle Bottom NNR, 16.6.96 (AMD).

[1482 *Homoeosoma nimbella* (Duponchel, 1837)

No recent record. The old ones (Goater, 1974) are vague and the presence of this species in Hampshire and the Isle of Wight needs confirmation.]

1483 *Phycitodes binaevella* (Hübner, 1813)

Scattered records, mostly singletons, from all three vice-counties.

■ vc10 Freshwater, a few every year in the 1990s (SAK-J); Whitwell, 1996; St Catherine's Point, several in June and July, 1995; Chale Green, 1991, 1994 (SRC).

■ vc11 Hengistbury Head, 15.7.97 (MJ); Cadlands House, 12.7.97, two at m.v. light (BG, JRL); Whitenap, Romsey, 8.7.95 (MJB); Kings Somborne, 30.6.95 (TJN); Chandlers Ford, 3.8.91, one at m.v. light (BG); Butser Hill, 13.7.97, three (AMD).

■ vc12 Magdalen Hill Down, 30.6.95 (PAB); Danebury, 2.7.99, several; Old Basing, 14.7.96; Odiham Common, 27.6.95; Castle Bottom NNR, 23.6.97; Rye

Common, 26.7.96, four (AMD); Selborne, fairly common, 21 specimens in 1995 (AEA); Noar Hill NR, 4.7.95 (AMJ).

1484 *Phycitodes saxicola* (Vaughan, 1870)

Probably seriously under-recorded: the only place where it is stated to be common is Southsea (Goater, 1992).

■ vc10 Freshwater, 27.5 and 15.6.99, genitalia det. BG (SAK-J); Parkhurst Forest, 22.7.96 (SAK-J); Chale Green, 1.8 and 20.8.95, one on each occasion (SRC).

■ vc11 Swanwick, 26.7.97, one female; Hamble Common, 1995–96; Fareham, 1999; all genitalia det. (RJD); Southsea, 2.9.98, genitalia checked (IRT).

1485 *Phycitodes maritima* (Tengström, 1848)

Under-recorded and confused with the previous species. It has been bred on several occasions from heads of ragwort *Senecio jacobaea*, from both coastal and inland localities (Goater, 1992).

■ vc10 Chale Green, 9.8.95, one (SRC); St Helens Spit, 26.7.94 (SAK-J).

■ vc11 Chandlers Ford, 18.8.91, one at m.v. light, genitalia det. (BG); Yew Hill, Kings Somborne, 21.8.96,

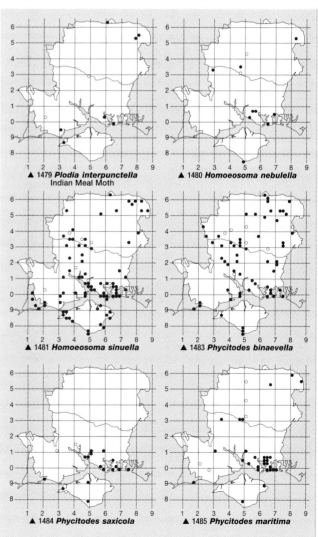

▲ 1479 *Plodia interpunctella*
Indian Meal Moth

▲ 1480 *Homoeosoma nebulella*

▲ 1481 *Homoeosoma sinuella*

▲ 1483 *Phycitodes binaevella*

▲ 1484 *Phycitodes saxicola*

▲ 1485 *Phycitodes maritima*

conf. BG (TJN); Fareham, five in 1993; Hook Lake, 1995–96; Portsdown Hill, 1999; all genitalia det. (RJD); Southsea, nine recorded between 16.7 and 18.8.98, conf. JRL (IRT).

■ vc12 Winnall Moors NR (DHS).

Thyrididae (1)

1486a *Telchines vialis* (Moore, 1883)

■ vc11 A male specimen of this Oriental species was taken at m.v. light in the Lower Itchen Valley on 7.10.1994 by Mr R. Houghton, who kindly presented it to the Natural History Museum, London. It was positively identified by M.R. Honey after examination of the genitalia. **New to Britain and Europe.**

Pterophoridae (28 + [2])

A distinctive family of moths comprising two subfamilies, the Agdistinae and Pterophorinae. The common name for the whole family, plume moths, derives from the form of the wings in the Pterophorinae. The forewings have one cleft or split, the hindwings two, giving the impression of feathers or plumes, especially as the lobes created by the clefts have long fringe hairs on the margins. The Agdistinae do not have these clefts, but the species of both subfamilies fold and roll their wings at rest and generally hold them at right angles to the body, thus forming a "T" shape. The body is relatively long and slender as are the legs. The larvae may feed in rootstocks or stems, or on foliage, flowers or seeds.

1488 *Agdistis bennetii* (Curtis, 1833)

Locally abundant in the saltmarshes of the Isle of Wight and S Hants (Goater, 1974, 1992).

■ vc11 Hengistbury Head, 1997 (MJ); Bucklers Hard salterns, 8.6.95, one at light (BG); Hamble Common; Titchfield Haven (RJD); Southsea, 7.8 and 21.9.96, at actinic trap (IRT); Gutner Point, Hayling Island, 24.7.94, abundant in saltmarsh (AMD).

1490 *Oxyptilus parvidactylus* (Haworth, 1811)

Locally common on unspoilt downland; recorded from all three vice-counties, but not recently from the Isle of Wight (Goater, 1974, 1992). The larva feeds on mouse-ear hawkweed *Pilosella vulgaris*.

1491 *Oxyptilus distans* (Zeller, 1847)

The larva of this species also feeds on mouse-ear hawkweed *Pilosella vulgaris*.

■ vc11 Southsea, 8.8.97, one at light, genitalia det. JRL (IRT). **New county record.**

1492 *Oxyptilus laetus* (Zeller, 1847)

■ vc11 Bournemouth, 3.7.47, S.C.S. Brown, det. C. Hart. (destined for BM, presently in hands of L. Christie, *teste* Hart, 11.3.95. **New county record.**
[Also vc9 Parley, Dorset, 3.8.46, S.C.S. Brown, det. C. Hart, in coll. C. Hart.]

1493 *Buckleria paludum* (Zeller, 1839)

Widespread in the bogs of the New Forest in the vicinity of the foodplant, round-leaved sundew *Drosera rotundifolia*, but not reported recently from NE Hampshire (Goater, 1974, 1992). The moth is easily disturbed in daytime, and flies naturally just before dusk.

1494 *Capperia britanniodactyla* (Gregson, 1869)

Local amongst wood-sage *Teucrium scorodonia* in all three vice-counties. The moth does not occur wherever the foodplant exists, and seems to prefer places where it grows out in the open, e.g., on shingle, or in open woodland rides.

■ vc10 Cranmore, 2.7.93; Parkhurst Forest, 22.7.96 (SAK-J).

■ vc11 Hamble Common, 1996; Portsdown (RJD); Browndown, 5.7.97, a few at dusk; Southsea, 22.6.92, one at m.v. light (JRL).

■ vc12 The Warren NR, Oakshott, 24.6.92 by J.A. Evans (AMD).

1495 *Marasmarchia lunaedactyla* (Haworth, 1811)

This species probably occurs wherever the foodplant, restharrow *Ononis* spp. occurs. It is easily disturbed by day, occasionally comes to light, and the early stages are easily detected on the foodplant.

■ vc10 Tennyson Down, locally common on *Ononis* (SAK-J, 1996); Totland Bay; Yarmouth; Apes Down; St Catherine's area (RJD).

■ vc11 Hengistbury Head, 1999 (MJ); Fareham (RJD).

■ vc12 Selborne (AEA).

1496 *Cnaemidophorus rhododactyla* ([Denis & Schiffermüller], 1775)

Known only from Botley Wood, S Hants, where it was first seen in 1977 (Goater, 1983). The larva feeds on wild rose *Rosa* spp. growing in open situations.

1497 *Amblyptilia acanthodactyla* (Hübner, 1813)

This and the next species have been confused in the past (Goater, 1974) and the older records are unreliable. The larvae of both species are somewhat polyphagous on herbaceous plants including hedge woundwort *Stachys sylvatica*, restharrow *Ononis* spp. and crane's-bill *Geranium* spp. Their distribution in the county is still imperfectly known: all verified records are given in Goater (1992) and below.

■ vc10 Freshwater, 9.10.94, one found indoors, four taken during 1996 (SAK-J); Southsea, 22.5.92, one at m.v. light (JRL), 1996 (IRT).

■ vc11 Fareham, 13.8.98, at m.v. light; Titchfield Haven, 11.9 and 25.9.96 (RJD); Southsea, 22.6.92, one at m.v. light (JRL); Milton Common, 12.8, 15.8 and 16.8.00, at m.v. light (IRT).

■ vc12 Harewood Forest, 26.10.97, one imago by day (DGG); Yateley, 26.8.96, one at m.v. light (AMD); Selborne, 1993, 1994 (AEA).

1498 *Amblyptilia punctidactyla* (Haworth, 1811)

■ vc11 Brockenhurst, 24.6.97, 30.6.98, both genitalia det. (JEC); Sparsholt College (AHD); Crab Wood,

20.9.97, one adult by day (JRL, *et al.*); Southsea, 22.6.94, one at m.v. light (JRL), 30.7.96, at actinic trap, conf. JRL (IRT).

■ vc12 Wildhern, nr Andover, 3.9.97 (DGG); The Warren NR, Oakshott, 24.6.92 by J.A. Evans (AMD).

[1500 *Platyptilia calodactyla* ([Denis & Schiffermüller], 1775)
The old and vague record from the Isle of Wight (Goater, 1974) has never been confirmed.]

1501 *Platyptilia gonodactyla* ([Denis & Schiffermüller], 1775)
Locally common amongst coltsfoot *Tussilago farfara*, and recorded from all three vice-counties (Goater, 1974, 1992).

1502 *Platyptilia isodactylus* (Zeller, 1852)
The foodplant, marsh ragwort *Senecio aquaticus* is locally common on the mainland but not often examined for larvae of this species. Hence there are few records (Goater, 1974, 1992), though it is almost certainly overlooked.

1503 *Platyptilia ochrodactyla* ([Denis & Schiffermüller], 1775)
The foodplant, tansy *Tanacetum vulgare*, is very local in Hampshire and so, therefore is this moth. Satisfactory records have been received only from the Portsmouth area, where it is common amongst the foodplant, especially after dark (JRL, DHS).

1504 *Platyptilia pallidactyla* (Haworth, 1811)
This species is very similar in appearance to *P. ochrodactyla*, but is associated with sneezewort *Achillea ptarmica*. It is locally common in damp places in all three vice-counties (Goater, 1974, 1992).

■ vc11 Brockenhurst, 8.7 and 9.7.98 (JEC); Sparsholt College (AHD); Hookheath Meadows NR, Southwick, 9.6.92, a few, and pupae found (JRL); Hamble Common; Wickham Common, 1996 (RJD); Browndown, 5.7.97, a few (JRL, IRT); Southsea, 1996, at actinic trap (IRT); Sandy Point NR, Hayling Island, 14.7.92, a few at m.v. light (JRL).

■ vc12 Brighton Hill, Basingstoke; Bartley Heath NR (AHD); Selborne, 1993, 1994 (AEA); Noar Hill, 21.7.93 (AMJ); Farnborough, 4.7.94 (RWP); Yateley, 2.7.97; Hazeley Heath, 5.7.97; Hawley Meadows, 23.7.96, four (AMD).

1505 *Stenoptilia pneumonanthes* (Büttner, 1880)
= *graphodactyla* auctt.
Recorded in the past from boggy areas of the New Forest (Goater, 1974), amongst the foodplant, marsh gentian *Gentiana pneumonanthes*. The plant is still there, but the moth has not been seen for many years. However, its recent rediscovery in Dorset suggests that is might still survive in Hampshire.

1507 *Stenoptilia zophodactylus* (Duponchel, 1840)
Although this species has been recorded from all three vice-counties (Goater, 1974, 1992), it is not often noticed. The larvae have be found on centaury *Centaurium erythraea* and autumn gentian *Gentianella amarella* in Hampshire but not, as far as is known, on yellow-wort

Blackstonia perfoliata, which is given as a foodplant by Beirne (1954). Recent records include those given below.
■ vc10 Freshwater, 18.10.97, resting on a door (SAK-J).
■ vc11 Dur Hill Down, 12.10.97, 12.10.98 (JEC).

1508 *Stenoptilia bipunctidactyla* (Scopoli, 1763)
This species is found in damp heaths, marshes and downland in all three vice-counties (Goater, 1974, 1992), where the larvae feed on field scabious *Knautia arvensis*, small scabious *Scabiosa columbaria* or devil's-bit scabious *Succisa pratensis*.
■ vc12 Wildhern, nr Andover, 16.7.99 (DGG); Selborne, 16.8.00 (AEA).

1509 *Stenoptilia pterodactyla* (Linnaeus, 1761)
Recorded from all three vice-counties (Goater, 1974, 1992, but with few records from the Isle of Wight. The larva feeds on germander speedwell *Veronica chamaedrys* growing along hedgerows and the edges of woods.
■ vc10 Cranmore, 13.8.97 (SAK-J).
■ vc11 Cadland Estate, Beaulieu, 12.7.97, one at m.v. light (BG, JRL); Sparsholt College (AHD); Old Winchester Hill NNR, 23.7.97, one (RJD, JRL); Botley Wood, 29.5.98, one larva (RJD); Butser Hill, 13.7.97, five (AMD); Sinah Common, Hayling Island (RJD).
■ vc12 Hazeley Heath, 5.7.97, five; Shortheath Common, 29.7.95, several; Rye Common, 5.8.96 (AMD); Farnborough, three in 1994 (RWP).

1510 *Merrifieldia (Pterophorus) leucadactyla* ([Denis & Schiffermüller], 1775)
= *tridactyla* auctt.
RJD writes that the record he gave for Oxenbourne Down (Goater, 1992) is not supported by voucher material and should therefore be regarded as suspect. Other records given in Goater, 1974, 1992) have not been added to, and that from the Isle of Wight still requires confirmation.

1512 *Merrifieldia (Pterophorus) baliodactylus* (Zeller, 1841).
Local amongst the foodplant, marjoram *Origanum vulgare* in all three vice-counties (Goater, 1974, 1992). This is a species of downland and waysides on the chalk.
■ vc10 Ventnor coast (RJD).
■ vc11 Portsdown, 19.4.92, several larvae (JRL).

1513 *Pterophorus pentadactyla* (Linnaeus, 1758)
White Plume Moth
Common throughout the three vice-counties, probably wherever bindweed *Calystegia sepium* or *C. sylvatica* are well-established.

1514 *Pterophorus galactodactyla* ([Denis & Schiffermüller], 1775)
Recorded from all three vice-counties (Goater, 1974, 1992) but not recently from the Isle of Wight. The moth is seldom encountered, but the larvae make characteristic large holes in the leaves of burdock *Arctium minus* and can often be found nearby, resting along the edge of a vein on the underside of the leaf. The moth seems to be commonest in open woodland on chalk.

◼ vc11 Parnholt Wood; Oxenbourne Down (RJD); Hen Wood, 26.5.97 and Clanfield, 15.4.97, larval feedings on *Arctium* (JRL, IRT).

◼ vc12 Wildhern, 9.4.98, larvae on *Arctium*, 15.7.98, imago (DGG); Micheldever, 7.4.97, a few larvae on *A. lappa* (JRL, IRT).

1515 *Pterophorus spilodactylus* (Curtis, 1827)

The only known locality in the area is on the cliffs between Freshwater and The Needles. Here the foodplant, white horehound *Marrubium vulgare* is common in patches along the cliff-edge, and the moth, in one or more stages of the life-cycle, can reliably be found.

1517 *Adaina microdactyla* (Hübner, 1813)

Locally common amongst hemp-agrimony *Eupatorium cannabinum* in all three vice-counties (Goater, 1974, 1992), especially when the plant is growing in drier localities.

◼ vc11 Sparsholt College (AHD); Fareham; Titchfield Haven; Portsdown, 30.5.98, several amongst the foodplant (RJD); Southsea, 28.7.97, one at m.v. light (JRL).

◼ vc12 Atners Towers, Stockbridge, 22.5.98 (JEC); Winnall Moors NR (DHS); Selborne, 1993, 1994 (AEA); Noar Hill, 14.6.94 (AMJ).

1518 *Ovendenia (Leioptilus) lienigianus* (Zeller, 1852)

Little is known of this species in Hampshire, but the records suggest that a systematic search of mugwort *Artemisia vulgaris* for the larvae could reveal its presence in other localities, particularly in the Winchester area between the valleys of the Itchen and Test. Previous records are all from N Hants: Leckford, Martyr Worthy, Micheldever and Polhampton (Goater, 1974, 1992).

◼ vc12 Odiham Common, 24.7.95, one at m.v. light (AMD).

[1520 *Hellinsia (Leioptilus) osteodactylus* (Zeller, 1841)

There is no compulsive evidence that this species has ever been found in Hampshire (Goater, 1974).]

1522 *Euleioptilus (Leioptilus) tephradactyla* (Hübner, 1813)

Recorded in the past from Baddesley Great Covert, now alas all but destroyed, and Ampfield (Goater, 1974), but not since. The larval foodplant is wild golden-rod *Solidago virgaurea*, which is thinly scattered and seldom common.

◼ vc12 Noar Hill, 21.6.93 (AMJ). **New vc record.**

1519 *Euleioptilus (Leioptilus) carphodactyla* (Hübner, 1813)

This local species has been recorded from all three vice-counties (Goater, 1974, 1992), though not recently from the Isle of Wight. The larva feeds on ploughman's spikenard *Inula conyza* on downland.

◼ vc8 Martin Down, 29.4.90 (S. Nash).

◼ vc10 Tennyson Down, 18.5.92, vacated larval feedings on *Inula conyza* (JRL, DHS, PHS); High Down, Freshwater, 25.7.95 (SAK-J).

◼ vc11 Hurn, one in 1999 (MJ); Cadland Estate, Beaulieu, 12.7.97, one at m.v. light (BG, JRL); Portsdown, 19.4.92, a few larvae on *I. conyza*; Southsea, 25.7.95, one at m.v. light and very occasionally since (JRL).

◼ vc12 Micheldever, 7.4.97, a few larvae (JRL, IRT); Selborne, 18.7.96, det. JRL from photograph (AEA).

1523 *Oidaematophorus lithodactyla* (Treitschke, 1833)

Local amongst the foodplants fleabane *Pulicaria dysenterica* and the less widespread ploughman's spikenard *Inula conyza*, but doubtless under-recorded. It has been found in all three vice-counties (Goater, 1974, 1992).

◼ vc11 Hamble Common; Titchfield Haven, 1996; Swanwick NR, 19.5.94 (RJD); Hookheath Meadows NR, Southwick, 10.6.94, one larva on fleabane, moth bred (JRL).

◼ vc12 Winnall Moors NR (DHS); Bartley Heath NR; Mapledurwell Fen, 25.7.99, two (AHD); Rye Common, 26.7.96 (AMD).

1524 *Emmelina monodactyla* (Linnaeus, 1758)

Common to abundant throughout the three vice-counties (Goater, 1974, 1992). The imago hibernates and comes to light early in the year; the larva is polyphagous on bindweeds *Calystegia* and *Convolvulus*, knotgrass *Polygonum aviculare* and other herbaceous plants and dwarf shrubs such as bilberry *Vaccinium myrtillus* and heather *Erica* spp. (Beirne, 1954).

Lasiocampidae (10)

1631 *Poecilocampa populi* (Linnaeus, 1758)
December Eggar

Widespread and common in wooded country in the three vice-counties, but doubtless still under-recorded because of the lateness of its flight period. The larva feeds on a variety of deciduous trees, including birch, oak, hawthorn and blackthorn.

1632 *Trichiura crataegi* (Linnaeus, 1758)
Pale Eggar

Very few recent records have come to hand, and these mostly of single specimens scattered through all three vice-counties, or single larvae. The species has suffered a serious decline in the area. The larva of this species is also polyphagous on deciduous trees and bushes.

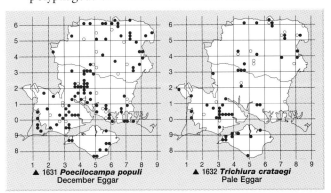

▲ 1631 *Poecilocampa populi*
December Eggar

▲ 1632 *Trichiura crataegi*
Pale Eggar

1633 *Eriogaster lanestris* (Linnaeus, 1758)
Small Eggar   **Notable/Nb**

Formerly widespread but local in all three vice-counties (Goater, 1974), but there have been no recent records. However, it holds on at Martin Down, at present politically in Hampshire but in vc8, S Wilts, and one or more nests of larvae are seen there each year, on hawthorn (LS).

1634 *Malacosoma neustria* (Linnaeus, 1758)
The Lackey

Widespread and usually fairly common to common in the three vice-counties, in gardens, orchards, hedgerows, bushy places and deciduous woodland. The gregarious larvae are a familiar sight on the foliage of trees such as wild cherry and hawthorn, though certainly much less common than 20 years ago.

1636 *Lasiocampa trifolii* ([Denis & Schiffermüller], 1775)
Grass Eggar   **Notable/Na**

Still quite frequent in south Hayling Island, though long since lost from the New Forest, and there has been no record from the Isle of Wight since 1954 (Goater, 1974). The larva feeds on a variety of low plants including coarse grasses, tree lupin *Lupinus arboreus* and shrubs such as broom *Cytisus scoparius* and blackthorn *Prunus spinosa*.

1637 *Lasiocampa quercus* (Linnaeus, 1758)
Oak Eggar

Male

Common on the heaths of the New Forest, more rarely, and in a different, more "typical" form elsewhere in the

county, especially along the coasts. The following records are considered noteworthy.

- vc11 Millbrook, 25.5.94, three larvae; Peartree Green, 1.8.84 (PAB); Woolston, 1990–97, common, maximum 30 in 1993 (ARC); Gosport, 30.7 to 2.8.95, female at light (DSW).
- vc12 Selborne, 18.7.99, female at m.v. light, first for district (AEA).

1638 *Macrothylacia rubi* (Linnaeus, 1758)
Fox Moth

Still common on heaths and along the coast. Sometimes, as at Needs Ore in 1996, larvae occur in the greatest profusion in autumn, though they evidently suffer considerable mortality during hibernation.

1639 *Dendrolimus pini* (Linnaeus, 1758)
Pine Lappet

- vc10 Freshwater, 12.8.96, male at m.v. light (Knill-Jones, 1997d). This is the third British record and the first since 1809. **New county record.**

1640 *Euthrix potatoria* (Linnaeus, 1758)
Drinker

Widespread in all three vice-counties but apparently much less common in recent years. Most frequent in marshy places and riversides, but also in drier grassy terrain. The larva feeds on coarse grasses Poaceae (Gramineae) favouring particularly common reed *Phragmites australis*.

- vc10 Arreton, 12.11.99, male seen by D. Peach (Knill-Jones, 2000). An extraordinary date.

1642 *Gastropacha quercifolia* (Linnaeus, 1758)
Lappet

Widespread in the three vice-counties but much less frequent than formerly. In the 1940s, when it was common, larvae could be found during the day by feeling around the stem bases of young blackthorn bushes growing in hedgerows.

Saturniidae (2)

1643 *Saturnia pavonia* (Linnaeus, 1758)
Emperor Moth

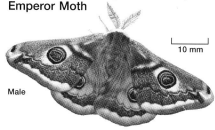

Male

Frequent on the heaths, less so in marshes, occasional elsewhere, where wandering females are sometimes taken

▲ 1633 *Eriogaster lanestris*
Small Eggar

▲ 1634 *Malacosoma neustria*
The Lackey

▲ 1636 *Lasiocampa trifolii*
Grass Eggar

▲ 1637 *Lasiocampa quercus*
Oak Eggar

at light. On heaths, the usual foodplant is ling *Calluna vulgaris*, and in marshes, meadowsweet *Filipendula ulmaria* or sallow.

■ vc12 Selborne, 6.4.95, one male at light; first seen in district (AEA).

1643a *Saturnia pyri* ([Denis & Schiffermüller], 1775)
Great Peacock Moth

One specimen, of unknown origin, recorded at Swaythling beside M27 motorway on 24.5.84 (Goater, 1992). **The only British record.**

Endromidae (1†)

1644 *Endromis versicolora* (Linnaeus, 1758)
Kentish Glory

No recent record and presumed long extinct in Hampshire (Goater, 1974, 1992).

Drepanidae (6)

1645 *Falcaria lacertinaria* (Linnaeus, 1758)
Scalloped Hook-tip

Common amongst birch, especially in thickets of young trees, in all three vice-counties.

1646 *Watsonalla binaria* (Hufnagel, 1767)
Oak Hook-tip

Common amongst oak in all three vice-counties.

1647 *Watsonalla cultraria* (Fabricius, 1775)
Barred Hook-tip

Frequent in beech woods both in the New Forest and on the chalk, but rare away from them.

1648 *Drepana falcataria* (Linnaeus, 1758)
Pebble Hook-tip

10 mm

Common amongst birch in all three vice-counties.
■ vc11 Chandlers Ford, 17.10.95, one at m.v. light – a very late date (BG).

1649 *Drepana curvatula* (Borkhausen, 1790)
Dusky Hook-tip

■ vc11 Totton, 21.8.91, one at m.v. light (Jeffes, 1995). **New county record.** First recorded in this country in 1960, this was the fifth of 11 recorded occurrences of this extremely scarce migrant (see Skinner, 1998).

1651 *Cilix glaucata* (Scopoli, 1763)
Chinese Character

Quite common in areas where hawthorn grows, but seemingly less so than formerly: for example, at Chandlers

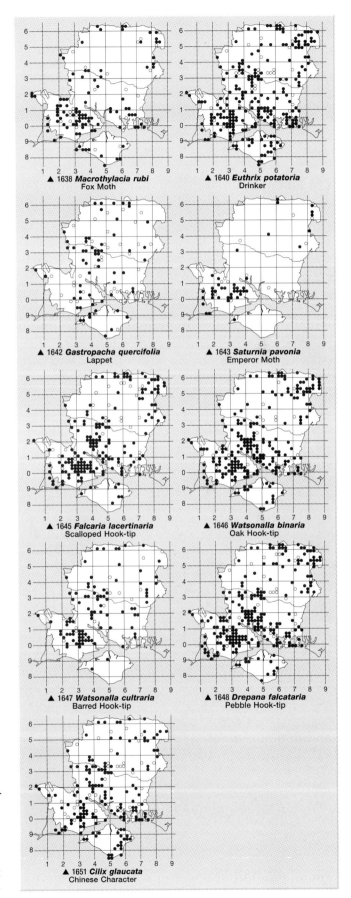

▲ 1638 *Macrothylacia rubi*
Fox Moth

▲ 1640 *Euthrix potatoria*
Drinker

▲ 1642 *Gastropacha quercifolia*
Lappet

▲ 1643 *Saturnia pavonia*
Emperor Moth

▲ 1645 *Falcaria lacertinaria*
Scalloped Hook-tip

▲ 1646 *Watsonalla binaria*
Oak Hook-tip

▲ 1647 *Watsonalla cultraria*
Barred Hook-tip

▲ 1648 *Drepana falcataria*
Pebble Hook-tip

▲ 1651 *Cilix glaucata*
Chinese Character

141

Ford, only one specimen has been recorded since 1990 where it used to be common.

Thyatiridae (9)

1652 *Thyatira batis* (Linnaeus, 1758)
Peach Blossom

Fairly common in all three vice-counties, especially in open, deciduous woodland where there is a good ground cover of bramble, the larval foodplant.

1653 *Habrosyne pyritoides* (Hufnagel, 1766)
Buff Arches
Usually common wherever light traps are operated in all three vice-counties. The foodplant is bramble.

1654 *Tethea ocularis* (Linnaeus, 1767)
Figure of Eighty
Fairly common in all three vice-counties; associated with poplars.

1655 *Tethea or* ([Denis & Schiffermüller], 1775)
Poplar Lutestring
Clearly much more local than the preceding species, but found wherever aspen *Populus tremula* is established. Isolated records include those given below.

- vc10 Cranmore, 12.5.93 (SAK-J); Binstead, 28.6.96, two, and 19.8.96, one (BJW).
- vc11 Chandlers Ford, 27.6.92, one at m.v. light (BG).
- vc12 Pamber Forest, 9.7.95 (AS); Bramley Frith NR, 4.7.95, one at m.v. light (AHD); Yateley Common, 8.6.96 (AMD).

1656 *Tetheella fluctuosa* (Hübner, 1803)
Satin Lutestring **Notable/Nb**
Well-established in parts of eastern Hampshire; recently discovered in Havant Thicket. The most westerly record to hand is Winchester, 23.6.83 (Goater, 1992). All post-1992 records are given below. The larva feeds on birch.
- vc11 Havant Thicket, 28.6.95, a few at m.v. light (JRL), 23.6.99, one at m.v. light (PRD *et al.*); Chappetts Copse, 1.7.00 (PAB, TJN).
- vc12 Conford, 21.6.95, one at m.v. light (JRL); Selborne, 7.7, 13.7, 14.7 and 26.7.95, 21.5.98, singletons at light (AEA); Noar Hill, 2.7.94, 14.7.95 (AMJ); Bentley Station Meadow, 28.7.95, four at light, 20.7.96, two (PAB); Whitehill, 20.5.98 (AGL); Waggoners Wells, 4.8.96, four (AMD); Alice Holt, 24.7.92 (Rothamsted Survey); Frith End, 24.6 and 1.7.95, singles at light (KW).

1657 *Ochropacha duplaris* (Linnaeus, 1761)
Common Lutestring
Locally fairly common amongst birch in all three vice-counties.

1658 *Cymatophorima diluta* ([Denis & Schiffermüller], 1775)
Oak Lutestring
Common in oak woodland in all three vice-counties, but sparse and evidently decreased away from extensive woods.

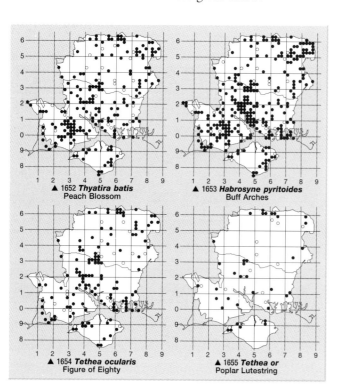

▲ 1652 *Thyatira batis*
Peach Blossom

▲ 1653 *Habrosyne pyritoides*
Buff Arches

▲ 1654 *Tethea ocularis*
Figure of Eighty

▲ 1655 *Tethea or*
Poplar Lutestring

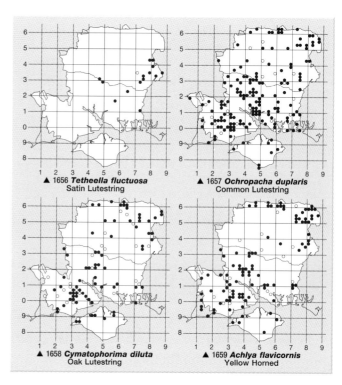

▲ 1656 *Tetheella fluctuosa*
Satin Lutestring

▲ 1657 *Ochropacha duplaris*
Common Lutestring

▲ 1658 *Cymatophorima diluta*
Oak Lutestring

▲ 1659 *Achlya flavicornis*
Yellow Horned

1659 *Achlya flavicornis* (Linnaeus, 1758)
Yellow Horned

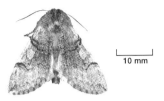

Common in birch country, especially on the heathland of the New Forest and in north-east Hampshire. In many places it has lost ground due to housing development.
■ vc11 Kings Somborne, 30.3.95 (TJN).

1660 *Polyploca ridens* (Fabricius, 1787)
Frosted Green
Still quite common in the oak woodlands in all three vice-counties.

Geometridae (252 + 3†)

1661 *Archiearis parthenias* (Linnaeus, 1761)
Orange Underwing
Seen less frequently nowadays than in the past. In many places, the decline, or loss, may be attributed to housing developments in erstwhile birch country. This species is now most often seen in the New Forest, in north-east Hampshire and in the north-east of the Isle of Wight, amongst the foodplant, birch. Unpredictable spring weather in recent years has made monitoring difficult: the moth flies in warm sunshine in March and April.

1662 *Archeiaris notha* (Hübner, 1803)
Light Orange Underwing   **Notable/Nb**
The larva is monophagous on aspen *Populus tremula*, and the species seems to be present wherever this tree is established. However, in places, such as Crab Wood, some of the few trees have been felled to the detriment of this and other local species.
■ vc11 Clumber Inclosure, 28.3.98, flying round aspen; Brockenhurst, 28.3.98, flying round and landing on aspen (JEC); Crab Wood, a strong colony, 1995 (RAB).
■ vc12 Pamber, commoner than *A. parthenias* (GJD, *teste* AECA).

1663 *Alsophila aescularia* ([Denis & Schiffermüller], 1775)
March Moth

Common in wooded country in all three vice-counties, but almost certainly under-recorded because of its early flying season. The larva is polyphagous on many deciduous trees and shrubs.

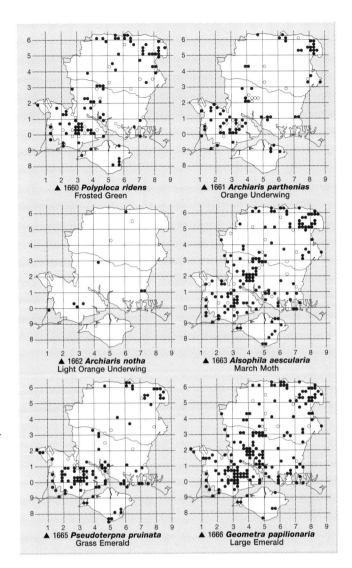

▲ 1660 *Polyploca ridens*
Frosted Green

▲ 1661 *Archiearis parthenias*
Orange Underwing

▲ 1662 *Archiaris notha*
Light Orange Underwing

▲ 1663 *Alsophila aescularia*
March Moth

▲ 1665 *Pseudoterpna pruinata*
Grass Emerald

▲ 1666 *Geometra papilionaria*
Large Emerald

1664 *Aplasta ononaria* (Fuessly, 1783)
Rest Harrow   **RDB3/Migrant**
Known in Hampshire only as a very occasional presumed migrant. There are only four records, all from vc11, the most recent being Southsea, 15.7.59 and Rowlands Castle, 9.7.62 (Goater 1974).

1665 *Pseudoterpna pruinata* (Hufnagel, 1767)
Grass Emerald
Mainly in the New Forest area and in north-east Hampshire, and also in the west and south-east of the Isle of Wight. Fairly common on damp heathland and in places along the coast, a rare wanderer elsewhere. The larva can be found on petty whin *Genista anglica* and also occurs on gorse and broom.
■ vc11 Woolston, three specimens on 25.7, 2.8 and 9.8.91 (ARC).

1666 *Geometra papilionaria* (Linnaeus, 1758)
Large Emerald
Still fairly frequent in birch country throughout the three vice-counties.

1667 *Comibaena bajularia* ([Denis & Schiffermüller], 1775)
Blotched Emerald
Fairly common in old oak woodland in all three vice-counties, but rather rare away from it.

1669 *Hemithea aestivaria* (Hübner, 1789)
Common Emerald
The species remains common in the three vice-counties. The larva is polyphagous on the foliage of many deciduous trees and shrubs.

1670 *Chlorissa viridata* (Linnaeus, 1758)
Small Grass Emerald   **Notable/Na**
Fairly common in the boggy areas of the New Forest, and in Emer Bog; formerly on heathy ground in Botley Wood, but no records to hand since 1960; no recent record from the Isle of Wight, and the old record for vc12 (Goater, 1974) remains unconfirmed.

1672 *Thalera fimbrialis* (Scopoli, 1763)
Sussex Emerald   **RDB1/Migrant**
There have been just two records within the region. The first is that cited in Goater (1974), from Bournemouth

on 30.7.46. News of the second came to the authors just before going to press.
■ vc10 A female at m.v. light at Binstead on 24.6.01 conf. BG (BJW). **New vc record.**

1673 *Hemistola chrysoprasaria* (Esper, 1795)
Small Emerald
Frequent amongst *Clematis* on the chalk, occasional elsewhere, where it is possibly using cultivated *Clematis* as a larval foodplant. The species seems to be virtually absent from the New Forest.
■ vc11 Chandlers Ford, 10.7.94, one at m.v. light (BG); Woolston, occasional at light (ARC).

1674 *Jodis lactearia* (Linnaeus, 1758)
Little Emerald
Still widespread in all three vice-counties but surely much less common than formerly.

1675 *Cyclophora pendularia* (Clerck, 1759)
Dingy Mocha   **RDB3**
The recent history of this species in Hampshire, and especially in the New Forest, is given by Goater (1992). There are extremely few recent records, yet the species undoubtedly persists at very low density, amongst small bushes of sallow *Salix* spp. in boggy areas, particularly in the extreme west of vc11.
■ vc10 Freshwater, 29.5.92, one at m.v. light (SAK-J, 1994), the third vc10 record since 1950.
■ vc11 Hurn, three in 1999, one on 27.7.00, all at m.v. light (MJ); St Ives, one record (JHC); Brockenhurst, four records (JEC), single larva beaten from an isolated small-leaved *Salix* spp., 23.9.00 (DGG).

1676 *Cyclophora annularia* (Fabricius, 1775)
The Mocha   **Notable/Nb**
Widespread in S Hants, southern N Hants and in the north of the Isle of Wight, but local and uncommon amongst field maple *Acer campestre*.

1677 *Cyclophora albipunctata* (Hufnagel, 1767)
Birch Mocha
Fairly frequent amongst birch, especially on boggy heathland, but undoubtedly less common than formerly. It occurs mainly in the south-west and north-east of mainland Hampshire, and locally on the Isle of Wight.

1678 *Cyclophora puppillaria* (Hübner, 1799)
Blair's Mocha
A scarce immigrant with about 24 records in the two counties to date. Recent records are given below.
■ vc10 Freshwater, 30.6.98 (DBW); Binstead, 19.9.99, one at m.v. light (BJW).
■ vc11 near Bransgore, 27.10.95 (G. Martin) (Skinner and Parsons, 1998).
■ vc12 Crawley, a female to m.v. light on 22.8.98 (RAB).

1679 *Cyclophora porata* (Linnaeus, 1767)
False Mocha
There are few recent records of this species, and none

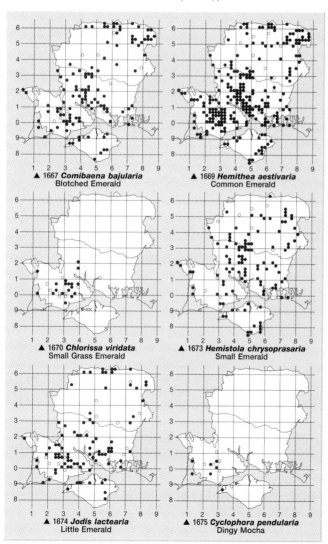

▲ 1667 *Comibaena bajularia*
Blotched Emerald

▲ 1669 *Hemithea aestivaria*
Common Emerald

▲ 1670 *Chlorissa viridata*
Small Grass Emerald

▲ 1673 *Hemistola chrysoprasaria*
Small Emerald

▲ 1674 *Jodis lactearia*
Little Emerald

▲ 1675 *Cyclophora pendularia*
Dingy Mocha

from the Isle of Wight. The species has declined dramatically during the second half of the 20th century. All known records were given in Goater (1992), many of them from pre-1940. It appears to require open, sunny, coppiced oak or areas of small oak bushes in order to thrive, and these conditions are largely lacking nowadays.
■ vc11 Roydon Woods, 25.8.91 (PAB); Brockenhurst, two records (JEC).

1680 *Cyclophora punctaria* (Linnaeus, 1758)
Maiden's Blush
This is the one *Cyclophora* species that seems to be recovering slightly in the area and is locally common in all three vice-counties. The larva feeds on oak.

1681 *Cyclophora linearia* (Hübner, 1799)
Clay Triple-lines
Fairly frequent in all three vice-counties, in beech woods on and off the chalk, but only occasional away from them.
■ vc11 Chandlers Ford, 29.6.92, one at m.v. light (BG).

1682 *Timandra griseata* Petersen, 1902
Blood-vein

10 mm

Widespread and fairly common in all three vice-counties.
■ vc10 Binstead, 8.11.99, one recorded by BJW (Knill-Jones, 2000). An extraordinary date.

1684 *Scopula nigropunctata* (Hufnagel, 1767)
Sub-angled Wave **RDB2**
■ vc10 Freshwater, 5.8.94, one at m.v. light (Knill-Jones, 1995). A presumed immigrant. **New county record.**

1687 *Scopula ornata* (Scopoli, 1763)
Lace Border **Notable/Na**
There remains just the single record given in Goater (1974) from Abbotstone Down vc12, on 25.6.60.

1688 *Scopula rubiginata* (Hufnagel, 1767)
Tawny Wave **RDB3**
■ vc11 Christchurch, 5.8.94, one at m.v. light (Jeffes, 1995). A presumed immigrant. **New county record.**

1689 *Scopula marginepunctata* (Goeze, 1781)
Mullein Wave
Fairly frequent along the coasts, rare inland, and there mainly on the chalk. All recent records are given.
■ vc11 Steamer Point Wood, 25.8.95 (PAB); Brockenhurst, few each year (JEC); Millbrook, 30.7.94 (PAB); Rownhams, 9.8.92, 5.5.95 (KG); Whitenap, Romsey, 5.8.95 (MJB); Chandlers Ford, 21.8.94, one at m.v. light (BG); Allbrook, 23.6 and 24.6.96 (ML); Woolston, 1990–93, common, maximum 60 in 1995 (ARC); Gosport, 21.5 to 22.9.95, total of 54 at light (DSW); Havant, 2.9.97 (CBC).

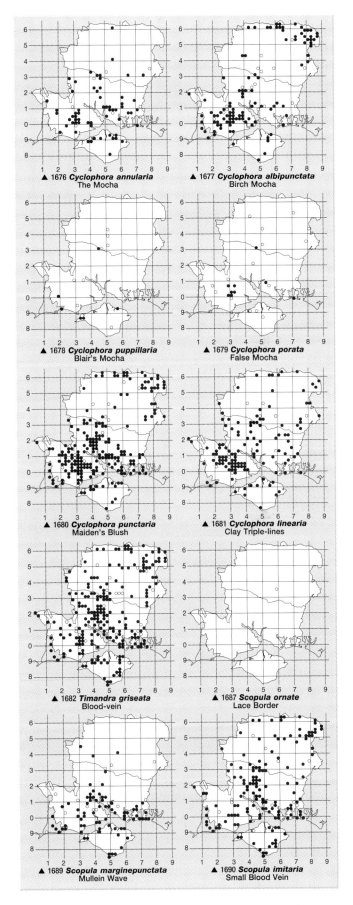

▲ 1676 *Cyclophora annularia*
The Mocha

▲ 1677 *Cyclophora albipunctata*
Birch Mocha

▲ 1678 *Cyclophora puppillaria*
Blair's Mocha

▲ 1679 *Cyclophora porata*
False Mocha

▲ 1680 *Cyclophora punctaria*
Maiden's Blush

▲ 1681 *Cyclophora linearia*
Clay Triple-lines

▲ 1682 *Timandra griseata*
Blood-vein

▲ 1687 *Scopula ornate*
Lace Border

▲ 1689 *Scopula marginepunctata*
Mullein Wave

▲ 1690 *Scopula imitaria*
Small Blood Vein

■ vc12 East Stratton, occasional, one or two each year (BI-J).

1690 *Scopula imitaria* (Hübner, 1799)
Small Blood Vein

Widespread in all three vice-counties, but only moderately common.

1691 *Scopula emutaria* (Hübner, 1809)
Rosy Wave   **Notable/Nb**

Found in two distinct habitats, in the coastal salterns and in boggy areas of the New Forest, where it is rather uncommon. Unrecorded from N Hants. All recent records are given below.

■ vc10 Newtown (SAK-J); St Helens Duver (PJC).
■ vc11 Hengistbury Head, 1997, common on saltmarsh (MJ); Brockenhurst, 24.6.92 (JEC); Lepe, 20.8.93 (NB); Cadlands House, 12.7.97, one flying at dusk (BG, JRL); Royal Victoria Country Park, Netley, 4.7.98 (P. Halliwell); Gilkicker Point, 29.7 and 24.8.97 (DSW); Southsea, 18.6.99, one at m.v. light (IRT); N Hayling Island, regular in garden (PRD).

1692 *Scopula immutata* (Linnaeus, 1758)
Lesser Cream Wave

This species has declined. It is found in scattered colonies on damp ground, in marshes and meadows.

1693 *Scopula floslactata* (Haworth, 1809)
Cream Wave

Fairly common, though less so than in former times, in deciduous woodland in all three vice-counties. It used often to be seen by day, resting on the upper surface of leaves.

1696 *Idaea ochrata* (Scopoli, 1763)
Bright Wave   **RDB1**

There has been no record since Bournemouth, 1900, given in Goater (1974).

1698 *Idaea muricata* (Hufnagel, 1767)
Purple-bordered Gold   **Notable/Nb**

Fairly frequent in the New Forest, on boggy moorland; we have no recent record from NE Hampshire where, in 1957, it was reported as being fairly common in the Farnborough area (Goater, 1974).

■ vc11 Beaulieu, 15.7.95 (BI-J).

1699 *Idaea rusticata* ([Denis & Schiffermüller], 1775)
Least Carpet

First recorded in 1977 at Ashurst, then Highcliffe and Hayling Island, 1984, all in vc11. The first Isle of Wight record was in 1991. Since then, very small numbers have occurred in all three vice-counties: it is evidently spreading westwards from its headquarters in the Thames Estuary. The first records for the county are detailed in Goater (1992), and all subsequent records are given below.

■ vc10 Niton, 6.8.92 (two) (*comm.* SAK-J); Chale Green, 6.8.94, 22.7.95, singles at m.v. light (SRC).

■ vc11 Brockenhurst, 23.7.96, one at m.v. light in garden (JEC); Totton, 14.8.91, one at m.v. light (Jeffes, 1995); Bitterne, 21.7.00, one at m.v. light (PAB); Botley Wood, 3.8.87 (JHC); Fareham, 17.7.99, one at m.v. light (MLO); Southsea, 5.7 and 11.7.99, singletons at m.v. light (IRT); Hayling Island, 6.8.84, 1.8.85, singles at m.v. light (JMW).

■ vc12 South Wonston, 11.7.99, one at m.v. light (PJSS); Pamber Forest, 1.7.95, one at light (AS), specimen kept (GJD); Selborne, 15.7 and 22.7.96 (Aston, 1997), 21.7.99, 307.00 (AEA); Bordon, 28.6.97 (AGL-G); Farnborough, 18.7.96 (RWP). **New vc record.**

■ vc22 Mortimer West End, 20.7.96, 15.7.97, singletons at m.v. light (GJD).

1701 *Idaea sylvestraria* (Hübner, 1799)
Dotted Border Wave   **Notable/Nb**

Scarce in the New Forest, north-east Hampshire and in the west and south-east of the Isle of Wight, with scattered records from elsewhere; some of these may have been unwarrantedly rejected, but there is no doubt other species are sometimes mistaken for it. The following recent records are regarded as sound.

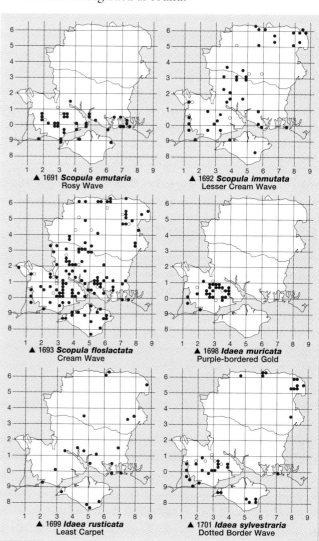

▲ 1691 *Scopula emutaria*
Rosy Wave

▲ 1692 *Scopula immutata*
Lesser Cream Wave

▲ 1693 *Scopula floslactata*
Cream Wave

▲ 1698 *Idaea muricata*
Purple-bordered Gold

▲ 1699 *Idaea rusticata*
Least Carpet

▲ 1701 *Idaea sylvestraria*
Dotted Border Wave

■ vc10 Freshwater, 9.7.98 (SAK-J).

■ vc11 Hengistbury, 1994 (MJ); Matchams, nr Ringwood, 1985, 1986 (GL); Vales Moor, 1996 (JEC); Beaulieu, 9.8.93 (BI-J); Brockenhurst, two records (JEC); Hayling Island, 17.8 and 22.8.87, singles at m.v. light (JMW).

■ vc12 Pamber Heath, 30.6 and 21.7.95 (AS); Yateley Common, 4.7 and 8.7.93, 18.6.97 (AMD); Farnborough, 3.8.94 (RWP).

1702 *Idaea biselata* (Hufnagel, 1767)
Small Fan-footed Wave

Very common in all three vice-counties.

1705 *Idaea fuscovenosa* (Goeze, 1781)
Dwarf Cream Wave

Fairly common, possibly under-recorded.

1706 *Idaea humiliata* (Hufnagel, 1767)
Isle of Wight Wave

Attempts to rediscover this species on the Isle of Wight have always failed, and there is no record since 1931. An isolated record from Portsmouth in 1954 gave hope that it may still lurk somewhere in the area (Goater, 1974).

1707 *Idaea seriata* (Schrank, 1802)
Small Dusty Wave

Still widely distributed, but evidently far less common than formerly.

1708 *Idaea dimidiata* (Hufnagel, 1767)
Single-dotted Wave

Widespread and fairly common in all three vice-counties.

1709 *Idaea subsericeata* (Haworth, 1809)
Satin Wave

Fairly common locally, on heaths and amongst tall grasses on downland.

1711 *Idaea trigeminata* (Haworth, 1809)
Treble Brown-spot

Widespread and usually common, in all three vice-counties.

1712 *Idaea emarginata* (Linnaeus, 1758)
Small Scallop

There are scattered records from all three vice-counties, but this moth is rather rarely reported nowadays. The decrease was noted by the end of the 1980s and all records pre-1992 were given in Goater (1992).

1713 *Idaea aversata* (Linnaeus, 1758)
Riband Wave

Still extremely common throughout; the plain form *remutata* Linnaeus rather outnumbers the typical banded form.

1714 *Idaea degeneraria* (Hübner, 1799)
Portland Ribbon Wave   **RDB3**

A presumed immigrant, or possibly a wanderer from the resident colony on Portland, Dorset. The only previous records are given in Goater (1974) from Sandown, Isle of

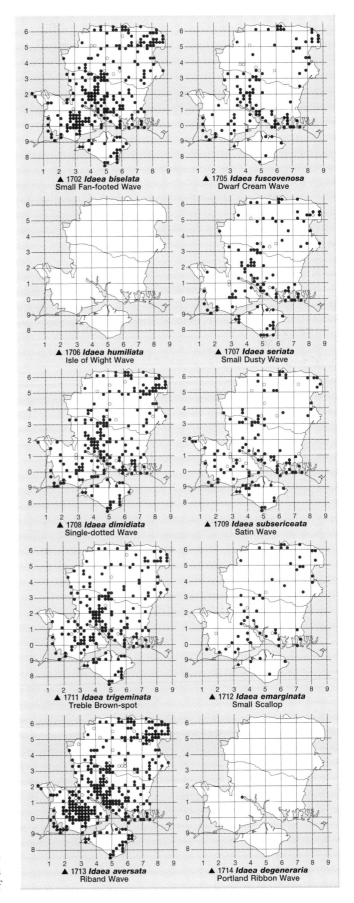

▲ 1702 *Idaea biselata*
Small Fan-footed Wave

▲ 1705 *Idaea fuscovenosa*
Dwarf Cream Wave

▲ 1706 *Idaea humiliata*
Isle of Wight Wave

▲ 1707 *Idaea seriata*
Small Dusty Wave

▲ 1708 *Idaea dimidiata*
Single-dotted Wave

▲ 1709 *Idaea subsericeata*
Satin Wave

▲ 1711 *Idaea trigeminata*
Treble Brown-spot

▲ 1712 *Idaea emarginata*
Small Scallop

▲ 1713 *Idaea aversata*
Riband Wave

▲ 1714 *Idaea degeneraria*
Portland Ribbon Wave

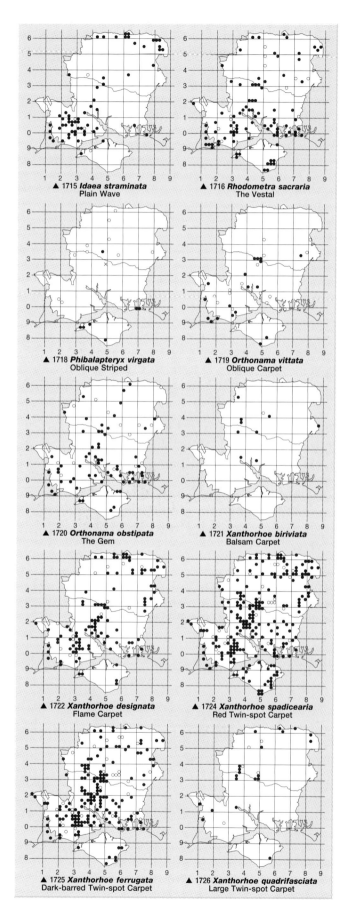

▲ 1715 *Idaea straminata*
Plain Wave

▲ 1716 *Rhodometra sacraria*
The Vestal

▲ 1718 *Phibalapteryx virgata*
Oblique Striped

▲ 1719 *Orthonama vittata*
Oblique Carpet

▲ 1720 *Orthonama obstipata*
The Gem

▲ 1721 *Xanthorhoe biriviata*
Balsam Carpet

▲ 1722 *Xanthorhoe designata*
Flame Carpet

▲ 1724 *Xanthorhoe spadicearia*
Red Twin-spot Carpet

▲ 1725 *Xanthorhoe ferrugata*
Dark-barred Twin-spot Carpet

▲ 1726 *Xanthorhoe quadrifasciata*
Large Twin-spot Carpet

Wight, 5.9.1902 and Brockenhurst, S Hants, October 1962.

■ vc10 Freshwater, 11.8.97, one at m.v. light (Knill-Jones, 1997b).

■ vc11 Totton, 26.8.90, one at m.v. light (Jeffes, 1995).

1715 *Idaea straminata* (Borkhausen, 1794)
Plain Wave

Local; uncommon but probably overlooked, and some of the sight records that have been submitted may have been unwarrantedly rejected. Most records are from the New Forest area and from Pamber Forest and Silchester.

■ vc10 Freshwater, 1.7.98 (SAK-J).

1716 *Rhodometra sacraria* (Linnaeus, 1767)
The Vestal

A common migrant, mainly in late summer and autumn; it appears all over the county, though most frequently on the Isle of Wight and towards the south coast of the mainland. It comes freely to light and can also be kicked up from stubble fields in which the usual foodplant, knotgrass *Polygonum aviculare*, is growing.

1718 *Phibalapteryx virgata* (Hufnagel, 1767)
Oblique Striped   **Notable/Nb**

Scarce, local and decreased. The foodplant is ladies' bedstraw *Galium verum*; the moth still occurs on the dunes at Hayling Island, but has virtually disappeared from the chalk. It is therefore gratifying to report the following records.

■ vc10 Freshwater, 15.7.98 (DBW, comm. SAK-J).

■ vc12 South Wonston, 5.4.97, one at m.v. light (PJSS).

1719 *Orthonama vittata* (Borkhausen, 1794)
Oblique Carpet

An uncommon marsh-inhabiting species, records of which are scattered thinly in the three vice-counties. The larva feeds on marsh bedstraw *Galium palustre* and other species of bedstraw.

■ vc11 Sholing, 18.8.99, one at m.v. light (ARC).

1720 *Orthonama obstipata* (Fabricius, 1794)
The Gem

A common migrant. There is sometimes an influx in May and June, after which the moth is common the following autumn, probably from progeny from the spring immigrants reinforced by further migration.

1721 *Xanthorhoe biriviata* (Borkhausen, 1794)
Balsam Carpet   **Notable/Na**

First reported at Wherwell, vc12, in 1964, and now established in the valley of the Upper Test, in damp woodland containing orange balsam *Impatiens capensis*, on which the larva feeds. It is also beginning to appear in the Itchen Valley, and there is one record from near the River Wey, at Waggoners Wells, given below.

■ vc11 Kings Somborne, 11.7.92 (TJN), photograph seen and identity confirmed (BG); Sholing, 18.8.99, one at m.v. light (ARC).

■ vc12 Leckford, now frequent in woodland in the river valley (BG *et al.*); Wildhern, 8.8.00 (DGG); Abbots Worthy, 2.8.94, two disturbed from herbage by River Itchen (AHD); East Stratton, 5.5.90, checked by DHS (BI-J); Waggoners Wells, 4.8.96, one at light (AMD).

1722 *Xanthorhoe designata* (Hufnagel, 1767)
Flame Carpet
Still fairly common and widespread in deciduous woodland and bushy places, though perhaps less so than formerly.

1724 *Xanthorhoe spadicearia* ([Denis & Schiffermüller], 1775)
Red Twin-spot Carpet
Common and widespread.

1725 *Xanthorhoe ferrugata* (Clerck, 1759)
Dark-barred Twin-spot Carpet
Common and widespread.

1726 *Xanthorhoe quadrifasciata* (Clerck, 1759)
Large Twin-spot Carpet

10 mm

Virtually confined to deciduous woodland in N Hants, where it is uncommon.
■ vc11 Kings Somborne, 20.7.95, 6.7.99 (TJN).
■ vc12 Winnall Moors NR (DHS); Yateley Common, 30.7.93, one (AMD).

1727 *Xanthorhoe montanata* ([Denis & Schiffermüller], 1775)
Silver Ground Carpet
A common species in deciduous woodland.

1728 *Xanthorhoe fluctuata* (Linnaeus, 1758)
Garden Carpet
Common, though distinctly less so than formerly.

1731 *Scotopteryx bipunctaria* ([Denis & Schiffermüller], 1775)
Chalk Carpet   **Notable/Nb**
This species has gone from many localities on the chalk, which were either ploughed up during the 1939–45 War, or developed for housing. It survives in one or two localities on the Isle of Wight, and on Broughton Down.
■ vc10 St Catherine's Point, several at light during July, 1995 (SRC, PC); Knighton Down, large colony discovered early 8.94, still thriving in 1996 (BJW).
■ vc11 St Ives, Ringwood, 29.8.87, one at m.v. light (JHC); Broughton Down, 27.7.94, 21.7.95 (NB), 7.7.00, seven seen during the day, and six on 8.8.00 (AHD).

1732 *Scotopteryx chenopodiata* (Linnaeus, 1758)
Shaded Broad-bar
Once known as "The Aurelian's Plague", this species is much less common than formerly, though colonies still occur locally in hollows on dunes and amongst scrub on downland.

1734 *Scotopteryx luridata* (Hufnagel, 1767)
July Belle
Frequent on the heaths of the New Forest and in the north-east of Hampshire, rare or absent elsewhere.
■ vc10 Cranmore, 9.6.94 (SAK-J). **Presence in vc 10 confirmed.**
■ vc11 Fareham, 8.7.97 (MO).

1735 *Catarhoe rubidata* ([Denis & Schiffermüller], 1775)
Ruddy Carpet   **Notable/Nb**
This species had become rare by the 1960s (Goater, 1974); it is now found most frequently in hedgerows on the chalk, near the foodplants hedge bedstraw *Galium mollugo* and ladies' bedstraw *G. verum*, and shows some signs of a modest recovery.
■ vc10 Wootton, 11.7.97 (TR); Newchurch, 12.7.94, Binstead, 5.7.93, 24.7.96, 25.6.98 (BJW).
■ vc11 Beaulieu, 13.7.95 (BI-J); Broughton Down, 21.7.95 (NB); Sholing, 27.6.99, one at m.v. light (ARC); Portsdown Hill, 7.7.98, four netted at dusk (RJD); Cosham, 17.6.97 (TJJ); N Hayling Island, 26.7.95 (PRD).
■ vc12 Danebury Hillfort, 2.7.99 (AMD); lane between Chilbolton and Crawley, 17.6.97, female netted at dusk

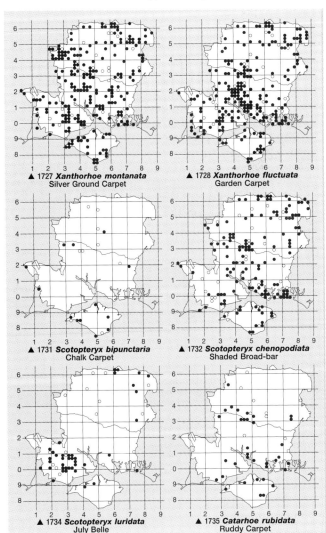

▲ 1727 *Xanthorhoe montanata*
Silver Ground Carpet

▲ 1728 *Xanthorhoe fluctuata*
Garden Carpet

▲ 1731 *Scotopteryx bipunctaria*
Chalk Carpet

▲ 1732 *Scotopteryx chenopodiata*
Shaded Broad-bar

▲ 1734 *Scotopteryx luridata*
July Belle

▲ 1735 *Catarhoe rubidata*
Ruddy Carpet

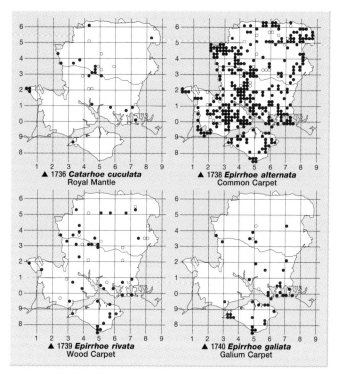

▲ 1736 *Catarhoe cuculata*
Royal Mantle

▲ 1738 *Epirrhoe alternata*
Common Carpet

▲ 1739 *Epirrhoe rivata*
Wood Carpet

▲ 1740 *Epirrhoe galiata*
Galium Carpet

(BG); Crawley, one in 1994: much rarer than in 1970s (RAB); Wildhern, nr Andover, 7.6.97, one in actinic trap (DGG); Magdalen Hill Down, 17.6.93 and three on 12.7.96 (PAB); Selborne, 28.6.94 (AEA); Noar Hill, 20.8.93 (AMJ).

1736 *Catarhoe cuculata* (Hufnagel, 1767)
Royal Mantle

Rare but fairly regular on what remains of the chalk country, in all three vice-counties. The larva of this species also lives on ladies' bedstraw *Galium verum*.
- vc11 Woolston, 21.7.90 (ARC); Leigh Park, Havant, 5.8.96 (CBC); Gutner Point, Hayling Island, 24.7.94 (AMD).
- vc12 Crawley, 1991 and 1995, in garden (RAB); Magdalen Hill Down, 12.7.96, two (PAB).

1738 *Epirrhoe alternata* (Müller, 1764)
Common Carpet

Widespread and locally abundant, particularly in meadows overrun by cleavers *Galium aparine*.

1739 *Epirrhoe rivata* (Hübner, 1813)
Wood Carpet

Uncommon, and almost confined to the chalk, where the larva feeds on hedge bedstraw *Galium mollugo* and ladies' bedstraw *G. verum*. It is easily confused with the previous species and some records may have been undeservedly rejected.
- vc10 Freshwater, 11.7.95 (SAK-J); Chale Green, 15.7.95, one (SRC).
- vc11 Fordingbridge, 2.7.92 (NHu); Broughton Down, 20.6.94 (BG); Kings Somborne, 20.7 and 28.7.95 (TJN); Wick Hill Hanger, 17.8.96, one (PAB); Gosport, 25.5, 27.5 and 29.5.95, singletons at light, conf. JRL (DSW); Leigh Park, Havant, 25.6.93 (CBC).

- vc12 Crawley, occasional in garden trap (RAB); Winnall Moors NR (DHS); East Stratton (BI-J).

1740 *Epirrhoe galiata* ([Denis & Schiffermüller], 1775)
Galium Carpet

This species remains fairly common in places on the coast, but is now very rare inland, on the chalk. Larva on bedstraws *Galium* spp.
- vc10 Chale Green, 2.6.94 (SRC).
- vc11 Butser Hill, 13.7.97 (AMD).
- vc12 South Wonston, 6.8.96 (PJSS).

1742 *Camptogramma bilineata* (Linnaeus, 1758)
Yellow Shell

Still reasonably common, especially on the chalk, but the moth comes to light rarely and so is certainly under-recorded. On the other hand, it is now much rarer in certain localities, such as Chandlers Ford.

1745 *Larentia clavaria* (Haworth, 1809)
The Mallow

Widespread but seldom more than a few specimens reported from any one locality. The foodplant, common mallow *Malva sylvestris* is scattered on waysides; the other foodplant, marsh mallow *Althaea officinalis*, is very local in coastal localities and the moth has so far not been associated with it in Hampshire. Recent records are given below.
- vc10 Binstead, 10.10 and 16.10.94, 3.10.97 (BJW).
- vc11 Brockenhurst, 5.10.86 (JEC); Beaulieu, 12.10.93 (BI-J); Rownhams, 30.9.94 (KG); Woolston, 28.9, 2.10 and 5.10.91 (ARC); Warsash, 28.9.95 (PAB), 15.10.96 (PMP); Gosport, 1.10.96 (DSW), Southsea, at least 14 between 28.9 and 4.11.97 (IRT).
- vc12 Crawley, 23.9.80, only one seen (RAB); Selborne, 25.9 and 26.9.98, 7.10 and 8.10.99, at m.v. light, first records (AEA).

1746 *Anticlea badiata* ([Denis & Schiffermüller], 1775)
Shoulder Stripe

Common in localities where dog-rose *Rosa canina* agg. grows.

1747 *Anticlea derivata* ([Denis & Schiffermüller], 1775)
The Streamer

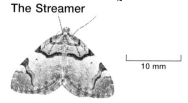

10 mm

Fairly common in localities where dog-rose *Rosa canina* agg. grows, emerging a little later in the spring than the preceding species.

1748 *Mesoleuca albicillata* (Linnaeus, 1758)
Beautiful Carpet

Widespread but scarce in deciduous and open coniferous woodland where there is a good growth of bramble.
- vc10 Parkhurst Forest, 22.7.96, first recent record (Knill-Jones, 1997d).

1749 *Pelurga comitata* (Linnaeus, 1758)
Dark Spinach

Local and uncommon in coastal localities, neglected corners of allotments, etc., where goosefoot *Chenopodium* spp. and orache *Atriplex* spp. are present. Recent records are given below.

■ vc11 St Ives, Ringwood, 1987, at m.v. light (JHC); Brockenhurst, three records (JEC); Southsea, 21.8.96 (JRL), six during August, 1997, at light (IRT); N Hayling Island, 9.8.98 (PRD).

■ vc12 Selborne, 28.7 and 29.7.99, only one previous record (AEA); Yateley Common, 24.7.93 (AMD).

1750 *Lampropteryx suffumata* ([Denis & Schiffermüller], 1775)
Water Carpet

10 mm

Usually local and uncommon, in damp woodland and along ditches and hedgerows where bedstraws *Galium* spp., including cleavers *G. aparine* occur.

■ vc10 Yarmouth, 17.5.92 (DHS).

■ vc11 Hengistbury, 19.4 to 20.6.94, six at m.v. light (MJ); Fordingbridge, 9.5.81 (NHu); Balmer Lawn, Brockenhurst, 21.5.92 (DHS); Brockenhurst, 20.5.99 (JEC); Broughton Down, 29.4.94, 29.4.95 (NB); Kings Somborne, 24.3.95, 6.4.96 (TJN).

■ vc12 East Stratton, 19.5.92, 24.4.93 (BI-J); Rye Common, 6.5.95, seven at m.v. light; Bentley Station Meadow, 5.5.95 (NB); Selborne, from 13.4.95, occasional at light (AEA); Noar Hill, 25.4.93, common in 1995, max. ten on 3.5 (AMJ); Alice Holt, seven between 22.4 and 25.5.92 (Rothamsted Survey).

1751 *Lampropteryx otregiata* (Metcalfe, 1917)
Devon Carpet   **Notable/Nb**

Not uncommon in parts of the New Forest, along the edges of damp rides, and in the north of the county, but still unrecorded from the Isle of Wight. Recent records outside the Forest are given below.

■ vc11 Yew Hill, 17.5.91 (JEC); Botley Wood, 11.5.98, one at actinic light (RJD).

■ vc12 Old Alresford Pond NR, 16.5.76, one disturbed by day, genitalia prep. 3926, conf. JRL (DMA, RJD).

1752 *Cosmorhoe ocellata* (Linnaeus, 1758)
Purple Bar

Widespread and common.

1754 *Eulithis prunata* (Linnaeus, 1758)
The Phoenix

A species that is certainly increasing in the county, though still extremely local on the Isle of Wight. The foodplants, red and black currants and gooseberry *Ribes* spp. are local in the wild, but the larva will also occur where these plants are cultivated.

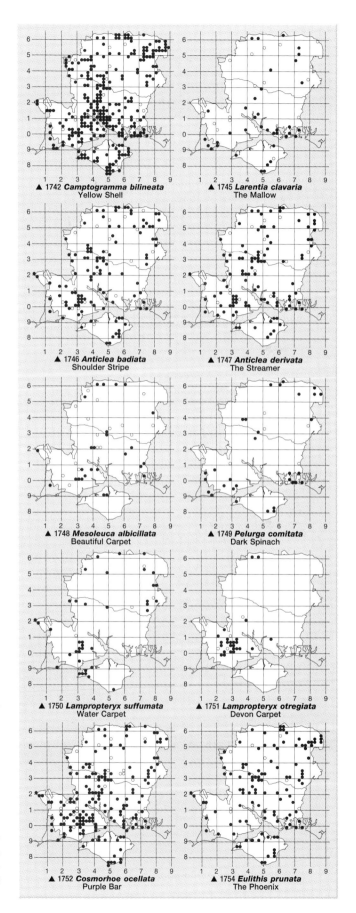

▲ 1742 *Camptogramma bilineata*
Yellow Shell

▲ 1745 *Larentia clavaria*
The Mallow

▲ 1746 *Anticlea badiata*
Shoulder Stripe

▲ 1747 *Anticlea derivata*
The Streamer

▲ 1748 *Mesoleuca albicillata*
Beautiful Carpet

▲ 1749 *Pelurga comitata*
Dark Spinach

▲ 1750 *Lampropteryx suffumata*
Water Carpet

▲ 1751 *Lampropteryx otregiata*
Devon Carpet

▲ 1752 *Cosmorhoe ocellata*
Purple Bar

▲ 1754 *Eulithis prunata*
The Phoenix

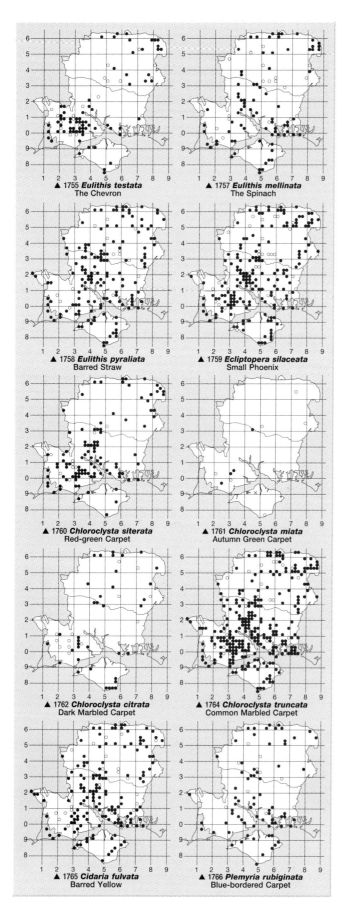

▲ 1755 *Eulithis testata*
The Chevron

▲ 1757 *Eulithis mellinata*
The Spinach

▲ 1758 *Eulithis pyraliata*
Barred Straw

▲ 1759 *Ecliptopera silaceata*
Small Phoenix

▲ 1760 *Chloroclysta siterata*
Red-green Carpet

▲ 1761 *Chloroclysta miata*
Autumn Green Carpet

▲ 1762 *Chloroclysta citrata*
Dark Marbled Carpet

▲ 1764 *Chloroclysta truncata*
Common Marbled Carpet

▲ 1765 *Cidaria fulvata*
Barred Yellow

▲ 1766 *Plemyria rubiginata*
Blue-bordered Carpet

1755 *Eulithis testata* (Linnaeus, 1761)
The Chevron

Frequent on heaths and boggy moorland in the New Forest and north-east Hampshire, and in suitable habitat elsewhere, including the Isle of Wight.
■ vc11 Rownhams, 23.8.94 (KG).

1757 *Eulithis mellinata* (Fabricius, 1787)
The Spinach

Widespread but much less common than formerly; very much an insect of cottage gardens where the foodplants, red and black currants *Ribes* spp. grow.

1758 *Eulithis pyraliata* ([Denis & Schiffermüller], 1775)
Barred Straw

Locally fairly common especially in areas where cleavers *Galium aparine* is well-established.

1759 *Ecliptopera silaceata* ([Denis & Schiffermüller], 1775)
Small Phoenix

Common wherever the smaller species of willowherb *Epilobium* spp. and rosebay *Chamerion angustifolium* occur.

1760 *Chloroclysta siterata* (Hufnagel, 1767)
Red-green Carpet

This is another species that has increased and extended its range recently. It used to be more-or-less confined in Hampshire to the New Forest, but is now rather widespread, especially in S Hants.

1761 *Chloroclysta miata* (Linnaeus, 1758)
Autumn Green Carpet

In contrast to the previous species, this has decreased in the county to the verge of extinction. The only recent records are given below.
■ vc11 Brockenhurst, 1994 (C. Donnelly, comm. DGG); Stubby Copse Inclosure, 23.4.87 (D.C.G. Brown, comm. DGG).
■ vc12 Crawley, 28.10.82, was last record until one in 1993 (RAB).

1762 *Chloroclysta citrata* (Linnaeus, 1761)
Dark Marbled Carpet

Rare but perhaps overlooked. The possibility of well-marked specimens of the next species being mistaken for *C. citrata* has been borne in mind, but all the following records are considered to be impeccable.
■ vc11 St Ives, Ringwood, 1987, at m.v. light (JHC); Beaulieu, 13.9.93 (BI-J); Sandy Point, Hayling Island, earliest specimens on 14.6.95 (PRD).
■ vc12 South Wonston, 31.8.93 (PJSS); East Stratton, 14.9.92 (BI-J); Pamber, 17.7.93 (GJD); Selborne, 16.7 and 13.8.95, singletons at light, identity carefully checked (AEA).

1764 *Chloroclysta truncata* (Hufnagel, 1767)
Common Marbled Carpet

Very common throughout, in two, sometimes three, broods.

152

1765 *Cidaria fulvata* (Forster, 1771)
Barred Yellow

Still widespread, but less common than formerly. It is most frequent in hedgerows on the chalk where the foodplant dog-rose *Rosa canina* agg. grows.

1766 *Plemyria rubiginata* ([Denis & Schiffermüller], 1775)
Blue-bordered Carpet

10 mm

All records pre-1992 were given in Goater (1992). This species remains uncommon in the area, except at Yateley; in the south of Britain, it seems to be associated particularly with blackthorn thickets.

■ vc11 Cadlands House, 12.7.97, one netted before dusk (BG, JRL); Woolston, 1990–95, up to three each year (ARC); Leigh Park, Havant, one in 1996 (CBC).
■ vc12 Chilbolton, hedgerow by old airfield, 17.6.97, one netted late evening (BG); Magdalen Hill Down, 1.7.94, 30.6.95 (PAB); Old Basing, 19.7.96; Yateley Common, fairly common since 1991 (AMD); Farnborough, 9.7.95, one at light (RWP).

1767 *Thera firmata* (Hübner, 1822)
Pine Carpet

Rather uncommon and usually encountered singly, mainly in the autumn. The larva feeds on Scots pine *Pinus sylvestris*.

1768 *Thera obeliscata* (Hübner, 1787)
Grey Pine Carpet

Very common in two broods wherever Scots pine occurs.

1769 *Thera britannica* (Turner, 1925)
Spruce Carpet

Nearly as frequent as the preceding species and often flying with it, but associated with plantations of Douglas fir *Pseudotsuga menziesii* and Norway spruce *Picea abies*.

1771 *Thera juniperata* (Linnaeus, 1758)
Juniper Carpet

Very local amongst juniper on the downs. Despite occasional records elsewhere, there is so far no real evidence that the species is taking to cultivated junipers in gardens, as it is in some other parts of the country.
■ vc12 Crawley, 4.11.82, the only one seen (RAB).

1771a *Thera cupressata* (Geyer, 1831)
Cypress Carpet

This recent arrival to Britain has its present stronghold in the area covered by Purbeck in Dorset, the Isle of Wight and south-west Hampshire. Its true status is difficult to monitor because of its association with cypresses which often grow on private property, but there is no doubt that is it becoming common very locally. It is now beginning to appear in SE Hampshire. For the species' early history in Britain, see Goater (1992) and references therein.

■ vc10 Freshwater, 13.10.95 (SAK-J), 15.10.97, three at light (SAK-J, BG); Freshwater, The Causeway, 11.7 and 13.7, 24.11 (two) and 26.11.94; 9, 21.6 and 29.6.95 (two), as well as in autumn; 24.7, 6.10 and 9.10.96 (DBW); St Lawrence, 17.9.92, two fresh males (JHC); Ventnor, 7.6.98 (I. Ferguson); Chale Green, 28.11.92 (Colenutt,1993), 22.7.95, one (SRC); Wootton, 5.10.97 (TR); Binstead, recorded for the first time in 1999, when 11 were seen between 12.10 and 11.11.99 (BJW).
■ vc11 Pennington, 10.6 to 5.7.95, eight specimens at least, including four on 10.6.95 (RC); 28.10.95, one male (in coll. BG); Lower Pennington, 1.11.95, two males at dusk amongst *Cupressus leylandii*, and two at m.v. light; 8.11.95, five (BG); Brockenhurst, 26.6 and 2.12.95, 30.6.98, singles at m.v. light (JEC); Sholing, 13.10.99, 15.7.00, singles at m.v. light (ARC); Rowner, five between 15.6 and 13.11.99 (LM); Milton Common, Southsea, 6.6.99, one at m.v. light, det. JRL (IRT); Waterlooville, 26.6, 29.6 and 1.7.00, single specimens at m.v. light (RJM); Gutner Point, 12.10.95, one at m.v. light (AMD); N Hayling Island, several at light in 1997,1998 and 1999 (PRD); Northney, 15, 21.6 and 25.6.99, 31.10.99 (Phillips, 2000), eight in 2000 (JWP).

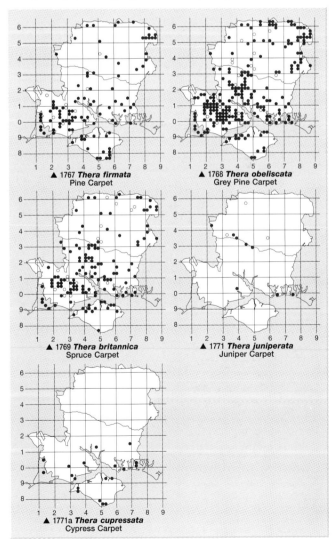

▲ 1767 *Thera firmata*
Pine Carpet

▲ 1768 *Thera obeliscata*
Grey Pine Carpet

▲ 1769 *Thera britannica*
Spruce Carpet

▲ 1771 *Thera juniperata*
Juniper Carpet

▲ 1771a *Thera cupressata*
Cypress Carpet

1773 *Electrophaes corylata* (Thunberg, 1792)
Broken-barred Carpet
Common in deciduous, especially birch, woodland.

1774 *Colostygia olivata* ([Denis & Schiffermüller], 1775)
Beech-green Carpet
This species has long been known from the south coast of the Isle of Wight, but its discovery in the Selborne area of N Hants in 1992, where it was seen annually over a period of five years was very interesting.
■ vc12 Selborne, several regularly at m.v. light between 16.8.92 and 27.7.97, but not since, possibly owing to destruction of habitat (AEA). (See Aston, 1993, where first date is given erroneously as 1982); Noar Hill NR, 20.8.95, two (AMJ). **New vc record.**

1775 *Colostygia multistrigaria* (Haworth, 1809)
Mottled Grey
Local and uncommon, but probably overlooked on account of its early flight season and sluggish habits. The larva feeds on bedstraws *Galium* spp. Recent records are given below.
■ vc10 Freshwater, 28.3.99, one at m.v. light (SAK-J).

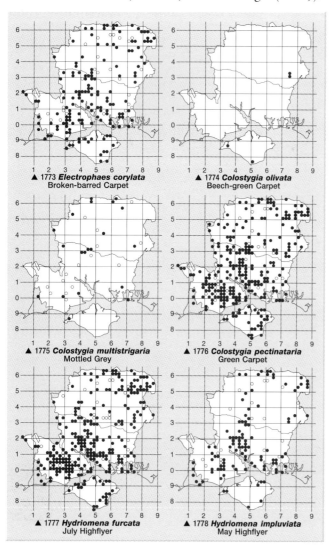

▲ 1773 *Electrophaes corylata*
Broken-barred Carpet

▲ 1774 *Colostygia olivata*
Beech-green Carpet

▲ 1775 *Colostygia multistrigaria*
Mottled Grey

▲ 1776 *Colostygia pectinataria*
Green Carpet

▲ 1777 *Hydriomena furcata*
July Highflyer

▲ 1778 *Hydriomena impluviata*
May Highflyer

■ vc11 Brockenhurst, 10.4.91 (JEC); Broughton Down, 1.4.95, 15.4.96 (NB); Sandy Point NR, Hayling Island, 9.4.84 (RJD).
■ vc12 Wildhern, nr Andover, 28.4.99 (DGG); Crawley, three on 17.4.96, new record for garden (RAB); East Stratton, 18.4.88 (BI-J); Newtown Common, 4.4.95, two in flight after dusk (AHD); Selborne, 28.3.92, one resting on cottage (AEA).

1776 *Colostygia pectinataria* (Knoch, 1781)
Green Carpet
Widespread and generally common.

1777 *Hydriomena furcata* (Thunberg, 1784)
July Highflyer
Usually very common wherever sallows *Salix* spp. grow.

1778 *Hydriomena impluviata* ([Denis & Schiffermüller], 1775)
May Highflyer
Fairly common to common amongst alder *Alnus glutinosa*.

1779 *Hydriomena ruberata* (Freyer, 1831)
Ruddy Highflyer
There are extremely few genuine records of this species in the area, but it is recorded from all three vice-counties (Goater, 1974, 1992). The larva feeds on sallow *Salix* spp. Recent records are given below.
■ vc10 Freshwater, May, 1986 (SAK-J).
■ vc11 Fordingbridge, 1.7.93, one at light, conf. BG. (NHu).

1781 *Horisme vitalbata* ([Denis & Schiffermüller], 1775)
Small Waved Umber
Common amongst wild *Clematis*, and therefore most frequent on the downs.
■ vc11 St Ives, Ringwood, 1987, at m.v. light (JHC); Brockenhurst, 30.7.92 (JEC); Chandlers Ford, 7.8.93, one at m.v. light (BG); Woolston, 1.8.95, one at light, second record for garden (ARC).
■ vc12 Yateley Common, 14.8.93; Rye Common, 5.8.96 (AMD).

1782 *Horisme tersata* ([Denis & Schiffermüller], 1775)
The Fern
For some reason this species which, like *H. vitalbata*, depends upon *Clematis*, has declined considerably since the early 1980s (Goater, 1992). It is still seen most often on the chalk.
■ vc11 Brockenhurst, 4.8.84 (JEC); Chandlers Ford, 2.8.91, one at m.v. light (BG); Portswood, 25.7.95 (A and CD); Woolston, 2.7.94 (ARC); Leigh Park, Havant, 22.7.96 (CBC).
■ vc12 Rye Common, 26.7.96, two (AMD).

1784 *Melanthia procellata* ([Denis & Schiffermüller], 1775)
Pretty Chalk Carpet
This *Clematis*-feeder has also shown some decline in recent years, and is seldom seen away from the chalk downland.
■ vc11 Brockenhurst, 23.6.86 (JEC); Chandlers Ford, 19.7.94, one at m.v. light (BG).

1785 *Pareulype berberata* ([Denis & Schiffermüller], 1775)
Barberry Carpet   **RDB1**

The *Berberis* bushes in the one known locality in
Hampshire were severely burnt when a stubble fire got
out of control in the early 1970s and the colony of
P. berberata was almost certainly destroyed. There have
been two further records of single specimens in different
parts of vc12 (Goater, 1992), but attempts to find a
breeding population have so far failed. **This species is
protected by the Wildlife and Countryside Act, 1981.
It is illegal to collect or disturb it in any of its stages.**

1787 *Rheumaptera hastata* (Linnaeus, 1758)
Argent and Sable   **Notable/Nb**

This species used to be very common flying by day over
birches in the New Forest and other extensive areas of
birch woodland during the 1940s, having previously been
rare. It is now rare once more, and absent from most of
its former strongholds. It was last seen at Botley Wood in
1988 (JEC) and at Fleet Pond in 1991. At Pamber, steps
are being taken to manage the woodland to favour *R.
hastata*, evidently with success. The only extant colonies
appear to be at Pamber and Harewood Forest, see below.
■ vc12 Harewood Forest, 10.6.94 (PAB), several seen in
different localities there during May–June, 1997–2000
(DGG, TJN); Pamber, steadily increasing since 1991, rides
having been opened in 1985; it then disappeared after 1994
and was not seen again until 27.5.99, one adult (GJD);
Fleet Pond, 25.5.88, 10.6.90, 20.5.91 (MAS, GCS).

1788 *Rheumaptera cervinalis* (Scopoli, 1763)
Scarce Tissue

Never common in the county, this species has declined
considerably and there are very few recent records, despite
the fact that the larva will thrive on cultivated *Berberis*,
and does so elsewhere in the country.
■ vc12 Yateley Common, 19.4.93, one (AMD);
Farnborough, 1.5.95, one at light (RWP).

1789 *Rheumaptera undulata* (Linnaeus, 1758)
Scallop Shell

Widespread but always uncommon. This moth is
associated with two unrelated foodplants, sallows, chiefly
Salix cinerea and bilberry *Vaccinium myrtillus*.
■ vc10 Binstead, 29.6.95, first record, 25.7.96 (BJW).

1790 *Triphosa dubitata* (Linnaeus, 1758)
The Tissue

Local and uncommon; the larva feeds on buckthorn
Rhamnus cathartica. All records are given in Goater
(1992). More recent ones are given below.
■ vc11 Broughton Down, 22.8.95 (NB).
■ vc12 Wildhern, nr Andover, 25.4.97, at actinic light
(DGG).

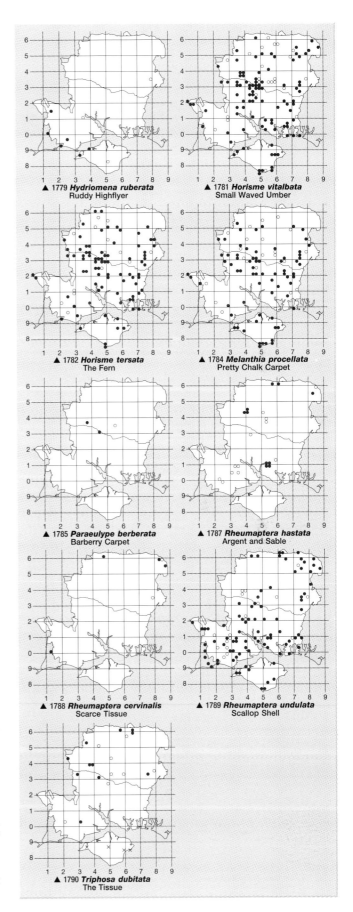

1791 *Philereme vetulata* ([Denis & Schiffermüller], 1775)
Brown Scallop
Another local species the foodplant of which is *Rhamnus catharctica*.
■ vc10 Cranmore, 6.7.96, two at m.v. light (PJC, BJW).
■ vc11 Romsey, beside canal, 13.7.96 (NB); Chandlers Ford, 29.6.92, one at m.v. light (BG); Downleaze Copse, Exton, 20.7.94 (PAB).
■ vc12 Magdalen Hill Down, 1.7.94, 3.8.96 (PAB); East Stratton (BI-J); Old Basing, 19.7.96, three (AMD).

1792 *Philereme transversata* (Hufnagel, 1767)
Dark Umber
This species also feeds on buckthorn, and like the two preceding ones, is local and rather uncommon. Recent records are given below.
■ vc10 Knighton, June 1989 (PC). **New vc record.**
■ vc11 Brockenhurst, 17.7.84 (JEC); Kings Somborne, 1.7.95 (TJN); Chandlers Ford, 24.7.94, 12.7.97, singles at m.v. light (BG); Downleaze Copse, Exton, 20.7.94 (PAB); Gosport, 24.7.95, one at light (DSW); Butser Hill, 13.7.97 (AMD).
■ vc12 Danebury Hillfort, 2.7.99, several; Rye Common, 26.7.96 (AMD); Magdalen Hill Down, 1.7.94, 30.6 and 5.8.95, 12.7.96 (PAB); East Stratton (BI-J); Ropley, 3.8.91 (PAB); Noar Hill NR, 14.7.95 (AMJ).

1793 *Euphyia biangulata* (Haworth, 1809)
Cloaked Carpet   **Notable/Nb**
There has been quite a spate of recent records, mostly of single specimens at light, but the indications are that it is gradually becoming more widespread in the area. All records received are included in Goater (1974, 1992) and below.
■ vc10 Queens Bower (NH); Binstead, 30.7.96, first record (BJW).

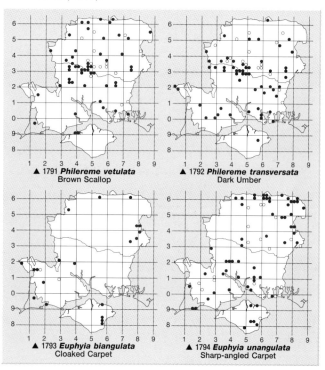

▲ 1791 *Philereme vetulata*
Brown Scallop

▲ 1792 *Philereme transversata*
Dark Umber

▲ 1793 *Euphyia biangulata*
Cloaked Carpet

▲ 1794 *Euphyia unangulata*
Sharp-angled Carpet

■ vc11 Hurn, 1.8.00, one at m.v. light (MJ); Highcliffe, still occurs rarely (EHW, 1991), 24.7.94 (RAC); Sandleheath, Fordingbridge, 30.6.92 (NHu); Linford, 1.8.97 (AGP); Plaitford Wood, 4.7.98 (NB); North Baddesley, 22.6.97, one at actinic trap, in coll. BG (DH).
■ vc12 Wildhern, nr Andover, 20.7 and 22.7.96, 1.7 and 5.7.97, 20.7.98, 8.7 and 27.7.99 at actinic light (DGG); Frith End, 16.7.94 (KW); Selborne, 13.7 and 17.7.95, 23.7.96, singletons at light (AEA); Bramshill Common, 1.8.96 (AMD); Bordon, 3.8.96 (AGL-G); Bentley Station Meadow, 28.7.95, six at light, 6.7 and 20.7.96, singles (PAB); Alice Holt, three between 8.7 and 8.8.92 (Rothamsted Survey).

1794 *Euphyia unangulata* (Haworth, 1809)
Sharp-angled Carpet
Widespread but local, apparently most frequent in the north-east of the county.
■ vc10 Chale Green, 18.6.94 (SRC); Wootton, 20.7.97 (TR); Binstead, 30.6.93 (BJW).

Epirrita Hübner, 1822. The problems of accurate identification of *Epirrita* species mean that all three are under-recorded. In general, it appears that *E. autumnata* is the commonest and most widespread, *E. dilutata* almost equally so, and that *E. christyi* is much less common and more attached to beechwoods.

1795 *Epirrita dilutata* ([Denis & Schiffermüller], 1775)
November Moth
■ vc10 Binstead, October 1995, of a series of six males, four were of this species, and two were *christyi*, genitalia det. BG (BJW).
■ vc11 Bentley Wood, Hants/Wilts border, of 184 male *Epirrita* examined from several sites during the autumn of 1994, 37 (20%) were this species (BF); Lower Pennington, 29.10.95, five at light, genitalia checked (BG); Smoky Hole, Bolderwood, 6.11.97, at m.v. light, genitalia checked (JEC, JS); Woolston, October 1995, four out of five *Epirrita* examined were this species, det. BG (ARC).
■ vc12 Stoke Charity, 1996, male, genitalia det. BG (PJSS); Bentley Station Meadow, 21.10.95, two males (PAB). Genitalia checked by BG.

1796 *Epirrita christyi* (Allen, 1906)
Pale November Moth
■ vc10 Binstead, October 1995, two *E. christyi* in a series of six males, the others of which were *E. dilutata*, genitalia det. BG (BJW).
■ vc11 Bentley Wood, Hants/Wilts border, of 184 male *Epirrita* examined from several sites during autumn 1994, 94 (51%) were this species (BF); Smoky Hole, Bolderwood, 6.11.97, at m.v. light, genitalia checked (JEC, JS).
■ vc12 Wildhern, 19.10.98, genitalia det. (DGG); Selborne, ten between 18.10 and 4.11.96 (AEA); Bentley Station Meadow, 21.10.95, one male (PAB). Genitalia checked by BG.

1797 *Epirrita autumnata* (Borkhausen, 1794)
Autumnal Moth
■ vc11 Bentley Wood, Hants/Wilts border, of 184 male

Epirrita examined from several sites during the autumn of 1994, 53 (29%) were this species (BF); Smoky Hole, Bolderwood, 6.11.97, at m.v. light, genitalia checked (JEC, JS); Woolston, October 1995, one out of five *Epirrita* examined was this species, det. BG (ARC).

◾ vc12 Wildhern, 10.10.98, genitalia det. (DGG); Bentley Station Meadow, 21.10.95, one male (PAB). Genitalia checked by BG.

1799 *Operophtera brumata* (Linnaeus, 1758)
Winter Moth

Extremely common in woodland and a well-known pest of orchards. The map shows an unjustified bias towards the New Forest. The larva is a staple diet of insectivorous birds in springtime.

1800 *Operophtera fagata* (Scharfenberg, 1805)
Northern Winter Moth

Much more local than the preceding, and found chiefly in birch woodland. It has disappeared from many localities, including Chandlers Ford, where it was quite common in the 1940s and 1950s.

1802 *Perizoma affinitata* (Stephens, 1831)
The Rivulet

Local and rather uncommon in open woodland where red campion *Silene dioica* flourishes, in the capsules of which the larva feeds.

◾ vc11 Whitenap, Romsey, 8.7.95 (MJB).

◾ vc12 Crawley, 23.5.95, only one seen (RAB); Selborne, 14.5, two; 28.5 and 30.5, 5.6.98, all at m.v. light (AEA).

1803 *Perizoma alchemillata* (Linnaeus, 1758)
Small Rivulet

Generally distributed and usually common; it occurs in places where hemp-nettle *Galeopsis tetrahit* is unknown, and there the larva is likely to feed in the fruiting heads of hedge woundwort *Stachys sylvatica* and other Lamiaceae.

1804 *Perizoma bifaciata* (Haworth, 1809)
Barred Rivulet

The larva of this species feeds on the ripening seeds of red bartsia *Odontites verna*, and the species is to be found in most places where this plant grows, which is mainly on the chalk. Occasional wanderers turn up elsewhere. These records are given below.

◾ vc10 Binstead, 30.7.94, first record (BJW).

◾ vc11 St Ives, Ringwood, 1987, at m.v. light (JHC); Chandlers Ford, 10.8.94, one at m.v. light (BG); Woolston, 6.8.95, one at light, first for garden; Sholing, 3.8.99, one at m.v. light (ARC); Gosport, 2.8 to 19.8.95, four at light, conf. PMP (DSW).

◾ vc12 Selborne, 19.8.95, one at light (AEA); Noar Hill, 24.7.93 (AMJ).

1807 *Perizoma albulata* ([Denis & Schiffermüller], 1775)
Grass Rivulet

Common amongst yellow rattle *Rhinanthus minor*, especially in grassy places on the downs. Wanderers include the two records given below.

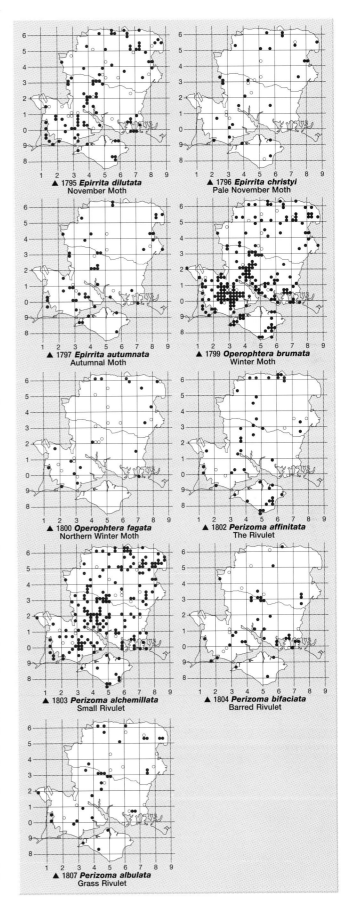

▲ 1795 *Epirrita dilutata*
November Moth

▲ 1796 *Epirrita christyi*
Pale November Moth

▲ 1797 *Epirrita autumnata*
Autumnal Moth

▲ 1799 *Operophtera brumata*
Winter Moth

▲ 1800 *Operophtera fagata*
Northern Winter Moth

▲ 1802 *Perizoma affinitata*
The Rivulet

▲ 1803 *Perizoma alchemillata*
Small Rivulet

▲ 1804 *Perizoma bifaciata*
Barred Rivulet

▲ 1807 *Perizoma albulata*
Grass Rivulet

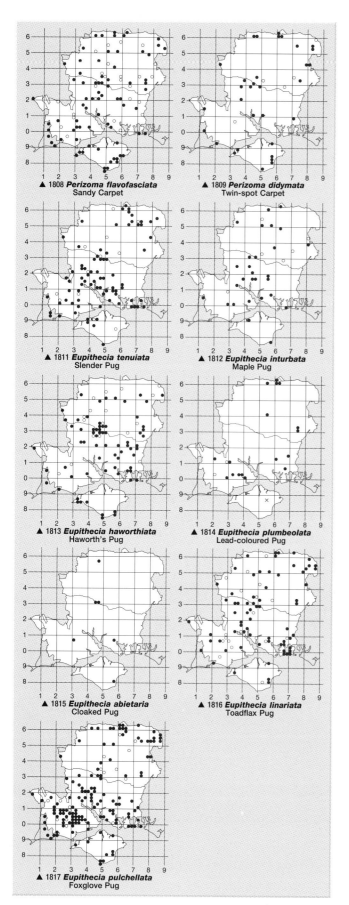

▲ 1808 *Perizoma flavofasciata*
Sandy Carpet

▲ 1809 *Perizoma didymata*
Twin-spot Carpet

▲ 1811 *Eupithecia tenuiata*
Slender Pug

▲ 1812 *Eupithecia inturbata*
Maple Pug

▲ 1813 *Eupithecia haworthiata*
Haworth's Pug

▲ 1814 *Eupithecia plumbeolata*
Lead-coloured Pug

▲ 1815 *Eupithecia abietaria*
Cloaked Pug

▲ 1816 *Eupithecia linariata*
Toadflax Pug

▲ 1817 *Eupithecia pulchellata*
Foxglove Pug

vc11 Brockenhurst, 27.6.84 (JEC); Chandlers Ford, 1.7.91, one at m.v. light (BG).

1808 *Perizoma flavofasciata* (Thunberg, 1792)
Sandy Carpet

This species used to be common in areas of open woodland with a strong growth of red campion *Silene dioica*, but has decreased considerably. The comments made in Goater (1974) and subsequently in Goater (1992) reflect this. There is little evidence of recovery.

vc10 Redcliff Bay, Sandown, 23.6.94 (SAK-J).

vc11 St Ives, Ringwood, 1987, at m.v. light (JHC); Whitenap, Romsey, 7.5.95 (MJB); Kings Somborne, 17.7.95 (TJN).

vc12 Danebury Hillfort, 2.7.99; Yateley Common, 24.5.93, 6.6.96 (AMD); Magdalen Hill Down, 30.6.95 (PAB); Selborne, from 15.6.95, seven specimens at light (AEA).

1809 *Perizoma didymata* (Linnaeus, 1758)
Twin-spot Carpet

Local and rare, certainly in recent years, although Fassnidge (1928–29) regarded it as common.

vc10 Binstead, 10.8.98, one at m.v. light (BJW).

vc11 Whitenap, Romsey, 23.6.94 (MJB); Woolston, 26.8.94 (ARC); Leigh Park, Havant, 13.7.94 (two), 15.7.94, not previously recorded (CBC).

vc12 Crawley, 10.7.81, only one seen (RAB); Pamber Forest, 9.7.95, one (AS); Greywell, 25.6.86, one at light (PB); Selborne, 17.7.95, one at light (AEA); Alice Holt, 7.7 and 10.7.92 (Rothamsted Survey).

Eupithecia Curtis. Caught specimens of this genus often cause problems of identification, especially when they are not retained for dissection, and many are ignored when they appear at light. Hence, all but the most conspicuous are seriously under-recorded.

1811 *Eupithecia tenuiata* (Hübner, 1813)
Slender Pug

Fairly common amongst sallow *Salix cinerea* in the catkins of which the larva may be found in spring.

1812 *Eupithecia inturbata* (Hübner, 1817)
Maple Pug

Very local: the larva requires well-grown field maple *Acer campestre*, on the flowers of which it feeds.

vc10 Bonchurch, 2.8.87, one at m.v. light (JRL, ECP-C). **New vc record.**

vc11 Chandlers Ford, 27.7.93, one at m.v. light (BG); Allbrook, 7.8.96, det. BG (ML).

1813 *Eupithecia haworthiata* Doubleday, 1856
Haworth's Pug

Common, probably wherever *Clematis* is established, though most frequent on the chalk.

1814 *Eupithecia plumbeolata* (Haworth, 1809)
Lead-coloured Pug   **Notable/Nb**

Local in woodlands where the foodplant, cow-wheat *Melampyrum pratense*, grows.

■ vc11 Brockenhurst, several each year, max. 22 in 1981 (JEC); Keeping Copse, Bucklers Hard, 8.6.95, two at light (BG).

■ vc12 East Stratton, occasional (BI-J); Pamber Forest and Silchester Common, locally common (GJD, 1995); Selborne, several in 1993 (AEA); Noar Hill, 23.6.93 (AMJ).

1815 *Eupithecia abietaria* (Goeze, 1781)
Cloaked Pug

The occasional records of this species in the area suggest migration, but it is possible that a resident population occurs, as it evidently did at one time in the New Forest. There are two recent records.

■ vc11 Park Hill Inclosure, 5.9.91, one at m.v. light (SPC); Fareham, 12.6.93, male at m.v. light (RJD).

1816 *Eupithecia linariata* ([Denis & Schiffermüller], 1775)
Toadflax Pug

The larva is often very common in the capsules of yellow toadflax *Linaria vulgaris* on waysides and waste ground.

1817 *Eupithecia pulchellata* Stephens, 1831
Foxglove Pug

Locally common in localities where foxglove *Digitalis purpurea* is established.

1818 *Eupithecia irriguata* (Hübner, 1813)
Marbled Pug   Notable/Nb

This species is a New Forest speciality, and there it is often common during May. It is seldom recorded anywhere else in the county (Goater, 1992), and has yet to be reported from the Isle of Wight. The larva feeds on oak.

■ vc11 Chandlers Ford, 15.5.92, one at m.v. light, specimen retained (BG).

■ vc12 East Stratton, 27.4.86, 19.5.89, 19.5 and 23.5.92 (BI-J).

1819 *Eupithecia exiguata* (Hübner, 1813)
Mottled Pug

Common, widespread and fairly easily identified

1820 *Eupithecia insigniata* (Hübner, 1790)
Pinion-spotted Pug   Notable/Nb

This beautiful pug has a stronghold north of Winchester, between the Test Valley and Alresford, but is nevertheless rare and elusive. There is only one record from vc11, and none from the Isle of Wight.

■ vc11 Beaulieu, 29.4.93 (BI-J).

■ vc12 South Wonston, 22.5.95 (PJSS); East Stratton, two in May 1971, 5.5.90, ten in 1992 (BI-J).

1821 *Eupithecia valerianata* (Hübner, 1813)
Valerian Pug   Notable/Nb

Rare and local, but sometimes found as a larva, if sought in the flowerheads of common valerian *Valeriana officinalis*. Recorders have frequently reported a high degree of parasitism, and this factor may be responsible for keeping numbers in check. The imago is inconspicuous and perhaps overlooked.

■ vc11 Beaulieu, 16.6.95, one at m.v. light (BI-J); Broughton

Down, 28.6.00, one taken at a lantern (AHD); Cherque, Gosport, 17.6.71, one male genitalia det. (DMA, RJD).

1823 *Eupithecia venosata* (Fabricius, 1787)
Netted Pug

The larva occurs in the capsules of bladder campion *Silene vulgaris* on the chalk, but apparently has not been reported in Hampshire from those of sea campion *S. uniflora*. The species appears to be rare, yet occasional specimens turn up as vagrants far from known sources of foodplant.

■ vc10 Binstead, 14.5.94 (BJW).

■ vc11 Beaulieu, 28.6.93 (BI-J); Brockenhurst, 3.6.85 (JEC); Cosham, 21.5.97 (TJJ); Havant, 17.6.97, one at m.v. light (CBC); Havant Thicket, 28.6.95, one at m.v. light (JRL).

■ vc12 Magdalen Hill Down, 30.6.95 (PAB); East Stratton, 25.5.92 (BI-J).

1824 *Eupithecia egenaria* Herrich-Schäffer, 1848
Pauper Pug   RDB3

This species is associated with small-leaved lime *Tilia platyphyllos* and has strongholds in the Wye Valley and in East Anglia. According to Brewis *et al.* (1996), there are

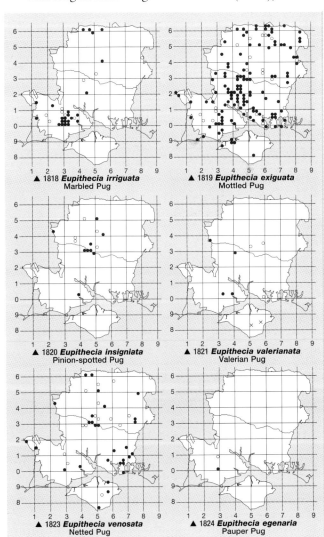

▲ 1818 *Eupithecia irriguata* Marbled Pug

▲ 1819 *Eupithecia exiguata* Mottled Pug

▲ 1820 *Eupithecia insigniata* Pinion-spotted Pug

▲ 1821 *Eupithecia valerianata* Valerian Pug

▲ 1823 *Eupithecia venosata* Netted Pug

▲ 1824 *Eupithecia egenaria* Pauper Pug

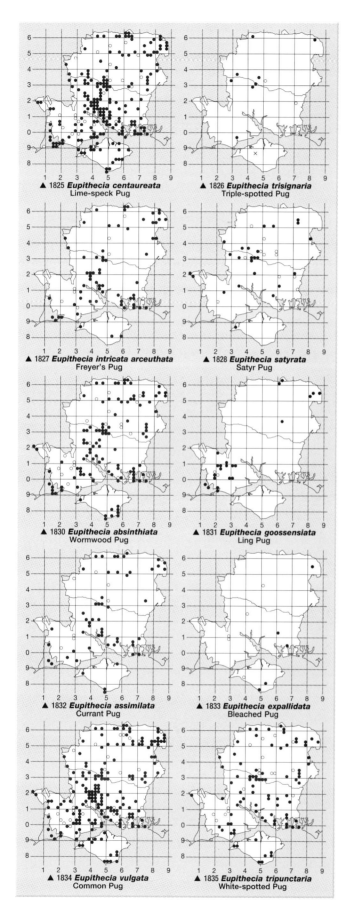

▲ 1825 *Eupithecia centaureata*
Lime-speck Pug

▲ 1826 *Eupithecia trisignaria*
Triple-spotted Pug

▲ 1827 *Eupithecia intricata arceuthata*
Freyer's Pug

▲ 1828 *Eupithecia satyrata*
Satyr Pug

▲ 1830 *Eupithecia absinthiata*
Wormwood Pug

▲ 1831 *Eupithecia goossensiata*
Ling Pug

▲ 1832 *Eupithecia assimilata*
Currant Pug

▲ 1833 *Eupithecia expallidata*
Bleached Pug

▲ 1834 *Eupithecia vulgata*
Common Pug

▲ 1835 *Eupithecia tripunctaria*
White-spotted Pug

many newly-discovered sites for the foodplant in Hampshire, and the moth may be expected to turn up again.

■ vc11 Emery Down, 7.6.79, one at m.v. light; Brockenhurst, 23.5.98, one at m.v. light, genitalia det. (JEC). **New county record.**

1825 *Eupithecia centaureata* ([Denis & Schiffermüller], 1775) Lime-speck Pug

10 mm

Perhaps the commonest, and surely the most easily identified species of pug.

1826 *Eupithecia trisignaria* Herrich-Schäffer, 1848 Triple-spotted Pug

This rare species is easily overlooked as a moth, but the larvae can be found in heads of hogweed *Heracleum sphondylium* or wild parsnip *Pastinaca sativa*, and should be sought in areas where the moth has been recorded.

■ vc11 Broughton Down, 13.7.94, 27.5.95, specimens seen by BG (NB).

■ vc12 Danebury, 19.7.96, genitalia det. (JEC); Yateley Common, 18.5.93 (AMD); Farnborough, 15.5.97 (RWP).

1827 *Eupithecia intricata arceuthata* (Freyer, 1842) Freyer's Pug

Once known, this large rather distinctive pug has been reported in numerous more-or-less suburban localities, where the larva feeds on species of cypress *Cupressus* and *Chamaecyparis*, and is often fairly common.

1828 *Eupithecia satyrata* (Hübner, 1813) Satyr Pug

Fairly common in places on the chalk, notably Broughton Down and Farley Mount, but easily overlooked as a moth, unless sought.

■ vc10 Freshwater, 5.6.98 (SAK-J). **New vc record.**

■ vc11 Broughton Down, June–July 1994, several at m.v. light (NB, BG); Butser Hill, 13.7.97 (AMD).

■ vc12 South Wonston, 28.5.97, conf. BG (PJSS); Alice Holt, 22.5.92 (Rothamsted Survey).

1830 *Eupithecia absinthiata* (Clerck, 1759) Wormwood Pug

Fairly common to common on waste ground and in woods and large gardens. The larva is fairly polyphagous but is encountered most often on mugwort *Artemisia vulgaris*.

1831 *Eupithecia goossensiata* Mabille, 1869 Ling Pug

This is possibly merely a heathland form of the preceding species, though its generally smaller size and slightly narrower wings, often with a purplish tint, together with its distinctive ecology, seem to set it apart. It is seldom recorded with confidence, however, except when bred from flowers of ling *Calluna vulgaris*.

■ vc12 Farnborough, 26.7.94, one at m.v. light (RWP).

1832 *Eupithecia assimilata* Doubleday, 1856
Currant Pug
Recorded in small numbers by careful observers in various parts of the three vice-counties, but easily overlooked. The larva feeds on two quite different kinds of plant, hop *Humulus lupulus* and red- and black currant *Ribes* spp.

1833 *Eupithecia expallidata* Doubleday, 1856
Bleached Pug   **Notable/Nb**
The rather distinctive larva of this species can be found on goldenrod *Solidago virgaurea* growing in open woodland, but is seldom encountered in Hampshire and has never been reported unequivocally from the Isle of Wight. Sight records of the imago, given below, have to be questioned. The only known localities are Ampfield Wood, where it has not been seen recently, Wickham and Havant Thicket.
■ vc11 Sandy Point, Hayling Island, 12.6 and 23.7.95, 1996, 11.8.97 and 7.8.98 single specimens, observer certain of identity, but specimens not kept (PS); Northney, Hayling Island, 1997 and 1998, observer likewise certain of identity, but no specimen kept (PRD).
■ vc12 East Stratton, 30.6.87, observer certain of identity, but specimen not kept (BI-J).

1834 *Eupithecia vulgata* (Haworth, 1809)
Common Pug
Common, but a constant source of worry to beginners trying to identify their pugs!

1835 *Eupithecia tripunctaria* Herrich-Schäffer, 1852
White-spotted Pug
The larva occurs among the ripening fruits of *Angelica*, but is often heavily parasitised; the moth is recorded at light in small numbers and is fairly easy to identify.

1836 *Eupithecia denotata* (Hübner, 1813)
Campanula Pug   **Notable/Na**
Locally common as a larva in seedheads of nettle-leaved bellflower *Campanula trachelium*. The record below is the only one we have away from a known source of foodplant.
■ vc11 Chandlers Ford, 18.7.94, female at m.v. light; slide 416 (BG).

1837 *Eupithecia subfuscata* (Haworth, 1809)
Grey Pug
Common, but another problem species for identification purposes.

1838 *Eupithecia icterata* (de Villers, 1789)
Tawny Speckled Pug
Widespread and fairly common, and readily identified.

1839 *Eupithecia succenturiata* (Linnaeus, 1758)
Bordered Pug
Another easily-recognised species. It appears to be less common than formerly.

1840 *Eupithecia subumbrata* ([Denis & Schiffermüller], 1775)
Shaded Pug
A species of chalk downland which hides in hedgerows and scrub during the day; the larva is somewhat polyphagous on the flowers of herbaceous plants such as field scabious *Knautia arvensis* and various yellow Asteraceae.

1841 *Eupithecia millefoliata* Rössler, 1866
Yarrow Pug   **NotableNb**
A fairly recent arrival in Hampshire, first recorded in 1951 (Goater, 1974) and now well-established on waste ground near the sea in south-east Hampshire and rediscovered on the Isle of Wight in 1998. There is only one record from vc12, given below. The stumpy, brown larvae can be found amongst the dead fruiting heads of yarrow *Achillea millefolium* in late autumn.
■ vc10 Cranmore and St Helens, autumn, 1998, larvae, moths bred in June, 1999 (SAK-J, BJW).
■ vc11 Browndown and Gilkicker Point, 8.97, larvae (SS, DSW); Southsea, 20.9.94, larvae common on waste ground, moths bred (BG, JRL), five at light, July–August 1997 (IRT); Northney, Hayling Island, October, 2000, larvae found along shore ((JWP).

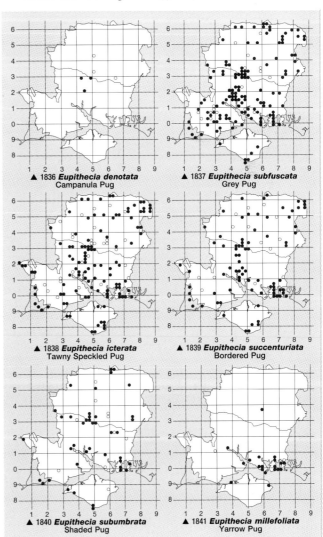

▲ 1836 *Eupithecia denotata*
Campanula Pug

▲ 1837 *Eupithecia subfuscata*
Grey Pug

▲ 1838 *Eupithecia icterata*
Tawny Speckled Pug

▲ 1839 *Eupithecia succenturiata*
Bordered Pug

▲ 1840 *Eupithecia subumbrata*
Shaded Pug

▲ 1841 *Eupithecia millefoliata*
Yarrow Pug

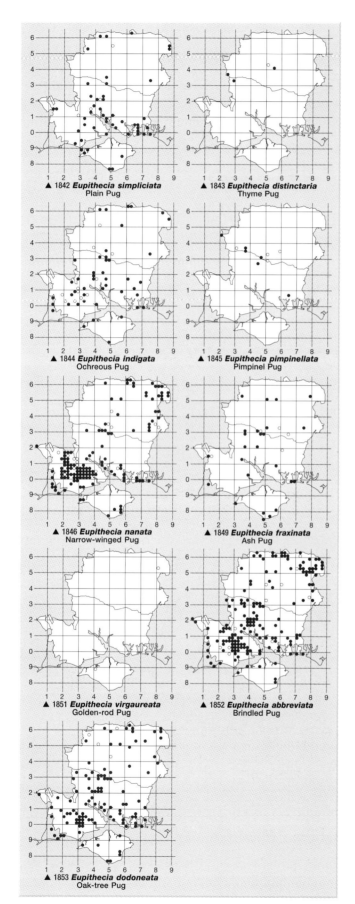

▲ 1842 *Eupithecia simpliciata*
Plain Pug

▲ 1843 *Eupithecia distinctaria*
Thyme Pug

▲ 1844 *Eupithecia indigata*
Ochreous Pug

▲ 1845 *Eupithecia pimpinellata*
Pimpinel Pug

▲ 1846 *Eupithecia nanata*
Narrow-winged Pug

▲ 1849 *Eupithecia fraxinata*
Ash Pug

▲ 1851 *Eupithecia virgaureata*
Golden-rod Pug

▲ 1852 *Eupithecia abbreviata*
Brindled Pug

▲ 1853 *Eupithecia dodoneata*
Oak-tree Pug

■ vc12 Abbotstone Down, 27.7.94, one at m.v. light (JRL). **New vc record.**

1842 *Eupithecia simpliciata* (Haworth, 1809)
Plain Pug

Uncommon and chiefly coastal, the larva feeding on the ripening fruits of goosefoot *Chenopodium* spp. and orache *Atriplex* spp.

■ vc10 Queens Bower, 7.8.92 (NH, *comm.* SAK-J).
■ vc11 Cadlands House, 12.7.97, one at m.v. light (BG, JRL); Kings Somborne, 23.7.93 (TJN); Woolston, 1.8.95, one at light, fourth record for garden (ARC).
■ vc12 South Wonston, 22.7.94 (PJSS); Wildhern, nr Andover, 9.7.97, at actinic light (DGG); Selborne, 27.7.94 (AEA).

1843 *Eupithecia distinctaria* Herrich-Schäffer, 1848
Thyme Pug   **Notable/Nb**

No recent record apart from the ones given below. The larva feeds on wild thyme *Thymus polytrichus*.

■ vc11 Broughton Down, 28.6.00, one taken at night with the aid of a lantern, and another in a Heath trap (AHD). **New vc record.**
■ vc12 Roche Court Down, Porton Down, 1.7.00, one at m.v. light (DGG).
■ vc12 East Stratton, 21.6.88, observer certain of identity, but specimen not kept (BI-J).

1844 *Eupithecia indigata* (Hübner, 1813)
Ochreous Pug

Fairly frequent in pine country; the only reliable record from the Isle of Wight until now is that given in Goater (1974), from St George's Down, 14.6.1941.

■ vc10 Binstead, 16.5.97 (BJW).

1845 *Eupithecia pimpinellata* (Hübner, 1813)
Pimpinel Pug

The moth is seldom seen, but larvae are often common, though usually very heavily parasitised, on burnet-saxifrage *Pimpinella saxifraga* on the downs.

1846 *Eupithecia nanata* (Hübner, 1813)
Narrow-winged Pug

Very common in heathy country; occasional records, like those given below, suggest it may be adapting to cultivated heathers *Calluna* and *Erica* spp.

■ vc11 Chandlers Ford, occasional at m.v. light (BG).
■ vc12 Rye Common, 24.4.97 (AMD); Farnborough, May 1994, three at m.v. light (RWP).

1849 *Eupithecia fraxinata* Crewe, 1863
Ash Pug

Rarely recorded. Usually associated with ash, and the record below is the first reported breeding from tamarisk *Tamarix gallica* in this area.

■ vc10 Chale Green, 23.7.95, one (SRC).
■ vc11 Chandlers Ford, 31.5.92, one at m.v. light (BG); Sinah Point, Hayling Island, reared from *Tamarix*, coll. 1.8.97, genitalia checked (JEC).
■ vc12 East Stratton (BI-J).

1851 *Eupithecia virgaureata* Doubleday, 1861
Golden-rod Pug

Though possibly overlooked as an imago, this species is almost certainly excessively rare or absent from Hampshire and the Isle of Wight. There is no record since those given in Goater (1974).

1852 *Eupithecia abbreviata* Stephens, 1831
Brindled Pug

Apart from Double-striped Pug *Gymnoscelis rufifasciata*, this is the first pug of the year to appear. It is very common in oak woodland throughout, and normally easy to identify once the melanic form is recognised.
■ vc11 Woolston, three at light in 1995, first for garden (ARC).

1853 *Eupithecia dodoneata* Guenée, 1857
Oak-tree Pug

This species emerges just as *E. abbreviata* is coming to an end. It is quite common in many places, and appears to have increased and extended its range in the area since the 1950s.

1854 *Eupithecia pusillata* ([Denis & Schiffermüller], 1775)
Juniper Pug

Fairly widespread, and attached to cultivated juniper as well as the very local wild populations.

1855 *Eupithecia phoeniceata* (Rambur, 1834)
Cypress Pug

Following the first Hampshire record in 1965, this species began to establish itself on the Isle of Wight and along the mainland coast from 1973. It is now quite common and has spread inland at least as far as Basingstoke (see below).
■ vc10 Wootton, 5.9.97 (TR).
■ vc11 St Ives, Ringwood, 1987, at m.v. light (JHC); Beaulieu, 30.7.94, seven between 9.8 and 9.9.95 (BI-J); Penerley Wood, 10.9.96, one at m.v. light (BG); Rownhams, first recorded 26.8.92, then every year (KG); Chandlers Ford, 21.8.94, 20.8.95, singles at m.v. light (BG); St Cross, 13.8.00, one at m.v. light (TWa); Bitterne, 14.8.95 (PAB); Woolston, 1990–97, up to 15 each year (ARC); Gosport, 26.5 to 8.10.95, total of 24 at light; Alverstoke, regular each year (DSW); Cosham, 8.8 and 14.8.94 (TJJ); Leigh Park, Havant, 5.8.96 (CBC).
■ vc12 South Wonston, 31.7.95 (PJSS); Kempshott, Basingstoke, 23.8.00, one at m.v. light (GH). **New vc record.**

1855a *Eupithecia ultimaria* Boisduval, 1840
Channel Islands Pug

This southern European species first appeared in Hampshire in June 1995, and subsequently the larvae were promptly discovered in unbelievable numbers on tamarisk *Tamarix gallica* on south Hayling Island (Langmaid, 1996b), and the following year diligent searching rewarded the Isle of Wight entomologists. So far, it has been looked for without success on other stands of foodplant along the Hampshire coast.
■ vc10 Old Park, St Lawrence, 13.7.97, one larva beaten

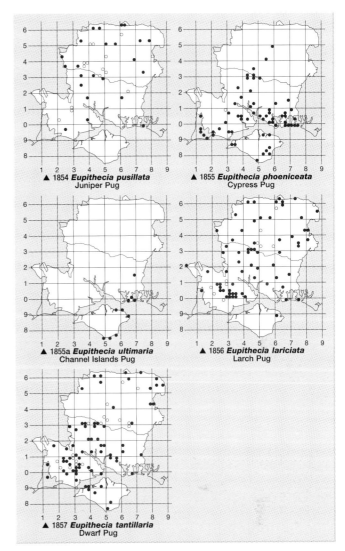

▲ 1854 *Eupithecia pusillata* Juniper Pug

▲ 1855 *Eupithecia phoeniceata* Cypress Pug

▲ 1855a *Eupithecia ultimaria* Channel Islands Pug

▲ 1856 *Eupithecia lariciata* Larch Pug

▲ 1857 *Eupithecia tantillaria* Dwarf Pug

from tamarisk (JMC); Ventnor, 1.8.99, one at m.v. light; Binstead, 1.8.99, one at m.v. light (BJW); Ryde Canoe Lake, 4.9 and 22.9.98; Bembridge, 14.7.97, a few larvae; Niton, 22.7.97, one larva (BJW). (Knill-Jones, 1997c). **New vc record.**
■ vc11 Southsea, 1995 (JRL), 16.8 and 19.8.97, at light (IRT); Waterlooville, 2.8.99, 15.6.00, single specimens at m.v. light (RJM); Sinah Common, Hayling Island, 31.7.96, larvae abundant on tamarisk, first moth emerged 10.9.96 (BG, JRL). **New county record.**

1856 *Eupithecia lariciata* (Freyer, 1841)
Larch Pug

Common in stands of larch throughout the mainland vice-counties, occasionally wandering from them.
■ vc10 Whitefield Wood, 17.4.95 (BJW). **Presence in vc10 confirmed.**

1857 *Eupithecia tantillaria* Boisduval, 1840
Dwarf Pug

Locally common amongst spruce, including well-established spruce *Picea* hedges. Other recent records include those given below.

■ vc11 Totton, 18.5.91 (MJ); Chandlers Ford, one or two most years at m.v. light (BG).

■ vc12 Bentley Station Meadow, 5.5.95 (PAB); Yateley Common, 18.5.93, 8.6.96 (AMD); Farnborough, May 1994, two at m.v. light (RWP).

1858 *Chloroclystis v-ata* (Haworth, 1809)
V-Pug

Fairly common throughout; the larva is polyphagous but seems to favour *Clematis* and hemp-agrimony *Eupatorium cannabinum*.

1859 *Chloroclystis chloerata* (Mabille, 1870)
Sloe Pug

First sought and discovered in Hampshire in 1972, when larvae were beaten from flowers of blackthorn; the moth is seldom seen or recognised, but larvae can be found by dint of appropriate effort in many localities: they seem to occur only on the high, arching branches at the tops of the bushes.

■ vc10 Cranmore, 10.6.98, one at m.v. light (PMW); Knighton Down and Brading Down, 12.4 and 18.4.98, larvae beaten by Brian Warne and Tony Redfern (Knill-Jones, 1998d).

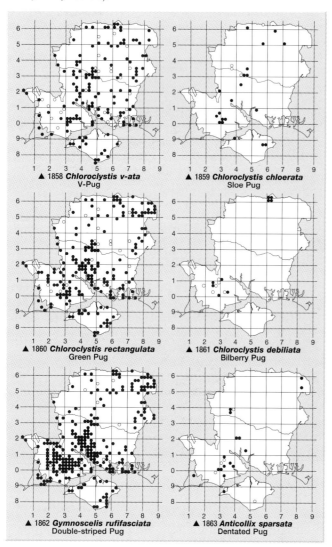
▲ 1858 *Chloroclystis v-ata*
V-Pug

▲ 1859 *Chloroclystis chloerata*
Sloe Pug

▲ 1860 *Chloroclystis rectangulata*
Green Pug

▲ 1861 *Chloroclystis debiliata*
Bilberry Pug

▲ 1862 *Gymnoscelis rufifasciata*
Double-striped Pug

▲ 1863 *Anticollix sparsata*
Dentated Pug

■ vc12 South Wonston, 1996, one female at light, genitalia det. BG (PJSS).

1860 *Chloroclystis rectangulata* (Linnaeus, 1758)
Green Pug

Common to very common in gardens, orchards, scrub and deciduous woodland. The larva is easily found in the flowers of cultivated apple *Malus domestica*.

1861 *Chloroclystis debiliata* (Hübner, 1817)
Bilberry Pug   **Notable/Nb**

Very local amongst bilberry *Vaccinium myrtillus* in open woodland in the New Forest, and reliably recorded also from Alice Holt and Pamber (see below).

■ vc12 Pamber Forest, 3.7.93, 30.6, two, and 9.7.95 (GJD); Pamber Heath, 2.7 and 9.7.95, singletons (AS).

1862 *Gymnoscelis rufifasciata* (Haworth, 1809)
Double-striped Pug

Common almost throughout the year.

1863 *Anticollix sparsata* (Treitschke, 1828)
Dentated Pug   **Notable/Na**

Very local in marshy woodland amongst the foodplant, yellow loosestrife *Lysimachia vulgaria*.

■ vc11 Hurn, occasional at m.v. light (Jeffes, 2000); Roydon Wood, 10.7.96 (PRD, JRL); Beaulieu, seven between 4.6 and 1.7.93, 5.7 and 6.7.94 (BI-J); Pig Bush, 4.7.98 (JEC); Bitterne, 1.7.93, one at m.v. light (PAB); Ramalley, Chandlers Ford, fairly common (BE, 1999).

■ vc12 South Wonston, 7.7.99, one at m.v. light, now in coll. BG (PJSS); Yateley Common, 30.6.92 (AMD); Eelmoor Marsh, 23.8.97, one at m.v. light (DGG). The observer commented on the late date but insisted that the specimen was fresh and had been carefully identified.

1864 *Chesias legatella* ([Denis & Schiffermüller], 1775)
The Streak

Common in thickets of broom, but under-recorded on account of the lateness of its season and the fact that it does not come readily to light.

■ vc10 Binstead, 12.11.95, one at light, the first in six years recording (BJW).

■ vc11 Beaulieu, 14.10.95 (BI-J); Needs Ore, 19.10.95, one at m.v. light; Chandlers Ford, 28.10.91, one at m.v. light (BG); Woolston, 16.10.95, one at light (ARC).

1865 *Chesias rufata* (Fabricius, 1775)
Broom-tip   **Notable/Nb**

Much more local and uncommon than the preceding species; the difficulty of finding it is compounded by the fact that it has such a long flight period.

■ vc11 Matchams, nr Ringwood, 1984 (GL); Woolston, recorded in 1990 and 1991 (ARC); Royal Victoria Country Park, Netley, 4.7.98 (P. Halliwell); Allington Gravel Pits, 16.4.82 (PAB).

■ vc12 Fleet, 25.7.90, one at m.v. light (MAS); Selborne, 26.3.99, wing found outside moth-trap, photo seen and confirmed BG (AEA).

1867 *Aplocera plagiata* (Linnaeus, 1758)
Treble-bar

Widespread and fairly common; most contributors can distinguish confidently between this and the next species.

1868 *Aplocera efformata* (Guenée, 1857)
Lesser Treble-bar

Widespread and fairly common, possibly outnumbering the preceding species in the New Forest, where the foodplant is likely to be slender St John's-wort *Hypericum pulchrum*.

1870 *Odezia atrata* (Linnaeus, 1758)
Chimney Sweeper

This day-flier is locally frequent in the Cholderton district of north-west Hampshire, where it was unknown in Fassnidge's day, and evidently a recent arrival in the Stockbridge/Farley Mount area, but conversely gone from the New Forest where it was then abundant. The foodplant is pignut *Conopodium majus*. All recent records received are detailed below.

■ vc8 Martin Down, 11.7.96, 18 seen by day (A.and LB).
■ vc11 Romsey, beside canal, 13.7.96, one at m.v. light (NB); Pitt Down, 22.6.98, 16 seen (DCM); St Catherine's Hill, Winchester, 10.7.86, one by day (PAB); Beacon Hill, Burghclere, 30.6 and 11.7.97 (Amanda Craig comm. AMD).
■ vc12 Cholderton district, widespread and quite common (HE); Shipton Bellinger, 5.7.95 (GCE); Perham Down, Tidworth, 13.7.96 (TJN); Woolbury Ring, 15.6.97, one seen (BG); Stockbridge Down, 19.6.94, c.7 (AB), fairly common in 1995, not seen before (RAB); Ashford Hill NNR, nine recorded between 25.6 and 9.7.95 (AS).

1872 *Discoloxia blomeri* (Curtis, 1832)
Blomer's Rivulet   **Notable/Nb**

The two specimens which turned up in 1974, one at Minstead in vc11 and one at Crawley in vc12 (Goater, 1992) remain the only records in the county.

1874 *Euchoeca nebulata* (Scopoli, 1763)
Dingy Shell

Locally frequent, in damp areas where alder flourishes. Isle of Wight records remain few and far between.
■ vc10 Freshwater, 2.7.94 (SAK-J); Arreton, fairly common among alders (Mr and Mrs Peach, comm. SAK-J).

1875 *Asthena albulata* (Hufnagel, 1767)
Small White Wave

This species really has decreased in the county, and gone are the days when it was "literally swarming" (Goater, 1992).
■ vc11 Chandlers Ford, 14.5.92, one at m.v. light, is the only recent record in an area where it used to be common in the 1940s (BG).

1876 *Hydrelia flammeolaria* (Hufnagel, 1767)
Small Yellow Wave

Widespread and fairly frequent in areas where field maple *Acer campestre* occurs, and evidently able to colonise isolated trees, as at Chandlers Ford.

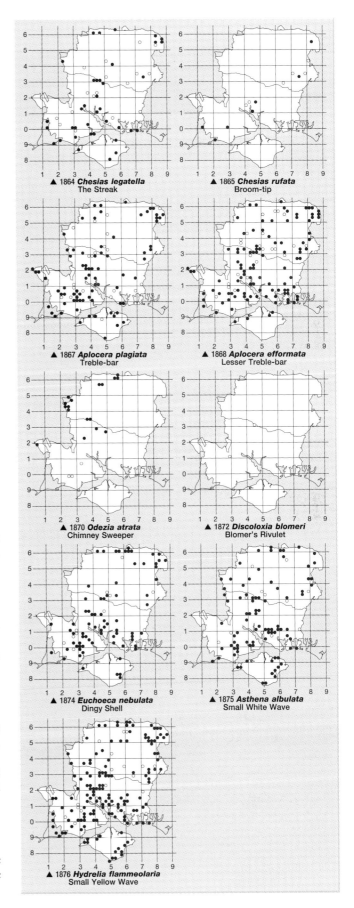

▲ 1864 *Chesias legatella*
The Streak

▲ 1865 *Chesias rufata*
Broom-tip

▲ 1867 *Aplocera plagiata*
Treble-bar

▲ 1868 *Aplocera efformata*
Lesser Treble-bar

▲ 1870 *Odezia atrata*
Chimney Sweeper

▲ 1872 *Discoloxia blomeri*
Blomer's Rivulet

▲ 1874 *Euchoeca nebulata*
Dingy Shell

▲ 1875 *Asthena albulata*
Small White Wave

▲ 1876 *Hydrelia flammeolaria*
Small Yellow Wave

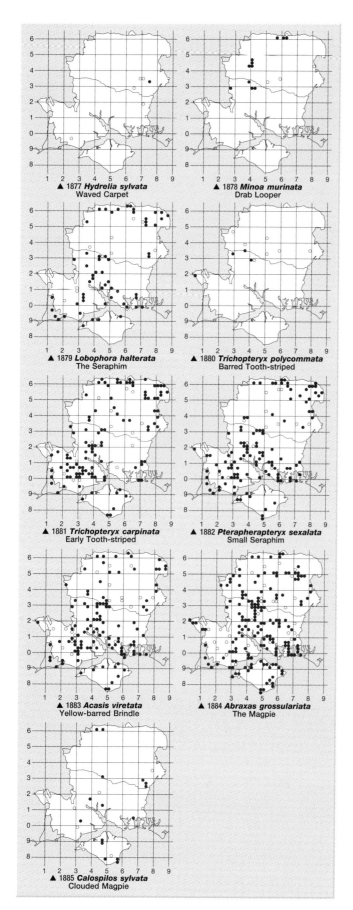

▲ 1877 *Hydrelia sylvata*
Waved Carpet

▲ 1878 *Minoa murinata*
Drab Looper

▲ 1879 *Lobophora halterata*
The Seraphim

▲ 1880 *Trichopteryx polycommata*
Barred Tooth-striped

▲ 1881 *Trichopteryx carpinata*
Early Tooth-striped

▲ 1882 *Pterapherapteryx sexalata*
Small Seraphim

▲ 1883 *Acasis viretata*
Yellow-barred Brindle

▲ 1884 *Abraxas grossulariata*
The Magpie

▲ 1885 *Calospilos sylvata*
Clouded Magpie

1877 *Hydrelia sylvata* ([Denis & Schiffermüller], 1775)
Waved Carpet   **Notable/Nb**

The few records of this species in Hampshire are detailed in Goater (1974). A single additional locality has come to hand since then; indeed it is the only record since 1975, when it was seen at Oxenbourne Down, vc11 (Goater, 1992). This species appears to be currently expanding its range in Sussex.

■ vc12 Selborne, 20.7.95, 16.7.96, singletons at light (AEA).

1878 *Minoa murinata* (Scopoli, 1763)
Drab Looper   **Notable/Nb**

Local in open, sunlit glades and clearings in deciduous woodland where wood spurge *Euphorbia amygdaloides* flourishes, flying by day. It has not been seen for several years in Crab Wood/West Wood and the remaining strongholds are now Pamber, Harewood Forest and Bentley Wood.

1879 *Lobophora halterata* (Hufnagel, 1767)
The Seraphim

Local amongst aspen *Populus tremula* and found occasionally in localities where this tree is absent. Here it is likely to be associated with another species of poplar.

■ vc11 Bitterne, 10.5, male and 13.5, female, in 1994 at m.v. light (PAB); Chandlers Ford, one or two most years at m.v. light (BG).

■ vc12 Rye Common, 6.5.95, two at m.v. light; Castle Bottom NNR, 11.5.98, fairly common; Yateley Common, fairly common (AMD).

1880 *Trichopteryx polycommata* ([Denis & Schiffermüller], 1775)
Barred Tooth-striped   **Notable/Na**

Once common in Crab Wood: most of the old privet bushes were grubbed up in making the car-park and other facilities for the Country Park and repeated efforts to refind the moth have failed. The localities cited in Goater (1974) need checking to see if the moth still survives in any of them.

■ vc8 Martin Down, 4.4.81, conf. BG (NHu).

■ vc11 Broughton Down, 15.4.96, one at m.v. light (NB); two males at rest on privet bushes after dark, 22.3.00, and two females on 1.4.00; one larva beaten from privet, 16.5.00 (AHD).

1881 *Trichopteryx carpinata* (Borkhausen, 1794)
Early Tooth-striped

Fairly common in deciduous woodland, especially where birch is present, but lost from or much rarer in several places.

1882 *Pterapherapteryx sexalata* (Retzius, 1783)
Small Seraphim

Common in woodland and marshy localities where sallow *Salix* spp. flourishes.

1883 *Acasis viretata* (Hübner, 1799)
Yellow-barred Brindle

Rather common in many localities ranging from wooded

garden to deciduous woodland. The larva feeds on several species of shrub, but seems here to favour holly and ivy.

1884 *Abraxas grossulariata* (Linnaeus, 1758)
The Magpie

Far less common than formerly, but still widespread. It used to swarm, for instance, along lanes between Lymington and Keyhaven and was also a common garden moth.

■ vc10 Freshwater, 11.8.94, ab. *dohrnii* (SAK-J).

1885 *Calospilos sylvata* (Scopoli, 1763)
Clouded Magpie

There are only two breeding colonies known in the area, in Parkhurst Forest vc10 (Goater, 1992) and in Happersnapper Hanger, vc12, but single specimens turn up from time to time all over the area. Recent records are given below.

■ vc10 Freshwater, 22.7.68, only record (SAK-J); Chale Green, 14.7.94 (SRC).

■ vc11 Rownhams, 1.7.93 (KG); Bitterne, 22.7.94, one at m.v. light in garden (PAB).

■ vc12 Crawley, 25.7.83, only one seen (RAB); Ashford Hangers NNR, 2.7.96, disturbed from bushes on Happersnapper Hanger, 5.7.96; Wheatham Hill, 9.7.96; Priors Dean (DB).

1887 *Lomaspilis marginata* (Linnaeus, 1758)
Clouded Border

Common and widely distributed wherever sallows *Salix* spp. are found.

1888 *Ligdia adustata* ([Denis & Schiffermüller], 1775)
Scorched Carpet

Widely distributed amongst spindle *Euonymus europaeus*, chiefly on the chalk but also in parts of the New Forest, and in gardens.

1889 *Macaria (Semiothisa) notata* (Linnaeus, 1758)
Peacock Moth

Fairly common in birch woodland; some care is needed to distinguish it from the next species where both occur together.

1890 *Macaria (Semiothisa) alternata* ([Denis & Schiffermüller], 1775)
Sharp-angled Peacock

More common and widespread than the previous species, the larva feeding chiefly on sallows *Salix* spp. in this area.

1893 *Macaria (Semiothisa) liturata* (Clerck, 1759)
Tawny-barred Angle

Common in pine country; the melanic ab. *nigrofulvata* Collins is rare.

1897 *Macaria (Semiothisa) wauaria* (Linnaeus, 1758)
The V-Moth

This is another species that has decreased, and all recent records are included below. Earlier records are detailed in Goater (1992). The larva feeds on the leaves of red and black currants and gooseberry *Ribes* spp.

■ vc11 Totton, 5.7, 16.7 and 20.7.91, at m.v. light (MJ); Sandy Point NR, Hayling Island, 23.8.98 (PS).

■ vc12 Pamber Heath, ten between 21.6 and 21.7.95; Lord's Wood, Pamber, 8.7.95, one (AS); Yateley Common, 30.6 and 8.7.92, 23.6 and 27.6 and 30.7.93, not since (AMD); Farnborough, 12.7.95, one at light (RWP).

1894 *Chiasmia (Semiothisa) clathrata* (Linnaeus, 1758)
Latticed Heath

The notes given in Goater (1974) hold good today: the species is still found quite commonly on the chalk and in

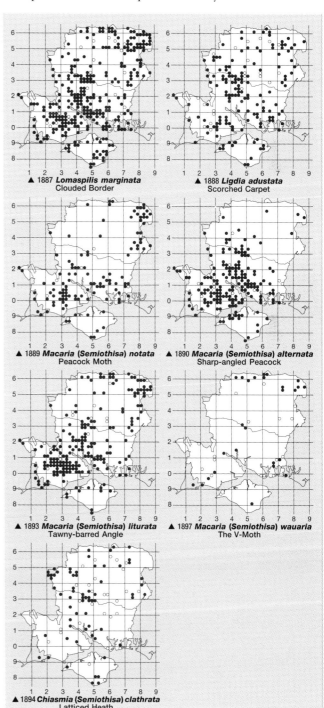

▲ 1887 *Lomaspilis marginata*
Clouded Border

▲ 1888 *Ligdia adustata*
Scorched Carpet

▲ 1889 *Macaria (Semiothisa) notata*
Peacock Moth

▲ 1890 *Macaria (Semiothisa) alternata*
Sharp-angled Peacock

▲ 1893 *Macaria (Semiothisa) liturata*
Tawny-barred Angle

▲ 1897 *Macaria (Semiothisa) wauaria*
The V-Moth

▲ 1894 *Chiasmia (Semiothisa) clathrata*
Latticed Heath

167

waste places where clovers are abundant, and in clover crops.

1896 *Itame (Semiothisa) brunneata* (Thunberg, 1784)
Rannoch Looper   **Notable/Na or Migrant**

An extremely scarce immigrant, with single records from each of the three vice-counties.

■ vc10 near Shalfleet, 18/19.6.97, one at a Robinson trap (Waring, 1998). **New vc record.**

■ vc11 St Ives, Ringwood, 31.7.88 (Goater, 1992).

■ vc12 Whitehill nr Bordon, 26.6.60 (Goater, 1974).

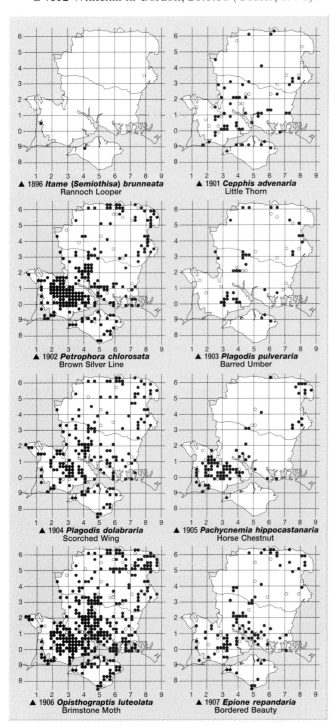

▲ 1896 *Itame (Semiothisa) brunneata*
Rannoch Looper

▲ 1901 *Cepphis advenaria*
Little Thorn

▲ 1902 *Petrophora chlorosata*
Brown Silver Line

▲ 1903 *Plagodis pulveraria*
Barred Umber

▲ 1904 *Plagodis dolabraria*
Scorched Wing

▲ 1905 *Pachycnemia hippocastanaria*
Horse Chestnut

▲ 1906 *Opisthograptis luteolata*
Brimstone Moth

▲ 1907 *Epione repandaria*
Bordered Beauty

1901 *Cepphis advenaria* (Hübner, 1790)
Little Thorn

Local but quite frequent in many woodland localities, associated either with bramble *Rubus fruticosus* agg., in neutral or basic habitats, or bilberry *Vaccinium myrtillus* in those which are acid.

1902 *Petrophora chlorosata* (Scopoli, 1763)
Brown Silver Line

Extremely common amongst bracken *Pteridium aquilinum* everywhere and well-recorded since it is so easily disturbed by day.

1903 *Plagodis pulveraria* (Linnaeus, 1758)
Barred Umber

Fassnidge's estimate in 1928–29, widely distributed but somewhat scarce, holds good today in the areas of deciduous woodland which survive.

1904 *Plagodis dolabraria* (Linnaeus, 1767)
Scorched Wing

10 mm

Generally distributed and fairly common throughout the three vice-counties, in and near deciduous woodland.

1905 *Pachycnemia hippocastanaria* (Hübner, 1799)
Horse Chestnut   **Notable/Nb**

A characteristic species of the heathlands of the New Forest and north and north-east Hampshire, and occasionally recorded elsewhere, for example, those given below.

■ vc11 Hengistbury, 16.8.94, one at m.v. light (MJ); Chandlers Ford, 1.8.91, one at m.v. light (BG); Woolston, 24.8.96, 30.7.97, singles at m.v. light (ARC); Warsash, 10.8.96 (PMP).

■ vc12 Crawley, 23.7.98, two at m.v. light (RAB); Selborne, 7.10.95, one at light, a new record for the locality and an extremely late date; 22.7, 6, 7, 11.8 and 15.8.96, at light, two on last date (AEA); Farnborough, 5.9.94, 17.8.95 (RWP).

1906 *Opisthograptis luteolata* (Linnaeus, 1758)
Brimstone Moth

One of the commonest, most conspicuous and well-recorded geometers in the area.

1907 *Epione repandaria* (Hufnagel, 1767)
Bordered Beauty

Few records of this attractive species have come to hand recently. It is an inhabitant of damp areas with sallows *Salix* spp. AMD states that it is regular in very small numbers at Yateley, vc12 (AMD, pers. comm.).

1909 *Pseudopanthera macularia* (Linnaeus, 1758)
Speckled Yellow

This attractive diurnal species is still quite common in

open woodland and bushy places where the principal foodplant, wood-sage *Teucrium scorodonia* grows.

1910 *Apeira syringaria* (Linnaeus, 1758)
Lilac Beauty

Although PJC, contributing to Goater (1992), states that it is becoming increasingly common in places on the Isle of Wight, the picture on the mainland is far less encouraging. Here, the records are sparse and it seems to have gone from certain localities, for instance Chandlers Ford, although the foodplant, honeysuckle, remains common.

■ vc10 Binstead, 1.10.95, second brood individual (BJW).

1911 *Ennomos autumnaria* (Werneburg, 1859)
Large Thorn   Notable/Nb

It is pleasing to learn that this moth still occurs at Southsea and in north Hayling Island, though no records have been received from the other old localities in south-east Hampshire, where it has always been extremely local.

■ vc11 Southsea, 7.9, 8.9 and 15.9.97, 6.9 and 24.9.98, 13 between 27.8 and 13.9.99, at light (IRT); Waterlooville, 17.9.00, one at m.v. light (RJM); Hayling Island, 24.9 and 25.9.86, singles at m.v. light (JMW); N Hayling Island, several in September 1994, 19.9.98 (PRD); Northney, 22.8.99, 6.9, 8.9 and 16.9.99 (Phillips, 2000), 11.9 and 13.9.00 (JWP).

1912 *Ennomos quercinaria* (Hufnagel, 1767)
August Thorn

Widespread and fairly common in well-established deciduous woodland.

1913 *Ennomos alniaria* (Linnaeus, 1758)
Canary-shouldered Thorn

Common and widespread in all three vice-counties.

1914 *Ennomos fuscantaria* (Haworth, 1809)
Dusky Thorn

Common and widespread in all three vice-counties.

1915 *Ennomos erosaria* ([Denis & Schiffermüller], 1775)
September Thorn

Common and widespread in all three vice-counties. Specimens appear in mid-July and again in September, and the exact relationship between the two emergences is obscure.

1917 *Selenia dentaria* (Fabricius, 1775)
Early Thorn

Common and widespread in all three vice-counties.

1918 *Selenia lunularia* (Hübner, 1788)
Lunar Thorn

There are a few old reports of this beautiful species in Hampshire, and two Isle of Wight localities are given (Goater, 1974), but nothing had been heard of it until the following three records, all in rather unexpected places. The Binstead specimen is of special interest in that it is an example of the very unusual second brood.

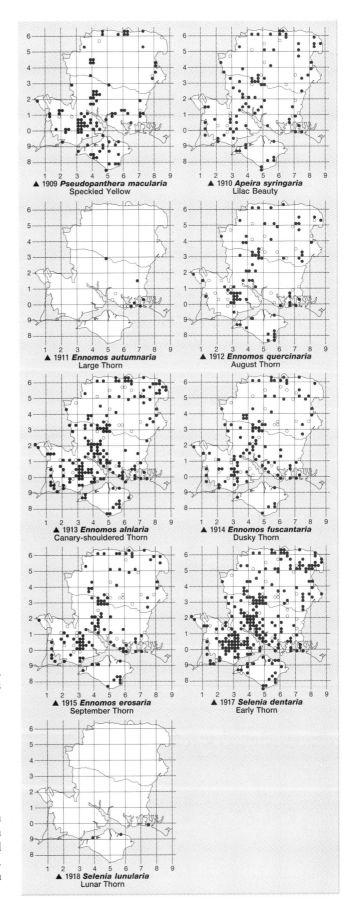

▲ 1909 *Pseudopanthera macularia* Speckled Yellow

▲ 1910 *Apeira syringaria* Lilac Beauty

▲ 1911 *Ennomos autumnaria* Large Thorn

▲ 1912 *Ennomos quercinaria* August Thorn

▲ 1913 *Ennomos alniaria* Canary-shouldered Thorn

▲ 1914 *Ennomos fuscantaria* Dusky Thorn

▲ 1915 *Ennomos erosaria* September Thorn

▲ 1917 *Selenia dentaria* Early Thorn

▲ 1918 *Selenia lunularia* Lunar Thorn

■ vc10 Ningwood Common, 30.5.95, one at m.v. light (PMW); Binstead, 2.8.94, male at m.v. light, conf. BG (BJW). See also Knill-Jones (1995).

■ vc11 Sandy Point, Hayling Island, 23.4.98, male at m.v. light (PS). I was given the remains of this specimen, and have made a slide of the wings and genitalia (BG).

1919 *Selenia tetralunaria* (Hufnagel, 1767)
Purple Thorn
Fairly common and widespread in all three vice-counties.

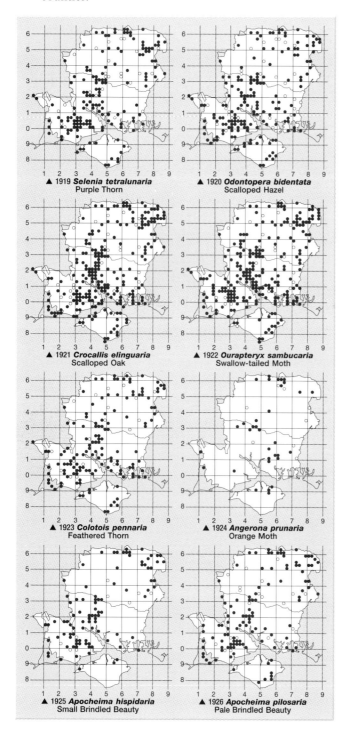

▲ 1919 *Selenia tetralunaria*
Purple Thorn

▲ 1920 *Odontopera bidentata*
Scalloped Hazel

▲ 1921 *Crocallis elinguaria*
Scalloped Oak

▲ 1922 *Ourapteryx sambucaria*
Swallow-tailed Moth

▲ 1923 *Colotois pennaria*
Feathered Thorn

▲ 1924 *Angerona prunaria*
Orange Moth

▲ 1925 *Apocheima hispidaria*
Small Brindled Beauty

▲ 1926 *Apocheima pilosaria*
Pale Brindled Beauty

1920 *Odontopera bidentata* (Clerck, 1759)
Scalloped Hazel
Fairly common and widespread in all three vice-counties.

1921 *Crocallis elinguaria* (Linnaeus, 1758)
Scalloped Oak
Common and widespread in all three vice-counties.

1922 *Ourapteryx sambucaria* (Linnaeus, 1758)
Swallow-tailed Moth
Common and widespread in all three vice-counties.
■ vc10 Freshwater, 6.11.97 – a very late date (Knill-Jones, 1998b).

1923 *Colotois pennaria* (Linnaeus, 1761)
Feathered Thorn
A common and widespread species of deciduous woodland in all three vice-counties. It flies very late in the year and is therefore under-recorded.

1924 *Angerona prunaria* (Linnaeus, 1758)
Orange Moth
This striking species has disappeared from a number of localities, but is still quite common in a few mature woodlands.
■ vc8 Damerham, 10.7.86, only record (PT).
■ vc10 Parkhurst Forest, 10.7.96, common (PJC, BJW).
■ vc11 Kings Somborne, 1.7.93, one at m.v. light (TJN); West Wood, Sparsholt, 17.7.96 (JWP); Downleaze Copse, Exton, 20.7.94 (PAB); Southwick, 1996 (JRL, EAP); Waterlooville, typical and f. *corylaria* recorded in 1999 (RJM).
■ vc12 South Wonston, 18.6.94, male at m.v. light (PJSS); East Stratton, very rare (BI-J); Odiham Common, 27.6.95, five at m.v. light (AMD); Eelmoor Marsh SSSI, 5.7.97, at m.v. light (DGG).

1925 *Apocheima hispidaria* ([Denis & Schiffermüller], 1775)
Small Brindled Beauty
Common and widespread in all three vice-counties; the flight period is short and the date is dependent on the vagaries of the weather in early spring.

1926 *Apocheima pilosaria* ([Denis & Schiffermüller], 1775)
Pale Brindled Beauty
One of the first species to emerge, often in early January, but very seldom before Christmas. It is common and widespread in all three vice-counties.
■ vc12 Stoke Charity, 2.10.97, one at m.v. light (PJSS).

1927 *Lycia hirtaria* (Clerck, 1759)
Brindled Beauty
This species is evidently rather common west of Ringwood (JHC records), but though widespread, it is unaccountably rare in most other parts of the area except in NE Hampshire (AMD, pers. comm.).
■ vc10 Freshwater, 7.4.99; Cranmore, 23.4.93 (SAK-J); Binstead, 12.4.94, first in five years recording (BJW).
■ vc11 Totton, 31.3.91 (MJ).

■ vc12 Bentley Station Meadow, 5.5.95 (PAB); Noar Hill, 19.4.93 (AMJ).

1930 *Biston stratatia* (Hufnagel, 1767)
Oak Beauty

10 mm

Common and widespread in all three vice-counties.

1931 *Biston betularia* (Linnaeus, 1758)
Peppered Moth
Common and widespread in all three vice-counties.

1932 *Agriopis leucophaearia* ([Denis & Schiffermüller], 1775)
Spring Usher
A common species in and around oak woodland in all three vice-counties, though less so than in the 1950s.

1933 *Agriopis aurantiaria* (Hübner, 1799)
Scarce Umber
Widespread and fairly common in all three vice-counties, though certainly under-recorded.
■ vc10 Freshwater, five during Nov.1995 – first since 1960s (SAK-J); Binstead, 24.11.94 (BJW, *comm.* SAK-J).

1934 *Agriopis marginaria* (Fabricius, 1776)
Dotted Border
Common and widespread in all three vice-counties.

1935 *Erannis defoliaria* (Clerck, 1759)
Mottled Umber
Common and widespread in all three vice-counties, though the larva is seldom so numerous as to be a pest.

1936 *Menophra abruptaria* (Thunberg, 1792)
Waved Umber
Widespread in all three vice-counties, but only moderately frequent.
■ vc12 South Wonston, 1993–95, pale and melanic forms (PJSS).

1937 *Peribatodes rhomboidaria* ([Denis & Schiffermüller], 1775)
Willow Beauty
Very common and widespread in all three vice-counties.

1937b *Peribatodes ilicaria* (Geyer, 1833)
Lydd Beauty
This suspected immigrant first occurred at Lydd, Kent on 27.8.90 and the records below are the third and fourth British records.
■ vc10 Ninham, 14.8.96, one male; 18.8.96, one female, by J. Reeve (Skinner and Parsons, 1999). **New county record.**

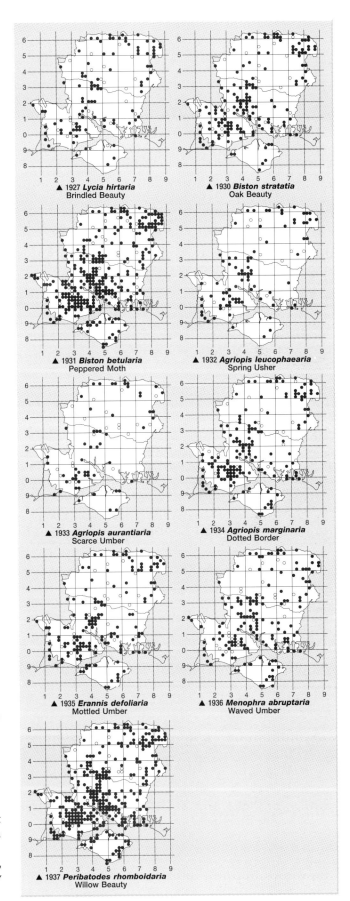

▲ 1927 *Lycia hirtaria*
Brindled Beauty

▲ 1930 *Biston stratatia*
Oak Beauty

▲ 1931 *Biston betularia*
Peppered Moth

▲ 1932 *Agriopis leucophaearia*
Spring Usher

▲ 1933 *Agriopis aurantiaria*
Scarce Umber

▲ 1934 *Agriopis marginaria*
Dotted Border

▲ 1935 *Erannis defoliaria*
Mottled Umber

▲ 1936 *Menophra abruptaria*
Waved Umber

▲ 1937 *Peribatodes rhomboidaria*
Willow Beauty

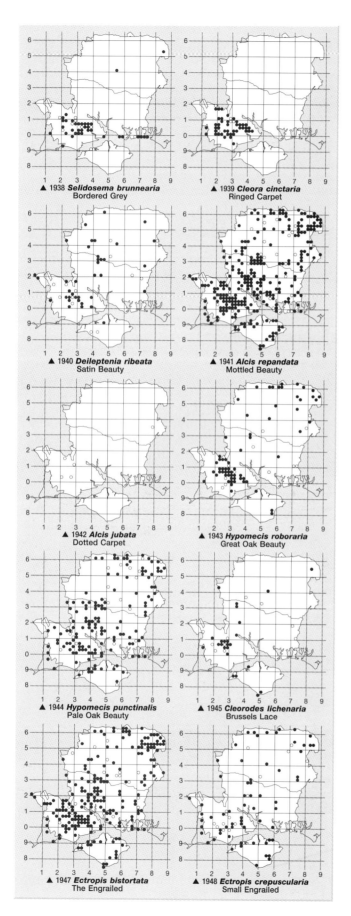

▲ 1938 *Selidosema brunnearia*
Bordered Grey

▲ 1939 *Cleora cinctaria*
Ringed Carpet

▲ 1940 *Deileptenia ribeata*
Satin Beauty

▲ 1941 *Alcis repandata*
Mottled Beauty

▲ 1942 *Alcis jubata*
Dotted Carpet

▲ 1943 *Hypomecis roboraria*
Great Oak Beauty

▲ 1944 *Hypomecis punctinalis*
Pale Oak Beauty

▲ 1945 *Cleorodes lichenaria*
Brussels Lace

▲ 1947 *Ectropis bistortata*
The Engrailed

▲ 1948 *Ectropis crepuscularia*
Small Engrailed

1938 *Selidosema brunnearia* (de Villers, 1789)
Bordered Grey   **Notable/Na**

Locally common on the heaths of the New Forest, and also on south Hayling Island, in the place where Dr Cockayne discovered larvae in 1930 (Goater, 1974).

■ vc11 Furzey Heath, New Forest, 12.8.95 (NB); Lepe Country Park, 14.8.96 (PMP); Sandy Point, Hayling Island, few at light in August (PRD).

■ vc12 East Stratton, 6.7.87, positively identified (BI-J).

1939 *Cleora cinctaria* ([Denis & Schiffermüller], 1775)
Ringed Carpet   **Notable/Na**

A speciality of the New Forest, where the moth can be found resting on the small pines on the heaths during May.

■ vc11 Lymington, one in 2000 (AJP); Beaulieu, 13.5.94 (BI-J); Holbury, 27.5.00, one at rest on a pine trunk (JEC, JS); these three records are from outside the normal range of the species in Hampshire.

1940 *Deileptenia ribeata* (Clerck, 1759)
Satin Beauty

Widespread in woodland, but usually very uncommon. The presence of the larval foodplants, yew, spruce or Douglas fir, is a requirement of the habitat.

■ vc10 Parkhurst Forest, 12.7.99 (SAK-J). First record since 1975.

■ vc11 Brockenhurst, 3.7.99, one at m.v. light (JEC); Frame Wood, 3.7.99, at m.v. light (DGG); West Wood, Sparsholt, 17.7.96 (JWP); Chandlers Ford, 1.7.99, male at m.v. light (BG).

■ vc12 Crawley, 4.8.96, one at m.v. light in garden (RAB); Wildhern, nr Andover, 15.8.96, at actinic light (DGG); East Stratton, 10.9.88, 4.7.89, 27.6.92, 10.7.92 (BI-J); Bentley Station Meadow, 28.7.95 (PAB).

1941 *Alcis repandata* (Linnaeus, 1758)
Mottled Beauty

Very common and widespread in all three vice-counties, though far less so than in the 1950s.

1942 *Alcis jubata* (Thunberg, 1788)
Dotted Carpet   **Notable/Nb**

Believed extinct in the area. This species used to be taken regularly in the New Forest and occasionally in the Chandlers Ford area, and in Woolmer Forest, but the last record to hand is of two at Rhinefields on 26.7.58, in coll. BG (Goater, 1974). The larva feeds on robust tree-lichens, and the moth is still plentiful in parts of the west and north Britain where these still thrive.

1943 *Hypomecis roboraria* ([Denis & Schiffermüller], 1775)
Great Oak Beauty   **Notable/Nb**

This species of ancient woodlands still occurs in the New Forest and other large woods that still survive, but it has gone from localities such as Chandler Ford, where housing development has destroyed the habitat.

■ vc11 Frenchmoor Copse, 26.6.93 (NB); Rownhams, 2.7.93 (KG); Southwick, 10.7.91, about 30 at m.v. light (Townsend and Wynne, 1992).

■ vc12 Pamber, fairly common (GRD, 1995); Odiham

Common, 27.6.95; Yateley Common, occasional (AMD); Farnborough, two in 1994 (RWP).

1944 *Hypomecis punctinalis* (Scopoli, 1763)
Pale Oak Beauty
Still fairly common in and around deciduous woodland in all three vice-counties.
■ vc10 Cranmore, 26.5.93 (SAK-J).

1945 *Cleorodes lichenaria* (Hufnagel, 1767)
Brussels Lace
This species all but disappeared after 1945, but there are some indications that it is returning. The larva is another that depends upon a vigorous growth of tree-lichens.
■ vc10 Freshwater, The Causeway, 13.7.94, 27.7.96 (DBW); St Catherine's Point, 30.6.95, two, 1.7.95, 11, at light (PMP).
■ vc11 Brockenhurst, 29.7.96, one at m.v. light in garden; Wood Crates, 1996 (JEC); Kings Somborne, 14.7.96, 5.6.97 (TJN).
■ vc12 East Stratton, 7.7.87 (BI-J).

1946 *Fagivorina arenaria* (Hufnagel, 1767)
Speckled Beauty
Extinct. During the 19th century, this species occurred rarely in the New Forest and hardly anywhere else in the country. It was last seen in numbers in 1872, and the very last record was in 1898 (Goater, 1974). The larva feeds on tree-lichens, and the imago was reputed to be an inhabitant of the tree-tops.

1947 *Ectropis bistortata* (Goeze, 1781)
The Engrailed
Common and widespread, in two broods, spring and late summer, in all three vice-counties.

1948 *Ectropis crepuscularia* ([Denis & Schiffermüller], 1775)
Small Engrailed
The moth known by this name flies in a single brood between those of *E. bistortata*, and its taxonomic status remains a subject of controversy. It appears to be confined to Britain, and the Continental authorities contend that *E. crepuscularia* and *E. bistortata* are synonymous. There appear to be no consistent structural differences.
■ vc11 Sims Wood, Exbury, 18.5.95, one (BG).
■ vc12 Noar Hill, 20.6.94 (AMJ).

1949 *Paradarisa consonaria* (Hübner, 1799)
Square Spot
Widespread and fairly common in deciduous woodland in all three vice-counties.

1950 *Parectropis similaria* (Hufnagel, 1767)
Brindled White-spot
Locally fairly common in deciduous woodland in all three vice-counties; elsewhere, it is rare.
■ vc11 Chandlers Ford, 6.6.96, one at light, first record (BG); Cosham, 26.6.96, one at m.v. light (TJJ).
■ vc12 Selborne, 7.6 and 19.6.96, first records (AEA).

1951 *Aethalura punctulata* ([Denis & Schiffermüller], 1775)
Grey Birch
Fairly frequent in birch woodland in all three vice-counties.

1952 *Ematurga atomaria* (Linnaeus, 1758)
Heath Moth
This species is very common on the heaths of the New Forest and north-east Hampshire, and less so, in a larger, yellower form, on chalk downland and sometimes in young plantations. Astonishingly, there is only one recent record from the Isle of Wight
■ vc11 Totton, 29.7.91, one by day (MJ).

1954 *Bupalus piniaria* (Linnaeus, 1758)
Bordered White
Fairly common in pine woodland in all three vice-counties, though apparently never the pest it sometimes is in other parts of the country.

1955 *Cabera pusaria* (Linnaeus, 1758)
Common White Wave
Common and widespread in all three vice-counties.

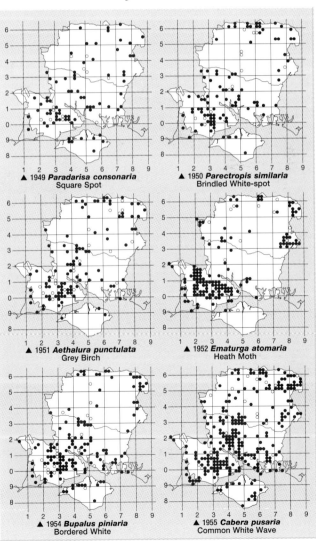

▲ 1949 *Paradarisa consonaria*
Square Spot

▲ 1950 *Parectropis similaria*
Brindled White-spot

▲ 1951 *Aethalura punctulata*
Grey Birch

▲ 1952 *Ematurga atomaria*
Heath Moth

▲ 1954 *Bupalus piniaria*
Bordered White

▲ 1955 *Cabera pusaria*
Common White Wave

1956 *Cabera exanthemata* (Scopoli, 1763)
Common Wave
Common and widespread in all three vice-counties, though more local than the previous species and more addicted to damp areas.

1957 *Lomographa bimaculata* (Fabricius, 1775)
White-pinion Spotted
Widespread in all three vice-counties, but seldom common.

1958 *Lomographa temerata* ([Denis & Schiffermüller], 1775)
Clouded Silver
Common and widespread in all three vice-counties.

1959 *Aleucis distinctata* (Herrich-Schäffer, 1839)
Sloe Carpet   **Notable/Nb**
The uncertainty of the weather in early spring has made the accurate monitoring of this species more difficult in recent years, and several attempts to relocate it in classical localities in the New Forest have failed. However, it is still present, and also in the Cranmore area of the Isle of Wight. The moth may be found after dark, resting on small blackthorn bushes at the time of flowering.

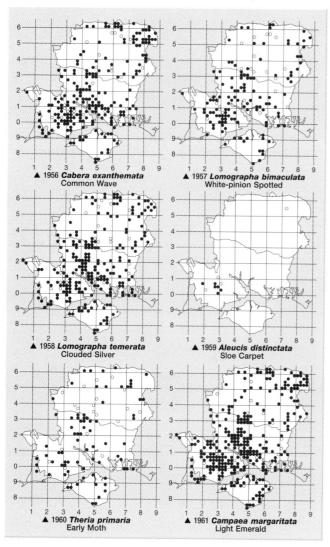

▲ 1956 *Cabera exanthemata*
Common Wave

▲ 1957 *Lomographa bimaculata*
White-pinion Spotted

▲ 1958 *Lomographa temerata*
Clouded Silver

▲ 1959 *Aleucis distinctata*
Sloe Carpet

▲ 1960 *Theria primaria*
Early Moth

▲ 1961 *Campaea margaritata*
Light Emerald

■ vc11 Linford, 2.4.97 (AGP); Fletchers Thorns, 1996 (JEC).
■ vc12 Hook, 24.3.77; specimen in coll. AHD and seen by BG. **New vc record.**

1960 *Theria primaria* (Haworth, 1809)
Early Moth
Common to abundant in late winter along hawthorn hedges and amongst isolated small bushes in open country and on the downs. The flightless females may be found sitting on the leafless twigs after dark.

1961 *Campaea margaritata* (Linnaeus, 1767)
Light Emerald
Very common and widespread in all three vice-counties.

1962 *Hylaea fasciaria* (Linnaeus, 1758)
Barred Red
Common in and near pine woodland in all three vice-counties.
■ vc11 Beaulieu, 3.11.94, one f. *prasinaria* at m.v. light (BI-J); in coll. BG.

1964 *Gnophos obscuratus* ([Denis & Schiffermüller], 1775)
The Annulet
Local and uncommon. In Hampshire, a dark form predominates on the heaths of the New Forest, and on the Freshwater cliffs, a quite different, white, form is found.
■ vc11 Matchams, nr Ringwood, 1982, 1985 (GL); Vales Moor, 1996 (JEC); East Denny Bog, 27.7.86; Netley Hill, 2.8.86 (PAB); Southsea, 26.7.96, one at actinic light, conf. JRL (IRT).
■ vc12 Eelmoor Marsh SSSI, 23.8.97, one at m.v. light (DGG).

1967 *Aspitates gilvaria* ([Denis & Schiffermüller], 1775)
Straw Belle   **RDB3**
There has been no record since those given in Goater (1974) from many years ago.

1968 *Semiaspilates (Aspitates) ochrearia* (Rossi, 1794)
Yellow Belle
Frequent on dunes and shingle in coastal localities, rare inland on the chalk.

1969 *Dyscia fagaria* (Thunberg, 1784)
Grey Scalloped Bar
Locally rather frequent on the New Forest heaths, especially near recently burned ground, on which the imago rests by day. Very occasional elsewhere. There has been one record from the Isle of Wight which reached the authors just before going to press.
■ vc10 Newtown Brickfields, 2.6.01 (M Tunmore, PMW). **New vc record.**
■ vc11 Sopley Common, 3.6.00 (MJ); Netley Hill, 17.7.93 (PAB).
■ vc12 Crawley, 21.5.81, only one seen (RAB).

1970 *Perconia strigillaria* (Hübner, 1787)
Grass Wave   **Notable/Nb**
Fairly common to common on the heaths of the New Forest, and also in north-east Hampshire; very local elsewhere.

■ vcll Emer Bog, 3.6.93 (NB).

■ vcl2 Pamber Heath, 17.6.95, one (AS); Conford, 21.6.95, one at m.v. light (JRL); Shortheath Common, 14.6.95, one at m.v. light; Castle Bottom NNR, 16.6.96, two at m.v. light; Yateley Common, fairly common (AMD); Hazeley Heath, 24.6.96, several by day (RWP).

Sphingidae (16 + [1])

1972 *Agrius convolvuli* (Linnaeus, 1758)
Convolvulus Hawk-moth
A fairly common migrant, usually appearing in September and October, but sometimes as early as June. There are scattered records from all three vice-counties, of moths taken at light or at flowers of *Petunia* and *Nicotiana*.

1973 *Acherontia atropos* (Linnaeus, 1758)
Death's-head Hawk-moth
Much less common than *A. convolvuli*, although the larvae are reported more often. The species is unable to survive the British winter. The most recent records are given below.

■ vcll Lymington, 14.9.92 (AJP).

■ vcl2 Chattis Hill, near Stockbridge, larva found early October by Mr HG North; moth emerged early November 1996 (comm. JHT); Selborne, 22.8.94, one at m.v. light (AEA).

1976 *Sphinx ligustri* Linnaeus, 1758
Privet Hawk-moth
Widespread and locally fairly common in all three vice-counties, though considerably less so than formerly. AMD remarks that he has seen the species only once in Hampshire in ten years (AMD, pers. comm.).

1978 *Hyloicus pinastri* (Linnaeus, 1758)
Pine Hawk-moth
The spread of this species in Hampshire in the 1940s is detailed in Goater (1974). Subsequently, there has been a decline, the moth remaining widespread in pine localities, but never common.

■ vcll Portchester, larvae reported feeding on *Pinus radiata*, 1997 and 1998 (A. Brookes).

1979 *Mimas tiliae* (Linnaeus, 1758)
Lime Hawk-moth

10 mm

Fairly common in all three vice-counties, especially in suburbia, where the moth is sometimes seen newly-emerged on the trunks of limes, and where the pupa can be dug under lime and elm trees.

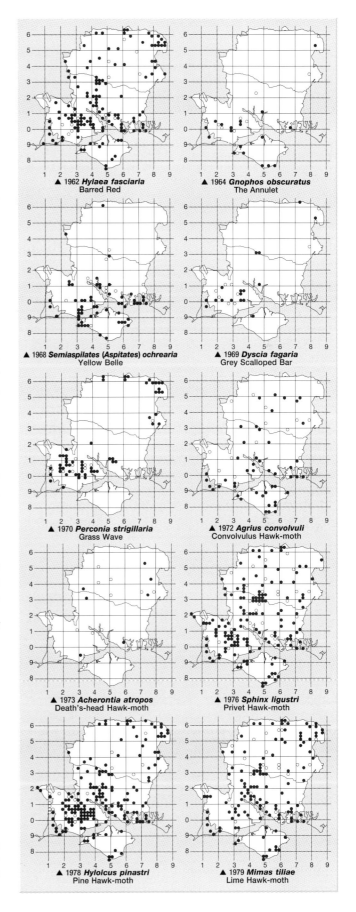

▲ 1962 *Hylaea fasciaria* Barred Red

▲ 1964 *Gnophos obscuratus* The Annulet

▲ 1968 *Semiaspilates (Aspitates) ochrearia* Yellow Belle

▲ 1969 *Dyscia fagaria* Grey Scalloped Bar

▲ 1970 *Perconia strigillaria* Grass Wave

▲ 1972 *Agrius convolvuli* Convolvulus Hawk-moth

▲ 1973 *Acherontia atropos* Death's-head Hawk-moth

▲ 1976 *Sphinx ligustri* Privet Hawk-moth

▲ 1978 *Hyloicus pinastri* Pine Hawk-moth

▲ 1979 *Mimas tiliae* Lime Hawk-moth

1980 *Smerinthus ocellata* (Linnaeus, 1758)
Eyed Hawk-moth
Widespread and fairly common in all three vice-counties, though less so than formerly.

1981 *Laothoe populi* (Linnaeus, 1758)
Poplar Hawk-moth
The most common and widespread hawk-moth in the area.

1982 *Hemaris tityus* (Linnaeus, 1758)
Narrow-bordered Bee Hawk-moth   **Notable/Na**

10 mm

Formerly local and moderately common, now virtually extinct in the area. There are recent encouraging signs that this day-flier can survive in low numbers on a site undetected.
■ vc11 Purewell, Christchurch, 8.6.00, one seen well and described (MJG); South of West Meon, 23.5.99, a freshly-emerged specimen found and taken on the hand and

sketched by Dr A. Barker, before being released; record confirmed by BG from the drawing.

1983 *Hemaris fuciformis* (Linnaeus, 1758)
Broad-bordered Bee Hawk-moth   **Notable/Nb**
This species staged a recovery in the 1970s, and now the moth is reported from time to time, chiefly in the New Forest, and larvae may be found, if sought on honeysuckle *Lonicera periclymenum* growing in exposed, well-illuminated places. Jeffes (2000) reported a larva at Hurn on a *Lonicera* (*nitida*) hedge, 12.7.99.

1984 *Macroglossum stellatarum* (Linnaeus, 1758)
Hummingbird Hawk-moth
A migratory species that appears every year in varying numbers. There have been a very few confirmed records of the adult found hibernating, and it is therefore possible that specimens found flying in the spring are not primary migrants, but have overwintered. The moth is mainly diurnal, when it is seen visiting flowers including *Aubrieta*, *Buddleia*, viper's bugloss *Echium vulgare*, red valerian *Centranthus ruber*, cultivated honeysuckle *Lonicera* spp., catmint *Nepeta*, *Petunia* and cultivated *Pulmonaria*.

1985 *Daphnis nerii* (Linnaeus, 1758)
Oleander Hawk-moth
An extremely scarce immigrant, not recorded in Hampshire or the Isle of Wight since 1975 (Goater, 1992).

[1986 *Hyles euphorbiae* (Linnaeus, 1758)
Spurge Hawk-moth
Two records from Southampton, 24.8.1871 and Bournemouth, 12.7.1908 are given by Goater (1974), with reservations about their provenance. The whereabouts of the specimens, if they exist, is unknown.]

1987 *Hyles gallii* (Rottemburg, 1775)
Bedstraw Hawk-moth

10 mm

A rare immigrant from the east. Recent records are given below.
■ vc11 Chandlers Ford, 30.6.95, male at light (BG); Southsea, 20.7.97, male at m.v. light (JRL).
■ vc12 East Stratton, 8.6.92, one at m.v. light, now in DHS coll. (BI-J); Odiham Common, 27.6.95, one at m.v. light (AMD). [The record given in Goater (1992) for Havant, 10.4.85 refers to *H. livornica* (CBC).]

1990 *Hyles livornica* (Esper, 1779)
Striped Hawk-moth
A rare immigrant species which, however, originates from

▲ 1980 *Smerinthus ocellata*
Eyed Hawk-moth

▲ 1981 *Laothoe populi*
Poplar Hawk-moth

▲ 1982 *Hemaris tityus*
Narrow-bordered Bee Hawk-moth

▲ 1983 *Hemaris fuciformis*
Broad-bordered Bee Hawk-moth

▲ 1984 *Macroglossum stellatarum*
Hummingbird Hawk-moth

▲ 1985 *Daphnis nerii*
Oleander Hawk-moth

southern Europe or perhaps north Africa. In 1949, it occurred in numbers which have been reached neither before nor since (Goater, 1974). Recent records are given below.

■ vc10 nr Shalfleet, 28.5.92 (Waring, 1992); Binstead, 14.6.96; Chale, 13.8.96, one in a conservatory belonging to Mr and Mrs Foss (BJW).

■ vc11 Boscombe, 2.6.92, one found dead by M.M. Brooks; East End, nr Lymington, 10.8.92 by D. Reas, Titchfield Haven LNR, 16.9.92 by A.F. Silcocks (Skinner, 1996); Brockenhurst, 6.4.85, 13.5.92 (JEC); Warsash, 6.6.96 (PMP); Havant, 10.4.85 (CBC).

1991 *Deilephila elpenor* (Linnaeus, 1758)
Elephant Hawk-moth
Widely distributed and often common in all three vice-counties. The larva is found chiefly on rosebay *Chamerion angustifolium* and willowherbs *Epilobium* spp.

1992 *Deilephila porcellus* (Linnaeus, 1758)
Small Elephant Hawk-moth
Much of the chalk downland that was a favoured habitat of this species has been lost; the moth is still present on that which survives, and also on coastal shingle and sandhills. Occasional elsewhere. The larva occurs mainly on ladies' bedstraw *Galium verum*.

1993 *Hippotion celerio* (Linnaeus, 1758)
Silver-striped Hawk-moth
A very scarce migrant. Recent records are given below.
■ vc10 Bonchurch, 16.8.94 (J. Halsey, *comm.* SAK-J); Wootton, 17.10.95 by G. Morey (Knill-Jones, 1997a).
■ vc11 Fordingbridge, 15.6.96 (NHu).

Notodontidae (22)

1995 *Cerura vinula* (Linnaeus, 1758)
Puss Moth
This species is widespread in the area, but is usually seen in very small numbers. Sometimes, however, small groups of larvae are discovered on small sallows *Salix* spp. and poplars *Populus* spp.
■ vc10 Ventnor, 3.9.99, one seen by J. Halsey (Knill-Jones, 2000). A very late date, and probably an example of a second brood.

1996 *Furcula bicuspis* (Borkhausen, 1790)
Alder Kitten
There remains but one confirmed Hampshire record, from New Milton, S Hants, in 1945 (Goater, 1974).

1997 *Furcula furcula* (Clerck, 1759)
Sallow Kitten
Widespread and moderately common in all three vice-counties

1998 *Furcula bifida* (Brahm, 1787)
Poplar Kitten
Rather rare and local, and all post-1992 records are detailed below.

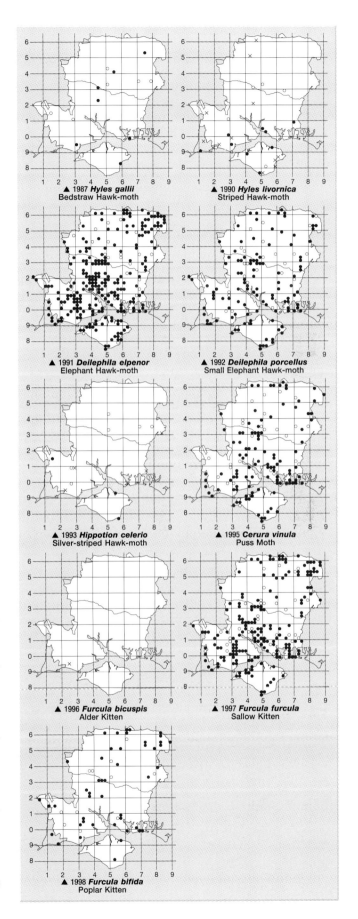

▲ 1987 *Hyles gallii*
Bedstraw Hawk-moth

▲ 1990 *Hyles livornica*
Striped Hawk-moth

▲ 1991 *Deilephila elpenor*
Elephant Hawk-moth

▲ 1992 *Deilephila porcellus*
Small Elephant Hawk-moth

▲ 1993 *Hippotion celerio*
Silver-striped Hawk-moth

▲ 1995 *Cerura vinula*
Puss Moth

▲ 1996 *Furcula bicuspis*
Alder Kitten

▲ 1997 *Furcula furcula*
Sallow Kitten

▲ 1998 *Furcula bifida*
Poplar Kitten

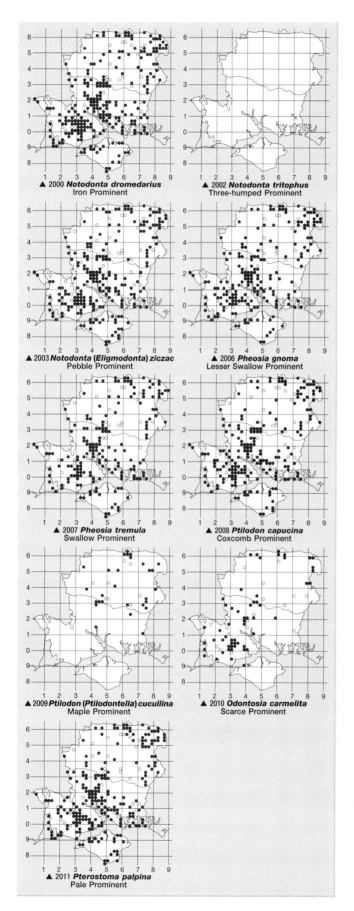

▲ 2000 *Notodonta dromedarius*
Iron Prominent

▲ 2002 *Notodonta tritophus*
Three-humped Prominent

▲ 2003 *Notodonta (Eligmodonta) ziczac*
Pebble Prominent

▲ 2006 *Pheosia gnoma*
Lesser Swallow Prominent

▲ 2007 *Pheosia tremula*
Swallow Prominent

▲ 2008 *Ptilodon capucina*
Coxcomb Prominent

▲ 2009 *Ptilodon (Ptilodontella) cucullina*
Maple Prominent

▲ 2010 *Odontosia carmelita*
Scarce Prominent

▲ 2011 *Pterostoma palpina*
Pale Prominent

■ vc11 Fordingbridge, 27.6.96 (NHu); Beaulieu, 3–5 each year (BI-J); Woodley, Romsey, 23.5.93, 6.6.95 (NB); Timsbury, 1994 (DT); Chandlers Ford, 6.5.95, one at light (BG); Allbrook, 13.6.96 (ML).

■ vc12 Crawley, 3.8.99 (RAB); East Stratton, fairly common (BI-J); Fugelmere Marsh, Fleet Pond NR, 17.6.94 conf. BG (PAB); Pamber Heath, 6.6.95 (AS); Selborne, 10.5.94, 13.6.96, at m.v. light, conf. BG (AEA); lane near west bank of River Blackwater, larva 25.9.95, moth emerged 14.6.96 (RWP); Rye Common, 6.5.95; Yateley Common, four in 1991, 11.6.94, 2.5.97 (AMD).

2000 *Notodonta dromedarius* (Linnaeus, 1758)
Iron Prominent

Common in birch country in all three vice-counties.

2002 *Notodonta tritophus* ([Denis & Schiffermüller], 1775)
Three-humped Prominent

Three records of this extremely scarce immigrant species are given in Goater (1974); further information on one of these is given by Phillips (1998), who states that the specimen taken by Sperring in 1920 is in his possession and is labelled S Hants, July 1920, A.H. Sperring, with a note saying "captured at Couplain (sic., for Cowplain), Hants, 1920. Goater, quoting South (1961) gives May, 1920 as the date. All records are given below, including a fourth which has recently been brought to the authors' attention.

■ vc10 Freshwater, 19.8.56; Cranmore, 2.8.60 by J. Lobb (Proc. IoW N.H. & Arch. Soc. **V**, Pt 7 (1962), *comm.* SAK-J.

■ vc11 Havant, 20.5.20; Waterlooville, July 1920.

2003 *Notodonta (Eligmodonta) ziczac* (Linnaeus, 1758)
Pebble Prominent

Fairly common in all three vice-counties. The foodplants are sallows and willows.

2006 *Pheosia gnoma* (Fabricius, 1776)
Lesser Swallow Prominent

Common in all three vice-counties wherever birch occurs.

2007 *Pheosia tremula* (Clerck, 1759)
Swallow Prominent

Frequent in all three vice-counties. The foodplants are poplar species.

2008 *Ptilodon capucina* (Linnaeus, 1758)
Coxcomb Prominent

Locally common in woodland in all three vice-counties, but mainly in the west of S Hants. The larva feeds on the foliage of many deciduous trees and bushes, including alder, birch, hazel, oak and sallow.

2009 *Ptilodon (Ptilodontella) cucullina* ([Denis & Schiffermüller], 1775)
Maple Prominent

A scarce species, found mainly in N Hants, and unrecorded from the Isle of Wight. The larva feeds on field maple *Acer campestre*, mainly on rather young trees in and around woodland.

■ vc11 West Wood, Sparsholt, 17.7.96 (JWP); Bramdean Common, 9.7.91, one at m.v. light (PAB); Portswood, 3.6.97, one at m.v. light (A and CD); Havant Thicket, one at m.v. light, 23.6.98 (IRT); Chappetts Copse, 1.7.00 (PAB, TJN).

■ vc12 South Wonston, 1993–96, annually (PJSS); East Stratton, 13.7.88, 28.8.89, six in 1992 (BI-J); Pamber Forest, 4.7.93 (GJD); Noar Hill NR, six in July 1995 (AMJ); Rye Common, 26.7.96, 3.7 and 6.7.00, a total of six seen (AMD); Frith End, 14.6.97, 6.6.98 (KBW); Fleet, 28.6.01 (MAS, WJS).

2010 *Odontosia carmelita* (Esper, 1799)
Scarce Prominent

Widespread but local and rather uncommon in birch country, mainly in the western half of S Hants.

■ vc10 Cranmore, 22.4.93, three at m.v. light (Knill-Jones, 1993b). **New vc record.**

■ vc12 Harewood Forest, 26.4.96, common (RAB); South Wonston, 18.4.97, one at m.v. light (PJSS); Pamber Heath, 14.4.95, one (AS); Bentley Station Meadow, 5.5.95 (PAB); Yateley Common, occasional (AMD).

2011 *Pterostoma palpina* (Clerck, 1759)
Pale Prominent
Widespread and fairly common in all three vice-counties. The larval foodplants are willows *Salix* spp.

2013 *Ptilophora plumigera* ([Denis & Schiffermüller], 1775)
Plumed Prominent   Notable/Na
This species was last reported in Hampshire on 10.11.84, from Crawley, vc12 (Goater, 1992), but it flies very late in the season and requires special search. It is considered likely to persist on the chalk in the Alton area, and perhaps elsewhere, in the vicinity of mature field maple *Acer campestre*.

2014 *Drymonia dodonaea* ([Denis & Schiffermüller], 1775)
Marbled Brown
Locally common in woodland in all three vice-counties, but evidently decreased since the 1950s. It is most frequent in the New Forest and north-east Hampshire.

■ vc10 Cranmore, 12.5.93 (SAK-J).

■ vc11 Chandlers Ford, 24.5.93, the only recent record; it was common on this exact site in the 1950s (BG).

■ vc12 Crawley, first record 4.5.95, two more later in same year (RAB).

2015 *Drymonia ruficornis* (Hufnagel, 1766)
Lunar Marbled Brown
Widespread and common in all three vice-counties. This is the first notodontid on the wing in springtime. The larva feeds on oak.

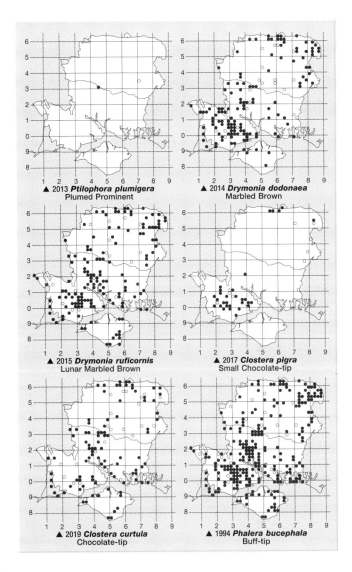

▲ 2013 *Ptilophora plumigera*
Plumed Prominent

▲ 2014 *Drymonia dodonaea*
Marbled Brown

▲ 2015 *Drymonia ruficornis*
Lunar Marbled Brown

▲ 2017 *Clostera pigra*
Small Chocolate-tip

▲ 2019 *Clostera curtula*
Chocolate-tip

▲ 1994 *Phalera bucephala*
Buff-tip

2017 *Clostera pigra* (Hufnagel, 1766)
Small Chocolate-tip   Notable/Nb
Known mainly from boggy areas in the New Forest in S Hants, but also in the north-east of N Hants, in similar habitat. In both areas, the larva is associated with creeping willow *Salix repens*, but elsewhere it has been found on other *Salix* spp. Unrecorded from the Isle of Wight.

■ vc12 Pamber, 23.7.95, female at light (GRD).

2019 *Clostera curtula* (Linnaeus, 1758)
Chocolate-tip

Widespread but uncommon, in all three vice-counties.

■ vc10 Binstead, five in 1995, including second brood specimens for the first time (BJW).

1994 *Phalera bucephala* (Linnaeus, 1758)
Buff-tip
Widespread and common in all three vice-counties.

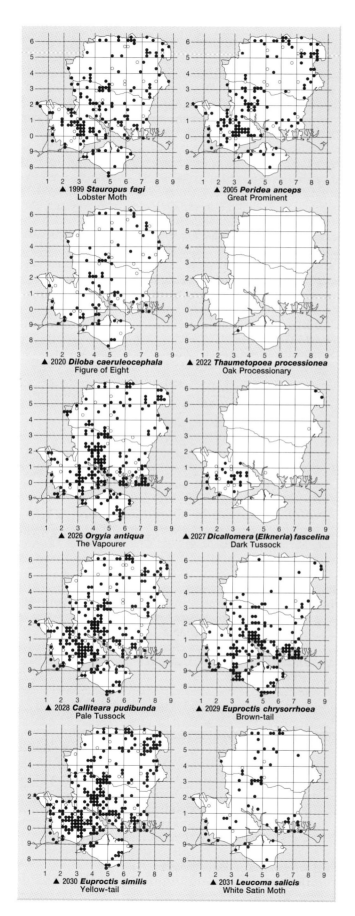

▲ 1999 *Stauropus fagi*
Lobster Moth

▲ 2005 *Peridea anceps*
Great Prominent

▲ 2020 *Diloba caeruleocephala*
Figure of Eight

▲ 2022 *Thaumetopoea processionea*
Oak Processionary

▲ 2026 *Orgyia antiqua*
The Vapourer

▲ 2027 *Dicallomera (Elkneria) fascelina*
Dark Tussock

▲ 2028 *Calliteara pudibunda*
Pale Tussock

▲ 2029 *Euproctis chrysorrhoea*
Brown-tail

▲ 2030 *Euproctis similis*
Yellow-tail

▲ 2031 *Leucoma salicis*
White Satin Moth

1999 *Stauropus fagi* (Linnaeus, 1758)
Lobster Moth

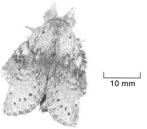

`|———|` 10 mm

Widespread and fairly common to common in beech woodland, and less often, amongst oak or birch in all three vice-counties, but especially in the New Forest.
■ vc10 Freshwater, 14.6.95, one f. *obscura* (SAK-J).

2005 *Peridea anceps* (Goeze, 1781)
Great Prominent
Locally common in oak woodland in all three vice-counties, but especially in the New Forest.

2020 *Diloba caeruleocephala* (Linnaeus, 1758)
Figure of Eight
Fairly common to common in all three vice-counties.

Thaumetopoeidae (1)

2022 *Thaumetopoea processionea* (Linnaeus, 1758)
Oak Processionary
All of the previous dozen or so records of this species (all males), since the first in 1983, were caught within the first three weeks of August. It is expanding its range on the continent and is resident on the Channel Islands.
■ vc10 Freshwater, 1.9 and 6.9.98, single males at m.v. light (SAK-J). **New county record.**

Lymantriidae (8 + 1†)

2025 *Orgyia recens* (Hübner, 1819)
Scarce Vapourer   **RDB3**
The last known locality for this species in Hampshire was Pamber Forest, and the last record was of two larvae found on 9.7.1944 (Goater, 1974).

2026 *Orgyia antiqua* (Linnaeus, 1758)
The Vapourer

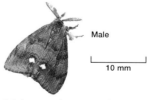

Male

`|———|` 10 mm

Male moths are often seen flying by day in August–September in all three vice-counties. Occasionally they come to light. The densest populations appear to be in S Hants and on the Isle of Wight.

2027 *Dicallomera (Elkneria) fascelina* (Linnaeus, 1758)
Dark Tussock
Local on heaths in the New Forest and in north-east Hampshire. In the former locality, it has certainly increased, though it is reported less frequently nowadays form the north-east.
▪ vc12 Farnborough, 25.7.95, one at light (RWP).

2028 *Calliteara pudibunda* (Linnaeus, 1758)
Pale Tussock
Widespread and common in all three vice-counties.

2029 *Euproctis chrysorrhoea* (Linnaeus, 1758)
Brown-tail
Formerly confined to a few places on the coast, notably Hayling Island, the Brown-tail has since spread with explosive suddenness. Winter nests of larvae are abundant in places such as Farlington Marshes and elsewhere along the whole of the coastline of the Isle of Wight and S Hants, mainly on hawthorn, blackthorn and bramble, and the moth is extending its range inland.
▪ vc11 Chandlers Ford, first recorded 22.7.91, now regular (BG).

▪ vc12 Noar Hill, 11.7.94 (AMJ); Yateley Common, 2.7.93, one (AMD).

2030 *Euproctis similis* (Fuessly, 1775)
Yellow-tail
Common and widespread in all three vice-counties.

2031 *Leucoma salicis* (Linnaeus, 1758)
White Satin Moth
Recorded very occasionally in all three vice-counties. The larva feeds on species of sallow, willow and poplar.
▪ vc10 Binstead, 11.7.95, third record (BJW).
▪ vc11 Woodley, Romsey, 1.7.94 (NB); Kings Somborne, 17.7 and 31.7.97 (TJN); Allbrook, 9.7.96 (ML); Browndown, 15.8.96 (DSW); Cosham, 25.7.96, 12.7.97, 6.7.99, one on each date (TJJ).
▪ vc12 South Wonston, 23.7.96 (PJSS); East Stratton, 19.7 and 26.7.91 (BI-J); Pamber Heath, 9.7 and 21.7.95, singletons; Lord's Wood, Pamber, 9.7.95, three (AS).

2033 *Lymantria monacha* (Linnaeus, 1758)
Black Arches
Common in and near deciduous or mixed woodland in all three vice-counties. The larva feeds on oak.
▪ vc11 Southsea, 31.7 and 10.8.96, new records for garden (JRL).

2034 *Lymantria dispar* (Linnaeus, 1758)
Gypsy Moth
Males are reported very occasionally as migrants (Goater, 1974, 1992). Old records of females, apparently genuine, suggest the species was once resident in the county. The only post-1992 records are given below.
▪ vc10 Chale Green, 4.9.93, one at m.v. light (SRC).
▪ vc11 "New Forest", 5.8.94, one male by D. Young (Skinner and Parsons, 1998).

Arctiidae (28 + 2†)

2035 *Thumatha senex* (Hübner, 1808)
Round-winged Muslin Moth
Scattered colonies in bogs and marshes in all three vice-counties, wandering occasionally.
▪ vc10 Parkhurst Forest, 10.7.96, one (PJC, BJW).
▪ vc11 Woolston, 23.7.96, one at m.v. light, first record (ARC).

2036 *Setina irrorella* (Linnaeus, 1758)
Dew Moth   **Notable/Na**
The headquarters of this species in the area are on the cliff-tops at Freshwater, Isle of Wight, and there is also a good colony at Hurst Castle on the mainland. Elsewhere, occasional presumed strays have been taken at light.
▪ vc10 Chale Green, 20.6.94, two at m.v. light (SRC).
▪ vc11 Beaulieu, 5.7.94, male at m.v. light (BI-J).

2037 *Miltochrista miniata* (Forster, 1771)
Rosy Footman
Widespread and fairly common in deciduous woodland

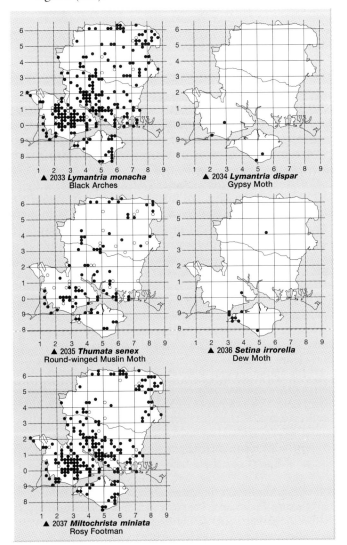

▲ 2033 *Lymantria monacha*
Black Arches

▲ 2034 *Lymantria dispar*
Gypsy Moth

▲ 2035 *Thumata senex*
Round-winged Muslin Moth

▲ 2036 *Setina irrorella*
Dew Moth

▲ 2037 *Miltochrista miniata*
Rosy Footman

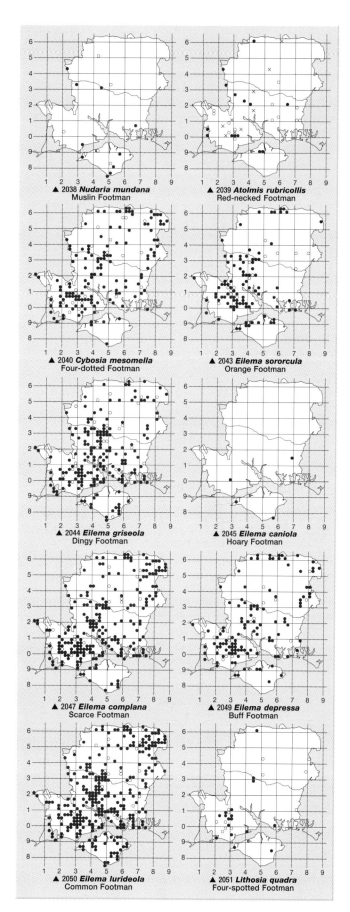

▲ 2038 *Nudaria mundana*
Muslin Footman

▲ 2039 *Atolmis rubricollis*
Red-necked Footman

▲ 2040 *Cybosia mesomella*
Four-dotted Footman

▲ 2043 *Eilema sororcula*
Orange Footman

▲ 2044 *Eilema griseola*
Dingy Footman

▲ 2045 *Eilema caniola*
Hoary Footman

▲ 2047 *Eilema complana*
Scarce Footman

▲ 2049 *Eilema depressa*
Buff Footman

▲ 2050 *Eilema lurideola*
Common Footman

▲ 2051 *Lithosia quadra*
Four-spotted Footman

in the Isle of Wight and S Hants, but mainly in the north-east of N Hants.

2038 *Nudaria mundana* (Linnaeus, 1761)
Muslin Footman

Very local and uncommon in the area. There are very scattered records from all three vice-counties.

■ vc10 St Catherine's Point, 30.7.95, one at m.v. light (SRC, PC).

2039 *Atolmis rubricollis* (Linnaeus, 1758)
Red-necked Footman

After a period of recession, this species appears to be making a come-back. All recent records are given below.
■ vc10 Parkhurst Forest, 25.6.96, one (PJC and BJW), several in July, 1996 (SAK-J).
■ vc11 Matchams, nr Ringwood, 12.7.83 (GL); Roydon Woods, 4.6 to 20.6.98, several at light (PAB); Frame Wood, 3.7.99, at m.v. light (DGG); Spearywell Wood, 19.6.98 (NB); Hilliers Arboretum, Ampfield, 20.6.98, five at m.v. light (TJN); Noads Copse, Winterslow, 23.8.97, one at m.v. light (BF).
■ vc12 Old Winchester Hill, 14.7.90, one (KW).

2040 *Cybosia mesomella* (Linnaeus, 1758)
Four-dotted Footman

Widespread but not particularly common, on damp heaths and in open woodland in all three vice-counties.

2041 *Pelosia muscerda* (Hufnagel, 1766)
Dotted Footman   **RDB3**

Ancient records from the New Forest are given in Goater (1974), but there has been no report of this moth in the county since 1891.

2043 *Eilema sororcula* (Hufnagel, 1766)
Orange Footman   **Notable/Nb**

Still fairly common to common in areas of oak woodland, mostly in the western half of S Hants and in the northern half of the Isle of Wight.

2044 *Eilema griseola* (Hübner, 1803)
Dingy Footman

Widespread in marshes and damp woodland in all three vice-counties.

2045 *Eilema caniola* (Hübner, 1808)
Hoary Footman   **Notable/Nb and Migrant**

■ vc10 Freshwater, 20.8.92, one at m.v. light (Knill-Jones, 1993), and another on 11.8.96 (SAK-J); Bonchurch, 13.8.96 by J. Halsey (Knill-Jones, 1997d). **New county record.**
■ vc11 Brockenhurst, 19.10.97, one at m.v. light, specimen retained (JEC); Waterlooville, 3.7.99, conf. from photograph BG (RJM). **New vc record.**

2047 *Eilema complana* (Linnaeus, 1758)
Scarce Footman

Widespread and fairly common in all three vice-counties.

2049 *Eilema depressa* (Esper, 1787)
= *deplana* (Esper, 1787)
Buff Footman
Rather local and uncommon; scattered records from all three vice-counties, but mainly in the New Forest.

2050 *Eilema lurideola* (Zincken, 1817)
Common Footman

10 mm

Widespread and common in all three vice-counties.

2051 *Lithosia quadra* (Linnaeus, 1758)
Four-spotted Footman
This species is still probably resident at low density in the New Forest. Elsewhere it is an uncommon presumed immigrant.
■ vc10 Freshwater, 18.9.00, one at m.v. light, (SAK-J).
■ vc11 Bolderwood, 5.7.97, one at m.v. light (JEC, JS); Lyndhurst area, July 1998, a total of seven seen (RAB); Rowner, 18.9.00, one at m.v. light (LM).

2053 *Coscinia cribraria* (Linnaeus, 1758)
subsp. ***bivittata*** (South, 1900)
Speckled Footman   **RDB1**
Likely habitats in the New Forest, where it was last reported in 1960, have been sought without success. However, the moth still persists in Dorset and it is possible it may reappear in some of its old Hampshire haunts which have not been destroyed by development.
subsp. ***arenaria*** (Lempke, 1937)
This rare immigrant has occurred once in Hampshire, at Chandlers Ford vc11, on 2.6.1945 (Goater, 1974).

2054 *Utetheisa pulchella* (Linnaeus, 1758)
Crimson Speckled Footman
A very scarce immigrant. All records received are given in Goater (1974, 1992) and below.
■ vc11 Sandy Point, Hayling Island, 19.9.92 by I. Thirlwell (Skinner, 1996).

2056 *Parasemia plantaginis* (Linnaeus, 1758)
Wood Tiger
A species that has decreased dramatically through loss of habitat. It is still present on the remaining areas of unspoilt downland.
■ vc8 Martin Down, 12.6.96, one (A.and LB).
■ vc11 Broughton Down, 19.6.82; Old Winchester Hill, 19.6.84 (PAB).
■ vc12 Porton Down, 7.7.91 (PAB); Tidworth Park, 8.7.95, one; Perham Down, 2.6.95, two; Great Shoddesden, 22.5.95, two (GE); Perham Down, 13.7.96 (TJN); Stockbridge Down, 19.6.94 (AB).

2056a *Pericallia ricini* (Fabricius, 1775)
■ vc11 Totton, 31.7.92, one at m.v. light, possibly originated from Southampton docks (Jeffes, 1995). This

is an Oriental species, first described from India. **New to Britain.**

2057 *Arctia caja* (Linnaeus, 1758)
Garden Tiger
This species, formerly so common both as a moth and as the classic "woolly bear" larva, has become much less so in recent years. It is still present in all three vice-counties.
■ vc11 Chandlers Ford, 24.7.94, is the only recent record here (BG).

2058 *Arctia villica* (Linnaeus, 1758)
Cream-spot Tiger
More or less confined to the coasts of the Isle of Wight and S Hants, where it is locally fairly common.

2059 *Diacrisia sannio* (Linnaeus, 1758)
Clouded Buff
This species was once locally frequent on the dry chalk (Goater, 1974), but nowadays it is known only from the damp heaths of the New Forest and north-east Hampshire, and recorded from the Cranmore and Parkhurst areas of the Isle of Wight, with occasional wanderers elsewhere.

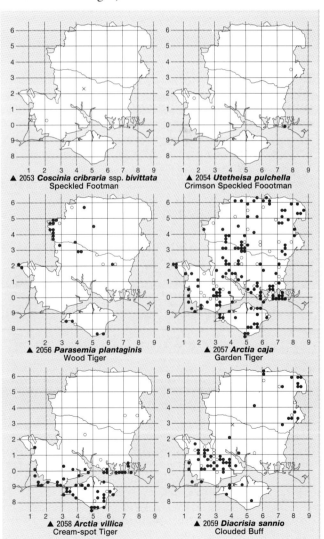

▲ 2053 *Coscinia cribraria* ssp. *bivittata*
Speckled Footman

▲ 2054 *Utetheisa pulchella*
Crimson Speckled Foootman

▲ 2056 *Parasemia plantaginis*
Wood Tiger

▲ 2057 *Arctia caja*
Garden Tiger

▲ 2058 *Arctia villica*
Cream-spot Tiger

▲ 2059 *Diacrisia sannio*
Clouded Buff

▪ vc10 Freshwater, 5.6.98 (SAK-J).

▪ vc11 Beaulieu, 23.6.95, male at m.v. light (BI-J); Woolston, 1993, one, 14.6.97, one at m.v. light (ARC).

▪ vc12 South Wonston, 26.8.99, one at m.v. light (PJSS); Pamber Heath, 20.6.95, one (AS); Conford, 21.6.95, one at m.v. light (JRL); Castle Bottom NNR, 23.6.95; Yateley Common, occasional (AMD).

2060 *Spilosoma lubricipeda* (Linnaeus, 1758)
White Ermine

Common and widespread in all three vice-counties.

2061 *Spilosoma luteum* (Hufnagel, 1766)
Buff Ermine

Common and widespread in all three vice-counties.

2062 *Spilosoma urticae* (Esper, 1789)
Water Ermine   **Notable/Nb**

Although always very local, in the past this species was not uncommon, especially in the valleys of the Avon and Stour. The last satisfactory records received are from Browndown 15.6.69 and Minstead 1976 (Goater, 1974, 1992).

2063 *Diaphora mendica* (Clerck, 1759)
Muslin Moth

Widespread in all three vice-counties. Males are sometimes fairly common at light and females are encountered occasionally making short daytime flights. There is evidence of a recent decline.

2064 *Phragmatobia fuliginosa* (Linnaeus, 1758)
Ruby Tiger

Widespread and sometimes common in all three vice-counties.

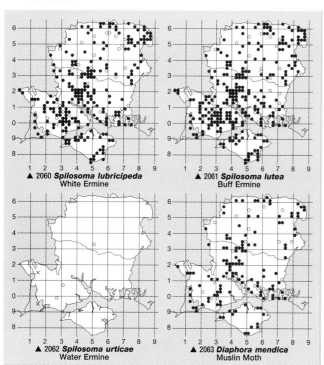

▲ 2060 *Spilosoma lubricipeda* White Ermine

▲ 2061 *Spilosoma lutea* Buff Ermine

▲ 2062 *Spilosoma urticae* Water Ermine

▲ 2063 *Diaphora mendica* Muslin Moth

2067 *Euplagia quadripunctaria* (Poda, 1761)
Jersey Tiger   **Notable/Nb**

This species has become established on the Isle of Wight during the 1990s, and is now locally frequent.

▪ vc10 Freshwater, 19.8.93, female at light; The Causeway, Freshwater, 21.8.93 by D. Wooldridge (Knill-Jones, 1994b); Freshwater, 16.8 and 30.8.95, two in August, 1996 (SAK-J); track below Nodes Beacon north of Tennyson Down, 13.8.00, one by day; Colwell, 1.8.00, one in garden (CDu); Farringford, 10.8.00, one by day (P. Jupp); Bonchurch, 13.8 and 20.8.94; over a dozen during August, 1996, and up to 20 a night during 2000 (J. Halsey, *comm.* SAK-J); Chale Green, 11.8.95, one f. *lutescens* (SRC).

▪ vc11 Pennington, 22.8.00, one at m.v. light (RC); Totton, 6.9.91, one at m.v. light (Jeffes, 1995).

2068 *Callimorpha dominula* (Linnaeus, 1758)
Scarlet Tiger

10 mm

This species is still common in the valleys of the Avon, Test and Itchen, and a report has been received of it abundance on the River Wey at Alton. Occasional wanderers are reported elsewhere, and are listed below.

▪ vc8 Martin Down, 11.7.97, one by day (MCH).

▪ vc11 Hengistbury Head, 14.7.94 (MJ); Brockenhurst, 29.6.92 (JEC); Beaulieu, 30.6.93 (BI-J); Totton, 30.6.92 (MJ); West Wood, Sparsholt, 17.7.96 (JWP); Chandlers Ford, 26.6.92 (BG); Portswood, 28.6.95 (A and CD); Woolston, 1.7.93 (ARC); Bridgemary, Gosport, 6.7 and 8.7.97 (DSW).

▪ vc12 South Wonston, 1.7.93, 14.7.95 (PJSS); East Stratton, 29.6.92 (BI-J); Alton, 1994–99, abundant along the River Wey (JD).

2069 *Tyria jacobaeae* (Linnaeus, 1758)
Cinnabar

Widespread and usually common, especially in the larval stage, on dunes, downs, open woodland and other places where the foodplant, ragwort *Senecio jacobaea* grows. The larva has also been found on Oxford ragwort *S. squalidus.*

Ctenuchidae (1)

2073a *Antichloris eriphia* (Fabricius, 1777)
▪ vc11 Winchester, January 2001, one found indoors resting on a fruit-bowl, evidently freshly emerged (M. Gibbons per TWa). Specimen in coll. BG. **New county record.**

Nolidae (4)

2075 *Meganola strigula* ([Denis & Schiffermüller], 1775)
Small Black Arches   **Notable/Na**

Moderately common in the large oakwoods – Parkhurst

Forest, the New Forest, Harewood and Pamber Forests; very occasional elsewhere.

■ vc10 Binstead, 11.7.96, one in garden, first record (BJW).

2076 *Meganola albula* ([Denis & Schiffermüller], 1775)
Kent Black Arches   **Notable/Nb**

Widespread but uncommon near the coasts of the Isle of Wight and S Hants, but still only four records from vc12 (Goater, 1974).

■ vc10 Chale Green, 25.7 and 30.7 and 1.8.94, 18.7.95 (SRC); Binstead, 5.7 and 9.7.98 (BJW).

■ vc11 Brockenhurst, five records, four in 1992; Frame Wood, 3.7.99, one (JEC); Beaulieu, occasional at m.v. light (BI-J); Woolston, 16.7.94, 17.7.97 (ARC); Botley Wood, 4.7.95, four at m.v. light (BG, JRL); Rowner, 31.7.99, one (LM); Gosport, 9.8 to 14.8.95, three at light (DSW); Cosham, 6.7 and 18.7.99, singletons at light (TJJ); Southsea, 28.7 and 3.8.96, at actinic trap (IRT); Leigh Park, Havant, 20.7.95, 22.7.96, 7.7 and 16.7.99, singles at light (CBC); Gutner Point, Hayling Island, 24.7.94, three; 16.8.96 (AMD); Sandy Point, Hayling Island, 27.7.87, over 20 at m.v. light (JMW); Havant, 8.7.97, one at m.v. light (CBC).

■ vc12 Selborne, 23.7.97, one at m.v. light, conf. BG (AEA). First recent record for the vice-county.

2077 *Nola cucullatella* (Linnaeus, 1758)
Short-cloaked Moth

10 mm

Still widespread and fairly common in all three vice-counties.

2078 *Nola confusalis* (Herrich-Schäffer, 1847)
Least Black Arches

Widespread and fairly common in oak woodland, though evidently less frequent than formerly.

■ vc10 Binstead, 7.5, 14.5 and 16.5.94, at m.v. light, first records (BJW).

■ vc11 Chandlers Ford, three recent records, 29.4.94, 7.6.97, 20.5.99 (BG); Woolston, 6.6.96, 1.5 and 6.6.97, singles at m.v. light, first record (ARC).

Noctuidae (312 + 5† + [3])

2080 *Euxoa obelisca* ([Denis & Schiffermüller], 1775)
Square-spot Dart   **Notable/Nb**

Probably still frequent on the chalk cliffs on the south side of the Isle of Wight, between The Needles and Ventnor.

2081 *Euxoa tritici* (Linnaeus, 1761)
White-line Dart

Chiefly on the sandy coasts of S Hants and the Isle of Wight, with a smaller, darker form frequent on the heaths of the New Forest and NE Hampshire. Rare elsewhere.

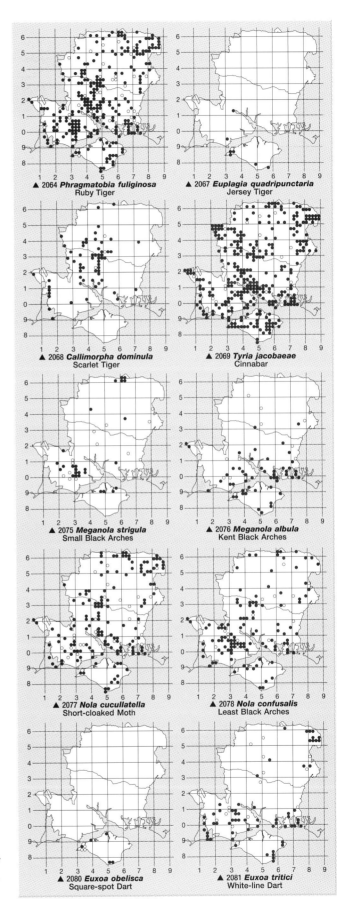

▲ 2064 *Phragmatobia fuliginosa*
Ruby Tiger

▲ 2067 *Euplagia quadripunctaria*
Jersey Tiger

▲ 2068 *Callimorpha dominula*
Scarlet Tiger

▲ 2069 *Tyria jacobaeae*
Cinnabar

▲ 2075 *Meganola strigula*
Small Black Arches

▲ 2076 *Meganola albula*
Kent Black Arches

▲ 2077 *Nola cucullatella*
Short-cloaked Moth

▲ 2078 *Nola confusalis*
Least Black Arches

▲ 2080 *Euxoa obelisca*
Square-spot Dart

▲ 2081 *Euxoa tritici*
White-line Dart

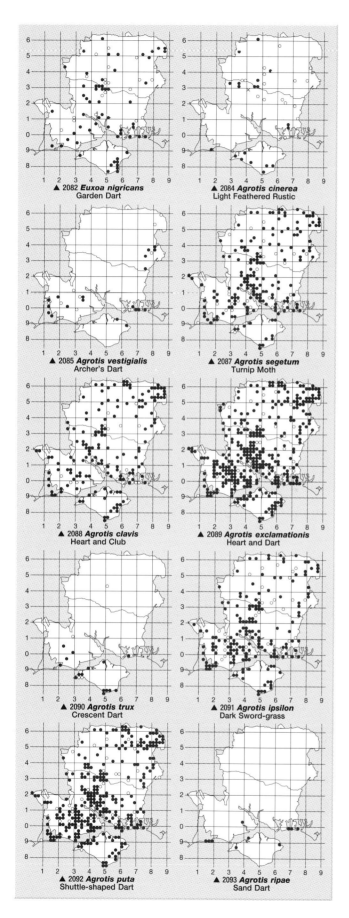

▲ 2082 *Euxoa nigricans*
Garden Dart

▲ 2084 *Agrotis cinerea*
Light Feathered Rustic

▲ 2085 *Agrotis vestigialis*
Archer's Dart

▲ 2087 *Agrotis segetum*
Turnip Moth

▲ 2088 *Agrotis clavis*
Heart and Club

▲ 2089 *Agrotis exclamationis*
Heart and Dart

▲ 2090 *Agrotis trux*
Crescent Dart

▲ 2091 *Agrotis ipsilon*
Dark Sword-grass

▲ 2092 *Agrotis puta*
Shuttle-shaped Dart

▲ 2093 *Agrotis ripae*
Sand Dart

vc11 Beaulieu, 5.8.95, one at m.v. light (BI-J); Totton, 30.7 and 10.8.90 (MJ, conf. BG); Woolston, occasional at m.v. light, 13 in 1997 from 29.7 (ARC).
vc12 Farnborough, 28.7.95, one at light (KW).

2082 *Euxoa nigricans* (Linnaeus, 1761)
Garden Dart
Scattered throughout, but there appears to have been a catastrophic decline in recent years.
vc11 Chandlers Ford, 9.8.91, not seen since though formerly common (BG); Woolston, occasional at m.v. light, max. 12 in 1992, seven in 1997 (ARC).

2084 *Agrotis cinerea* ([Denis & Schiffermüller], 1775)
Light Feathered Rustic   **Notable/Nb**
This species still occurs on the chalk downland of the Isle of Wight and along the borders of S and N Hants, and also on Portsdown Hill above Portsmouth, but is much less common than formerly.
vc10 Freshwater, 24.5.93; Afton Down, 6.6.96 (SAK-J).
vc11 Hengistbury, 16.5.00 (MJ); Broughton Down, 20.5.95 (NB); Kings Somborne, 8.6.96 and 26.5.97 (TJN).
vc12 Wildhern, nr Andover, 26.5.99, one at m.v. light (DGG); East Stratton, 31.5.87, 9.6.90, 2.6.92 (BI-J).

2085 *Agrotis vestigialis* (Hufnagel, 1766)
Archer's Dart

10 mm

Frequent on the sand dunes of Hayling Island, less so in other coastal localities; the dark form from the New Forest and NE Hampshire is seldom reported nowadays, and recent records are given below.
vc10 Binstead, 21.6.95, first record (BJW).
vc12 Selborne, 4.7.95, one at light, new record for locality (AEA); Frith End, 12.8.95, one at light (KW); Shortheath Common, 13.8.97, several; Broxhead Common, 18.8.97, one (AMD).

2087 *Agrotis segetum* ([Denis & Schiffermüller], 1775)
Turnip Moth
Found throughout, but less frequently than in the past; numbers are sometimes augmented by immigration.

2088 *Agrotis clavis* (Hufnagel, 1766)
Heart and Club
Fairly common to common in all three vice-counties, mainly on the coast and on the chalk.

2089 *Agrotis exclamationis* (Linnaeus, 1758)
Heart and Dart
This is usually one of the commonest moths during the summer months, throughout the area.

2090 *Agrotis trux* (Hübner, 1824)
Crescent Dart   **Notable/Nb**
Found mainly on the coasts of the Isle of Wight, where it is locally common. Very rare on the mainland, where it is evidently a vagrant. Mainland records are given in Goater (1974, 1992) and below.
■ vc11 Bashley, 11.9.93, male at m.v. light (RAC, conf. BG); Brockenhurst, 12.7.82 (JEC); Southsea, 14.8.00, one at m.v. light (JRL).

2091 *Agrotis ipsilon* (Hufnagel, 17 66)
Dark Sword-grass
One of the commonest immigrant species, abundant in certain years.

2092 *Agrotis puta* (Hübner, 1803)
Shuttle-shaped Dart
Widespread and common in the three vice-counties.

2093 *Agrotis ripae* (Hübner, 1823)
Sand Dart   **Notable/Nb**
Common on the dunes of Hayling Island vc11 and at Bembridge and St Helens vc10, less so at Hengistbury vc11. An occasional wanderer elsewhere.
■ vc10 Freshwater, The Causeway, 13.7.94 (DBW, *comm.* SAK-J).
■ vc11 Beaulieu, 13.7.95, one at m.v. light (BI-J).

2094 *Agrotis crassa* (Hübner, 1803)
Great Dart
So far, there are two records of this very rare immigrant, given below.
■ vc10 Freshwater, 12.8.96, one at m.v. light on the same night as a Pine Lappet (Knill-Jones, 1997d). **New vc record.**
■ vc11 Beaulieu, 5.8.96, male at m.v. light, now in coll. Nat. Hist. Mus., London (BI-J). **New county record.**

2097 *Actinotia polyodon* (Clerck, 1759)
Purple Cloud
There is but a single ancient record of this species in Hampshire, of one found in a spider's web at Ashford, some time before 1855 (Goater, 1974).

2098 *Axylia putris* (Linnaeus, 1761)
The Flame
Common in all three vice-counties.

2099 *Actebia praecox* (Linnaeus, 1758)
Portland Moth   **Notable/Nb**
This moth has been sought without success in its old haunt around Hengistbury Head, but has not been reported since 1929, when nine specimens and one larva were found there (Goater, 1974).

2101 *Ochropleura flammatra* ([Denis & Schiffermüller], 1775)
Black Collar
The ancient records given in Goater (1974) from the Isle of Wight, at Freshwater in 1859 and 1876, remain the only ones for the area.

2102 *Ochropleura plecta* (Linnaeus, 1761)
Flame Shoulder
Common in all three vice-counties.

2104 *Standfussiana lucernea* (Linnaeus, 1758)
Northern Rustic
This species is still recorded very occasionally on the Isle of Wight (Goater, 1992), and there are two very old undated records from Bassett and the Meon Valley in S Hants (Goater, 1974).

2105 *Rhyacia simulans* (Hufnagel, 1766)
Dotted Rustic
Very occasionally recorded when the species is doing well nationally. All records received are given in Goater (1974, 1992) and below.
■ vc10 Freshwater, 18.7.94 (SAK-J); Chale Green, 14.7.94 (SRC). (Knill-Jones, 1994f). **New vc record.**
■ vc11 St Ives, Ringwood, 12.9.87, at m.v. light (JHC); Brockenhurst, 13.8.85 (JEC); Fareham, 24.6.88 (RJD); Alverstoke, 3.9 and 8.9.88 (DSW); Sandy Point, Hayling Island, 14.7.95 (PRD), 14.8.98 (PS).
■ vc12 Old Burghclere Chalk Pit, 16.7.86, one at m.v.

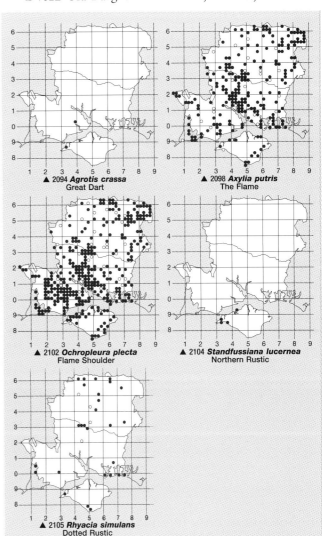

▲ 2094 *Agrotis crassa*
Great Dart

▲ 2098 *Axylia putris*
The Flame

▲ 2102 *Ochropleura plecta*
Flame Shoulder

▲ 2104 *Standfussiana lucernea*
Northern Rustic

▲ 2105 *Rhyacia simulans*
Dotted Rustic

light (GGE-F); Wheathold, 1981, one at m.v. light (PRB); Greywell, 3.10.86, one at light (PB); Ropley, 15.8.92 (PAB); Selborne, 1.9.93, 25.9.94 (AEA).

2107 *Noctua pronuba* Linnaeus, 1758
Large Yellow Underwing
Very common in all three vice-counties.

2108 *Noctua orbona* (Hufnagel, 1766)
Lunar Yellow Underwing   **Notable/Na**
This species has become extremely local nationally, and

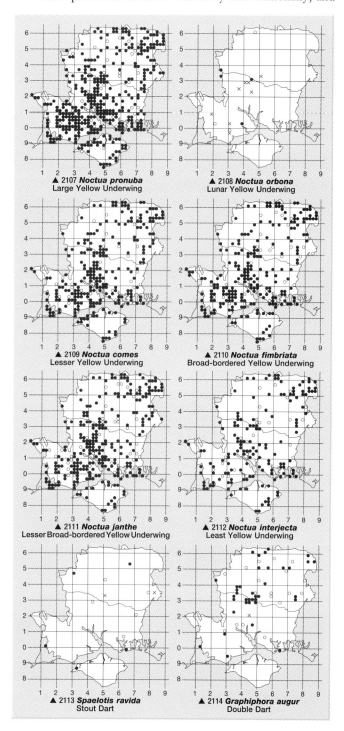

▲ 2107 *Noctua pronuba*
Large Yellow Underwing

▲ 2108 *Noctua orbona*
Lunar Yellow Underwing

▲ 2109 *Noctua comes*
Lesser Yellow Underwing

▲ 2110 *Noctua fimbriata*
Broad-bordered Yellow Underwing

▲ 2111 *Noctua janthe*
Lesser Broad-bordered Yellow Underwing

▲ 2112 *Noctua interjecta*
Least Yellow Underwing

▲ 2113 *Spaelotis ravida*
Stout Dart

▲ 2114 *Graphiphora augur*
Double Dart

the strong colony at Porton Down, on the Wiltshire/Hampshire border is therefore of great importance. The only records received since those given in Goater (1974, 1992) are given below.

■ vc11 Beaulieu, 6.8.96 (BI-J). Identity confirmed by recorder, but specimen not retained.

■ vc12 Porton Down, common (S. Miles, conf. BG, JRL); Isle of Wight Woods, Porton Down, two on 15.7.97 and 17 on 3.7.00 at m.v. light; Roche Court Down, Porton Down, 3.7.00, four to m.v. light (DGG); Crawley, 22.9.89 by R.A. Bell (Chalmers-Hunt and Bretherton, 1993).

2109 *Noctua comes* Hübner, 1813
Lesser Yellow Underwing
Common in all three vice-counties.

2110 *Noctua fimbriata* (Schreber, 1759)
Broad-bordered Yellow Underwing
Widely distributed and fairly common, especially in deciduous woodland.

2111 *Noctua janthe* (Borkhausen, 1792)
Lesser Broad-bordered Yellow Underwing
Common in all three vice-counties.

2111a *Noctua janthina* ([Denis & Schiffermüller], 1775)
■ vc11 Southsea, 9.7.01, male at m.v. light (JRL, conf. BG). **New to Britain.**

2112 *Noctua interjecta* Hübner, 1803
Least Yellow Underwing
Widespread but never very common.

2113 *Spaelotis ravida* ([Denis & Schiffermüller], 1775)
Stout Dart
Rare, and irregular in its appearance. All post-1980 records are given below. All older records received are given in Goater (1974, 1992).

■ vc10 Freshwater: the specimen recorded as *Graphiphora augur*, taken 20.8.86 (Goater, 1992), was in reality this species (comm. SAK-J). **New vc record.**

■ vc11 Matchams, nr Ringwood, 8.9.85 (GL); Southsea, 27.9.87 (JRL); Portsdown, 12.8.73 (KJW comm. RJD).

■ vc12 Weyhill, 26.7.82 (M. Jordan); Old Basing, 30.7 and 21.8.82 (PD).

2114 *Graphiphora augur* (Fabricius, 1775)
Double Dart
Widespread in the mainland vice-counties, but seldom common. It is found in open woodland and bushy places on and off the chalk, but has decreased considerably during the last decade.

■ vc10 The record for Freshwater, 20.8.86 in Goater (1992) refers to *S. ravida*, see above. There is one record for vc10, Alverstone, undated, but before 1937, given in Goater (1974).

■ vc11 Kings Somborne, 7.7.95, 20, 23.6 and 30.6.99, singles at light (TJN).

■ vc12 Wheathold and Ashford Hill Meadows, scarce

(PRB); Selborne, 10.7.95, one at light (AEA); Noar Hill NR, 14 between 4.7 and 20.7.95 (AMJ); Yateley Common, 21.7.94, one (AMD); Farnborough, 3.7.95, one at light (RWP).

2117 *Paradiarsia glareosa* (Esper, 1788)
Autumnal Rustic

Locally frequent in all three vice-counties, with occasional wanderers turning up away from established localities.
■ vc11 Totton, 25.9.90 (MJ); Woolston, 10.9 and 25.9.90 (ARC).
■ vc12 Crawley, 9.9.84, 26.8.85, 4.8.99 (RAB); Noar Hill, 27.8.94, 5.9.95 (AMJ); Yateley Common, common, e.g. 70 at m.v. light on 2.9.96 (AMD); Farnborough, 22.9.95, one at light (RWP).

2118 *Lycophotia porphyrea* ([Denis & Schiffermüller], 1775)
True Lover's Knot

Very common in heathy country and increasingly so in the vicinity of gardens where heathers are grown.

2119 *Peridroma saucia* (Hübner, 1808)
Pearly Underwing

A fairly common migrant.
■ vc10 Freshwater, 9.12.98, a very late date (SAK-J).

2120 *Diarsia mendica* (Fabricius, 1775)
Ingrailed Clay

Widespread and common in open, deciduous woodland in all three vice-counties.

2122 *Diarsia brunnea* ([Denis & Schiffermüller], 1775)
Purple Clay

Much less common than formerly; in the summer of 1892, for instance, at Brockenhurst it was stated to be a continual pest at sugar (Goater 1974). It occurs in deciduous woodland, and nowadays it is usually recorded as single specimens.

2123 *Diarsia rubi* (Vieweg, 1790)
Small Square-spot

This species is found in a wide variety of habitats (Goater, 1974) throughout the three vice-counties.

2126 *Xestia c-nigrum* (Linnaeus, 1758)
Setaceous Hebrew Character

A common species throughout the three vice-counties, especially in autumn when it may become extremely abundant.

2127 *Xestia ditrapezium* ([Denis & Schiffermüller], 1775)
Triple-spotted Clay

There are very few recent records; most of the old ones are from N Hants, from woodland on chalk.
■ vc12 Wildhern, nr Andover, 22.7.96, at actinic light (DGG).

2128 *Xestia triangulum* (Hufnagel, 1766)
Double Square-spot

Common throughout the three vice-counties.

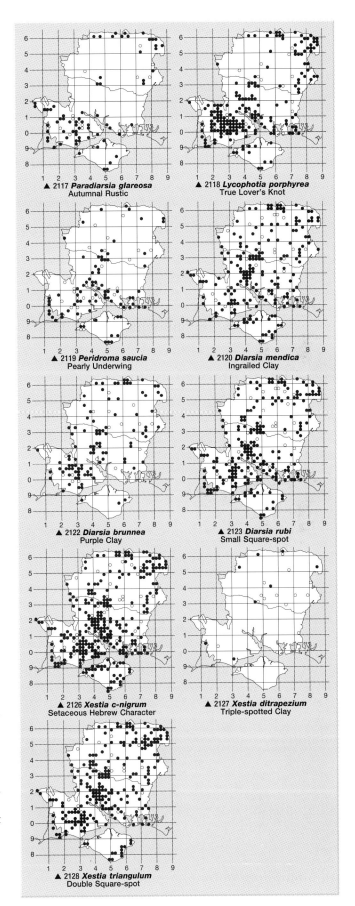

▲ 2117 *Paradiarsia glareosa*
Autumnal Rustic

▲ 2118 *Lycophotia porphyrea*
True Lover's Knot

▲ 2119 *Peridroma saucia*
Pearly Underwing

▲ 2120 *Diarsia mendica*
Ingrailed Clay

▲ 2122 *Diarsia brunnea*
Purple Clay

▲ 2123 *Diarsia rubi*
Small Square-spot

▲ 2126 *Xestia c-nigrum*
Setaceous Hebrew Character

▲ 2127 *Xestia ditrapezium*
Triple-spotted Clay

▲ 2128 *Xestia triangulum*
Double Square-spot

2130 *Xestia baja* ([Denis & Schiffermüller], 1775)
Dotted Clay
Local, and most frequent in heathy localities.

2131 *Xestia rhomboidea* (Esper, 1790)
Square-spotted Clay   **Notable/Nb**
There have been no records of this species in the area since 1968. In the past, it was stated to be locally fairly common, e.g. Brockenhurst, Farley Mount and Michelmersh vc11, Harewood Forest and Micheldever vc12 (Goater, 1974, 1992).
  ■ vc11 Hazelton Gardens, Horndean, 6.7.64, at m.v. light (M.E. Castle, Diary); Fassnidge (1923–24), gave "Horndean, not common".

2132 *Xestia castanea* (Esper, 1798)
Neglected Rustic
Common in heathy country in the mainland vice-counties, especially in the New Forest and NE Hampshire. Formerly common in acid oak woodland at Chandlers Ford. There have been no recent records from the Isle of Wight. The red form, not uncommon in NE Hampshire, does not seem to occur in the New Forest.

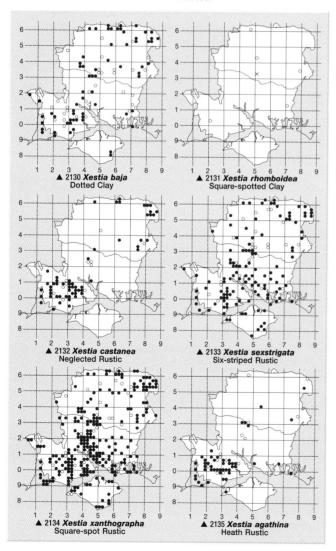

▲ 2130 *Xestia baja*
Dotted Clay

▲ 2131 *Xestia rhomboidea*
Square-spotted Clay

▲ 2132 *Xestia castanea*
Neglected Rustic

▲ 2133 *Xestia sexstrigata*
Six-striped Rustic

▲ 2134 *Xestia xanthographa*
Square-spot Rustic

▲ 2135 *Xestia agathina*
Heath Rustic

  ■ vc11 Woolston, 1.9 and 4.9.91 (ARC).
  ■ vc12 Selborne, 19.8.95, one of red form at light, new record for locality; 3.9 and 5.9.96, both of red form (AEA).

2133 *Xestia sexstrigata* (Haworth, 1809)
Six-striped Rustic
Locally common in two quite different types of terrain, namely low-lying damp ground such as water meadows and damp woodland on heavy soils, and on the dry chalk downs; less common on heaths (Goater, 1974). Insofar as these habitats survive, this observation remains true.

2134 *Xestia xanthographa* ([Denis & Schiffermüller], 1775)
Square-spot Rustic
A common species of grasslands and open woodland, but especially so among rank grasses on the chalk downs.

2135 *Xestia agathina* (Duponchel, 1827)
Heath Rustic
Locally common on heaths, especially in the New Forest; lost through habitat destruction in several places such as Hiltingbury Common vc11, and an occasional wanderer elsewhere; it appears to be, or to have become, very rare on the heaths of NE Hampshire: it was stated to be fairly common and variable at Whitehill (DW in Goater, 1974), but AMD (pers. comm.) says that he has never encountered it on the heaths he works.
  ■ vc10 Freshwater, 15.9.94, 13.9 and 16.9.96 (SAK-J).
  ■ vc11 Winchester, 12.9.98, one at m.v. light (TWa); Warsash, 24.8.96 (PMP).
  ■ vc12 East Stratton, 12.9, 13.9 and 17.9.92, singletons at m.v. light (BI-J); Selborne, 22.9.98, at m.v. light (AEA).

2136 *Naenia typica* (Linnaeus, 1758)
The Gothic
Rather an uncommon species, but the moth does not come readily to light and is probably overlooked to some extent. Most recent records have been of single specimens at light or at flowers such as *Buddleia*.

2137 *Eurois occulta* (Linnaeus, 1758)
Great Brocade   **Notable/Na or Migrant**
A scarce migrant, recorded from time to time in all three vice-counties. All records are given in Goater (1974, 1992) and below.
  ■ vc10 Whitwell, 20.8.96 by S. Colenutt (Knill-Jones, 1997d). This is apparently the first Isle of Wight record since 1857 (see Goater, 1974).
  ■ vc11 Cosham, 2.9.96, one at m.v. light, conf. JRL (TJJ).
  ■ vc12 Cholderton, 27.7.84 (HE); Crawley, 15.8.83, one at m.v. light in garden (RAB); Bentley, 7.8.96, one at m.v. light. (MC).

2138 *Anaplectoides prasina* ([Denis & Schiffermüller], 1775)
Green Arches
Found in deciduous woodland in all three vice-counties.

It was a common woodland species up to about 1930 (Goater, 1974) but seldom so today.

2139 *Cerastis rubricosa* ([Denis & Schiffermüller], 1775)
Red Chestnut

Widespread but seldom common. In the author's experience, it has decreased considerably.

■ vc11 Chandlers Ford, 10.4.92, 5.4.96 are the only recent records from this locality (BG); Woolston, 27.4.95, first record for garden (ARC).

2140 *Cerastis leucographa* ([Denis & Schiffermüller], 1775)
White-marked   **Notable/Nb**

Very local. Nearly all records are from N Hants, where it is found in widely scattered localities, and those given for S Hants from Winchester, 1980 and East Meon, 1974, two (Goater, 1992) are exceptional.

■ vc12 Bramley Frith Wood, 22.3.98, one at m.v. light (AHD); Selborne, several each year, eight in 1995 and 1996 (AEA); Noar Hill, 18.4.93 (AMJ); Frith End, 29.4.95, one at light (KW); Rye Common, 15.4.96, two (AMD).

2142 *Anarta myrtilli* (Linnaeus, 1761)
Beautiful Yellow Underwing

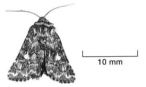

10 mm

Common on heathland, mainly in the New Forest and in NE Hampshire. The moth is usually diurnal, but is recorded occasionally at light.

■ vc11 Bitterne, 22.7.94, one at m.v. light in garden; Netley Common, 9.9.89, one larva; Netley Hill, 2.8.86 (PAB).

■ vc12 Pamber Heath, 10.7.95, one (AS); Farnborough, 17.8.95, one at light (RWP).

2145 *Discestra trifolii* (Hufnagel, 1766)
The Nutmeg

Widespread in the three vice-counties, often in the vicinity of allotments and gardens, but less common than in the 1960s and 1970s.

2147 *Hada plebeja* (Linnaeus, 1761) (= *nana* (Hufnagel, 1766))
The Shears

Recorded in many places in the three vice-counties, but most common on the chalk and along the coast.

2148 *Polia bombycina* (Hufnagel, 1766)
Pale Shining Brown   **Notable/Nb**

Once locally common (Goater, 1974), this species has virtually disappeared from the county, and we have received no record since 1990. The ecology is little understood and, alarmingly, recent attempts to find the species on Porton Down where it was once common, and where the habitat appears to be unchanged, have proved negative. The records given in Goater (1992) are repeated below, together with three additional ones.

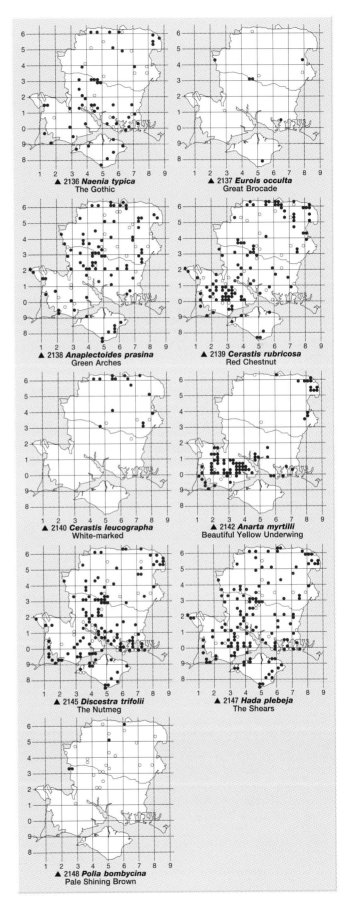

▲ 2136 *Naenia typica*
The Gothic

▲ 2137 *Eurois occulta*
Great Brocade

▲ 2138 *Anaplectoides prasina*
Green Arches

▲ 2139 *Cerastis rubricosa*
Red Chestnut

▲ 2140 *Cerastis leucographa*
White-marked

▲ 2142 *Anarta myrtilli*
Beautiful Yellow Underwing

▲ 2145 *Discestra trifolii*
The Nutmeg

▲ 2147 *Hada plebeja*
The Shears

▲ 2148 *Polia bombycina*
Pale Shining Brown

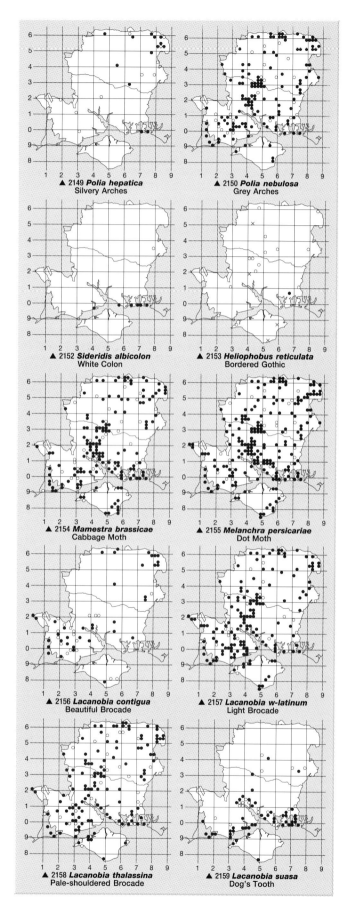

▲ 2149 *Polia hepatica*
Silvery Arches

▲ 2150 *Polia nebulosa*
Grey Arches

▲ 2152 *Sideridis albicolon*
White Colon

▲ 2153 *Heliophobus reticulata*
Bordered Gothic

▲ 2154 *Mamestra brassicae*
Cabbage Moth

▲ 2155 *Melanchra persicariae*
Dot Moth

▲ 2156 *Lacanobia contigua*
Beautiful Brocade

▲ 2157 *Lacanobia w-latinum*
Light Brocade

▲ 2158 *Lacanobia thalassina*
Pale-shouldered Brocade

▲ 2159 *Lacanobia suasa*
Dog's Tooth

■ vc11 Noad's Copse, 12.6.90 (BF); Winchester, 4.7.75, 26.6.76 (DHS); Upham, 2.7.75, two at m.v. light (DWHF).
■ vc12 Cholderton, 23.9.79, last record from this site (HE); Leckford, 30.6.74 (WRLG); Crawley, a few, but not since 1976 (RAB); Overton, 1981, 12 at m.v. light (AHD); East Stratton, 1.7.71, only record (BI-J); Tadley, 30.6.81, the only record (PRB); Lindford, one in 1970 and six in 1971 (JWOH).

2149 *Polia hepatica* (Clerck, 1759)
Silvery Arches   **Notable/Nb**

Local and uncommon in heathy areas, where the larvae can be found at night in spring, feeding on the opening buds of birch saplings growing amongst heather. This species seems to be maintaining itself fairly well in NE Hampshire, but to have disappeared from the New Forest, as well as from places in the centre of the county where the habitat has been destroyed.
■ vc11 Sandy Point, Hayling Island, 27.7.87, one at m.v. light (JMW).
■ vc12 East Stratton, 17.7.86, 28.6.87, 30.6.88, 14.6 and 27.6.92 (BI-J); Bramdean Common, 9.7.94 (PAB); Warren Heath, Bramshill, 26.6 to 1.7.83, total of 30 at m.v. light in four sessions (MAS); Eelmoor Marsh, 4.7.98, one at m.v. light (DGG); Castle Bottom NNR, 23.6.95, three at m.v. light, 16.6.96, one; Yateley Common, 14.6 and 17.6.93 (AMD).

2150 *Polia nebulosa* (Hufnagel, 1766)
Grey Arches

Still frequent in deciduous woodland in the three vice-counties.

2152 *Sideridis albicolon* (Hübner, 1813)
White Colon   **Notable/Nb**

Very local along the coast of S Hants, Hayling Island being the best-known locality. There has been no recent record of the small, dark form from the heaths of north-east Hampshire (Goater, 1974) although it is likely still to occur.

2153 *Heliophobus reticulata* (Goeze, 1781)
Bordered Gothic   **Notable/Na**

This species seems to have disappeared from Hampshire and from many other of its former localities as part of a massive national decline. All the old records are given in Goater (1974, 1992) and below, the most recent being from Widley, S Hants, in 1986, two specimens on separate dates.
■ vc12 Cholderton, 27.6.76 is the last sighting at this location (HE).

2154 *Mamestra brassicae* (Linnaeus, 1758)
Cabbage Moth

Regarded as common until recently, since when it has shown a considerable decline.

2155 *Melanchra persicariae* (Linnaeus, 1761)
Dot Moth

Widespread and common in all three vice-counties.

2156 *Lacanobia contigua* ([Denis & Schiffermüller], 1775)
Beautiful Brocade
Now found mainly on the birch heaths of the New Forest and NE Hampshire, where it has become rare; formerly more widespread.

▪ vc10 Chale Green, 22.6.93 (SRC, *comm.* SAK-J).

2157 *Lacanobia w-latinum* (Hufnagel, 1766)
Light Brocade
This species remains widespread and locally fairly common in all three vice-counties.

2158 *Lacanobia thalassina* (Hufnagel, 1766)
Pale-shouldered Brocade
Though still widespread in all three vice-counties, this insect has most certainly decreased recently.

2159 *Lacanobia suasa* ([Denis & Schiffermüller], 1775)
Dog's Tooth
Common on the coastal salterns of S Hants, but rare inland. It is local on the Isle of Wight, but there are few records from N Hants.

2160 *Lacanobia oleracea* (Linnaeus, 1758)
Bright-line Brown-eye
Widespread and common in all three vice-counties. The larva is often abundant on orache *Atriplex* spp., goosefoot *Chenopodium* spp. and redshank *Persicaria maculosa* on allotments and waste places near the sea.

2161 *Lacanobia blenna* (Hübner, 1824)
The Stranger
The three 19th century records from Freshwater vc10 given in Goater (1974) remain the only ones. There has been only one other British record, from Sussex in 1886.

2163 *Ceramica pisi* (Linnaeus, 1758)
Broom Moth
Most frequent in heathy places in the New Forest and NE Hampshire, occasional elsewhere.

2164 *Aetheria bicolorata* (Hufnagel, 1766)
Broad-barred White
Widespread and fairly common, especially on the coast and inland on the chalk.

2166 *Hadena rivularis* (Fabricius, 1775)
The Campion
Widely distributed in Hampshire and the Isle of Wight, but reported much less often than formerly. The larva appears to show a preference for the unripe seedheads of ragged-robin *Lychnis flos-cuculi*, which grows in damp water meadows.

▪ vc10 Freshwater, three at m.v. light during July and August, 1998 (SAK-J).

2167 *Hadena perplexa* ([Denis & Schiffermüller], 1775)
Tawny Shears
The larva of this species feeds on sea campion *Silene uniflora* on the coast and bladder campion *S. vulgaris* on the chalk

downs. The latter habitat has been largely destroyed and here the moth is much less common than formerly.

▪ vc10 Binstead, 16.7.94 (BJW, *comm.* SAK-J).

▪ vc11 Pennington, 21.7.95, one at light (RC); Beaulieu, 2.8.94, one at m.v. light (BI-J); Rownhams, 16.7.92 (KG); Woolston, 25.7.91 (ARC); Whitenap, Romsey, 5.7.95 (MJB).

▪ vc12 Selborne, 12.7.98, one at m.v. light, first record (AEA).

2169 *Hadena luteago* ([Denis & Schiffermüller], 1775)
subsp. ***barrettii*** Doubleday
Barrett's Marbled Coronet   **Notable/Na**
The single specimen taken at Freshwater in 1952 (Goater, 1974) is the only one known from the area.

2170 *Hadena compta* ([Denis & Schiffermüller], 1775)
Varied Coronet
The first appearance of this species in the county was in 1983 (Goater, 1983). Since then it has spread rapidly and is now recorded from all three vice-counties. It is essentially a garden moth, the larva feeding on the seeds of sweet-william *Dianthus barbatus*. Details of mainland

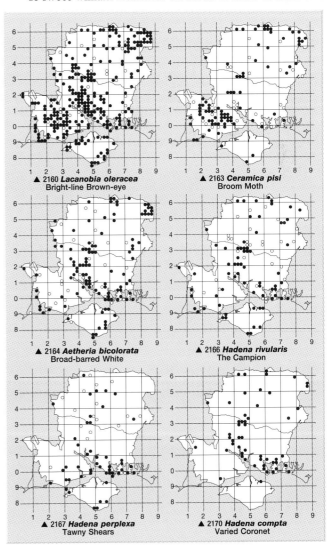

▲ 2160 *Lacanobia oleracea*
Bright-line Brown-eye

▲ 2163 *Ceramica pisi*
Broom Moth

▲ 2164 *Aetheria bicolorata*
Broad-barred White

▲ 2166 *Hadena rivularis*
The Campion

▲ 2167 *Hadena perplexa*
Tawny Shears

▲ 2170 *Hadena compta*
Varied Coronet

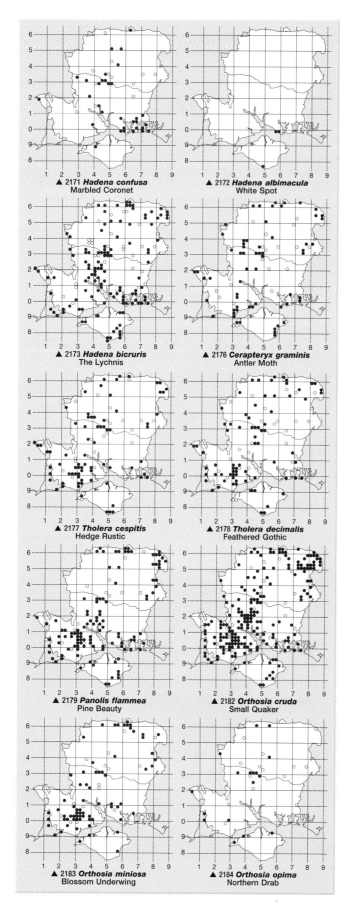

▲ 2171 *Hadena confusa*
Marbled Coronet

▲ 2172 *Hadena albimacula*
White Spot

▲ 2173 *Hadena bicruris*
The Lychnis

▲ 2176 *Cerapteryx graminis*
Antler Moth

▲ 2177 *Tholera cespitis*
Hedge Rustic

▲ 2178 *Tholera decimalis*
Feathered Gothic

▲ 2179 *Panolis flammea*
Pine Beauty

▲ 2182 *Orthosia cruda*
Small Quaker

▲ 2183 *Orthosia miniosa*
Blossom Underwing

▲ 2184 *Orthosia opima*
Northern Drab

records up to 1996 are given below, since when it has become too numerous to merit mention.

■ vc10 Binstead, 16.5.98, one at m.v. light (BJW). **New vc record.**

■ vc11 Highcliffe, 12.7.94 (RAC); Fordingbridge, 11.6.96 (NHu); Totton, 7.7.92 (MJ); Whitenap, Romsey, several in 1990, 25.6 and 29.6.95, 26.6.96 (MJB); Chandlers Ford, 7.7.91 (BG); Allbrook, 16.6 and 7.7.96 (ML); Bitterne, 4.7.95 (PAB); Rownhams, 2.6.94, 7.7.95 (KG); Portswood, 21.6.95 (A and CD); Woolston, 1990–1996, up to three each year (ARC); Botley Wood, 4.7.95, one at m.v. light (BG, JRL); Fareham, 30.6.93, one at m.v. light (RJD); Gosport, 27.6 and 9.7.96 (DSW); Widley, Portsdown, 10.6.90 (PMP); Portchester, 24.7.96 (PMP); Cosham, first recorded 15.6.94, now regular in small numbers (TJJ); Leigh Park, Havant, 29.6.87, 19.6.94, 20.7.95, 25.6 and 26.6.96, (CBC); Southsea, 18.6, 23.6 and 24.6.95, singletons at m.v. light (JRL), 24.6.96 (IRT); Hayling Island, 26.6.96 (PIVS), 29.6.96 (PD).

■ vc12 South Wonston, 24.6.93, 16.6.94, 28.5.95 (PJSS); East Stratton, 6.7 and 18.7.86, 3.7.87, 26.6.88, 6.7, 16.7, 26.7 and 27.7.91, 12.6.92 (BI-J); Whitchurch, 30.6.94 (DGG); Pamber Heath, three between 20.6 and 1.7.95 (AS); Selborne, 9.6.93, 17.6 to 29.6.94 (four), 1.7 to 20.7.94 (three), nine in 1995, 33 in 1996 (AEA); Farnborough, 29.6.94 (RWP); Frith End, 6.7.96 (KW).

2171 *Hadena confusa* (Hufnagel, 1766)
Marbled Coronet

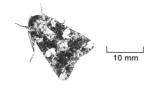

10 mm

Like that of *H. perplexa*, the larva of this species feeds on sea campion *Silene uniflora* on the coast and bladder campion *S. vulgaris* on the chalk downs. It has never been a common species in the three vice-counties.

■ vc11 Whitenap, Romsey, 29.6.93, identity confirmed (M. Baker); Kings Somborne, 24.6.95 (TJN); Woolston, 28.6.91 (ARC).

■ vc12 South Wonston, 1993–95, annually (PJSS).

2172 *Hadena albimacula* (Borkhausen, 1792)
White Spot   **RDB2**

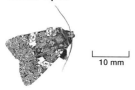

10 mm

Very local on shingle amongst the foodplant, Nottingham catchfly *Silene nutans* at Browndown. A recent record from the Isle of Wight suggests that it may also occur there, where *S. nutans* exists along a cliff-edge.

■ vc10 Chale Green, 24.5.93 (SRC, Knill-Jones, 1994c). **New vc record.**

■ vc11 Browndown, 29.6.85, one male, one female (S. Swift), 5.7.97, three at m.v. light (JRL,IRT, *et al.*).

2173 *Hadena bicruris* (Hufnagel, 1766)
The Lychnis
Widespread and common. Larvae can be found in the capsules of white campion *Silene latifolia* and red campion *S. dioica* in most places where these plants grow.

2176 *Cerapteryx graminis* (Linnaeus, 1758)
Antler Moth
Widespread but usually rather uncommon in grassy places in marshes and on heaths, chalk downs and commons. Some of its favoured habitat has been lost and many of the locations shown on the map refer to single specimens.
■ vc11 Totton, 19.8.91 (MJ).
■ vc12 Selborne, 18.8.95, one at light, first record (AEA).

2177 *Tholera cespitis* ([Denis & Schiffermüller], 1775)
Hedge Rustic
There are scattered records through the three vice-counties, but the moth is nowhere common in the area.

2178 *Tholera decimalis* (Poda, 1761)
Feathered Gothic
Scattered records through the three vice-counties, but considerably decreased. In the 1950s, it was quite abundant on the heaths and in some of the rides in the New Forest, coming freely to the light of a paraffin lantern; now it is seldom reported. The first evidence of decline, cited in Goater (1974) was that given by DWHF who stated that, prior to 1950, it was common in the Itchen Valley vc12, but had become scarce.
■ vc12 Wildhern, 23.9.00 (19) at m.v. light; 30.9.00 (four) (DGG).

2179 *Panolis flammea* ([Denis & Schiffermüller], 1775)
Pine Beauty
Widespread in and near pine woods, but not particularly common in the area.
■ vc11 Totton, 9.3.92 (MJ).

2182 *Orthosia cruda* ([Denis & Schiffermüller], 1775)
Small Quaker
Widespread and usually very common in all three vice-counties.

2183 *Orthosia miniosa* ([Denis & Schiffermüller], 1775)
Blossom Underwing
Scattered in all three vice-counties, and locally fairly common, as in parts of the New Forest. It is possible that some of these records relate to migrants rather than residents (Tunmore 1999).
■ vc11 Totton, 24.4.91 (MJ); Woolston, 30.3 and 31.3.91 (ARC).
■ vc12 Selborne, 6.4.95, one at light, first record (AEA).

2184 *Orthosia opima* (Hübner, 1809)
Northern Drab
Much less common than formerly. Records are scattered through the three vice-counties, but there are few recent

ones. At Freshwater, for example, it was reported as fairly common (Goater, 1974), but by 1992, SAK-J stated "no recent record" (Goater, 1992), and recorded it only once since, below.
■ vc10 Freshwater, 9.5.95; Cranmore, 8.4.95 (SAK-J); Binstead, 17.4 and 30.4.96, first records (BJW).
■ vc11 St Ives, Ringwood, 21.4.87, at m.v. light (JHC); Matchams, nr Ringwood, 21.5.85 (GL); Yew Hill, 8.5.88 (JEC).

2185 *Orthosia populeti* (Fabricius, 1775)
Lead-coloured Drab
Locally frequent in the vicinity of well-established aspen *Populus tremula*.

2186 *Orthosia gracilis* ([Denis & Schiffermüller], 1775)
Powdered Quaker
Widespread and fairly common in all three vice-counties. The New Forest is noteworthy for a "red" population which is very variable, the larva of which feeds on bog-myrtle *Myrica gale*. Little or no gene exchange appears to take place between these "red" populations and those nearby which are of the normal pale stone-colour.

2187 *Orthosia cerasi* (Fabricius, 1775)
Common Quaker
Widespread and usually very common in all three vice-counties.
■ vc10 Binstead, 13.12.98 (BJW).

2188 *Orthosia incerta* (Hufnagel, 1766)
Clouded Drab
Widespread and usually very common in all three vice-counties.

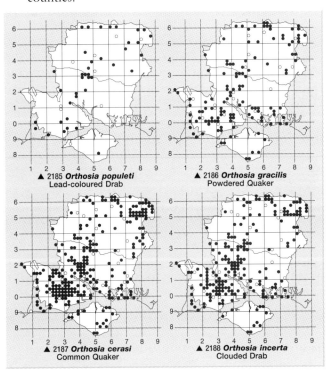

▲ 2185 *Orthosia populeti*
Lead-coloured Drab

▲ 2186 *Orthosia gracilis*
Powdered Quaker

▲ 2187 *Orthosia cerasi*
Common Quaker

▲ 2188 *Orthosia incerta*
Clouded Drab

2189 *Orthosia munda* ([Denis & Schiffermüller], 1775)
Twin-spotted Quaker
Widespread and fairly common in all three vice-counties.

2190 *Orthosia gothica* (Linnaeus, 1758)
Hebrew Character
Widespread and usually very common in all three vice-counties.

2191 *Mythimna turca* (Linnaeus, 1761)
Double Line   **Notable/Nb**
There have been no records of this species since one trapped at Emer Bog on 29.7.78 (Goater, 1992). Former strongholds were Havant Thicket vc11 and parts of Woolmer Forest vc12. It has long since gone from the New Forest. Reasons for its decline are not understood.

2192 *Mythimna conigera* ([Denis & Schiffermüller], 1775)
Brown-line Bright-eye
This is another species that has decreased considerably. The map shows many more pre-1980 records than more recent ones, and nowhere has it been reported as anything like common.

2193 *Mythimna ferrago* (Fabricius, 1787)
The Clay
Still widespread and fairly common to common in all three vice-counties.

2194 *Mythimna albipuncta* ([Denis & Schiffermüller], 1775)
White-point
A moderately frequent migrant species, recorded mainly on the Isle of Wight and near the coast in S Hants. At the time of writing, it seems to be at least temporarily established on the Isle of Wight and near the S Hants coast, perhaps since about 1990.
■ vc12 Crawley, 1.9.98, male at m.v. light (RAB); South Wonston, 31.8.99, one at m.v. light (PJSS); East Stratton, 15.8.92 (BI-J). The only previous records for N Hants are those given in Goater (1974).

2195 *Mythimna vitellina* (Hübner, 1808)
The Delicate
A moderately frequent migrant species, recorded mainly on the Isle of Wight and near the coast in S Hants. It was particularly common in 1992, when it was recorded in many places, including several in N Hants.

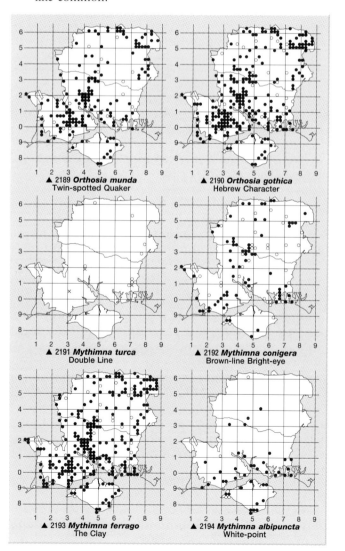

▲ 2189 *Orthosia munda*
Twin-spotted Quaker

▲ 2190 *Orthosia gothica*
Hebrew Character

▲ 2191 *Mythimna turca*
Double Line

▲ 2192 *Mythimna conigera*
Brown-line Bright-eye

▲ 2193 *Mythimna ferrago*
The Clay

▲ 2194 *Mythimna albipuncta*
White-point

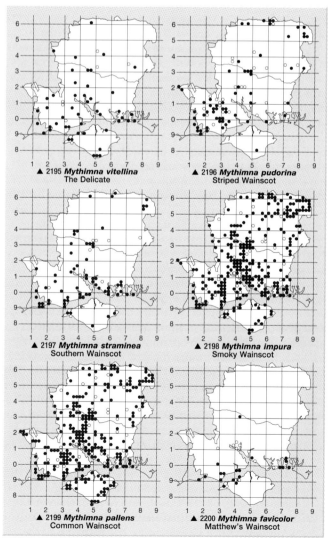

▲ 2195 *Mythimna vitellina*
The Delicate

▲ 2196 *Mythimna pudorina*
Striped Wainscot

▲ 2197 *Mythimna straminea*
Southern Wainscot

▲ 2198 *Mythimna impura*
Smoky Wainscot

▲ 2199 *Mythimna pallens*
Common Wainscot

▲ 2200 *Mythimna favicolor*
Matthew's Wainscot

2196 *Mythimna pudorina* ([Denis & Schiffermüller], 1775)
Striped Wainscot
Local in marshes and bogs and damp moorland in the mainland vice-counties.
■ vc10 Godshill, 12.7.94 by P. Cramp (Knill-Jones, 1995). **New vc record.**
■ vc12 Crawley, 27.6 to 6.7.74, four (RAB). This record was given incorrectly in Goater (1992) under *Simyra albovenosa* (comm. RAB).

2197 *Mythimna straminea* (Treitschke, 1825)
Southern Wainscot
Locally common in marshes and reed-beds in the mainland vice-counties.
■ vc10 Chale Green, 29.6 and 1.9.95, singles (SRC).
■ vc11 Chandlers Ford, 8.7.94 (BG).
■ vc12 Winnall Moors NR (DHS); Yateley Common, 26.7.93, one (AMD).

2198 *Mythimna impura* (Hübner, 1808)
Smoky Wainscot
Very common in grassy places in the mainland vice-counties.

2199 *Mythimna pallens* (Linnaeus, 1758)
Common Wainscot
Very common in grassy places in the mainland vice-counties.

2200 *Mythimna favicolor* (Barrett, 1896)
Matthew's Wainscot   **Notable/Na**
This species, if species it is, is more or less confined to coastal salterns where it replaces *M. pallens*. It is very occasionally reported inland.
■ vc11 Brockenhurst, two records (JEC, 1994).

2201 *Mythimna litoralis* (Curtis, 1827)
Shore Wainscot   **Notable/Nb**
Locally common on coastal sand-dunes, especially those in south Hayling Island.
■ vc11 Browndown, 5.7.97, one at m.v. light (JRL, IRT, *et al.*).

2202 *Mythimna l-album* (Linnaeus, 1767)
White L Wainscot   **Notable/Nb**
This erstwhile scarce migrant appears to be established, at least temporarily, on the Isle of Wight and in the Titchfield Haven area of S Hants. Recent records include the following.
■ vc10 Freshwater, The Causeway, 6.10.96, three, 9.10.96, two (DBW); Hacketts Land, 1km W of Branstone, 25.6.97 (PP); Binstead, 4.7.98, one at m.v. light (BJW).
■ vc11 Brockenhurst, 1.10.92 (JEC); Beaulieu, 9.7.00 (BI-J); Timsbury, 1994 (DT); Lower Test Marshes, 19.6, 22.6, 25.6 and 27.6.95 (JP); Woolston, 10.10.90, 1.10.96, 8.9 and 25.9.97 (ARC); Warsash, 7.7.96, 17.9, 22.9 and 25.9.96, ten between 15.10 and 21.10.96; Titchfield Haven, 20.9 to 27.9.94, eight at m.v. light (PMP); Brownwich cliffs, 10.7.96, two on

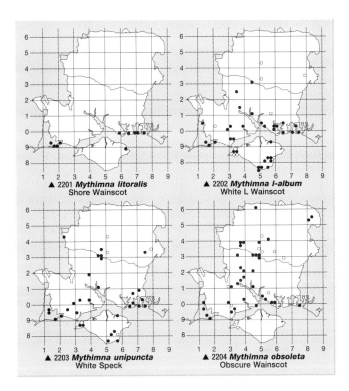

▲ 2201 *Mythimna litoralis*
Shore Wainscot

▲ 2202 *Mythimna l-album*
White L Wainscot

▲ 2203 *Mythimna unipuncta*
White Speck

▲ 2204 *Mythimna obsoleta*
Obscure Wainscot

honeydew, one on privet flowers (RJD); Fareham, 12.9.99, one at m.v. light (MLO); Rowner, 21.9.99, one at m.v. light (LM); Bedenham, Gosport, 18.9.97; Bridgemary, 15.9.97 (DSW); Cosham, 18.6.99, 11.9.99 (TJJ); Southsea, 13.9.99, one at m.v. light (IRT); Hayling Island, eight in August, 1995, five in September and one on 7.10.95 (PRD), 24 between 17.9 and 14.10.96 (PIVS); Sandy Point, Hayling Island, apparently well established: 9.10 and 12.10.78, 30.9.81, 14.7.82, 17.9.87 (JMW).
■ vc12 Crawley, 22.9.89, second record (RAB).

2203 *Mythimna unipuncta* (Haworth, 1809)
White Speck
In recent years, this hitherto very scarce migrant has been reported with increasing frequency on the Isle of Wight and in S Hants, but there are still very few records from N Hants, given in Goater (1974) and below.
■ vc10 Freshwater, 14.12.98, a very late date (SAK-J).
■ vc11 Winchester, 9.9.00, three at m.v. light (JCl); Hayling Island, 13.10 to 5.12.78, total of 95 at m.v. light (JMW), is an exceptionally large number.
■ vc12 South Wonston, 8.10.00, one at m.v. light (PJSS); Selborne, 22.8.96, 25.9.98, singles at m.v. light (AEA).

2204 *Mythimna obsoleta* (Hübner, 1803)
Obscure Wainscot
Local in reed-beds, only occasionally wandering from them. It appears to be present in all the large reed-beds in the area.
■ vc11 Brockenhurst, 22.6.89 (JEC); Kings Somborne, 22.6.92 (TJN); Woolston, 27.6.91 (ARC); Chandlers Ford, 4.6.97, only record (BG).

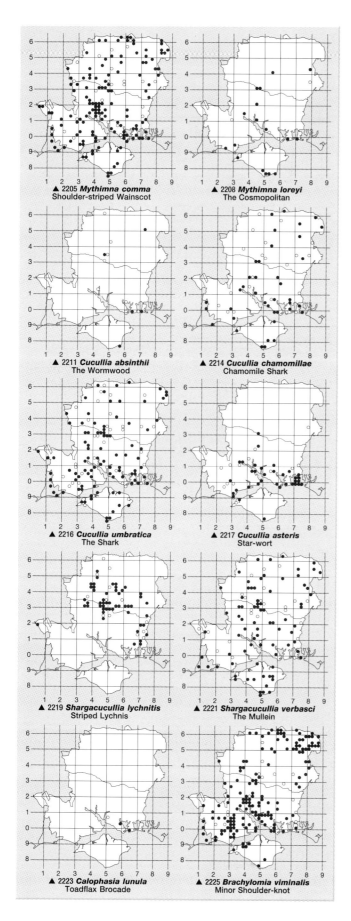

▲ 2205 *Mythimna comma*
Shoulder-striped Wainscot

▲ 2208 *Mythimna loreyi*
The Cosmopolitan

▲ 2211 *Cucullia absinthii*
The Wormwood

▲ 2214 *Cucullia chamomillae*
Chamomile Shark

▲ 2216 *Cucullia umbratica*
The Shark

▲ 2217 *Cucullia asteris*
Star-wort

▲ 2219 *Shargacucullia lychnitis*
Striped Lychnis

▲ 2221 *Shargacucullia verbasci*
The Mullein

▲ 2223 *Calophasia lunula*
Toadflax Brocade

▲ 2225 *Brachylomia viminalis*
Minor Shoulder-knot

2205 *Mythimna comma* (Linnaeus, 1761)
Shoulder-striped Wainscot
Widespread and moderately common in grassy places in the three vice-counties.

2206 *Mythimna putrescens* (Hübner, 1824)
Devonshire Wainscot   Notable/Na
The single record given in Goater (1974), Boscombe, 1901, remains the only one.

2208 *Mythimna loreyi* (Duponchel, 1827)
The Cosmopolitan
A very scarce migrant species which appeared in unusual numbers in 1992 and appears to be on the increase. It is thought that many of the late summer specimens that were seen in that year were locally bred (Skinner 1998). All known records are given in Goater (1974, 1992) and below.

■ vc10 Freshwater, 21.11.89, 28.10.95, 1.9.96 (SAK-J); St Lawrence, 12.9.92 (JHC); Bonchurch, 23.10.94 (J. Halsey, *comm.* SAK-J); Chale Green, 23.5 and 6.8.92 (SRC). The first record for vc10 was in 1988.

■ vc11 Highcliffe, 29.10.99, a pupa excavated from the cliff by Mrs A. Calway while fossil-hunting; the moth emerged on 3.11. 99, was set, and its identity confirmed by DGG (M. Calway, pers. comm.). This is the first wild pupa ever discovered in Britain. Lymington, 5.11.89 (AJP); Chandlers Ford, 6.8.92 (BG); Winchester, 27.8.92 (DHS); Woolston, 13.9.92 (ARC); Solent Court, 8.6.95 (PMP); Southsea, 10.9.92 (JRL); Hayling Island, 15.8.83, 10.7.86, singles at m.v. light (JMW).

■ vc12 East Stratton, 4.9.92 (BI-J); Bentley, 29.8.92 (MC).

2209 *Senta flammea* (Curtis, 1828)
Flame Wainscot   Notable/Na and Migrant
The only records of this suspected immigrant for the area are of the one taken at Titchfield Haven vc11 in 1948 (Goater, 1974) and at Shanklin vc10 in 1971 and 1975 (Goater, 1992).

2211 *Cucullia absinthii* (Linnaeus, 1761)
The Wormwood   Notable/Nb
The status of this species in Hampshire and the Isle of Wight remains uncertain. There are scattered records, mostly of single specimens, in all three vice-counties, but no direct evidence that it has ever bred in the area.

■ vc10 Bonchurch, 14.7.98 by J. Halsey (Knill-Jones, 1999b).

■ vc11 Portchester, (KJW, comm. RJD); Hayling Island, 7.8.79, 5.8.85, 16.8.88, singles at m.v. light (JMW).

■ vc12 South Wonston, 19.7.98 (PJSS); Greywell, 23.7.01, conf. AHD (PB).

2214 *Cucullia chamomillae* ([Denis & Schiffermüller], 1775)
Chamomile Shark
Thinly scattered through the three vice-counties, but scarcer than formerly, probably on account of changed agricultural techniques.

■ vc11 Chandlers Ford, 16.4.93, rare but regular in the 1950s (BG); Woolston, 7.5.97, one at m.v. light, second record (ARC).

2216 *Cucullia umbratica* (Linnaeus, 1758)
The Shark

This species is still fairly frequent in places, especially near the coast of S Hants.

■ vc11 Chandlers Ford, 28.6.92, the only recent record (BG); M3 works S of Winchester, 16 larvae seen in 1996 (RAB).

2217 *Cucullia asteris* ([Denis & Schiffermüller], 1775)
Star-wort   **Notable/Nb**

Larvae are reported from time to time on sea aster *Aster tripolium* in the salterns along the coast of S Hants, and the moth is occasionally taken at light or visiting flowers. In the past, larvae were also found abundantly on wild goldenrod *Solidago virgaurea* at Baddesley Great Covert and Botley Wood. There is still only one record from N Hants (Goater, 1992), from Whitehill in 1951.

■ vc11 Keyhaven, 25.8.84, larva on sea aster; Dibden Bay, 8.9.91, larva on sea aster (PAB); Lepe Country Park, 14.8.96, one at m.v. light (PMP); Hythe, larvae on *Aster tripolium*, 4.9 to 5.9.83, 8.9 to 25.9.84, 6.9.85, 15.9.88; specimens found at rest, 17.7.84, 12.7 and 17.7.88, 21.7.89 and 21.6.95, and visiting flowers in garden 13 to 31.7.90, 7.8.91 and 16.8.92 (IWS); Fareham, 20.7.90 (RJD); Gilkicker Point, 20.8.97, over 20 larvae on sea aster (DSW); N Hayling Island, 1.8.98 (PRD).

2218 *Cucullia gnaphalii* (Hübner, 1813)
The Cudweed

The larvae in Botley Wood in 1941 and 1943, the second of which was bred (Goater, 1974) are the only records of this species in the area.

2219 *Shargacucullia lychnitis* (Rambur, 1833)
Striped Lychnis   **Notable/Na**

Very locally frequent in an area on each side of the boundary between North and S Hants. The larva has been found only on dark mullein *Verbascum nigrum*, where it feeds on the flower spikes, especially where the plants are temporary colonists of disturbed ground such as roadsides. The moth comes to light very rarely.

■ vc11 Kings Somborne, 8.7.95, one at m.v. light (TJN).
■ vc12 Crawley, 6.7.95, 14.7.99, at m.v. light (RAB); Magdalen Hill Down, 30.6.95, one at light (PAB); South Wonston, 1993–95, annually (PJSS); Selborne, 11.7 and 12.7.95, singletons at light, new for locality (AEA).

2221 *Shargacucullia verbasci* (Linnaeus, 1758)
The Mullein

Larvae are seen frequently on mullein *Verbascum* spp, where they feed mainly on the leaves but sometimes on the flowers, and often appear shortly after the foodplant has temporarily colonised an area; also on figwort *Scrophularia nodosa* and occasionally on *Buddleia*. The moth comes to light very occasionally.

■ vc11 Chandlers Ford, 29.4.95, one at m.v. light (BG); Bitterne, 28.4.95, one at m.v. light (PAB); Fareham, 5.5.99, one at light (MLO).
■ vc12 Yateley Common, 21.5.92, one at m.v. light (AMD).

2223 *Calophasia lunula* (Hufnagel, 1766)
Toadflax Brocade   **RDB3**

This species is considered likely to become established on shingle along parts of the Hampshire coast. The larvae should be sought not only on yellow toadflax *Linaria vulgaris* but also on purple toadflax *L. purpurea* (M. Parsons, pers. comm.). All records are given below.

■ vc11 Locksheath, 13.5.71 (R. Hayward); Southsea, 11.8.92 (JRL); Gosport, 18.8.96, one at m.v. light, conf. JRL (DSW).

2225 *Brachylomia viminalis* (Fabricius, 1776)
Minor Shoulder-knot

Fairly common to common in damp places amongst sallow *Salix* spp. in all three vice-counties. The larvae are often common in spun shoots of the foodplant.

2226 *Leucochlaena oditis* (Hübner, 1822)
Beautiful Gothic   **RDB3**

Probably still frequent along the Freshwater cliffs on the Isle of Wight, although not sought recently. Occasionally, it strays a little way inland.

■ vc10 Freshwater, 18.10.97, 11.9.99, at m.v. light in garden (SAK-J).

2227 *Brachionycha sphinx* (Hufnagel, 1766)
The Sprawler

Widespread in oak woodland but by no means common.
■ vc11 Kings Somborne, 25.10.93 (TJN); Chandlers Ford, 22.11.91, 8.11.95 (BG).

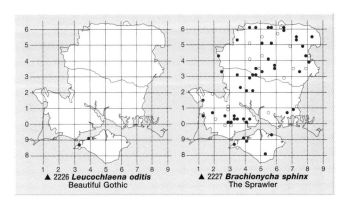

▲ 2226 *Leucochlaena oditis*
Beautiful Gothic

▲ 2227 *Brachionycha sphinx*
The Sprawler

2229 *Dasypolia templi* (Thunberg, 1792)
Brindled Ochre
There is an established population in the Freshwater area of the Isle of Wight, and a scattering of records in SW Hampshire. The larva lives in the roots of hogweed *Heracleum sphondylium*.
■ vc11 Linford, 11.10.96, one at m.v. light (AGP).

2230 *Aporophyla australis* (Boisduval, 1829)
Feathered Brindle   **Notable/Nb**
Common on the Freshwater cliffs, Isle of Wight.
■ vc11 Hengistbury Head, 2.10.96, second Hampshire mainland record (MJ). The first was at Southsea on 20.9.88 (Goater, 1992).

2231 *Aporophyla lutulenta* ([Denis & Schiffermüller], 1775)
Deep-brown Dart
This species is very locally fairly common, and occasional wanderers turn up away from known colonies.
■ vc11 Rownhams, 1.9.94 (KG); Chandlers Ford, 24.9.94 (BG); Gaters Mill, Mansbridge, 30.9.89 (PAB); Woolston, fairly common, up to 14 each year, 1990–1995, 18 in 1997 (ARC); Gosport, 23.9 to 10.10.95, five at light

(DSW); Cosham, small numbers at light every year (TJJ).
■ vc12 Bentley Station Meadow, 23.9.95 (PAB); Yateley Common, fairly common (AMD); Frith End, 23.9.95, seven, and 30.9.95, five, at light (KW); Farnborough, two in 1994 (RWP).

2232 *Aporophyla nigra* (Haworth, 1809)
Black Rustic
Nowadays, a common autumn-flying species in all three vice-counties.

2233 *Lithomoia solidaginis* (Hübner, 1803)
Golden-rod Brindle
There is but a single record of this scarce presumed immigrant, from Burghclere vc12, in 1954 (Goater, 1974).

2235 *Lithophane semibrunnea* (Haworth, 1809)
Tawny Pinion
This species still occurs at very low density in all three vice-counties. It is unusual for more than one or two specimens to be recorded in any one locality each year. Nowadays, the majority are taken at light after hibernation.

2236 *Lithophane socia* (Hufnagel, 1766)
Pale Pinion
Slightly more widespread and less rare than *L. semibrunnea*, and like that species, seen more often in early spring after hibernation, either at light or at sallow bloom.

2237 *Lithophane ornitopus* (Hufnagel, 1766)
Grey Shoulder-knot
Following a period of scarcity during the post-War years, this species has recovered quite well and is now not uncommon in oak woodland in all three vice-counties. In the New Forest, it is often found resting on the trunks of pine trees in mixed woodland.

2240 *Lithophane leautieri* (Boisduval, 1829)
Blair's Shoulder-knot
The first British record was at Freshwater in 1951 (see Goater, 1974). It is now one of the commonest autumn moths throughout the county, particularly in parks, suburbs and villages where cypresses *Cupressus* spp. are grown.

2241 *Xylena vetusta* (Hübner, 1813)
Red Sword-grass
Most of the records of this species are from the New Forest, where it is widespread but rare. There are scattered records from elsewhere in the three vice-counties, recent ones are given below.
■ vc10 Chale Green, 14.4.95, one (SRC).
■ vc11 Beaulieu, 21.10.95, one at m.v. light (BI-J); Frenchmoor, 22.2.97 (NB); Titchfield Haven NR, 30.3.95, one at light (PMP).
■ vc12 Crawley, 19.10.90, second record (RAB).

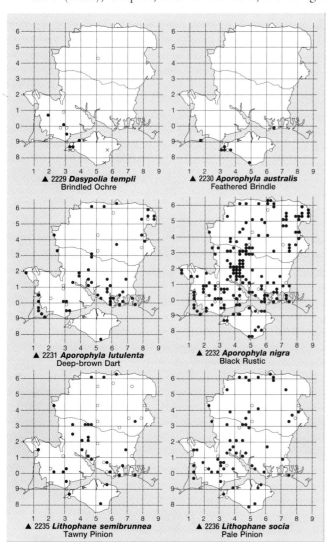

▲ 2229 *Dasypolia templi*
Brindled Ochre

▲ 2230 *Aporophyla australis*
Feathered Brindle

▲ 2231 *Aporophyla lutulenta*
Deep-brown Dart

▲ 2232 *Aporophyla nigra*
Black Rustic

▲ 2235 *Lithophane semibrunnea*
Tawny Pinion

▲ 2236 *Lithophane socia*
Pale Pinion

2242 *Xylena exsoleta* (Linnaeus, 1758)
Sword-grass **Notable/Nb**
Formerly resident in all three vice-counties, now an extremely scarce presumed immigrant. The only recent record is of one taken at sugar at Freshwater on 7.10.78 (PJC).

2243 *Xylocampa areola* (Esper, 1789)
Early Grey
Widespread and common in the three vice-counties.

2245 *Allophyes oxyacanthae* (Linnaeus, 1758)
Green-brindled Crescent

10 mm

Widespread but much less common than formerly.

2246a *Dryobota labecula* (Esper, 1788)
Oak Rustic
This species was found in Jersey in 1991 (Burrow, 1996) and is now established on evergreen oak *Quercus ilex* in the Channel Islands, but the records given below are the first for Britain.
■ vc10 Freshwater, 15.10.99, one at m.v. light (Rogers, 2000), 22.11.99, one worn specimen at m.v. light (SAK-J). **New to Britain.**

2247 *Dichonia aprilina* (Linnaeus, 1758)
Merveille du Jour

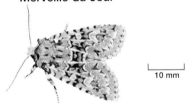

10 mm

Common in mature oak woodland. In spring the larvae may be found by day, wedged into crevices in the bark of old oak trees.

2248 *Dryobotodes eremita* (Fabricius, 1775)
Brindled Green
Fairly common in the vicinity of oak woods in all three vice-counties, but especially in the New Forest area.

2250 *Mniotype adusta* (Esper, 1790)
Dark Brocade
Numerous records of this insect were given in Goater (1974), and in some places it was quite common. It has now virtually disappeared, and there has been only a handful of records since the 1960s.
■ vc10 Freshwater, 27.6.92, one at m.v. light (SAK-J, 1994).
■ vc11 Matchams, nr Ringwood, 1983, 1984, 1986 (GL).
■ vc12 Wildhern, 8.8.00, one to m.v. light (DGG);

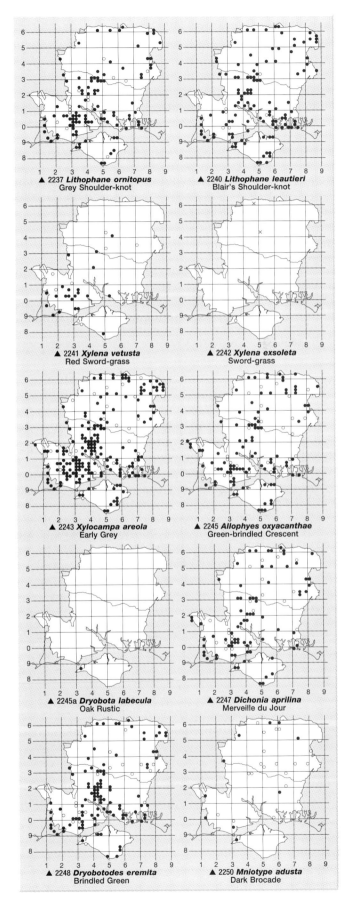

▲ 2237 *Lithophane ornitopus*
Grey Shoulder-knot

▲ 2240 *Lithophane leautieri*
Blair's Shoulder-knot

▲ 2241 *Xylena vetusta*
Red Sword-grass

▲ 2242 *Xylena exsoleta*
Sword-grass

▲ 2243 *Xylocampa areola*
Early Grey

▲ 2245 *Allophyes oxyacanthae*
Green-brindled Crescent

▲ 2245a *Dryobota labecula*
Oak Rustic

▲ 2247 *Dichonia aprilina*
Merveille du Jour

▲ 2248 *Dryobotodes eremita*
Brindled Green

▲ 2250 *Mniotype adusta*
Dark Brocade

Greywell, 9.7.84, one in house; recorder confident of identity (PB).

2251 *Trigonophora flammea* (Esper, 1785)
Flame Brocade

An extinct resident of Sussex, this species remains an extremely scarce migrant. It is being reported with increasing regularity, and its re-establishment as a breeding species is considered quite likely. All records are given below.

■ vc10 Freshwater, 18.10.90 (two), 20.10.90 (Knill-Jones, 1991); again on 18.10.95, 14.10.96, 26.10.99 (SAK-J); The Causeway, Freshwater, 28.10.99 by DBW (*comm.* SAK-J). **New vc record.**

■ vc11 Highcliffe, 27.10.95, one at light, now in coll. Nat. Hist. Mus., London (RAC); Lymington, 3.10.68 conf. JWP (D. Fish); Sandy Point, Hayling Island, 14.10.96, one at m.v. light (PS).

2252 *Polymixis flavicincta* ([Denis & Schiffermüller], 1775)
Large Ranunculus

Very local and by no means common except in the Alton/Selborne area of vc12. All recent records are given below.

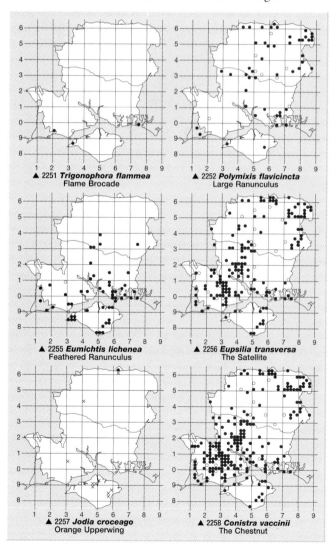

▲ 2251 *Trigonophora flammea*
Flame Brocade

▲ 2252 *Polymixis flavicincta*
Large Ranunculus

▲ 2255 *Eumichtis lichenea*
Feathered Ranunculus

▲ 2256 *Eupsilia transversa*
The Satellite

▲ 2257 *Jodia croceago*
Orange Upperwing

▲ 2258 *Conistra vaccinii*
The Chestnut

■ vc11 Kings Somborne, 25.9.99, one at light in garden (TJN); Chandlers Ford, 18.10.97, first record (BG); Leigh Park, Havant, 26.9.92, 28.9.94, 12.10.95, 30.9.96, 28.9.98, 8.10.99 (CBC).

■ vc12 Crawley, 27.9 and 28.9.98, resting on side of house; first for many years (RAB); Magdalen Hill Down, 4.10.97 (PAB); South Wonston, 1993–95, annually in September (PJSS); Tadley, 21.9.96, one at m.v. light (AHD); Selborne, common at light, 44 specimens in 1995 (AEA); Yateley Common, occasional (AMD); Frith End, 30.9.95, two at light (KW); Farnborough, five in September 1994 (RWP).

■ vc22 Mortimer West End, 26.9.98, one seen at m.v. light (GJD).

2255 *Eumichtis lichenea* (Hübner, 1813)
Feathered Ranunculus

This species is now well-established on the coast of S Hants and is extending its range inland, with several isolated records from N Hants. The data given below make an interesting comparison with those given in Goater (1974, 1992).

■ vc11 Pennington, 30.10.95 (RC); Beaulieu, 2.10 to 14.10.95, four at m.v. light, 23.9.96 (BI-J); Holbury, common between 29.9 and 23.10.00, including a total of 31 at m.v. light on 29.9 and 20 on 30.9; Chandlers Ford, 25.9.98, male at m.v. light (BG); Bitterne, 9.10.95, one at light (PAB); Woolston, 10.10.95, one at light, first since three in 1991, six between 20.9 and 10.10.96, nine in 1997; Sholing, 30.9 and 10.10.98 (ARC); Fareham, 64 between 18.9 and 12.10.97 (MO); Rowner, 39 in 1999 (LM); Gosport, 4.9 to 16.10.95, total of 203 at light (DSW), 10.10.95, 14 at light (SS); Southsea, now common (JRL); N Hayling Island (PRD).

■ vc12 Crawley, occasional, first record 28.9.81, most recent 27.9.92 (RAB); Selborne, 8.10.94, one at light (Aston, 1995), 12.10 and 13.10.95, singletons (AEA).

2256 *Eupsilia transversa* (Hufnagel, 1766)
The Satellite

Widespread but most definitely far less common than it was three decades ago.

2257 *Jodia croceago* ([Denis & Schiffermüller], 1775)
Orange Upperwing   **RDB1**

The records given in Goater (1974) have proved impossible to map because of their vagueness, and nothing has been heard of this moth in any of the three vice-counties since that time. One of the old localities was Pamber Forest vc12, and the following sight record from just over the boundary into vc22, Berks, leads one to hope the moth may be rediscovered.

■ vc22 Mortimer West End, 15.2.92, one seen at m.v. light (GJD).

2258 *Conistra vaccinii* (Linnaeus, 1761)
The Chestnut

Widespread and common in woodlands in all three vice-counties.

2259 *Conistra ligula* (Esper, 1791)
Dark Chestnut
There is a wide scattering of records through all three vice-counties, but the moth is nowhere common and appears to have decreased.

2260 *Conistra rubiginea* ([Denis & Schiffermüller], 1775)
Dotted Chestnut   **Notable/Nb**
This species appears to have become much more widespread in recent years, though still at low density. Up until the 1970s, its stronghold was on the Bagshot Sands area in NE Hampshire but recently there have been many records from the western half of S Hants.
■ vc10 Cranmore, 6.5.95 (SAK-J).
■ vc11 Hurn, 12.3.00; Hengistbury Head, 23.2.00 (MJ); Matchams, nr Ringwood, regular in small numbers after hibernation (GL); Roydon Woods, 14.5.98 (PAB); Beaulieu, 13.3.94, 20.4.96, 4.5.00 (BI-J); Broughton Down, 15.4.96, four at m.v. light; Woodley, Romsey, 5.5.92 (NB); Kings Somborne, 11.4.92, 16.4.96, 20.4.96 (two), 8.4.97, three between 17.3 and 8.4.98 (TJN); Chandlers Ford, 27.2.92, 20.4.96 (BG); Allbrook, 21.4.96 (ML); Woolston, 16.4.96; Sholing, 17.2 and

19.2.98 (ARC); Itchen Valley Country Park, 10.4.96 (MTC).
■ vc12 Brockley Warren, 6.4.97, two (TJN); South Wonston, 24.3.96 (PJSS); East Stratton, two in 1971 (BI-J); Pamber Heath, 2.4.95, one (AS); Fleet Pond, 21.4.98 (DGG); Selborne, seven at m.v. light between 26.2 and 8.4.98 (AEA); Noar Hill, 15.3.93, 31.3.95 (AMJ); Bentley Station Meadow, 5.5.95 (PAB); Hazeley Heath, 9.3.97, two; Rye Common, 22.3.94, 15.4.96, two; Castle Bottom NNR, 4.4.98, two; Zebon Copse, 20.3.98; Yateley Common, occasional (AMD); Frith End, 1.4.95, 28.3.98, singles at light (KW); Farnborough, 6.4.95, one at light (RWP), 26.4.96 (KW).

2261 *Conistra erythrocephala* ([Denis & Schiffermüller], 1775)
Red-headed Chestnut
The two records, from the Bournemouth district in 1902 (Goater, 1974) are the only ones for the area.

2262 *Agrochola circellaris* (Hufnagel, 1766)
The Brick
Widely distributed in all three vice-counties and often common. It is most frequent in areas of mature ash *Fraxinus excelsior*, and less so in localities where the larval foodplant has to be catkins of sallows or poplars.

2263 *Agrochola lota* (Clerck, 1759)
Red-line Quaker
Common throughout the area in localities where the foodplants, sallows and willows *Salix* spp. grow.

2264 *Agrochola macilenta* (Hübner, 1809)
Yellow-line Quaker
Common in deciduous woodland in all three vice-counties, though apparently less so than in the 1950s.

2264a *Agrochola haematidea* (Duponchel, 1827)
Southern Chestnut   **RDB2**
This species was discovered in Hampshire in 1996 at Linford by AGP, who took a number at light in his garden. It has subsequently been found to occur widely in the area, but attempts to find it in new grid squares have been thwarted by unfavourable weather. Possibly it is a new arrival in the country, but it could well have been overlooked on account of its late season and short flight period, for about half an hour at dusk. It was first found in W Sussex in 1990 (Haggett and Smith, 1993) and has now been found in Dorset (P.H. Sterling, pers. comm.).
■ vc11 Sopley Common, 21.5.00, larvae swept at night (MJ); Linford, October, 1996, 20 at light; W of Slufters Enclosure, 16.10.96, two at light; Picket Hill, 28.6.97, one larva on cross-leaved heath *Erica tetralix*, one swept from ling *Calluna vulgaris* or *E. tetralix*; Ridley Plain, 19.10.96, two at light; Bratley Plain, 29.9.97, one; Dur Hill Down, 11.10.97, one (JEC); Whitemoor, W of Emery Down, 30.9 to 6.10.97, several at m.v. light (JEC, BG); Picket Post, 12.10.97, five at light (BG, R. Dyke); Vales Moor, 19.10.96, two at light; Black Gutter, 4.10.97, one at m.v. light (BG). **New county record.**

▲ 2259 *Conistra ligula*
Dark Chestnut

▲ 2260 *Conistra rubiginea*
Dotted Chestnut

▲ 2262 *Agrochola circellaris*
The Brick

▲ 2263 *Agrochola lota*
Red-line Quaker

▲ 2264 *Agrochola macilenta*
Yellow-line Quaker

▲ 2264a *Agrochola haematidea*
Southern Chestnut

2265 *Agrochola helvola* (Linnaeus, 1758)
Flounced Chestnut
Present in all three vice-counties, but usually at low density and mainly in deciduous woodland.
■ vc11 Chandlers Ford, 24.10.92 (BG); Black Gutter, 4.10.97, one at m.v. light (BG, TJN); Picket Post, 12.10.97, one at light (BG, R. Dyke).

2266 *Agrochola litura* (Linnaeus, 1758)
Brown-spot Pinion
Thinly distributed in the mainland vice-counties; few records from the Isle of Wight.

2267 *Agrochola lychnidis* ([Denis & Schiffermüller], 1775)
Beaded Chestnut
Widespread and often common in all three vice-counties.

2268 *Parastichtis suspecta* (Hübner, 1817)
The Suspected
This species occurs in birch-heath country, mainly in the New Forest and north-east Hampshire. There are two records from the Isle of Wight, one very old (Goater, 1974).

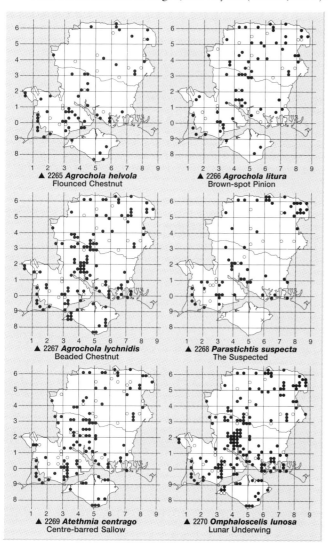

▲ 2265 *Agrochola helvola*
Flounced Chestnut

▲ 2266 *Agrochola litura*
Brown-spot Pinion

▲ 2267 *Agrochola lychnidis*
Beaded Chestnut

▲ 2268 *Parastichtis suspecta*
The Suspected

▲ 2269 *Atethmia centrago*
Centre-barred Sallow

▲ 2270 *Omphaloscelis lunosa*
Lunar Underwing

■ vc12 Pamber Heath, 9.7 to 26.7.95, total of 22 recorded (AS).

2269 *Atethmia centrago* (Haworth, 1809)
Centre-barred Sallow
Widespread but rather local in all three vice-counties. The moth requires mature ash, preferably isolated trees, on the opening buds of which the larva feeds in spring.

2270 *Omphaloscelis lunosa* (Haworth, 1809)
Lunar Underwing
This is usually one of the commonest autumn-flying moths on downland and grassy heaths, and also in deciduous woodland where, however, it is less frequent.

2271 *Xanthia citrago* (Linnaeus, 1758)
Orange Sallow
This species probably occurs wherever there are mature stands and avenues of lime: hence it is something of a suburban moth. Its true frequency in an area is best gauged by searching for larvae in late spring or sugaring the foliage of the trees in autumn.
■ vc11 Pennington, 1.9.95 (RC); Rownhams, 20.9.93 (KG); Chandlers Ford, 24.9.94, 30.9.97 (BG); Woolston, 16.9.95, first record for garden, 30.9.97 (ARC); Bedenham, Gosport, 18.9.97 (DSW).
■ vc12 Wildhern, nr Andover, 13.5.97, five larvae on lime (DGG); Selborne, 14.10.96 (AEA).

2272 *Xanthia aurago* ([Denis & Schiffermüller], 1775)
Barred Sallow
Widespread and often common in the mainland vice-counties, mainly but not only in beech woodland on the chalk. The larva feeds on the buds, and later the foliage, of beech and field maple *Acer campestre*.
■ vc12 Brighton Hill, Basingstoke, 24.9.94, one at m.v. light (AHD).

2273 *Xanthia togata* (Esper, 1788)
Pink-barred Sallow

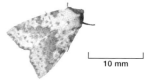

10 mm

Widespread in all three vice-counties in damp ground amongst sallows and poplars, in the catkins of which the larvae occur in early spring, later feeding on the foliage.

2274 *Xanthia icteritia* (Hufnagel, 1766)
The Sallow
This moth has the same habits as the preceding, but is generally much more common.

2275 *Xanthia gilvago* ([Denis & Schiffermüller], 1775)
Dusky-lemon Sallow
There are very few recent records of this moth, most from the SE of Hampshire. In the past, scattered small colonies

occurred amongst wych elm *Ulmus glabra* in all three vice-counties. Alas, this tree has all but died out, the moth with it.

■ vc11 Funtley, 4.10.98, one at m.v. light, conf. RJD (MLO); Hayling Island, 6.10.76, 4.10.77, singles at m.v. light (JMW).

■ vc12 Cholderton, 20.9.76 (HE); East Stratton, 5.8 and 20.8.68, conf. CHD (BI-J).

2276 *Xanthia ocellaris* (Borkhausen, 1792)
Pale-lemon Sallow **Notable/Na**

■ vc10 Wootton, 5.10.97 at actinic light by Tony Redfern (Knill-Jones, 1998d). **New county record.**

2277 *Moma alpium* (Osbeck, 1778)
Scarce Merveille du Jour **RDB3**

10 mm

This species is still quite common in the New Forest oakwoods. It is still present in the woods near Wickham and in Havant Thicket, but has disappeared from localities such as Chandlers Ford, where it was fairly common up until the early 1950s. There has been no recent record from Parkhurst Forest, Isle of Wight, though it may well still occur there.

2278 *Acronicta megacephala* ([Denis & Schiffermüller], 1775)
Poplar Grey

Widespread in the vicinity of poplars in all three vice-counties.

2279 *Acronicta aceris* (Linnaeus, 1758)
The Sycamore

Widespread and fairly common in all three vice-counties, particularly in the suburbs. The larva feeds on maples *Acer* spp. including sycamore, horse chestnut and other trees.

2280 *Acronicta leporina* (Linnaeus, 1758)
The Miller

Widespread and fairly common in all three vice-counties, in the vicinity of the foodplants, birch and alder.

2281 *Acronicta alni* (Linnaeus, 1767)
Alder Moth

Considered to be a very rare moth until the advent of m.v. light; it is now known to be widespread and fairly common, though only recorded from the north of the Isle of Wight. The larva feeds on a wide variety of deciduous trees, particularly birch, oak and hawthorn.

■ vc10 Freshwater, 26.5.93 (SAK-J); Binstead, 23.5 and 24.5.93 (BJW).

■ vc11 Woolston, 6.5 and 9.6.90 (ARC).

■ vc12 South Wonston, 26.6.96 (PJSS).

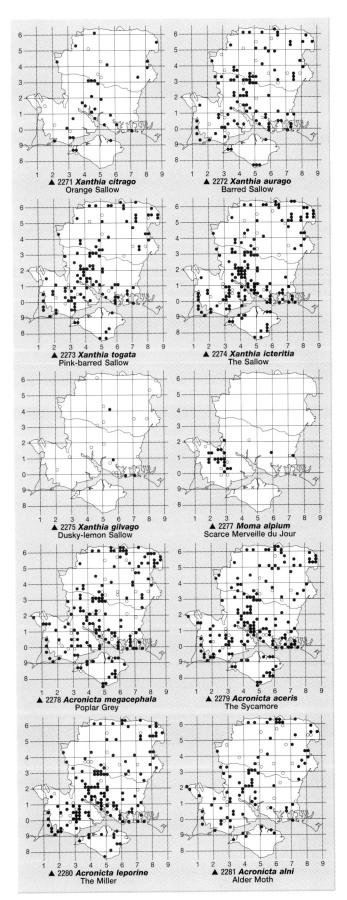

▲ 2271 *Xanthia citrago*
Orange Sallow

▲ 2272 *Xanthia aurago*
Barred Sallow

▲ 2273 *Xanthia togata*
Pink-barred Sallow

▲ 2274 *Xanthia icteritia*
The Sallow

▲ 2275 *Xanthia gilvago*
Dusky-lemon Sallow

▲ 2277 *Moma alpium*
Scarce Merveille du Jour

▲ 2278 *Acronicta megacephala*
Poplar Grey

▲ 2279 *Acronicta aceris*
The Sycamore

▲ 2280 *Acronicta leporine*
The Miller

▲ 2281 *Acronicta alni*
Alder Moth

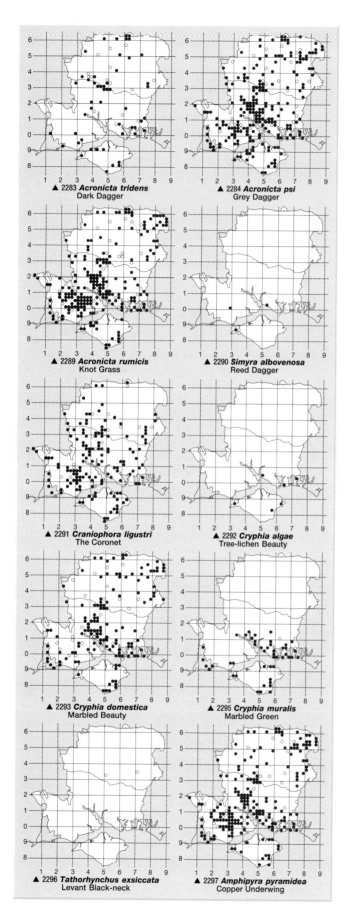

▲ 2283 *Acronicta tridens*
Dark Dagger

▲ 2284 *Acronicta psi*
Grey Dagger

▲ 2289 *Acronicta rumicis*
Knot Grass

▲ 2290 *Simyra albovenosa*
Reed Dagger

▲ 2291 *Craniophora ligustri*
The Coronet

▲ 2292 *Cryphia algae*
Tree-lichen Beauty

▲ 2293 *Cryphia domestica*
Marbled Beauty

▲ 2295 *Cryphia muralis*
Marbled Green

▲ 2296 *Tathorhynchus exsiccata*
Levant Black-neck

▲ 2297 *Amphipyra pyramidea*
Copper Underwing

2283 *Acronicta tridens* ([Denis & Schiffermüller], 1775)
Dark Dagger

This species can only be positively identified by dissection or by finding the very distinctive larva. It is certainly uncommon in the area, though probably under-recorded.

■ vc11 Brockenhurst, 9.7.81 (JEC); Rownhams, 7.6.96, female, genitalia det. BG (KG); Chandlers Ford, 13.7.92, female (BG); Cosham, 9.7.96, genitalia det. (TJJ).

■ vc12 Danebury, 19.7.96, genitalia det. (JEC); Wildhern, nr Andover, 1.9.96, larvae, 20.7.98, 9.7.99, both genitalia det. (DGG); Magdalen Hill Down, 30.8.00, larva on hawthorn (PAB); Brighton Hill, Basingstoke, 3.8.96, two males, genitalia det. (AHD).

2284 *Acronicta psi* (Linnaeus, 1758)
Grey Dagger

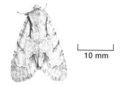

10 mm

Widespread and common in all three vice-counties. The majority of specimens examined turn out to be this species rather than *A. tridens* and of "odd" individuals subjected to genitalic examination, most also have proved to be *A. psi*.

2287 *Acronicta auricoma* ([Denis & Schiffermüller], 1775)
Scarce Dagger

Apart from the record given below, the only other is of a single specimen at Luccombe Chine, Isle of Wight, in 1947 (Goater, 1974)

■ vc11 Warsash, 7.8 to 9.8.96, one at m.v. light (PMP). **New vc record.**

2289 *Acronicta rumicis* (Linnaeus, 1758)
Knot Grass

Widespread and common in all three vice-counties. The larva is polyphagous, and may be found on herbaceous plants such as dock *Rumex* spp. and plantain *Plantago* spp. as well as deciduous trees and shrubs.

2290 *Simyra albovenosa* (Goeze, 1781)
Reed Dagger   **Notable/Nb**

The present status of this moth in Hampshire and the Isle of Wight is not known. There was, and probably still is, a colony in Freshwater Marsh, Isle of Wight, though the most recent record available is dated 1952. It has also been reliably reported from Browndown (Goater, 1974) but since then the area has been largely filled in. It is an inhabitant of reed-beds, the larva feeding on common reed *Phragmites australis*. All other records are detailed below.

■ vc10 Freshwater, 1992, one at garden m.v. light (SAK-J).

■ vc11 Brockenhurst, 12.7.82, one at light (JEC); Titchfield Haven, 7.5.00, one at m.v. light, photographed (B. Duffin comm. M. Honey).

■ vc12 [Crawley, 1973 (Goater, 1992) is incorrect: the record refers to *Mythimna pudorina* (RAB)].

2291 *Craniophora ligustri* ([Denis & Schiffermüller], 1775)
The Coronet
Widespread and locally frequent in the Isle of Wight and S Hants, but there appear to be no records from NE Hampshire. The larva feeds on ash and wild privet.

2292 *Cryphia algae* (Fabricius, 1775)
Tree-lichen Beauty
The present status of this species, hitherto an extremely scarce immigrant, is uncertain. There have been several recent records from the Isle of Wight and S Hants, and some indication that it may be breeding the Warsash area. All records are given below.
■ vc10 Freshwater, 27.8.92, one at m.v. light (Knill-Jones, 1993); Ninham, 23.8.96, by J. Reeve (Skinner and Parsons, 1999); Brading Marsh RSPB Reserve, 29.7.01 (CWP). **New vc record.**
■ vc11 Warsash, 2.8.95, 7.8 to 12.8.96, four, 2.9.96 (PMP); Warsash Common, 9.8.00, one (PAB), in coll. Nat. Hist. Mus., London; Southsea, 26.7.95 (JRL); Southsea, 21.8.91, one at m.v. light (JRL); Northney, Hayling Island, 31.7.99 (Phillips, 2000).

2293 *Cryphia domestica* (Hufnagel, 1766)
Marbled Beauty
Widespread in the vicinity of walls and buildings where lichens grow, in all three vice-counties.

2294 *Cryphia raptricula* ([Denis & Schiffermüller], 1775)
Marbled Grey
The only Hampshire record is of one at Southsea in 1955 (Goater, 1974).

2295 *Cryphia muralis* (Forster, 1771)
Marbled Green
Locally common all round the Isle of Wight coast and that of S Hants east of Southampton, here extending some distance inland. The larva feeds on lichens on rocks and old walls.
■ vc11 Hengistbury, 1994 (MJ); Woolston, 3.8.90, 1.8.97 (ARC); Sholing, 13.8 and 21.8.98 (ARC); Bitterne, 31.8.96 (PAB); Rowner, 31 in 1999 (LM); Gosport, 9.7 to 29.8.95, total of 57 at light (DSW); Waltham Chase, August 95 (EAP).

2296 *Tathorhynchus exsiccata* (Lederer, 1855)
Levant Black-neck
An extremely scarce immigrant, of which there are four Hampshire records, perhaps surprisingly all in vc12 and not since 1967 (Goater, 1974). All records are summarised below.
■ vc12 Martyr Worthy, two on 2.2.67 and another on the following night DWHF); Farringdon, 20.3.52 (H. S. Robinson).

2297 *Amphipyra pyramidea* (Linnaeus, 1758)
Copper Underwing
Widespread in deciduous woodland in all three vice-counties, but particularly common in the New Forest. Most recorders have confidently distinguished between

this and the next species, but in the maps, there may be some bias in favour of *A. pyramidea*.

2298 *Amphipyra berbera* Rungs, 1949
Svensson's Copper Underwing
This species appears to have the same distribution and habitat preferences as *A. pyramidea*; the fewer records suggest it may be somewhat under-recorded. Their flight-periods overlap, but in general, *A. berbera* starts to emerge about a fortnight ahead of *A. pyramidea*. Both species are seen far more commonly at sugar than at light.

2299 *Amphipyra tragopoginis* (Clerck, 1759)
Mouse Moth
The Mouse Moth is present in all three vice-counties but has evidently decreased, judging from the high proportion of pre-1980 records on the map. Like the other *Amphipyra* species, it is commoner at sugar than at light.

2300 *Mormo maura* (Linnaeus, 1758)
Old Lady
This is another species that comes rarely to light and it is therefore likely to be under-recorded. It favours water-courses through deciduous woodland, and is sometimes found roosting communally under bridges over streams. The majority of the records come from S Hants, and especially the New Forest. The larva can be found in spring at night on blackthorn and other trees and shrubs.
■ vc10 Hacketts Land, 1km W of Branstone, 14.8.97 (D and PP); Binstead, 17.8.93 (BJW).
■ vc11 Bartley, New Forest, 18.8.95, one at m.v. light (AHD); Lepe Country Park, 6.9.97, two in toilets (JK); Woolston, 1990–95, between one and four every year, at light (ARC); Merryoak, Southampton, 6.8.84; Gaters Mill, Mansbridge, 12.8.89 (PAB).

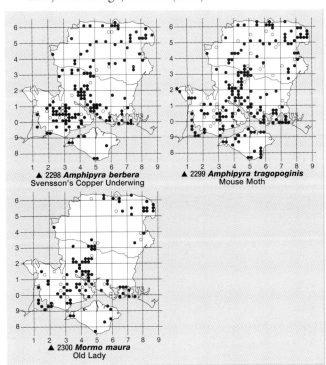

▲ 2298 *Amphipyra berbera*
Svensson's Copper Underwing

▲ 2299 *Amphipyra tragopoginis*
Mouse Moth

▲ 2300 *Mormo maura*
Old Lady

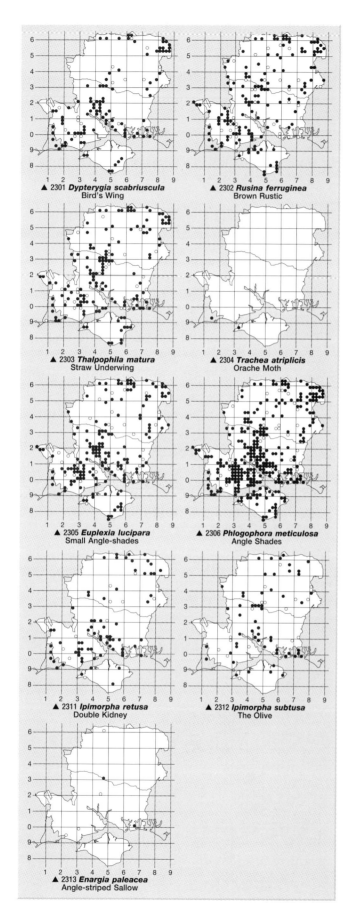

▲ 2301 *Dypterygia scabriuscula*
Bird's Wing

▲ 2302 *Rusina ferruginea*
Brown Rustic

▲ 2303 *Thalpophila matura*
Straw Underwing

▲ 2304 *Trachea atriplicis*
Orache Moth

▲ 2305 *Euplexia lucipara*
Small Angle-shades

▲ 2306 *Phlogophora meticulosa*
Angle Shades

▲ 2311 *Ipimorpha retusa*
Double Kidney

▲ 2312 *Ipimorpha subtusa*
The Olive

▲ 2313 *Enargia paleacea*
Angle-striped Sallow

■ vc12 Selborne (AEA); Yateley Common, 18.8.93 (AMD).

2301 *Dypterygia scabriuscula* (Linnaeus, 1758)
Bird's Wing

10 mm

Widely distributed in all three vice-counties, but most frequent in S Hants.

2302 *Rusina ferruginea* (Esper, 1785)
Brown Rustic

Widespread and fairly common in all three vice-counties, in a wide variety of habitats, in wooded and open country.

2303 *Thalpophila matura* (Hufnagel, 1766)
Straw Underwing

This species is also widespread and fairly common, favouring particularly heathland, chalk downland and coastal localities.

2304 *Trachea atriplicis* (Linnaeus, 1758)
Orache Moth

The two records given below are the only ones for the area. However, other specimens have appeared recently in other parts of the country and we may expect to see more.

■ vc10 Freshwater, 9.8.96, one at m.v. light (Knill-Jones, 1997d). **New vc record.**

■ vc11 Christchurch, 31.7.95, one at m.v. light (Jeffes, 1995). **New county record.**

2305 *Euplexia lucipara* (Linnaeus, 1758)
Small Angle-shades

This species is common in deciduous woodland, mainly on acid soils, in all three vice-counties. The larva is one of the few species to feed on bracken *Pteridium aquilinum* and other ferns.

2306 *Phlogophora meticulosa* (Linnaeus, 1758)
Angle Shades

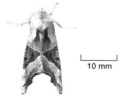

10 mm

Common all over the area, numbers of the resident population being regularly reinforced by immigration. The imago has been recorded in every month of the year, but is most frequent in early autumn.

[2307 *Pseudenargia ulicis* (Staudinger, 1859)
The Berber

The only British specimen was said to have been taken at sugar at Brockenhurst on 16 August 1935 (Goater, 1974).

The early date given, together with the small price made when it was sold in 1943, would appear to throw some doubt upon the veracity of the record.]

2311 *Ipimorpha retusa* (Linnaeus, 1761)
Double Kidney
Widespread though not usually very common, in damp areas where the larva feeds in the shoots of common sallow *Salix cinerea* and other species of sallow and willow.

2312 *Ipimorpha subtusa* ([Denis & Schiffermüller], 1775)
The Olive
Scattered through the three vice-counties. The larva lives between spun leaves of poplar *Populus* spp., usually rather high up on the tree.
■ vc10 Binstead, 10.8.98, one at m.v. light (BJW).

2313 *Enargia paleacea* (Esper, 1788)
Angle-striped Sallow   **Notable/Nb and Migrant**
Whilst this species is resident from the Midlands northwards, the nine records to date in our area are thought to be immigrants (see Goater, 1974, 1992). All are listed below.
■ vc11 New Milton, 21.7.67 (M.D.Noble); Sandydown, 15.7.67 (R.W.Watson); Chandlers Ford, 26.7.51 and 18.7.52 (BG); Winchester, 10.8.80 (DHS); Southsea, 11.8.97, one at light (IRT).
■ vc12 Burghclere, 15.8.64 (two) and another on 18.8.64 (Saundby).

2314 *Enargia ypsillon* ([Denis & Schiffermüller], 1775)
Dingy Shears
Scattered through the three vice-counties, mainly along the river valleys. The larva feeds on narrow-leaved willows and may often be found in numbers hiding under loose bark near the base of the tree, in May.
■ vc10 Godshill, 12.7.94 (PJC, *comm.* SAK-J).

2315 *Dicycla oo* (Linnaeus, 1758)
Heart Moth   **RDB3**
This species is notoriously erratic in its appearance in Britain, and little has been heard of it in Hampshire for many years (Goater, 1974, 1992). The larva feeds on oak *Quercus* spp. and the moth comes to sugar very early in the evening, well before darkness has set in. Later in the night, it comes to light. Recent records are given below.
■ vc12 Pamber, 1.7.93, 17.7.93 (GJD); Wheathold, singles on 30.6 and 5.7.81 at m.v. light (PRB); Wellington Country Park, 1982 (D. Young).

2316 *Cosmia affinis* (Linnaeus, 1767)
Lesser-spotted Pinion
Dutch elm disease has played havoc with the populations of the elm-feeding *Cosmia* species. Formerly, *C. affinis* was fairly widespread and not uncommon locally where there were tall elms *Ulmus* spp.; now, it has all but disappeared.
■ vc10 Binstead, 4.8.95, first record, 30.7.96 (BJW).
■ vc11 Ringwood, 1994, eight bred (RAB); Beaulieu, 16.8.96 (BI-J); Chandlers Ford, 23.7.93 (BG); Gosport,

5.8.95, one at light, conf. PMP, 20.8 and 22.8.96 (DSW).
■ vc12 Yateley, 12.8.97 (AMD).

2317 *Cosmia diffinis* (Linnaeus, 1767)
White-spotted Pinion   **Notable/Na**
Always local and rare in the county, this is another elm-feeder that has virtually gone. Old records are given in Goater (1974, 1992), to which may be added the following.
■ vc11 Linford, 3.8.96, one at m.v. light, observer confident of identity but specimen not retained (AGP); Solent Court, Warsash, 6.8.91 (PMP).
■ vc12 Pamber Forest, 22.8.93 (GJD).
■ vc22 Mortimer West End, singles on the very early dates of 2.7 and 15.7.93 (GJD).

2318 *Cosmia trapezina* (Linnaeus, 1758)
The Dun-bar
The larva of this species is polyphagous on the foliage of elms *Ulmus* spp. and many other deciduous trees and is also a notorious carnivore which eats the larvae of other Lepidoptera, in particular those of the Winter Moth *Operophtera brumata*. We can find no actual evidence that it is strictly a cannibal which feeds on larvae of its own kind.

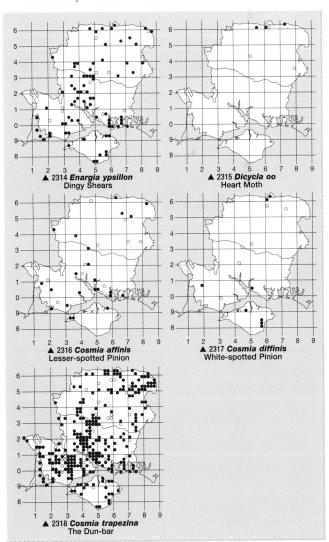

▲ 2314 *Enargia ypsillon*
Dingy Shears

▲ 2315 *Dicycla oo*
Heart Moth

▲ 2316 *Cosmia affinis*
Lesser-spotted Pinion

▲ 2317 *Cosmia diffinis*
White-spotted Pinion

▲ 2318 *Cosmia trapezina*
The Dun-bar

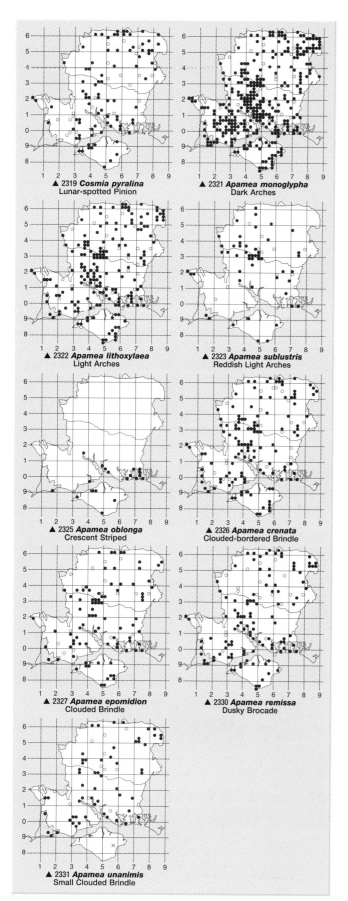

▲ 2319 *Cosmia pyralina*
Lunar-spotted Pinion

▲ 2321 *Apamea monoglypha*
Dark Arches

▲ 2322 *Apamea lithoxylaea*
Light Arches

▲ 2323 *Apamea sublustris*
Reddish Light Arches

▲ 2325 *Apamea oblonga*
Crescent Striped

▲ 2326 *Apamea crenata*
Clouded-bordered Brindle

▲ 2327 *Apamea epomidion*
Clouded Brindle

▲ 2330 *Apamea remissa*
Dusky Brocade

▲ 2331 *Apamea unanimis*
Small Clouded Brindle

2319 *Cosmia pyralina* ([Denis & Schiffermüller], 1775)
Lunar-spotted Pinion

Though favouring elm, the larvae of this species will also feed on the foliage of fruit-trees *Prunus* and *Pyrus* spp., blackthorn and other trees and shrubs, so the moth has not suffered as badly as those of its congeners which are strictly confined to elm. It is still widespread and moderately common, though certainly less so than formerly.

■ vc11 Kings Somborne, 21.7.99, one at light in garden (TJN); Rownhams, 23.7.93 (KG); Chandlers Ford, 7.8.91 (BG); Bitterne, 13.7.95 (PAB); Woolston, 21.7.90, 8.7.95 (ARC).

2321 *Apamea monoglypha* (Hufnagel, 1766)
Dark Arches

Widespread and very common in all three vice-counties.
■ vc10 Freshwater, 1.12.97 an extremely late date (Knill-Jones, 1998b).

2322 *Apamea lithoxylaea* ([Denis & Schiffermüller], 1775)
Light Arches

Widespread and fairly common in all three vice-counties.

2323 *Apamea sublustris* (Esper, 1788)
Reddish Light Arches

Locally common on the chalk and in places on the coast. Well-known localities are Martin Down (vc8), Broughton Down vc11, Danebury Hillfort vc12 and other places on the chalk around Winchester, and Noar Hill vc12.
■ vc11 Woolston, 19.7.91, 3.7 and 10.7.96, 15.7.97 (ARC).
■ vc12 South Wonston, 14.7.96 (PJSS); Old Burghclere Chalk Pit, 16.7.86, at m.v. light (GGE-F).

2325 *Apamea oblonga* (Haworth, 1809)
Crescent Striped   **Notable/Nb**

Confined to the coastal salterns of S Hants and the Isle of Wight, where it is locally fairly common; its headquarters appear to be on Hayling Island.
■ vc11 Pennington, 19.8.92 (NB); Southsea, 26.7.96, at actinic trap (IRT).

2326 *Apamea crenata* (Hufnagel, 1766)
Clouded-bordered Brindle

Widespread and fairly common in all three vice-counties.

2327 *Apamea epomidion* (Haworth, 1809)
Clouded Brindle

Widespread and fairly common in all three vice-counties, though generally less so than *A. crenata*, and more of a woodland species.

2330 *Apamea remissa* (Hübner, 1809)
Dusky Brocade

Widespread and fairly common in all three vice-counties.

2331 *Apamea unanimis* (Hübner, 1813)
Small Clouded Brindle

Local in marshy places and river valleys on the mainland, but, surprisingly, only one old record from the Isle of Wight (Goater, 1974) has been found.

2333 *Apamea anceps* ([Denis & Schiffermüller], 1775)
Large Nutmeg

This species has decreased in recent years. There are scattered records from both mainland vice-counties, mostly of single specimens, and no recent ones from the Isle of Wight.

■ vc11 Woolston, 9.7.96, first record, 12.6.97 (ARC).
■ vc22 Mortimer West End, 20.6.98, one seen at m.v. light (GJD).

2334 *Apamea sordens* (Hufnagel, 1766)
Rustic Shoulder-knot

Widespread and fairly common in all three vice-counties, though there is evidence that it has decreased.

2335 *Apamea scolopacina* (Esper, 1788)
Slender Brindle

Widespread and fairly common in all three vice-counties. Since the 1950s, it has appeared in many new localities on the mainland and is now known from several places on the Isle of Wight. On the other hand, there is a cluster of squares in the New Forest from which old records but no recent ones have been received. The moth is regarded as an inhabitant of open woodland, the larva feeding on grasses such as wood millet *Milium effusum* and wood melick *Melica uniflora* and wood rush *Luzula* spp., but recent records, the more interesting of which are given below, suggest its requirements may be becoming more catholic.

■ vc10 Freshwater, 31.7.94 (SAK-J); Godshill, 5.8.94 (PJC, *comm*. SAK-J); Chale Green, 25.7.94 (SRC); Binstead, 17.7 and 1.8.94, 6.7.98 at m.v. light (BJW). **New vc record.**
■ vc11 Kings Somborne, 16.7.94 (TJN); Chandlers Ford, few each year, first recorded 3.8.91 (BG); Bitterne, 22.7.94, at m v. light (PAB).
■ vc12 Selborne, one or two at light each year (AEA); Noar Hill NR, 14.7.95 (AMJ); Farnborough, two in July, 1994 (RWP).

2336 *Apamea ophiogramma* (Esper, 1794)
Double Lobed

Local in marshes and occasional in gardens. In the first-named localities, the larva feeds within the stems of reed canary-grass *Phalaris arundinacea*, and in gardens in the ornamental ribbon grass *P. arundinacea* var. *picta*.

■ vc10 Freshwater, 7.8.94, one at m.v. light (SAK-J).
■ vc11 Fordingbridge, 25.7.80 (NHu); Bitterne, 27.7.94, at m.v. light; Gaters Mill, Mansbridge, 14.7.90; Moorgreen Meadows, 1.7.95; Itchen Valley Country Park, 19.7.95 (PAB); Woolston, 27.7.95, first record for garden (ARC); Gosport, 14.8.96 (DSW); Southsea, 25.7.96 (JRL); Leigh Park, Havant, 5.8.96 (CBC); Hayling Island, 28.7.96 (PD).
■ vc12 Winnall Moors NR (DHS); South Wonston, 27.7.95 (PJSS); Farnborough, three in July, 1994 (RWP).

Oligia. The following three species, especially their melanic forms, should only be recorded following dissection of genitalia. With experience, many of the other forms can be assigned to one or other species with reasonable confidence, and such records of *O. strigilis* and *O. latruncula* are treated as acceptable

for mapping. Accepted records of *O. versicolor*, however, refer only to specimens which have been critically examined.

2337 *Oligia strigilis* (Linnaeus, 1758)
Marbled Minor

In its typical form, the most easily recognised of the three critical species: a short, black projection from the postmedian line into the white area outside it, near the dorsum, appears to be diagnostic. It is widespread and common in all three vice-counties.

■ vc11 Bentley Wood, Hants/Wilts border, of 90 *Oligia* species examined from several sites during the autumn of 1994, eight (9%) were this species (BF); Woolston, 1993, genitalia det. BG (ARC); Southsea, 4.7.96, at actinic trap, genitalia det. (IRT).

2338 *Oligia versicolor* (Borkhausen, 1792)
Rufous Minor

This appears to be the least common of the three critical species, though it is probably under-recorded on account of the *caveat* expressed above. Even so, it does seem to have increased in the last 25 years, and is evidently the commonest species by far in Bentley Wood (see below).

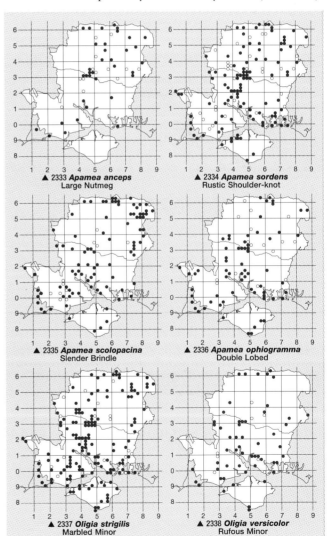

▲ 2333 *Apamea anceps*
Large Nutmeg

▲ 2334 *Apamea sordens*
Rustic Shoulder-knot

▲ 2335 *Apamea scolopacina*
Slender Brindle

▲ 2336 *Apamea ophiogramma*
Double Lobed

▲ 2337 *Oligia strigilis*
Marbled Minor

▲ 2338 *Oligia versicolor*
Rufous Minor

■ vc10 Freshwater, 1.7 and 6.7.98 (SAK-J); Knowles Farm, 22.6 and 24.6.96, genitalia det. (TS). **New vc record.**
■ vc11 Cadlands House, 13.6.97, at least two at light, genitalia slide 533 (BG), 13.7.97, one (BG, JRL); Bentley Wood, Hants/Wilts border, of 90 *Oligia* species examined from several sites during the autumn of 1994, 58 (64.5%) were this species (BF); Woolston, 1993, genitalia det. BG (ARC); Locks Heath, two in 2000, first on 20.7.00, genitalia det. (PCa); The Moors, 17.7.98; Fareham, 1996, 6.7.98, genitalia det. (RJD); Southsea, 6.6.99, one at m.v. light, det. JRL (IRT).
■ vc12 Danebury, 19.7.96, genitalia det. (JEC).

2339 *Oligia latruncula* ([Denis & Schiffermüller], 1775)
Tawny Minor
This is probably the commonest of the three critical species, and usually recognisable by the coppery hue to the forewings.
■ vc10 Binstead, six male *Oligia* taken in June 1995 were this species, det. BG (BJW).
■ vc11 Bentley Wood, Hants/Wilts border, of 90 *Oligia* species examined from several sites during the autumn of 1994, 21 (23%) were this species (BF); Woolston, 1993, genitalia det. BG (ARC); Southsea, 19.6 and 26.6.96, at actinic trap, genitalia det. (IRT).
■ vc12 Danebury, 19.7.96, genitalia det. (JEC).

2340 *Oligia fasciuncula* (Haworth, 1809)
Middle-barred Minor
Widespread and fairly common in all three vice-counties, though generally less so than the other three *Oligia* species.
■ vc11 Bentley Wood, Hants/Wilts border, of 90 *Oligia* species examined from several sites during the autumn of 1994, three (3.5%) were this species (BF).

2341 *Mesoligia furuncula* ([Denis & Schiffermüller], 1775)
Cloaked Minor
This species is particularly common along the coast and inland on the chalk.

2342 *Mesoligia literosa* (Haworth, 1809)
Rosy Minor
M. literosa is also found mainly on the coast and on the chalk downs, where it is less frequent than *M. furuncula*.
■ vc11 Woolston, 1990–93, common (ARC).

Mesapamea. Since the discovery, made in the 1980s, that "*Mesapamea secalis*" consisted of two sibling species, both polymorphic, it has been shown that both are present in Hampshire and the Isle of Wight and are probably widespread. However, genitalic examination is essential for proper determination and very few recorders have done this. It has therefore been deemed worthwhile to map the recorded distribution of the aggregate (see Map 2342a) as well as that of the two segregates. "*M. remmi*" is probably a hybrid between these two.

2343 *Mesapamea secalis* (Linnaeus, 1758) *sens.str.*
Common Rustic
All confirmed records are given in Goater (1992) and below.

■ vc10 Bonchurch (JRL).
■ vc11 Strodgemoor Bottom, 1996, genitalia det.; Vales Moor, 1996, genitalia det.; South Oakley Inclosure, 16.8.96, genitalia det. (JEC); Romsey, 26.7.78 (AKD); North Baddesley, July 1997 (DH), genitalia det. BG; Allbrook, July 1995, male (ML), genitalia det. BG; Fareham; Chilling Copse; Titchfield Haven, all genitalia det. (RJD).
■ vc12 Danebury, 19.7.96, genitalia det. (JEC); Winnall Moors NR (DHS); South Wonston, 1996, male genitalia det. BG (PJSS); Wildhern, 25.7.98, genitalia det. (DGG); Bramley Frith NR, 8.7.81 and 3.8.93; Bartley Heath NR, 20.7.95 (AKD, genitalia det. BG; Farnborough, 23.7.94 (2m), 5.8.94 (1m), genitalia det. BG (RWP).

2343a *Mesapamea didyma* (Esper, 1788)
Lesser Common Rustic
All confirmed records are given in Goater (1992) and below.
■ vc10 Bonchurch (JRL).
■ vc11 Strodgemoor Bottom, 1996, genitalia det.; Vales Moor, 1996, genitalia det.; Two Beeches Bottom, 5.8.96, genitalia det. (JEC); Allbrook, July 1995, male (ML), genitalia det. BG; Fareham; Titchfield Haven, both genitalia det. (RJD).
■ vc12 Danebury Hillfort, 2.7.99, genitalia det. BG (AMD); Winnall Moors NR (DHS); Wildhern, 23.7.98, genitalia det. (DGG); Basingstoke, 23.8.93; Bramley Frith NR, 3.8.93 (AKD) genitalia det. BG; Farnborough, 17.7.94, 23.7.94, 3.8 and 5.8.94, single males from each night's catch genitalia det. BG (RWP).

2345 *Photedes minima* (Haworth, 1809)
Small Dotted Buff
Frequent in damp localities in open woodland and meadows

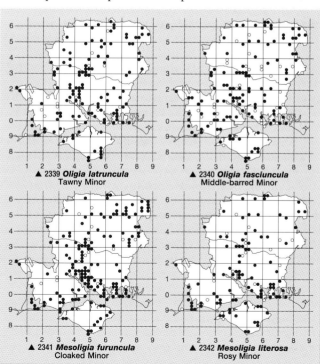

▲ 2339 *Oligia latruncula*
Tawny Minor

▲ 2340 *Oligia fasciuncula*
Middle-barred Minor

▲ 2341 *Mesoligia furuncula*
Cloaked Minor

▲ 2342 *Mesoligia literosa*
Rosy Minor

where the foodplant, tufted hair-grass *Deschampsia caespitosa* grows. The larva lives inside the shoots.

■ vc10 Binstead, 9.8.94, first record (BJW).

2349 *Chortodes fluxa* (Hübner, 1809)
Mere Wainscot   **Notable/Nb**
A small colony in the reedbed at Browndown on the coast of S Hants, discovered in 1968, still persists. Occasional wanderers have been reported nearby and there are two old records from the Sandown district in vc10 (Goater, 1974).

■ vc11 Browndown, 1.9.63, 30.8.84, 14.8.87, two (S. Swift), 3.8.96 (P. Davey, 1997); Rowner Wild Grounds, 4.8.96 (DSW); Sandy Point, Hayling, 20.7.97 (PS).

2350 *Chortodes pygmina* (Haworth, 1809)
Small Wainscot
Locally common in marshes in all three vice-counties, occasional wanderers appearing at light elsewhere.

2352 *Eremobia ochroleuca* ([Denis & Schiffermüller], 1775)
Dusky Sallow
This species has increased and expanded its range spectacularly since the 1950s (Goater, 1974), and is now widespread. It is particularly common on the chalk and in places along the coast.

■ vc11 Totton, 20.7 and 23.7, 1.8.90 (MJ); Woolston, 1990–1995, up to ten each year, (ARC); Bitterne, 21.7.95 (PAB).

■ vc12 Farnborough, 4.8.96 (RWP).

2353 *Luperina testacea* ([Denis & Schiffermüller], 1775)
Flounced Rustic
Widespread in all three vice-counties, though it has perhaps decreased in numbers since the 1950s.

2354 *Luperina nickerlii* (Freyer, 1845)
Sandhill Rustic   **Notable/Na**
The one taken at Farringdon vc12 in 1950, a presumed immigrant (Goater, 1974) is the only record for the county.

2355 *Luperina dumerilii* (Duponchel, 1826)
Dumeril's Rustic
An extremely scarce immigrant, the seven earlier records from the area all emanated from Freshwater, the most recent being in 1962 (Goater, 1974).

■ vc11 Southsea, 27.8.64, one at m.v. light, recently det. B. Skinner (RH). **New vc record.**

2358 *Amphipoea fucosa* (Freyer, 1830)
Saltern Ear
Locally common on the coastal salterns, with occasional records inland.

■ vc11 Brockenhurst, five records (JEC, 1994); N of St Leonards, nr Beaulieu, 29.8.96, two at light (BG).

2360 *Amphipoea oculea* (Linnaeus, 1761)
Ear Moth
In the 1950s this moth was commonly seen by day on flowers of ragwort *Senecio jacobaea*, on the downs, on heaths

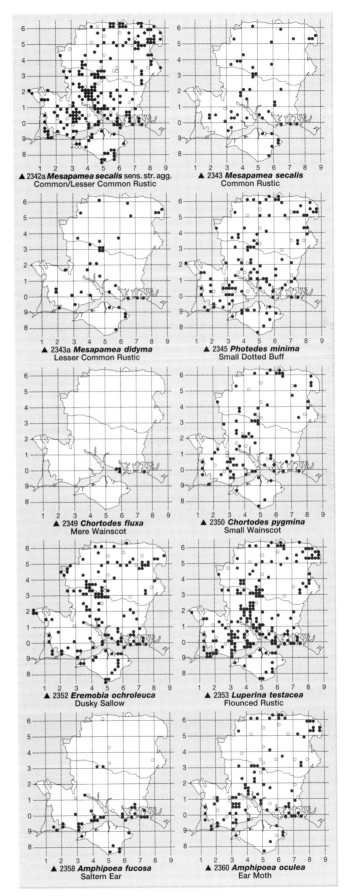

▲ 2342a *Mesapamea secalis* sens. str. agg.
Common/Lesser Common Rustic

▲ 2343 *Mesapamea secalis*
Common Rustic

▲ 2343a *Mesapamea didyma*
Lesser Common Rustic

▲ 2345 *Photedes minima*
Small Dotted Buff

▲ 2349 *Chortodes fluxa*
Mere Wainscot

▲ 2350 *Chortodes pygmina*
Small Wainscot

▲ 2352 *Eremobia ochroleuca*
Dusky Sallow

▲ 2353 *Luperina testacea*
Flounced Rustic

▲ 2358 *Amphipoea fucosa*
Saltern Ear

▲ 2360 *Amphipoea oculea*
Ear Moth

and along the coast. It is seldom encountered thus today, but occasional specimens are reported at light across the area.

2361 *Hydraecia micacea* (Esper, 1789)
Rosy Rustic
Widespread and locally common in all three vice-counties. The larva feeds in the tap-roots of plants such as docks *Rumex* spp. and burdocks *Arctium* spp.

2362 *Hydraecia petasitis* Doubleday, 1847
Butterbur Moth
Owing to its secretive habits, this is a moth that requires looking for. It probably occurs in every extensive patch of butterbur *Petasites hybridus* on the Hampshire mainland, especially around the Winchester area in the valleys of the Test and Itchen, but many of the records shown on the map are pre-1980. It has not been recorded from the Isle of Wight.

■ vc11 Beaulieu, 1.9.93 (BI-J); Havant, 2.9.97, one at m.v. light, new for garden (CBC).

■ vc12 East Stratton, 20.8.68, 30.8 and 31.8 and 9.9.92 (BI-J).

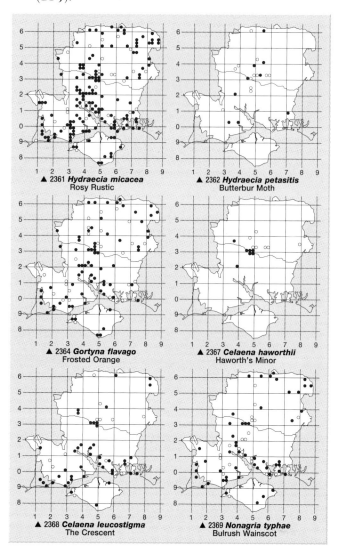

▲ 2361 *Hydraecia micacea*
Rosy Rustic

▲ 2362 *Hydraecia petasitis*
Butterbur Moth

▲ 2364 *Gortyna flavago*
Frosted Orange

▲ 2367 *Celaena haworthii*
Haworth's Minor

▲ 2368 *Celaena leucostigma*
The Crescent

▲ 2369 *Nonagria typhae*
Bulrush Wainscot

2364 *Gortyna flavago* ([Denis & Schiffermüller], 1775)
Frosted Orange
Fairly common in all three vice-counties. The larva feeds in the roots and lower stems of burdock *Arctium* spp., thistles *Carduus* and *Cirsium* spp., foxglove *Digitalis* and other herbaceous plants.

2367 *Celaena haworthii* (Curtis, 1829)
Haworth's Minor
Frequent in the Itchen valley above Winchester, straying into vc11, and occasionally recorded in the Test valley north of Stockbridge. An old record for the Isle of Wight is given in Goater (1974). The larval foodplant in Hampshire is unknown.

2368 *Celaena leucostigma* (Hübner, 1808)
The Crescent
Local in marshes, mainly near the coast of S Hants. The larva lives in the stems of yellow iris *Iris pseudacorus* and greater pond-sedge *Carex riparia*.

■ vc11 Gaters Mill, Mansbridge, 12.8.89 (PAB); Leigh Park, Havant, 14.8.96 (CBC).

■ vc12 Pamber Forest, 5.8.97 (GJD); Yateley Common, 23.7.93 (AMD).

2369 *Nonagria typhae* (Thunberg, 1784)
Bulrush Wainscot
This species probably occurs wherever reed-mace *Typha latifolia* is established. After the 1939–45 War, flooded cellars on the bombed sites in Southampton were soon colonised by the plant, and soon the stems were found to contain larvae or pupae of this moth (BG, pers. obs.). Moths taken at light away from known breeding localities are invariably wandering females.

■ vc10 Freshwater, 15.8.94, f. *fraterna* (SAK-J).

2370 *Archanara geminipuncta* (Haworth, 1809)
Twin-spotted Wainscot
Locally abundant in reed-beds, especially those along the coast at Keyhaven, Lower Test and Titchfield Haven, and extending inland along the valleys of the Avon, Test and Itchen. The larva lives in the stems of common reed *Phragmites australis*, causing the central leaves to wither.

■ vc11 Rownhams, 6.8.94, 28.7.95 (KG); Kings Somborne, 31.7.95 (TJN); Woolston, 15.8.96, first since 1990 (ARC).

2371 *Archanara dissoluta* (Treitschke, 1825)
Brown-veined Wainscot
Present in the reed-beds of Hampshire and the Isle of Wight, mostly near the coast, but much less common than *A. geminipuncta*. The larva pupates lower down the stem of the foodplant, head downwards: in *A. geminipuncta*, the pupa lies head upwards, higher in the stem, and is easier to find.

■ vc11 Rownhams, 29.7.95 (KG); Brockenhurst, 8.8.92 (JEC); Kings Somborne, 14.8.93 (TJN); Woolston, 27.7.91 (ARC).

■ vc12 Greywell Moors NR, 3.8 and 16.8.94, at m.v. light (AHD).

2373 *Archanara sparganii* (Esper, 1790)
Webb's Wainscot   **Notable/Nb**

Locally common in the marshes of the Isle of Wight and S Hants, but unrecorded from N Hants.

■ vc10 Binstead, 12.8.96, first record for garden (BJW).
■ vc11 St Ives, Ringwood, 31.8.87, at m.v. light (JHC); Totton, 22.8.91 (MJ).

2374 *Archanara algae* (Esper, 1789)
Rush Wainscot   **RDB3**

The two mysterious but genuine records given in Goater (1974), from Hengistbury Head on 6.8.53, and Southampton Common on 9.8.69, both vc11, are the only ones for this highly colonial species, the larva of which lives in the stems chiefly of common club-rush *Schoenoplectus lacustris* and lesser reed-mace *Typha angustifolia*.

2375 *Rhizedra lutosa* (Hübner, 1803)
Large Wainscot

Widely distributed in the drier parts of reed-beds in all three vice-counties, where the larva feeds in the roots and lower stems of common reed. Occasional wanderers, nearly always females, are taken at light elsewhere.

2376 *Sedina buettneri* (Hering, 1858)
Blair's Wainscot   **RDB1**

This species, discovered in Freshwater Marsh in 1945, was lost about 1952 when the marsh was drained and burned. However, its discovery in Dorset in 1996 leads one to hope it may be refound in this area. The larva feeds in the stems of lesser pond-sedge *Carex acutiformis*.

2377 *Arenostola phragmitidis* (Hübner, 1803)
Fen Wainscot

Common to abundant in reed-beds, mainly near the coast of S Hants.

■ vc11 Totton, 26.7.90 (MJ); Kings Somborne, 12.8.95 (TJN); Allbrook, 8.8.96 (ML); Bitterne, 19.7.95 (PAB); Woolston, 1990–93, common (ARC).

2378 *Oria musculosa* (Hübner, 1808)
Brighton Wainscot   **Notable/Na**

This species spread into the wheatfields of N Hants from the Salisbury area just before and during the War years of 1939–45, and became locally common. Subsequently, there were a few records from S Hants and one from Freshwater Marsh, Isle of Wight (Goater, 1974). After flourishing in N Hants for several years, the species suddenly showed a population crash in the late 1970s, and the last report received was of one at Burghclere in 1983 (Goater, 1992). The species is now on the brink of extinction in this country.

■ vc12 Cholderton, 16.7.70, last record at this location (HE).

2379 *Coenobia rufa* (Haworth, 1809)
Small Rufous

Widespread but local in bogs and marshes in all three vice-counties, but most common in the New Forest.

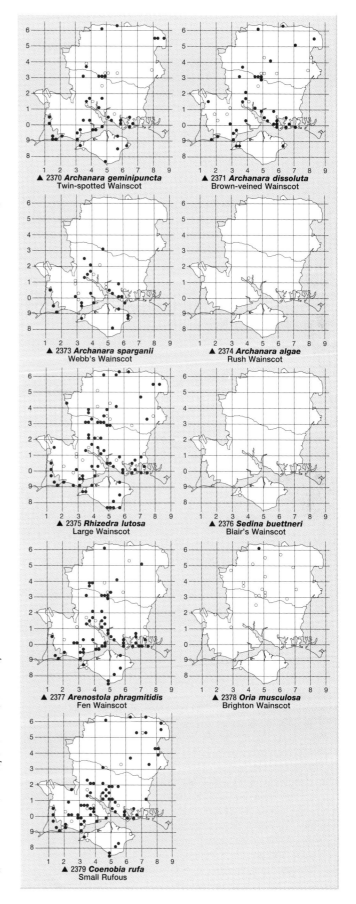

▲ 2370 *Archanara geminipuncta*
Twin-spotted Wainscot

▲ 2371 *Archanara dissoluta*
Brown-veined Wainscot

▲ 2373 *Archanara sparganii*
Webb's Wainscot

▲ 2374 *Archanara algae*
Rush Wainscot

▲ 2375 *Rhizedra lutosa*
Large Wainscot

▲ 2376 *Sedina buettneri*
Blair's Wainscot

▲ 2377 *Arenostola phragmitidis*
Fen Wainscot

▲ 2378 *Oria musculosa*
Brighton Wainscot

▲ 2379 *Coenobia rufa*
Small Rufous

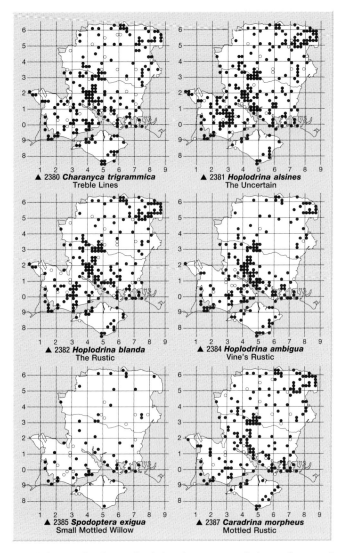

▲ 2380 *Charanyca trigrammica*
Treble Lines

▲ 2381 *Hoplodrina alsines*
The Uncertain

▲ 2382 *Hoplodrina blanda*
The Rustic

▲ 2384 *Hoplodrina ambigua*
Vine's Rustic

▲ 2385 *Spodoptera exigua*
Small Mottled Willow

▲ 2387 *Caradrina morpheus*
Mottled Rustic

There, the larva feed in the stems of sharp-flowered rush *Juncus acutiflorus*; in marshes, the foodplant is soft rush *J. effusus*. Isolated records of interest are given below.

■ vc11 Whitenap, Romsey, 16.8.95 (MJB); Chandlers Ford, 3.8.91 (BG).
■ vc12 Crawley, 7.8.81, only one seen (RAB).

2380 *Charanyca trigrammica* (Hufnagel, 1766)
Treble Lines
Widespread and usually common in open woodland and grassy places in all three vice-counties.

2381 *Hoplodrina alsines* (Brahm, 1791)
The Uncertain
Common in all three vice-counties. Most recorders have shown themselves competent to distinguish this from the next species.

2382 *Hoplodrina blanda* ([Denis & Schiffermüller], 1775)
The Rustic
Common in all three vice-counties, though rather less so than the preceding species.

2384 *Hoplodrina ambigua* ([Denis & Schiffermüller], 1775)
Vine's Rustic
Now common in all three vice-counties, but especially so in S Hants.

2385 *Spodoptera exigua* (Hübner, 1808)
Small Mottled Willow
One of the commoner migrant species. It appears in greater or lesser numbers most years in all three vice-counties.
■ vc22 Mortimer West End, 28.7 and 29.7.98, singletons seen at m.v. light (GJD).

2386 *Spodoptera littoralis* (Boisduval, 1833)
Mediterranean Brocade
The specimen taken at Lymington on 13.10.78 (AJP) was a probable immigrant (Goater, 1992). It is also occasionally imported with bananas, tomatoes and other fruits (Skinner, 1998).

2387 *Caradrina morpheus* (Hufnagel, 1766)
Mottled Rustic
Widespread and fairly common in all three vice-counties.

2389 *Paradrina clavipalpis* (Scopoli, 1763)
Pale Mottled Willow
Widespread and common, especially in built-up areas, towns, villages and farms.

2391 *Chilodes maritima* (Tauscher, 1806)
Silky Wainscot
Resident in the large reed-beds in all three vice-counties, and along the river valleys. Occasional wanderers turn up at light some distance from their breeding grounds.
■ vc10 Freshwater, 1.9.95, f. *bipunctatus* (SAK-J); Chale Green, 25.7.94 (SRC); St Catherine's Point, 30.6.95 (PMP).
■ vc11 Beaulieu, 30.7.94, one f. *bipunctatus* (BI-J); Rownhams, 20.7.96, f. *bipunctatus* (KG); Chandlers Ford, 6.6.96, one at light, first record (BG); Bitterne, 27.6.96, one (PAB); Gosport, 15.7.96 (DSW).
■ vc12 Fleet Pond (NB).

2392 *Athetis pallustris* (Hübner, 1808)
Marsh Moth   **RDB3**
The one ancient record of this species in Hampshire, a female taken flying by day at Ringwood in 1870, is detailed in Goater (1974).

2393 *Acosmetia caliginosa* (Hübner, 1813)
Reddish Buff   **RDB1**
Still resident on the Isle of Wight. Attempts are currently under way to reintroduce the moth to mainland Hants. **This species is protected by the Wildlife and Countryside Act, 1981. It is illegal to collect or disturb it in any of its stages.**

2394 *Stilbia anomala* (Haworth, 1812)
The Anomalous
More or less confined to the New Forest, and there very local, favouring dry railway banks and other places where the common grass is wavy hair-grass *Deschampsia flexuosa*;

it is possibly associated also with other fine-leaved grasses such as bristle-bent *Agrostis curtisii* and fine-leaved sheep's fescue *Festuca filiformis*. Fassnidge (1923–24) gave Ch[andlers] F[or]d, loc. c. R[obertson], and in the "Ludlow" coll., there are two specimens from Chandlers Ford taken by R.B. Robertson dated 1912 and others, without captor, dated 29.8.09 and 29.8.11 (HCCMS).

■ vc10 Chale Green, 19.9.94 (SRC).

■ vc11 Pennington, 4.9.95, male at light (RC); Roydon Woods, 31.8.90 (PAB); Beaulieu, 29.8.95, male, 5.9.95, female at m.v. light (BI-J); Woolston, 14.9.90, 2.9.95; Sholing, 27.8.99 (ARC).

2396 *Elaphria venustula* (Hübner, 1821)
Rosy Marbled   **Notable/Nb**

Recorded with increasing frequency in both the mainland vice-counties, and now known from the Isle of Wight. It has become especially frequent in the New Forest. It favours bracken-clad open woodland and heath-margins where the foodplant, tormentil *Potentilla erecta* grows. All records received since 1992 are detailed below.

■ vc10 Binstead, 19.6.98, one at m.v. light (BJW); Freshwater, 13.6.92, one at m.v. light (Knill-Jones, 1994). **New vc record.**

■ vc11 Hazleton Gardens, Horndean, 30.5.64, netted at dusk (M.E. Castle, Diary) appears to be the second Hampshire record; Sopley Common, 3.6.00, one at m.v. light (MJ); Matchams, nr Ringwood, 16.6.86, 2.7.86 (GL); Linwood, 6.6.98 (AGP); Brockenhurst, up to four each year; Bratley Inclosure, 11.7.96 (JEC); Set Thorns Inclosure, 22.6.99, at m.v. light; Frame Wood, 3.7.99, at m.v. light (DGG); Beaulieu, 19.6 to 20.6.95, three at m.v. light, six between 26.6 and 10.7.96, 15.6.00 (BI-J); Rownhams, 18.6.95 (KG); Broughton Down, 27.7.95 (NB); Southwick, 10.7.91, one at m.v. light (Townsend and Wynne, 1992); Fareham, 16.6.99, one at m.v. light (MLO); Havant Thicket, 28.6.95, one at m.v. light (JRL).

■ vc12 Conford, 21.6.95, one at m.v. light (JRL); Pamber Forest, 4.7.93; Silchester Common, 29.6.95, one (GJD); Selborne, 9.7 and 19.7.96, first records, 20.6.98 (AEA); Castle Bottom NNR, 23.6.97, several; Yateley Common, 7.6 and 26.6.94 (AMD); Alice Holt, 10.6.92 (Rothamsted Survey); Farnborough, 27.6.96, two (RWP).

■ vc22 Mortimer West End, 20.6.98, one seen at m.v. light (GJD).

2397 *Panemeria tenebrata* (Scopoli, 1763)
Small Yellow Underwing

Scattered colonies of this moth occur in all three vice-counties in meadows and on downs, but it is largely absent from the New Forest.

■ vc10 Ashey, 15.5.93, by day; Knighton Down, 12.6.96, one by day (BJW).

■ vc11 Woodley, Romsey, 1.6.95 (NB); Barce River, Romsey, 19.5.87 (PAB); Casbrook Common, 20.5.00 (TJN); Hum Hole, Bitterne, 6.6.96 (PAB); Bishops Waltham, 1995, fairly common (RAB).

■ vc12 Ashford Hill NNR, 28.5 and 29.5.00 (A and LB, TJN); Bartley Heath NR, Hook, 10.5.94, very small colony (AHD); Blacksmiths Meadow, Selborne, 6.6.96,

two seen (AEA); Odiham Common, 1996; Rye Common, 1994; Yateley Common, 1995 (AMD).

2398 *Periphanes delphinii* (Linnaeus, 1758)
Pease Blossom

No recent record (see Goater, 1974).

2399 *Pyrrhia umbra* (Hufnagel, 1766)
Bordered Sallow

This is now a rare species, and more or less confined to coastal localities and a few places on the chalk. The foodplant

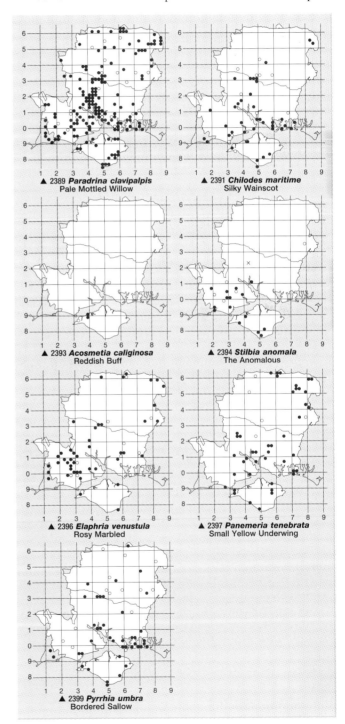

▲ 2389 *Paradrina clavipalpis*
Pale Mottled Willow

▲ 2391 *Chilodes maritime*
Silky Wainscot

▲ 2393 *Acosmetia caliginosa*
Reddish Buff

▲ 2394 *Stilbia anomala*
The Anomalous

▲ 2396 *Elaphria venustula*
Rosy Marbled

▲ 2397 *Panemeria tenebrata*
Small Yellow Underwing

▲ 2399 *Pyrrhia umbra*
Bordered Sallow

is restharrow *Ononis* spp. Occasional wanderers turn up at light away from established populations.

■ vc10 Chale Green, 1.7.93 (SRC *comm.* SAK-J).

■ vc11 Kings Somborne, 12.7.97 (TJN); Woolston, 1990–96, up to seven each year (ARC); Downleaze Copse, Exton, 16.6.95 (PAB); Gosport, 23.7.95, one at light (DSW), Cosham, 19.7.99, first record (TJJ); Southsea, 12.8.97, one at light (IRT); Gutner Point, Hayling Island, 24.7.94 (AMD).

2400 *Helicoverpa armigera* (Hübner, 1808)
Scarce Bordered Straw

A moderately frequent immigrant species, recorded from all three vice-counties. Larvae are often found on imported tomatoes, peppers and peas but, as far as is known, they have only once been recorded in the wild.

■ vc10 Binstead, regularly recorded at light. In 1997, five larvae were found in garden on red geranium, first moth emerged early December (BJW).

2401 *Heliothis viriplaca* (Hufnagel, 1766)
Marbled Clover   RDB3

Occasional specimens are reported at light on or near chalk

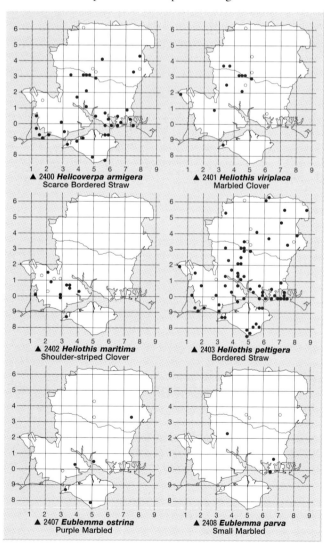

▲ 2400 *Helicoverpa armigera*
Scarce Bordered Straw

▲ 2401 *Heliothis viriplaca*
Marbled Clover

▲ 2402 *Heliothis maritima*
Shoulder-striped Clover

▲ 2403 *Heliothis peltigera*
Bordered Straw

▲ 2407 *Eublemma ostrina*
Purple Marbled

▲ 2408 *Eublemma parva*
Small Marbled

downland. Whether these are representatives of a tiny surviving resident population or immigrants is uncertain. In the past, the moth was found more often though irregularly in such habitat, which was then more extensive.

■ vc10 Freshwater, 27.7.85, 13.8 and 14.8.96, singles at m.v. light (Knill-Jones, 1997d).

■ vc11 Wood Crates, 19.10.95 (JEC and JMS); Timsbury, 1994 (DT).

■ vc12 Leckford, (BG, BS); Stockbridge Down, 15.7.95, one by day (GAC); Crawley, 6.8 and 7.8.94, 1995, two at m.v. light in garden, 20.8.96 (RAB); Magdalen Hill Down, 22.8.97, one seen by day (PAB, DGG).

2402 *Heliothis maritima* de Graslin, 1855
Shoulder-striped Clover   RDB3

In Hampshire, this species is more or less confined to the New Forest, where it occurs on damp heathland, although recent records have been few. Surprisingly, there is only one record from the heaths of NE Hampshire (see below), for in the past it has been not uncommon on the neighbouring Surrey heaths.

■ vc10 Freshwater, 27.7.85, originally identified as *H. viriplaca* (Goater, 1992), but later corrected to this species (Knill-Jones, 1994f). **New vc record.**

■ vc11 East Denny Bog, 27.7.86 (PAB); Shatterford, 2.7.99 (JEC).

■ vc12 Fleet, 5.7.52, two specimens captured on heather (Kindred, 1954). **New vc record.** This previously overlooked record was pointed out to the authors by David Green. The exact locality is uncertain.

2403 *Heliothis peltigera* ([Denis & Schiffermüller], 1775)
Bordered Straw

10 mm

A fairly common migrant species. It often produces a locally-bred generation, but so far seems to be unable to survive the British winter. Larvae are found on coastal shingle on sticky groundsel *Senecio viscosus* and sometimes on marigolds in cottage gardens.

■ vc11 Sinah Common, 19.6.96, c.8 flying between 1730 and 1830 hrs, some ovipositing on restharrow *Ononis repens* and others feeding at flowers of viper's bugloss *Echium vulgare* (GRE).

2405 *Protoschinia scutosa* ([Denis & Schiffermüller], 1775)
Spotted Clover

There is a single record of this species, taken at Seaview on the Isle of Wight on 3.7.59 (Goater, 1974).

2407 *Eublemma ostrina* (Hübner, 1808)
Purple Marbled

All known 20th century records of this very scarce immigrant species are summarised below. In addition there are four 19th century records in Goater (1974).

■ vc10 Chale Green, 20.5.92, three at m.v. light (SRC,

comm. SAK-J); Freshwater, 26.8.92, one f. *carthami* at m.v. light (SAK-J, 1994).

■ vc11 Sandydown, nr Lymington, 30.10.52 (P.J.M.Robinson); Beaulieu, 15.10.95, one at light, in coll. BG (BI-J); Bishops Waltham, 8.8.92 by Dr J. Fisher (Skinner, 1996); Solent Court, Warsash, 15.5.92 (PMP).

■ vc12 Micheldever, 30.6.57 (C.H. Dixon); Martyr Worthy, 15.5 and 23.5.69 (D.W.H. ffennell); Selborne, 1.10.99, one at m.v. light, now in Nat. Hist. Mus., London (AEA).

2408 *Eublemma parva* (Hübner, 1808)
Small Marbled

Hampshire and the Isle of Wight benefited from small influxes of this moth in 1953 and to a lesser extent in 1968 (Goater, 1974). A further specimen was taken at Southsea on 7.8.80 (Goater, 1992). Since then, two further records of this scarce immigrant have come to hand.

■ vc11 Hilliers Arboretum, Ampfield, 21.7.98, one at m.v. light (PAB); Widley, 24.7.89 (PMP).

[2409 *Eublemma minutata* (Fabricius, 1794)
Scarce Marbled

There is one ancient record from Freshwater (Goater, 1974), which is considered to require confirmation.]

2410 *Protodeltote pygarga* (Hufnagel, 1766)
Marbled White Spot

Fairly common to common in open woodland and damp heaths in all three vice-counties. The larva feeds on purple moor-grass *Molinia caerulea* and other grasses.

2412 *Deltote uncula* (Clerck, 1759)
Silver Hook

The colonies of this species, an inhabitant of marshes and boggy heathland, have diminished greatly since the 1950s, but remain scattered on the mainland. The current status of *D. uncula* on the Isle of Wight is uncertain.

■ vc10 Godshill, 2.7.86 (PJC) is the only recent record.

■ vc11 Brockenhurst, 13.6.80, 29.5.89 (JEC); Beaulieu, 8.7.94 (BI-J).

■ vc12 Crawley, 13.7.83, only one seen (RAB); Winnall Moors NR (DHS); Ashford Hill NNR, 8.7.95, one (AS).

2415 *Acontia lucida* (Hufnagel, 1766)
Pale Shoulder

■ vc11 Linford, 19.8.96, one at m.v. light (AGP). **New county record.**

2418 *Earias clorana* (Linnaeus, 1761)
Cream-bordered Green Pea　　　　　　Notable/Nb

An inhabitant of marshes and damp woodland in the river valleys where the larva feeds on osier and various species of willow *Salix* spp.

■ vc10 Freshwater, 25.6.93 (SAK-J); Godshill, 22.7.94 (PJC, *comm.* SAK-J); St Catherine's Point, 30.6.95, two, 1.7.95, six, at light (PMP); Chale Green, 27.6 and 29.6.93 (SRC, *comm.* SAK-J).

■ vc11 Hengistbury, fairly common at two sites (MJ);

Matchams, nr Ringwood, 1985, 1986 (GL); Pennington, 7.7.95 (RC); Titchfield Haven, 29.6.00, one at m.v. light (BD).

2419 *Earias biplaga* Walker, 1866
Spiny Bollworm

Only two British specimens are currently known. The second of these was taken at Lymington on 23.7.82 (see Goater, 1992).

2420 *Earias insulana* (Boisduval, 1833)
Egyptian Bollworm

The second specimen to be found in Britain occurred at Brockenhurst on 8.10.67 (Goater, 1974).

2421 *Bena bicolorana* (Fuessly, 1775)
Scarce Silver-lines

Locally fairly common in oak woodland in all three vice-counties.

2422 *Pseudoips prasinana* (Linnaeus, 1758)
Green Silver-lines

Generally commoner and more widespread than the

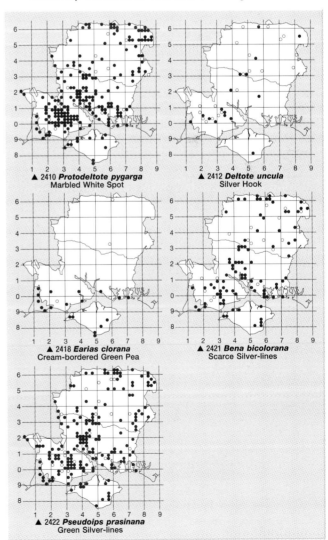

▲ 2410 *Protodeltote pygarga*
Marbled White Spot

▲ 2412 *Deltote uncula*
Silver Hook

▲ 2418 *Earias clorana*
Cream-bordered Green Pea

▲ 2421 *Bena bicolorana*
Scarce Silver-lines

▲ 2422 *Pseudoips prasinana*
Green Silver-lines

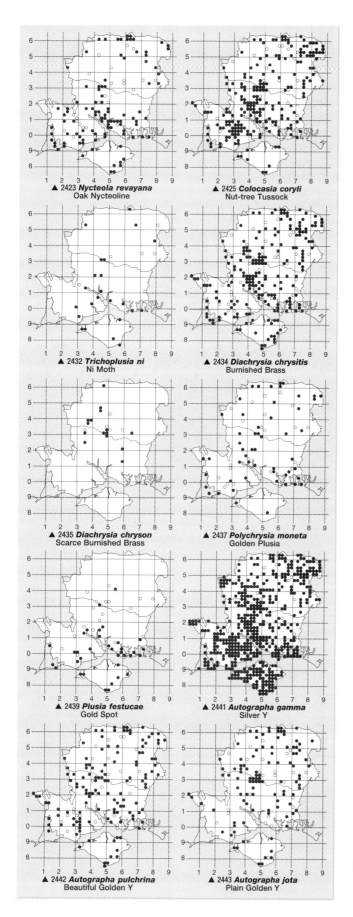

▲ 2423 *Nycteola revayana*
Oak Nycteoline

▲ 2425 *Colocasia coryli*
Nut-tree Tussock

▲ 2432 *Trichoplusia ni*
Ni Moth

▲ 2434 *Diachrysia chrysitis*
Burnished Brass

▲ 2435 *Diachrysia chryson*
Scarce Burnished Brass

▲ 2437 *Polychrysia moneta*
Golden Plusia

▲ 2439 *Plusia festucae*
Gold Spot

▲ 2441 *Autographa gamma*
Silver Y

▲ 2442 *Autographa pulchrina*
Beautiful Golden Y

▲ 2443 *Autographa jota*
Plain Golden Y

previous species, the larva having a wider range of foodplants which includes oak, birch and beech.

2423 *Nycteola revayana* (Scopoli, 1772)
Oak Nycteoline

Widely distributed in oak and mixed deciduous woodland in all three vice-counties. The moth comes to light before and after hibernation; in the autumn it visits the flowers of ling and during the winter it may be beaten from yew trees in woodland, and from thickets of blackthorn.

[2424 *Nycteola degenerana* (Hübner, 1799)
Sallow Nycteoline

New Forest, 1905 (see Goater, 1974). There remains some doubt as to the true identity of this specimen.]

2425 *Colocasia coryli* (Linnaeus, 1758)
Nut-tree Tussock

10 mm

A common species in and near deciduous woodland in all three vice-counties. The moth is double-brooded and the larva feeds on a range of deciduous trees and shrubs, including hazel, birch and beech.

2428 *Chrysodeixis chalcites* (Esper, 1789)
Golden Twin-spot

Seven records of this very scarce immigrant are known for the area, three from Freshwater, two from Highcliffe, and one each from Warsash and Crawley.

■ vc10 Freshwater, 5.10.65 by SAK-J (Goater, 1974); Freshwater, 19.10.88, recorded as *C. acuta* (Goater, 1992), was really this species; Freshwater, 20.12.98, moth bred from a larva found on celery in Somerfields Supermarket, 19.11.98 (SAK-J).

■ vc11 Highcliffe, 9.9.85 by EHW (Goater, 1992), 2.10.90 (EHW); Solent Court, Warsash, 6.8.91, conf. JRL (PMP).

■ vc12 Crawley, 23.9.98, female at m.v. light (RAB). **New vc record.**

2429 *Chrysodeixis acuta* (Walker, 1858)
Tunbridge Wells Gem

There are two genuine records of this extremely scarce immigrant, one from Burghclere vc12 on 5.11.55 (Goater, 1974) and the following one from the Isle of Wight.

■ vc10 Binstead, 27.10.95, one at m.v. light at a time when several others were recorded along the south coast; identity confirmed by BG (BJW) (see Knill-Jones, 1997d). **New vc record.** [The Freshwater record (Goater, 1992) has been reidentified as *C. chalcites* and must be deleted. See above.]

2430 *Ctenoplusia limbirena* (Guenée, 1852)
Scar Bank Gem

This is another extremely rare immigrant plusiid, of which

there have been two records from Freshwater, Isle of Wight (Goater, 1974, 1992) and the following one from S Hants.

■ vc11 Southsea, 10.6.97, one at m.v. light (Langmaid, 1998). **New vc record.**

2432 *Trichoplusia ni* (Hübner, 1803)
Ni Moth

Another scarce immigrant species which has been taken occasionally in all three vice-counties.

■ vc10 Freshwater, 15.5.94 (Knill-Jones, 1994e), 25.11.94, 11.6.96 (SAK-J); Freshwater, 3.8.96 by D.B. Wooldridge; Bonchurch, 12.8.96 and five on 13.8.96 by J. Halsey; Godshill, 19.8.96 by P.J. Cramp (Knill-Jones, 1997d); Binstead, 16.8.96 (BJW). **New vc record.**

■ vc11 Brockenhurst, 17.9.92, 2.12.94 (JEC); Beaulieu, 14.8.96 (BI-J); Totton, 25.7.92 (Jeffes, 1995); Chandlers Ford, 8.8.92 (BG), 31.8.00 (BE); Winchester, 28.7 and 31.7.92, singles (DHS); Woolston, 26.7.92 (ARC); Warsash, 5.8.96, 12.8.96 (three), 20.8.96 (PMP); Bridgemary, Gosport, 5.8.96 (DSW); Southsea, 21.7.92, 14.8 and 1.9.96 (JRL); Hayling Island, 12.10.82, one at m.v. light, in coll. J. Phillips (JMW).

■ vc12 Wildhern, 28.6.00 (DGG); Bentley, 7.8.92 (MC).

2433 *Thysanoplusia orichalcea* (Fabricius, 1775)
Slender Burnished Brass

The 11 records for the area of this scarce immigrant are detailed in Goater (1974 and 1992) and summarised below. Precise locations for some records are not known.

■ vc10 Freshwater, 20.9.61, 8.10.62 and 20.9.87 by SAK-J.

■ vc11 New Milton, 8.10.69 by M.D.Noble; Minstead, 9.10.69 by L.W.Siggs; Lymington, 1.9 and 5.9.80 by AJP; Highcliffe, 21.3.85 by EHW; Boldre, 29.7.83; Brockenhurst, 15.8.87 by A.D.Russwurm.

■ vc12 East Stratton, 4.9.88 by BI-J.

2434 *Diachrysia chrysitis* (Linnaeus, 1758)
Burnished Brass

Widespread and common in all three vice-counties.

2435 *Diachrysia chryson* (Esper, 1789)
Scarce Burnished Brass   **Notable/Na**

10 mm

In Hampshire, the headquarters of this nationally very local species are in the Test valley north and south of Stockbridge; there is another colony in the Winchester area, in the valley of the Itchen. The larva feeds on hemp-agrimony *Eupatorium cannabinum* growing in carr and along the margins of fen woodland but not, apparently, in dry places.

■ vc11 Kings Somborne, 8.7.94, four during July, 1995, 11.7 and 27.7.96 (TJN); Downleaze Copse, Exton, 20.7.94, three at m.v. light (PAB).

■ vc12 Winnall Moors NR (DHS); Ropley, 3.8.91 (PAB).

2436 *Macdunnoughia confusa* (Stephens, 1850)
Dewick's Plusia

There have been three records in our area to date of this rare migrant that is expanding its range into Western Europe.

■ vc11 Portsmouth, 28.8.91 by I.Lakin (Goater, 1992); Northney, N Hayling Island, 25.9.99, one at m.v. light (PRD): *Atropos* **10**, Pl.2 fig.4.

■ vc12 Greywell, 2.10.98, moth found indoors fluttering against a window (PB): specimen in coll. AHD. **New vc record.**

2437 *Polychrysia moneta* (Fabricius, 1787)
Golden Plusia

This moth became established in Hampshire towards the end of the 19th century and became a moderately common cottage garden species, the larva feeding on cultivated larkspur *Delphinium* spp. and monkshood *Aconitum* spp. It has decreased rather dramatically in the last 30 years, probably due to the increased use of insecticide sprays by gardeners, but is still reported occasionally.

■ vc11 Fordingbridge, 21.9.96 (NHu); Pennington, 22.6.95 (RC); Totton, 1991–92, several (MJ); Whitenap, Romsey, 26.6.93 (MJB); Kings Somborne, 28.7.95 (TJN); Chandlers Ford, 11.7.94 (BG); Allbrook, 25.6.96 (ML); Woolston, 1990–97, one or two every year (ARC); Leigh Park, Havant, 20.7.95, one at light (CBC).

■ vc12 South Wonston, 1.7.93, 23.6.95 (PJSS); Pamber Heath, 1.7.95, one (AS); Selborne, 3.7.94, 5.7 and 25.7.96 (AEA); Farnborough, 2.7.94 (RWP).

2439 *Plusia festucae* (Linnaeus, 1758)
Gold Spot

This has always been an uncommon resident species in the area, mainly in the coastal marshes and to a lesser extent in the river valleys. Occasional wanderers turn up elsewhere.

■ vc10 Freshwater, 8.7.89 (SAK-J); Binstead, 27.7.90, 29.7 and 30.7.94, 5.8.94 (BJW).

■ vc11 Christchurch, 11.8.94, Totton, 19.8.91 (MJ); Gosport, 31.7.95, one at light (DSW), Southsea, 6.8 and 21.8.97, at light (IRT).

2441 *Autographa gamma* (Linnaeus, 1758)
Silver Y

A common immigrant which may breed during the summer. In 1996, it was present in extreme abundance, almost certainly occurred in every 2 km square in the area.

2442 *Autographa pulchrina* (Haworth, 1809)
Beautiful Golden Y

Widespread and fairly common in all three vice-counties.

2443 *Autographa jota* (Linnaeus, 1758)
Plain Golden Y

Widespread and fairly common in all three vice-counties, and usually slightly more frequent than *A. pulchrina* except on acid soils, where the reverse is the case.

2444 *Autographa bractea* ([Denis & Schiffermüller], 1775)
Gold Spangle

Two records (Goater, 1974), from Bournemouth on 19.7.33, and Minstead on 26.7.73, both in S Hants. This is predominantly a northern species in Britain.

2447 *Syngrapha interrogationis* (Linnaeus, 1758)
Scarce Silver Y

A resident in Wales and northern Britain and a rare immigrant in the south.
■ vc11 Woolston, 10.8.95, one at m.v. light (ARC) in coll. Nat. Hist. Mus., London; 3rd county record.

2448 *Cornutiplusia circumflexa* (Linnaeus, 1767)
Essex Y

The only fully authenticated British record is the one from Sway on 29.7.79 (Goater, 1992 and Skinner, 1998).

2449 *Abrostola triplasia* (Linnaeus, 1758)
Dark Spectacle

This has always been a very uncommon species in the area (Goater, 1974, 1992). All recent records are given below.
■ vc10 Freshwater, 2.9.90 (SAK-J); Chale Green, four in July 1993, first records (SRC); Binstead, 31.7.95, 20.9, 22.9 and 27.9.98, at m.v. light (BJW).
■ vc11 Hurn, 29.6.98 (MJ); Brockenhurst, three records (JEC); Solent Court, Warsash, one record (PMP); Titchfield Haven, 16.9.92 (PMP); Bridgemary, Gosport, 10.5.95, one at light, conf. JRL (DSW); Southsea, 26.7.95 (JRL), Milton Common, 18.6.00, one at m.v. light (IRT); Hayling Island, 6.10.85, 10.7.86, singles at m.v. light (JMW); N Hayling Island (PRD).
■ vc12 Crawley, 25.9.99 (RAB); Selborne, 7.8 and 30.8 and 8.9.95, singletons at light (AEA).

2450 *Abrostola tripartita* (Hufnagel, 1766)
The Spectacle

Widespread and common in all three vice-counties.

2451 *Catocala fraxini* (Linnaeus, 1758)
Clifden Nonpareil

This spectacular immigrant has been reported from time to time in all three vice-counties but has so far failed to become established. Despite its name, the moth is normally associated with aspen *Populus tremula* woods, though ash *Fraxinus excelsior* is listed as a foodplant by Continental authors. There were 11 records before 1950 (Goater, 1974) and all subsequent ones are listed below.
■ vc10 Freshwater, 7.10.86 by C.Pope; 9.10.96, 4.10.98, singles at m.v. light (SAK-J); Gurnard Marsh, 24.9.96 by Mr Downer (Knill-Jones, 1997d).
■ vc11 Lymington, 1.10.81 by Mr. Harmer; Highcliffe, 10.9.82 by EHW; Matchams, nr Ringwood, 1985 (GL); Christchurch, 12.10.95, worn specimen at m.v. light (MJ).

2452 *Catocala nupta* (Linnaeus, 1767)
Red Underwing

The most widely-distributed *Catocala* in the area, though far less common than formerly. In the early 1950s it was possible to find upwards of half a dozen specimens resting on the trees in Southampton Avenue by patrolling the road on a bicycle!

2454 *Catocala promissa* ([Denis & Schiffermüller], 1775)
Light Crimson Underwing   **RDB3**

This and the next species are two for which the New Forest is famous. Both still occur there, but numbers fluctuate from year to year. Formerly, *C. promissa* was rather more widespread. Former localities have been mapped where possible. For other records, the reader is referred to Goater (1974, 1992).
■ vc10 Shanklin, 12.9.79 and 14.8.82 by JMC (Goater, 1992) are the only two records.
■ vc11 Highcliffe, 4.8.82, and two subsequently (EHW, 1991); Totton, 21.7.92 (MJ).

2455 *Catocala sponsa* (Linnaeus, 1767)
Dark Crimson Underwing   **RDB2**

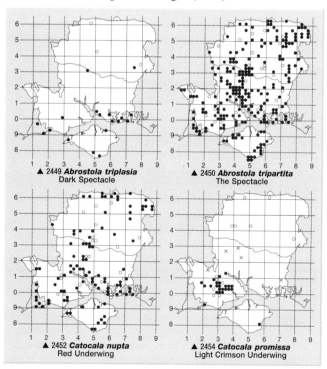

▲ 2449 *Abrostola triplasia*
Dark Spectacle

▲ 2450 *Abrostola tripartita*
The Spectacle

▲ 2452 *Catocala nupta*
Red Underwing

▲ 2454 *Catocala promissa*
Light Crimson Underwing

The few records of this species outside the New Forest suggest that it may occasionally migrate. The native population is closely associated with ancient oak woodland.

There are two records from vc10, at Sandown on 22.7.1893 and Freshwater on 12.8.58 (Goater, 1974).
■ vc11 Royal Victoria Country Park, Netley, 26.7.93 (D. Holt); Southsea, 2.8.84 by JRL (Goater, 1992); Hayling Island, 19.8.86, one at m.v. light (JMW).

2455a *Catocala nymphagoga* (Esper, 1788)
Oak Yellow Underwing
Of the two British records of this species, one occurred at Denny Lodge, New Forest, vc11, on 31.7.82 (Goater, 1992).

2456 *Minucia lunaris* ([Denis & Schiffermüller], 1775)
Lunar Double-stripe
The only record is of the specimen at Lee-on-Solent on 29.5.54 (Goater, 1974). It is a very scarce migrant which has shown it can establish itself for a short period.

2462 *Callistege mi* (Clerck, 1759)
Mother Shipton
This diurnal species is locally fairly common on downland, in rough grassland and waste places where clovers and trefoils *Trifolium* spp., medick or lucerne *Medicago* spp. occur.

2463 *Euclidia glyphica* (Linnaeus, 1758)
Burnet Companion

10 mm

This is another common diurnal species in all three vice-counties, which is found in similar locations to those favoured by *C. mi*.

2464 *Catephia alchymista* ([Denis & Schiffermüller], 1775)
The Alchymist
Apart from the ancient records given in Goater (1974) from the Isle of Wight, this species has never been reported in the county.

2465 *Tyta luctuosa* ([Denis & Schiffermüller], 1775)
The Four-spotted   **RDB3**
Alas, this appears to be one of our "lost" species. In the 1950s, it was locally fairly common on downland in a wide area around Winchester, and used also to be fairly frequent on the Isle of Wight (Goater, 1974). A possible sighting from Martin Down in 1982 (vc8) offers slight hope it may yet be found there.

2466 *Lygephila pastinum* (Treitschke, 1826)
The Blackneck
Still widespread in all three vice-counties, although it has decreased and become more local. It is found in marshes, rough grassland, hay fields and along railway banks where the foodplant, tufted vetch *Vicia cracca* grows.
■ vc10 Brading Down, 21.6.95, several by day (BJW).

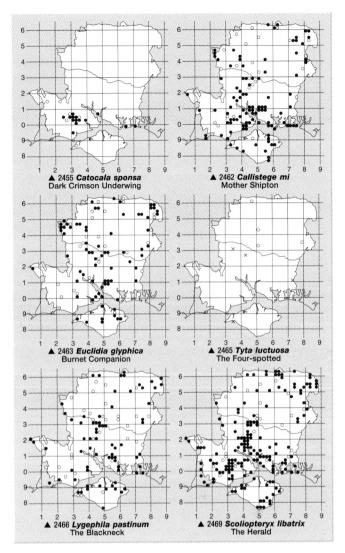

▲ 2455 *Catocala sponsa*
Dark Crimson Underwing

▲ 2462 *Callistege mi*
Mother Shipton

▲ 2463 *Euclidia glyphica*
Burnet Companion

▲ 2465 *Tyta luctuosa*
The Four-spotted

▲ 2466 *Lygephila pastinum*
The Blackneck

▲ 2469 *Scoliopteryx libatrix*
The Herald

■ vc11 Beaulieu, 3.7.94 (BI-J); Whitenap, Romsey, 27.6.95 (MJB); Chandlers Ford, 30.6.95, one at m.v. light (BG); Woolston, 18.7.94 (ARC); Botley Wood, 4.7.95, common at m.v. light (BG, JRL); Gosport, 21.7.95, one at light (DSW).
■ vc12 Porton Down, 7.7.91 (PAB); Magdalen Hill Down, 30.6.95 (PAB); South Wonston, 1993–95, annually (PJSS); Tadley, present in meadows in considerable numbers in 1994, not seen before (AECA); Noar Hill NR, 14.7.95 (AMJ); Farnborough, 24.7.94 (RWP); Odiham Common, 11.7.97; Hawley Meadows NR, 23.7.96 (AMD).

2469 *Scoliopteryx libatrix* (Linnaeus, 1758)
The Herald
Widespread and generally common in all three vice-counties. The moth comes freely to sugar, and also to light before and after hibernation, and the larva is often encountered on bushes of sallow and willow or poplar in late summer. Hibernating moths are sometimes found in groups in outhouses, and during the War years, they were common in the (rather damp) surface air-raid shelters along the local roads in Chandlers Ford.

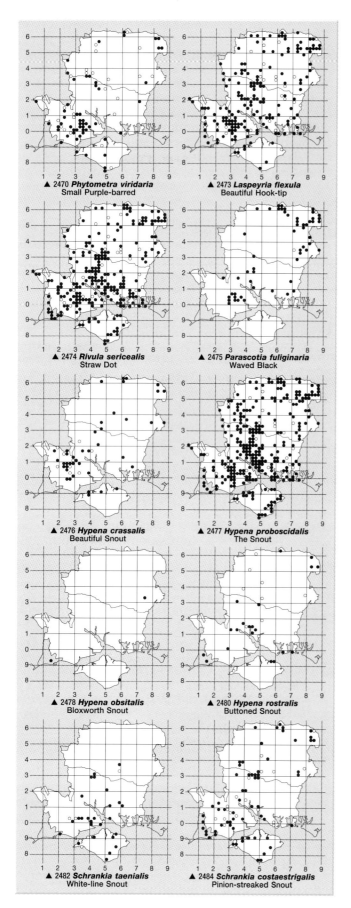

▲ 2470 *Phytometra viridaria*
Small Purple-barred

▲ 2473 *Laspeyria flexula*
Beautiful Hook-tip

▲ 2474 *Rivula sericealis*
Straw Dot

▲ 2475 *Parascotia fuliginaria*
Waved Black

▲ 2476 *Hypena crassalis*
Beautiful Snout

▲ 2477 *Hypena proboscidalis*
The Snout

▲ 2478 *Hypena obsitalis*
Bloxworth Snout

▲ 2480 *Hypena rostralis*
Buttoned Snout

▲ 2482 *Schrankia taenialis*
White-line Snout

▲ 2484 *Schrankia costaestrigalis*
Pinion-streaked Snout

2470 *Phytometra viridaria* (Clerck, 1759)
Small Purple-barred

Widespread and locally common in two quite different types of habitat, chalk downland and heaths. The common factor is the presence of the foodplants, species of milkwort *Polygala* spp.

2473 *Laspeyria flexula* ([Denis & Schiffermüller], 1775)
Beautiful Hook-tip

A widely-distributed woodland species in all three vice-counties. The larva feeds on lichens and algae *Desmococcus* growing on tree trunks.

2474 *Rivula sericealis* (Scopoli, 1763)
Straw Dot

Fairly common to common in marshes and bogs and in open, grassy woodland in all three vice-counties. The larva feeds at night on species of grass Poaceae (Gramineae), favouring purple moor-grass *Molinia caerulea* and false brome-grass *Brachypodium sylvaticum*.

2475 *Parascotia fuliginaria* (Linnaeus, 1761)
Waved Black   **Notable/Nb**

This interesting species, at one time more or less confined to the Bagshot Sands area of NE Hants, has extended its range and is now reported in small numbers across much of the mainland in pine-birch-heath country. The larva feeds communally on bracket fungi growing on decaying logs in damp woodland.

■ vc11 Brockenhurst, one in 1994, seven in 1995, two in 1997 (JEC); Beaulieu, 27.7 and 5.8.95, 4.8 and 6.8.96, 15.7 and 20.7.00 (BI-J); Chandlers Ford, 3.8.91 (BG); W Chandlers Ford, several in 1999 (BE); Allbrook, 22.7.91, 23.6.96 (ML); Portswood, 26.7.00, one (A and CD); Woolston, 25.7.91, 4.8.96, 23.7 and 4.8.97 (ARC); Widley, Portsdown, 21.6.89 (PMP); Havant, 27.7.97, one at m.v. light, new for garden (CBC); Waterlooville, 26.6.00, one at m.v. light (RJM).

■ vc12 Crawley, one worn specimen in July 1994, only one seen (RAB); Bartley Heath NR, 20.7.95, two at m.v. light (AHD); Pamber Forest, 13.8.91, three in 1997 (GJD), 9.7.95; Lord's Wood, Pamber, 9.7.95, one; Pamber Heath, 8.7 to 24.7.95, five recorded (AS); Selborne, one or two each year from 1993 (AEA); Castle Bottom NNR, 15.7.95 (NB); Rye Common, 26.7 and 5.8.96; Shortheath Common, 29.7.95, one; Yateley Common, 4.7 and 28.7.93, 7.7.97; Waggoners Wells, 4.8.96, two at light (AMD); Alice Holt, ten between 22.6 and 31.7.92 (Rothamsted Survey); Frith End, 15.7 and 22.7.95, singletons at light (KW); Farnborough, two in July, 1994 (RWP).

■ vc22 Mortimer West End, 28.7.98, two seen at m.v. light (GJD).

2476 *Hypena crassalis* (Fabricius, 1787)
Beautiful Snout

Local amongst bilberry *Vaccinium myrtillus*, mainly in the New Forest.

■ vc10 Binstead, 9.7.95, first record (BJW).

■ vc11 Bratley Inclosure, 11.7.96 (JEC); Rownhams, 11.7.95 (KG); Crab Wood, 14.7.93, single specimen at m.v. light (RAB); Chandlers Ford, 5.7.00, female at m.v. light (BG).

■ vc12 South Wonston, 6.7.00, one at m.v. light (PJSS); Yateley Common, 7.7.97, one at m.v. light, far from known stand of foodplant; Waggoners Wells, 4.8.96, three (AMD).

2477 *Hypena proboscidalis* (Linnaeus, 1758)
The Snout

10 mm

Very common in the vicinity of common nettle *Urtica dioica*, in all three vice-counties.

2478 *Hypena obsitalis* (Hübner, 1813)
Bloxworth Snout　　　　　　　　**RDB2/Migrant**

There have been three records, one from each of the three vice-counties. This species is an extremely scarce migrant, but has become established recently in the West Country, and may possibly do so here. The larva feeds on pellitory-of-the-wall *Parietaria judaica*.

■ vc10 Shanklin, 27.1.68 (AH Greenham, *teste* BFS). **New county record.**

■ vc11 Christchurch, 2.5.95, one at m.v. light (Jeffes, 1995). **New vc record.**

■ vc12 Selborne, 12.11.94, one at m.v. light (Aston, 1995b), now in coll. Nat. Hist. Mus., London. **New vc record.**

2480 *Hypena rostralis* (Linnaeus, 1758)
Buttoned Snout　　　　　　　　**Notable/Nb**

Very local and rather scarce. The larva feeds on wild hop *Humulus lupulus* and garden cultivars.

■ vc10 Ryde, 24.5 and 24.5 and 2.6.94, 6.6.95, 7.6.95, two, 31.8.95, three in 1998 (D and PP, *comm.* BJW); Binstead, 23.5.92, 6.6.92, 29.6.95, 12.5 and 4.6.98 (BJW).

■ vc11 Christchurch, 23.7 and 28.9.94 (MJ); Brockenhurst, 15.10.91 (JEC); Totton, 20.5.91 (MJ); Rownhams, 13.5.92 (KG); Kings Somborne, 13.5.99, one at light in garden (TJN); Portswood, 16.10.95 (A and CD); Bitterne Park, 31.5.96, one amongst ivy in garden (P and PW); Woolston, 1990–93, common (ARC); Southsea, 19.6.95, one at m.v. light (JRL).

■ vc12 Yateley Common, 11.5.93 (AMD); Farnborough, 9.4.96 (KW).

■ vc22 Mortimer West End, 15.5.98, one seen at m.v. light (GJD).

2482 *Schrankia taenialis* (Hübner, 1809)
White-line Snout　　　　　　　　**Notable/Nb**

Very local and usually uncommon, but probably overlooked. All post-1992 records are given.

■ vc10 High Down and Fort Victoria, July/August 1995, common (SAK-J); Walters Copse, Newtown, two in 1997

(AB); Queens Bower, 6.7.93 (NH); Firestone Copse, common flying at dusk (BJW).

■ vc11 Brockenhurst, 25.7.85 (JEC); Ladycross, 27.7.99, four at sugar-ropes (DGG); N of St Leonards, nr Beaulieu, 29.8.96, one at light; Spearbed Copse, Exbury, 5.10.95, one at m.v. light (BG); Southwick, 1996 (JRL, EAP); Botley Wood, 1.7.98, one netted at dusk; Titchfield Haven, 1996 (RJD).

2484 *Schrankia costaestrigalis* (Stephens, 1834)
Pinion-streaked Snout

Widespread and fairly common in marshy and boggy areas.

2485 *Hypenodes humidalis* Doubleday, 1850
Marsh Oblique-barred　　　　　　　**Notable/Nb**

Very locally abundant in bogs.

■ vc10 Freshwater, 20.8.96 (SAK-J).

■ vc11 Emer Bog, 19.8.93 (NB).

■ vc12 Shortheath Common, 13.8.97, two (AMD).

2488 *Pechipogo strigilata* (Linnaeus, 1758)
Common Fan-foot　　　　　　　　**Notable/Na**

This species has declined seriously, and until recently the only known surviving Hampshire colony was in Pamber Forest. It is most gratifying therefore to report a second locality in N Hants and in a third site, in the Test valley near Romsey. It is still present on the Isle of Wight, in Parkhurst Forest (PMW).

2489 *Zanclognatha tarsipennalis* Treitschke, 1835
The Fan-foot

Widespread and common, chiefly in deciduous woodland.

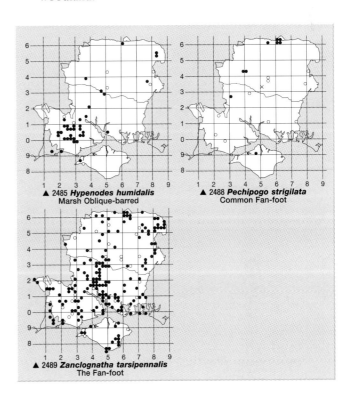

▲ 2485 *Hypenodes humidalis*
Marsh Oblique-barred

▲ 2488 *Pechipogo strigilata*
Common Fan-foot

▲ 2489 *Zanclognatha tarsipennalis*
The Fan-foot

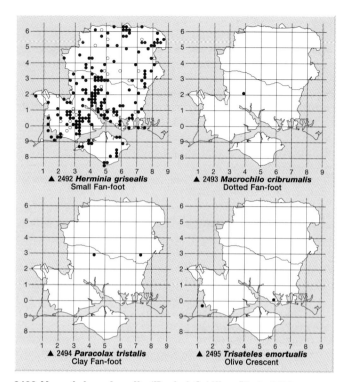

▲ 2492 *Herminia grisealis*
Small Fan-foot

▲ 2493 *Macrochilo cribrumalis*
Dotted Fan-foot

▲ 2494 *Paracolax tristalis*
Clay Fan-foot

▲ 2495 *Trisateles emortualis*
Olive Crescent

2492 *Herminia grisealis* ([Denis & Schiffermüller], 1775)
Small Fan-foot
Widespread and common, chiefly in deciduous woodland.

2493 *Macrochilo cribrumalis* (Hübner, 1793)
Dotted Fan-foot   **Notable/Nb**
The isolated colony in Emer Bog vc11 has been known for many years and still persists. The moth is not known anywhere else in the area.
■ vc11 Emer Bog, 26.6.93 (NB).

2494 *Paracolax tristalis* (Fabricius, 1794)
Clay Fan-foot   **Notable/Na**
First recorded in Hampshire in 1971 at Alice Holt vc12 (see Goater, 1974). None since until those given below. Its true status in the county remains a mystery, but it appears to be extremely rare.
■ vc11 Crab Wood, 14.7.93, single specimen at m.v. light (RAB). **New vc record.**
■ vc12 Ashford Hangers, 16.7.95, specimen seen by BG (PMP).

2495 *Trisateles emortualis* ([Denis & Schiffermüller], 1775)
Olive Crescent   **RDB3**
There are three records of presumed immigrants, given below.
■ vc10 Ventnor, July 1939, one by day by C.H. Simmonds (Goater, 1974). The exact location is not known.
■ vc11 Rowner, 8.7.99, one at m.v. light (LM, conf. BG); Hurn, 18.7.01, a worn individual at m.v. light (MJ). **New vc record.**

Appendix 1
Gazetteer of Localities Mentioned in the Text

vc8 South Wilts

Bentley Wood	SU2530
Damerham	SU1015
Martin Down NNR	SU0419

vc10 Isle of Wight

Afton Down	SZ3685
Afton Marsh	SZ3486
Alum Bay	SZ3085
Alverstone	SZ5785
Apes Down	SZ4587
Apse Heath	SZ5683
Arreton	SZ5387
Ashey	SZ5789
Ashey Down	SZ5787
Bembridge	SZ6286
Billingham	SZ4880
Binstead	SZ5792
Bonchurch	SZ5777
Borthwood	SZ5784
Bouldnor	SZ3789, SZ3790
Brading	SZ6086
Brading Chalk Pit	SZ6086
Brading Down	SZ5986
Brighstone	SZ4282
Brighstone Forest	SZ4284, SZ4384
Brook	SZ3983
Carisbrooke	SZ4886
Chale	SZ4877
Chale Green	SZ4879
Compton Chine	SZ3685
Cowes	SZ4995
Cranmore	SZ3989
Cridmoor Bog	SZ5082
Culver Cliff	SZ6385
Dodnor	SZ5090
Fattingpark Copse	SZ5290
Firestone Copse	SZ5591
Five Houses	SZ4287
Fort Victoria	SZ3389
Freshwater	SZ3486
Gatcombe	SZ4984, SZ4985
Godshill	SZ5281
Grammars Common	SZ4084
Gurnard	SZ4795
Hacketts Land	SZ5583
Hamstead	SZ4091
Headon Warren	SZ3185

Hurst Stake	SZ5090
Knighton Down	SZ5787
Knowles Farm	SZ4875, SZ4975
Lake Common	SZ5884
Locks Copse	SZ4490
Locksgreen	SZ4489
Luccombe Chine	SZ5879
Mill Copse, Yarmouth	SZ3488
Moortown	SZ4283
Nettlestone	SZ6290
Newport	SZ5090
Newtown	SZ4290
Ninham	SZ5782
Ninham Withybed	SZ5783
Ningwood	SZ4088
Niton	SZ5176
Northwood	SZ5092
Norton Green	SZ3488
Nunney's Wood,	SZ4089
Nunwell	SZ5987
Osborne	SZ5094
Osborne Estate	SZ5195
Parkhurst Forest	SZ4791
Priory Bay	SZ6390
Priory Woods	SZ6288
Queens Bower	SZ5685
Redcliff Bay	SZ6285
Reeth Bay	SZ5075
Ricket's Hill	SZ6088
Roud	SZ5080
Rowridge Valley	SZ4586
Ryde	SZ5992
St Boniface Down	SZ5678
St Catherine's Point	SZ4975
St George's Down	SZ5186
St Helens	SZ6288
St Helens Duver	SZ6388, SZ6389
St Lawrence	SZ5376
Sandown Levels	SZ6086
Seagrove Bay	SZ6290
Seaview	SZ6291
Shalcombe	SZ3884
Shalcombe Down	SZ3884
Shalfleet	SZ4189
Shamblers Copse	SZ4994
Shanklin	SZ5781, SZ5881
Shide	SZ5086
Steephill	SZ5576
Tennyson Down	SZ3285
Tolt Down	SZ4884
Totland	SZ3286

Ventnor	SZ5677
Walter's Copse	SZ4390
Watchingwell	SZ4488, SZ4489
Werrar	SZ5092
West High Down	SZ3284
Westover Farm	SZ4186
Westover Plantation	SZ4084
Whitecroft	SZ4886
Whitefield Wood	SZ6088
Whitwell	SZ5277
Wootton	SZ5492
Yafford	SZ4482
River Yar marshes	SZ3588
Yarmouth	SZ3589

vc11 South Hants

Allbrook	SU4521
Allington Gravel Pits	SU4716
Alver Valley NR	SU5800
Alverstoke	SZ6098
Ampfield Wood	SU3924, SU4024
Anses Wood	SU2212
Ashurst	SU3310
Baddesley Great Covert	SU4019, SU4119
Bashley	SZ2497
Battramsley	SZ3099
Beacon Hill NNR, Warnford	SU6022
Beaulieu	SU3802
Beaulieu Road	SU3406
Bedenham	SU5903, SU5904
Bishops Dyke	SU3404
Bitterne	SU4612
Bitterne Park	SU4413
Black Gutter	SU2016
Bolderwood	SU2308
Botany Bay	SU4511
Botley Wood	SU5410
Bournemouth	
Braishfield	SU3725
Bramshaw Woods	SU2516
Bratley	SU2208
Bratley Plain	SU2108, SU2109
Brick Kiln Inclosure	SU2906
Bridgemary	SU5803
Brockenhurst	SU3002
Broughton Down NR	SU2833, SU2932

Ringwood	SU1505	Testwood Park	SU3514,
Riverside Park	SU4314,		SU3614
	SU4315	The Moors NR	SU5517,
Round Coppice	SU5309		SU5616,
Rowbarrow	SU3504		SU5617
Rowner Wild Grounds LNR	SU5801	Thornhill	SU4712
Rownhams	SU3816	Thorns Beach	SZ3996
Royal Victoria		Timsbury	SU3424
Country Park	SU4707,	Titchfield Haven NNR	SU5302
	SU4708	Totton	SU3613
Roydon Woods	SU3100,	Tournebury Wood	SZ7399
	SU3200	Town Common	SZ1396,
Rufus Stone	SU2712		SZ1496
St Catherine's Hill,		Upper Hamble	SU4911
Christchurch	SZ1395,	Country Park to	SU5012
	SZ1495	Upper Pennington	SZ3095
St Catherine's Hill,		Vales Moor	SU1904
Winchester	SU4827	Wallington	SU5807
St Cross	SU4728	Waltham Chase	SU5615
St Denys	SU4313	Warsash	SU5005
St Ives	SU1204	Westbourne	SZ0790
St Leonards	SZ4098	West Meon	SU6424
Sack Copse	SU2821	West Walk	SU5912
Sandleheath	SU1214	West Wood	SU4129
Sandy Balls	SU1614	Weston Common	SU4511,
Sandy Point LNR	SZ7498		SU4611
Sarisbury	SU5008	Weston Shore	SU4409
Segensworth	SU5208	Whitemoor, nr Emery Down	SU3108
Shatterford	SU3405,	Whitenap	SU3720
	SU3406	Whitley Wood	SU2905
Shedfield Common	SU5513	Wickham Common	SU5810
Sims Wood	SU4101	Widley, Portsdown	SU6606,
Sinah Common	SZ6999		SU6706
Sloden Inclosure	SU2112	Winchester (south)	
Slufters Inclosure	SU2210,	Wood Crates	SU2608,
	SU2310		SU2708
Smoky Hole	SU2307	Woodfidley	SU3404
Soberton	SU6116	Woodley, Romsey	SU3622
Solent Court	SU5004	Woolston	SU4310,
Sopley Common	SZ1297		SU4410
South Bentley Inclosure	SU2312	Yew Hill NR	SU4526
Southampton Common	SU4114		
Southsea	SZ6598		
Sparsholt College	SU4231	**vc12 North Hants**	
Spearbed Copse	SU4001		
Stanpit Marsh	SZ1692,	Abbots Worthy	SU5032
	SZ1792	Abbotstone Down	SU5835,
Staunton Country Park	SU7009		SU5836
Steamer Point Wood	SZ1993	Alice Holt	SU8042
Stephill Bottom	SU3505	Alresford Pond	SU5932,
Stoke Park Wood	SU4719		SU5933
Strodgemoor Bottom	SU1803	Anton Lakes NR	SU3546
Stubbington	SU5403	Ashford Hangers NNR	SU7326,
Studley Wood	SU2215,		SU7426
	SU2216	Ashford Hill NNR	SU5661
Swanwick	SU5109,	Bartley Heath NR	SU7253
	SU5209	Basing Forest	SU6455
Swaythling Grange	SU4415	Basing House	SU6652
Teg Down	SU4529	Beacon Hill NR, Highclere	SU4557
Telegraph Woods	SU4713	Bentley	SU7843

Bentley Station Meadow NR	SU7942
Bentley Wood	
(Hampshire part)	SU2532
Bordon	SU7835
Bramdean Common	SU6329
Bramley Frith Wood NR	SU6459,
	SU6460
Bramshill Plantation	SU7461,
	SU7561
Bramshott Common	SU8633
Bricksbury Hill	SU8249
Brighton Hill	SU6249
Brockley Warren	SU4136
Broxhead Common LNR	SU8037
Burghclere	SU4757
Castle Bottom NNR	SU7959
Chawton Park Wood	SU6736
Cheesefoot Head	SU5327
Chilbolton	SU3940
Cholderton	SU2242
Church Crookham	SU8152
Conford Moor	SU8133
Cow Down Copse	SU5850,
	SU5851
Crawley	SU4234
Danebury Hillfort	SU3237
East Stratton	SU5439,
	SU5440
Eelmoor Marsh	SU8353
Farnborough	SU8753
Farringdon	SU7135
Fleet Pond LNR	SU8254,
	SU8255
Frenchmoor	SU2728
Frith End	SU8139
Fugelmere Marsh, Fleet	SU8254
Greywell Moors NR	SU7251
Happersnapper Hanger	SU7327
Harewood Forest	SU3842
to	SU4046
Hawkley Warren	SU7228,
	SU7328
Hawley Meadows NR	SU8560
Hazeley Heath	SU7558
Hillside Common	SU7550
Hook Common	SU7153
Isle of Wight Woods,	
Porton Down	SU2436,
	SU2437
Itchen Abbas	SU5232
Leckford	SU3737
Liss	SU7728
Longmoor	SU8031
Longstock	SU3537
Ludshott Common	SU8535
Magdalen Hill Down NR	SU5029
Mapledurwell Fen	SU6951
Martyr Worthy	SU5132
Micheldever	SU5139
Micheldever Wood	SU5338

Monkwood	SU6730	St John's Copse	SU5850	Whitmoor Vale	SU8635
Monxton	SU3043	Selborne	SU7433	Wick Hill Hanger	SU7533
Newtown Common	SU4762	Shipton Bellinger	SU2345,	Winchester (north)	
Noar Hill NR	SU7431		SU2346	Winchfield Hurst	SU7754
Northington	SU5637	Shortheath Common	SU7736	Wildhern	SU3552
Oakley	SU5750	Shroner Wood	SU5135,	Winnall Moors NR	SU4830
Odiham Common	SU7552,		SU5235	Wolverton Marsh	SU5558
	SU7553	Silchester Common	SU6262	Woolbury Ring	SU3735
Old Basing	SU6652	South Wonston	SU4635	Woolmer Forest	SU8032
Old Burghclere Chalk Pit	SU4757	Stockbridge Down	SU3735	Worthy Down	SU4534,
Overton	SU5149	Stoke Charity	SU4839		SU4634
Pamber Forest	SU6160	Tadley	SU6060	Yateley	SU8259
Perham Down, Tidworth	SU2648	Tangley	SU3252,	Zebon Copse	SU8051
Porton Down			SU3352		
(Hampshire part)	SU2336,	Waggoners Wells	SU8534	**vc22 Berkshire**	
	SU2337	The Warren NR	SU7328		
Redenham	SU3049	Wheatham Hill	SU7427	Benyon's Inclosure	SU6263
Ropley	SU6431	Wheathold	SU5560	Mortimer West End	SU6363
Rye Common	SU7650,	Whitchurch	SU4647		
	SU7850	Whitehill	SU7934		

Appendix 2
List of Contributors

The following people have contributed records towards the Hampshire and Isle of Wight Branch of Butterfly Conservation database and for use in this book. Where individual records are detailed in the text the initials used are those indicated below.

David Agassiz (DJLA)

Alan Albery
Pamber; Ashford Hill

Chris Allen (CA)
West End

D.M. Appleton (DMA)

Alasdair Aston (AEA)
Selborne

Mike Baker (MJB)
Romsey

Dave Ball
Ashford Hangers

Andy and Linda Barker (A&LB)
Stockbridge Down

Reg Bell (RAB)
Crawley

David Biggs
Gurnard and elsewhere

Norman Binsted (NB)
Broughton Down;
Romsey and elsewhere

Paul Boswell (PB)
Greywell

Andrew Brookes
Portchester

Peter Brough (PRB)
Wheathold; Ashford Hill

Phil Budd (PAB)
Bitterne

Andy Butler (AB)
Isle of Wight

Patrick Carden
Fordingbridge

Peter Carr (PCa)
Locks Heath and elsewhere

Mike Cartwright
Bursledon; Itchen Valley CP

Bob Chapman (RAC)
Highcliffe; Farlington Marsh

John Chainey (JEC)
Brockenhurst

Jim Cheverton (JMC)
Shanklin

Marina Christopher (MC)
Bentley

Sean Clancy (SPC)
New Forest and elsewhere

Jane/Adrian Clark
Lymington

Julian Clarke (JHC)
Ringwood and elsewhere

Sue Clarke
Froyle

Peter Clarkson (PHC)
Farnborough and elsewhere

Andrew Cleave MBE
Bramley Frith

Jon Clifton
New Forest

John Cloyne (JCl)
Winchester

Simon Colenutt (SRC)
Chale Green

Andrew Collins (ARC)
Woolston; Sholing

Barry Collins (CBC)
Leigh Park, Havant

Raymond Cook (RRC)
New Forest

Richard Coomber (RC)
Pennington

Trevor Crabb (TAC)
Widley

Peter Cramp (PC)
Godshill

Jos Creese (JCr)
Bishops Waltham

Peter Davey (PD)
vc11 (Dorset)

Tony Davis (AMD)
Many localities, mostly in
NE Hampshire

Alan and Caroline Dawson (A&CD)
Portswood

Graham Dennis (GJD)
Pamber

Jonty Denton (JD)
Alton and district

Richard Dickson (RJD)
Fareham

David Dimmock (DPD)
Church Crookham

Tony Dobson (AHD)
Basingstoke

Caroline Dudley (CDu)
West Wight

Barry Duffin (BD)
Titchfield Haven

Pete Durnell (PRD)
Hayling Island

Henry Edmunds (HE)
Cholderton

Rob Edmunds (RE)
Fleet

Brian Elliott (BE)
Chandlers Ford; Ramalley

Mary Elliott
Soberton

Sue Ellis
Meon Valley

George Else (GRE)

the late Maitland Emmet (AME)

Glynne and Sheila Evans
Chilbolton

Justin Evans

Ian Ferguson (IDF)
Ventnor

Brian Fletcher
Winchester and elsewhere

Barry Fox (BF)
Winterslow

Mike Gibbons (MJG)
Hengistbury

Edwin and Joyce Gifford (E&JG)
Bartley

Warren Gilchrist (WRLG)
Monk Sherborne

Barry Goater (BG)
Chandlers Ford

Keith Godfrey
Rownhams

David and Madge Goodall
Otterbourne

Brian Goodey
National Moth Night Organiser

David and Audrey Graham
Bordon

David Green (DGG)
Whitchurch; Wildhern

Chris Hall (CRH)
Fleet

Phil Halliwell
Royal Victoria CP, Netley

James Halsey
Ventnor

Martin Harvey (MCH)
Berkshire Lepidoptera Recorder

Roger Hayward (RH)

Bob Heckford (RJH)

G. Henwood (GH)
Kempshott, Basingstoke

Neale Hider
Royal Victoria CP, Netley

Barry Hilling (BH)
  Milford-on-Sea
Robert Hoare (RJBH)
  Winchester
J. Hobbs (JH)
Donald Hobern (DH)
  North Baddesley;
  Hursley Park
Peter Hodge (PH)
  Westwood Woodland Park,
  Netley
Norman Holland (NH)
  Queens Bower, Isle of Wight
Ralph Hollins
Daniel Houghton
  Fareham
Norman Hutchinson (NHu)
  Fordingbridge
Brian Ivon-Jones (BI-J)
  East Stratton; Beaulieu
Tony James (AMJ)
  Selborne
Mike Jeffes (MJ)
  Totton; Christchurch
Terry Jennings (TJJ)
  Cosham
Janet Jones
  Winchfield
Peter Jupp
  Isle of Wight
Jennifer Keddie (JK)
  Netley; Lepe Country Park
Tony King
  Swaythling
Paul Kitchener (PK)
  Linwood
Sam Knill-Jones (SAK-J)
  Freshwater
David and Rosalind Langley
John Langmaid (JRL)
  Southsea and many other localities
Martin Laux (ML)
  Allbrook; Chandlers Ford
Gordon Le Pard (GL)
  Matchams
Tony Leveson-Gower (AGL-G)
  Bordon, Grayshott
Bob Lord
  Needs Ore and elsewhere
Lee Marshall (LM)
  Rowner and Gosport area
Sarah Miles
  Porton Down
D.L.H. Miller (DLHM)
  Arreton, Isle of Wight
Richard Moore (RJM)
  Waterlooville
Charlie Morris (DCM)
  Dibden Bay and elsewhere

Tony Mundell (ARGM)
  Church Crookham
Tim Norriss (TJN)
  Kings Somborne
Maurice Opie (MLO)
  Funtley
Peter Orchard
  Kings Somborne
Andy Page (AGP)
  Linford
Jess Pain
  Lower Test Marshes
C. Palmer (HCCMS)
  Hampshire County Council
  Museums Service
R.M. Palmer (RMP)
Ron Parfitt (RWP)
  Farnborough
Mark Parsons (MSP)
David and Pauline Peach (D&PP)
  Ryde
John Phillips (JWP)
  Hayling Island
Chris Piatkiewicz
  Woolston
Tony Pickles (AJP)
  Lymington
Bryan Pinchen (BJP)
Colin Plant (CWP)
Keith and Jane Plumridge (K&JP)
  Chandlers Ford
John Poland (JPP)
  Portswood
Colin Pope
  Ryde
Peter Potts (PMP)
  Titchfield Haven
Ted Pratt (EAP)
  Waltham Chase
Ted and Penny Raynor
Graham, Mark and Theo Roberts
  Cosham
John Rowell
  Whippingham
Mick Scott (MAS)
  Fleet Pond
William Scott (WJS)
  Fleet Pond
Peter Sewell (PS)
  Hayling Island
A.F.Silcocks
  Titchfield Haven
Bernard Skinner (BS)
A.C. Smallbone
  Petersfield
Linda Smith (LS)
  Martin Down
Peter Smith (PJSS)
  South Wonston

Richard Smout
  Newport
Jenny Spence (JMS)
Ian W. Staples (IWS)
  Hythe
Tony Steele (TS)
  Knowles Farm, Isle of Wight
Graham Stephenson (GCS)
  Fleet
Phil Sterling (PHS)
  vc11 (Dorset) and elsewhere
Dougie Sterling (DHS)
  Winchester
Andy Swash (AS)
  Pamber
Stuart Swift (SS)
  Gosport area
John Taverner
David Thelwell (DAT)
  Timsbury
Ian Thirlwell (IRT)
  Southsea
Paul Toynton (PT)
  Damerham
David Tinling (DJAT)
  Alverstoke
Paul Troake (PTr)
  Martin Down
the late Darren Walker (DSW)
  Gosport area
Tim Walker (TWa)
  Winchester
John Walters
  Hayling Island
Brian Warne (BJW)
  Binstead
Paul Waring (PMW)
  Isle of Wight
Paul Warren
  Brockenhurst
Keith Wheeler (KJW)
  Portchester
the late Ted Wild (EHW)
  Highcliffe
Mike Wildish
  Andover
Audrey Wilkinson
  Niton, Isle of Wight
Ken Willmott
Keith Wills (KBW).
  Farnborough, Frith End
Tim Winter (TW)
  Alice Holt
David Wooldridge (DBW)
  Freshwater
Simon Young
  Isle of Wight
George Yorke (CGY)
  Shawford

Appendix 3
List of Photographs

Cover

Catocala sponsa Dark Crimson Underwing
    Paul Waring
Frame Wood, New Forest
    Terry Heathcote

Plate 1

Hengistbury Head
    John Taverner
2301 *Dypterygia scabriuscula* Bird's Wing
    Tony Mundell
Latchmore Bottom, New Forest
    John Taverner
2264a *Agrochola haematidea* Southern Chestnut
    Tim Norriss
Mark Ash Wood, New Forest
    John Taverner
1999 *Stauropus fagi* Lobster Moth
    Alan Barnes

Plate 2

Frame Wood, New Forest
    Terry Heathcote
2455 *Catocala sponsa* Dark Crimson Underwing
    David Green
Compton Down, Isle of Wight
    Jim Asher
2226 *Leucochlaena oditis* Beautiful Gothic
    David Green
Bonchurch Down, Isle of Wight
    Andy Butler
0374 *Synanthedon vespiformis* Yellow-legged Clearwing
    Tim Norriss

Plate 3

Harewood Forest
    David Green
1878 *Minoa murinata* Drab Looper
    David Green
Titchfield Haven NR
    Barry Duffin
1640 *Euthrix potatoria* Drinker
    Alan Barnes
Browndown Ranges
    Tim Norriss
2172 *Hadena albimacula* White Spot
    Tim Norriss

Plate 4

Sinah Dunes, Hayling Island
    Pete Durnell
1636 *Lasiocampa trifolii* Grass Eggar
    Tim Norriss
Sandy Point, Hayling Island
    Pete Durnell
Odiham Common
    Tim Norriss
0163 *Adscita statices* Forester
    Tim Norriss
Noar Hill
    John Taverner
2463 *Euclidia glyphica* Burnet Companion
    Tim Norriss

Plate 5

0014 *Hepialus humuli* Ghost Moth
    Phil Sterling
0077 *Stigmella tityrella*
    Phil Sterling
0129 *Incurvaria pectinea*
    Phil Sterling
0148 *Nemophora degeerella*
    Tony Mundell
0161 *Zeuzera pyrina* Leopard Moth
    Tony Mundell
0162 *Cossus cossus* Goat Moth
    Tony Mundell

Plate 6

0163 *Adscita statices* Forester
    Tim Norriss
0171 *Zygaena lonicerae* Narrow-bordered Five-spot Burnet
    Tim Norriss
0173 *Apoda limacodes* Festoon
    David Green
0174 *Heterogenea asella* Triangle
    David Green
0192 *Pachythelia villosella*
    Tim Norriss
0196 *Morophaga choragella*
    Tim Norriss

Plate 7

0374 *Synanthedon vespiformis* Yellow-legged Clearwing
    Tim Norriss

0377 *Synanthedon flaviventris* Sallow Clearwing
Tim Norriss
0530 *Coleophora lixella*
David Green
0538 *Coleophora vibicella*
Phil Sterling
0651 *Oecophora bractella*
Phil Sterling
0809 *Pexicopia malvella*
Tim Norriss
0925 *Phtheochroa rugosana*
Tim Norriss

Plate 8

1073 *Olethreutes schulziana*
Tony Mundell
1288 *Alucita hexadactyla* Twenty-plume Moth
Tony Mundell
1359 *Cynaeda dentalis*
Tim Norriss
1362 *Pyrausta purpuralis*
Tony Mundell
1398 *Nomophila noctuella* Rush Veneer
Tim Norriss
1405 *Pleuroptya ruralis* Mother of Pearl
Tim Norriss
1438 *Trachycera (Numonia) suavella*
Tim Norriss
1513 *Pterophorus pentadactyla* White Plume Moth
Alan Barnes

Plate 9

1633 *Eriogaster lanestris* Small Eggar larval nest
David Green
1637 *Lasiocampa quercus* Oak Eggar
Alan Barnes
1640 *Euthrix potatoria* Drinker
Alan Barnes
1643 *Saturnia pavonia* Emperor Moth
Alan Barnes
1645 *Falcaria lacertinaria* Scalloped Hook-tip
Tony Mundell
1648 *Drepana falcataria* Pebble Hook-tip
Ken Willmott
1651 *Cilix glaucata* Chinese Character
Ken Willmott

Plate 10

1652 *Thyatira batis* Peach Blossom
Alan Barnes
1656 *Tetheella fluctuosa* Satin Lutestring
Tim Norriss
1660 *Polyploca ridens* Frosted Green
David Green

1675 *Cyclophora pendularia* Dingy Mocha
David Green
1680 *Cyclophora punctaria* Maiden's Blush
David Green
1682 *Timandra griseata* Blood-vein
Alan Barnes
1747 *Anticlea derivata* The Streamer
Tim Norriss

Plate 11

1750 *Lampropteryx suffumata* Water Carpet
Tim Norriss
1771a *Thera cupressata* Cypress Carpet
Tim Norriss
1787 *Rheumaptera hastata* Argent and Sable
David Green
1825 *Eupithecia centaureata* Lime-speck Pug
Alan Barnes
1852 *Eupithecia abbreviata* Brindled Pug
Tony Mundell
1878 *Minoa murinata* Drab Looper
David Green
1919 *Selenia tetralunaria* Purple Thorn
Alan Barnes

Plate 12

1947 *Ectropis bistortata* The Engrailed
Tim Norriss
1979 *Mimas tiliae* Lime Hawk-moth
Tony Mundell
1982 *Hemaris tityus* Narrow-bordered Bee Hawk-moth
David Green
1994 *Phalera bucephala* Buff-tip
Alan Barnes
1999 *Stauropus fagi* Lobster Moth
Alan Barnes
2010 *Odontosia carmelita* Scarce Prominent
Tim Norriss
2019 *Clostera curtula* Chocolate-tip
Alan Barnes
2026 *Orgyia antiqua* The Vapourer
Alan Barnes

Plate 13

2028 *Calliteara pudibunda* Pale Tussock
Alan Barnes
2033 *Lymantria monacha* Black Arches
Alan Barnes
2037 *Miltochrista miniata* Rosy Footman
Tony Mundell
2050 *Eilema lurideola* Common Footman
Alan Barnes
2057 *Arctia caja* Garden Tiger
Tim Norriss

2068 *Callimorpha dominula* Scarlet Tiger
Jim Asher
2069 *Tyria jacobaeae* Cinnabar
Tim Norriss

Plate 14

2077 *Nola cucullatella* Short-cloaked Moth
Paul Harris
2107 *Noctua pronuba* Large Yellow Underwing
Alan Barnes
2142 *Anarta myrtilli* Beautiful Yellow Underwing
Tim Norriss
2172 *Hadena albimacula* White Spot
Tim Norriss
2214 *Cucullia chamomillae* Chamomile Shark larva
Tony Mundell
2219 *Shargacucullia lychnitis* Striped Lychnis larva
Tim Norriss

Plate 15

2226 *Leucochlaena oditis* Beautiful Gothic
David Green
2247 *Dichonia aprilina* Merveille du Jour
David Green
2264a *Agrochola haematidea* Southern Chestnut
Tim Norriss
2301 *Dypterygia scabriuscula* Bird's Wing
Tony Mundell
2421 *Bena bicolorana* Scarce Silver-lines
David Green
2437 *Polychrysia moneta* Golden Plusia
Tim Norriss

Plate 16

2441 *Autographa gamma* Silver Y
Alan Barnes
2455 *Catocala sponsa* Dark Crimson Underwing larva
Tim Norriss
2455 *Catocala sponsa* Dark Crimson Underwing
David Green
2463 *Euclidia glyphica* Burnet Companion
Tim Norriss
2475 *Parascotia fuliginaria* Waved Black
David Green
2477 *Hypena proboscidalis* The Snout
Tony Mundell
2480 *Hypena rostralis* Buttoned Snout
Alan Barnes

Black and white photographs used in the systematic list

Jim Asher – 2068
Alan Barnes – 1376, 1637, 1643, 1652, 1682, 1825, 1999,
2019, 2026, 2050, 2403
Peter Creed – 0150, 2306
Brian Fletcher – 0998
David Green – 0173, 0530, 1659, 1663, 1787, 1982, 2226,
2247, 2277, 2455
Paul Harris – 2077
Tony Mundell – 0161, 1073, 1362, 1378, 1979, 2301, 2477
Tim Norriss – 0163, 0171, 0196, 0374, 0718, 0925, 0986,
1001, 1037, 1048, 1082, 1113, 1261, 1366, 1405, 1642,
1726, 1747, 1750, 1766, 1904, 1930, 1987, 2010, 2085,
2142, 2171, 2172, 2219, 2245, 2273, 2284, 2425, 2435,
2463
Phil Sterling – 0014, 0651
Ken Wilmott – 1648

References

Agassiz, D.J.L. 1991. Microlepidoptera Review of the Year 1989. *Entomologist's Rec. J. Var.* 103: 141–153.

Agassiz, D.J.L. 2000. The 1997 Presidential Address – Part 2 Why do Names change? *Br. J. Ent. Nat. Hist.* 13: 41–49.

Agassiz, D.J.L., Heckford, R.J. and Langmaid, J.R. 1997. Microlepidoptera Review of 1995. *Entomologist's Rec. J. Var.* 109: 169–187.

Agassiz, D.J.L., Heckford, R.J. and Langmaid, J.R.. 1998. Microlepidoptera Review of 1996. *Entomologist's Rec. J. Var.* 110: 97–114.

Agassiz, D.J.L. and Karsholt, O. 1989. *Cydia medicaginis* (Kuznetzov, 1962) (Lepidoptera: Tortricidae) in the British Isles. *Entomologist's Gaz.* 40: 193–196.

Aston, A.E. 1993. *Colostygia olivata* (D.& S.) (Lep. Geometridae) – new to north Hampshire. *Entomologist's Rec. J. Var.* 105: 291.

Aston, A.E. 1995. *Eumichtis lichenea lichenea* (Hb.) Feathered Ranunculus (Lep.: Noctuidae) in north-east Hampshire. *Entomologist's Rec. J. Var.* 107: 32.

Aston, A.E. 1995b. *Hypena obsitalis* (Hb.) the Bloxworth Snout (Lep.: Noctuidae) new to mainland Hampshire. *Entomologist's Rec. J. Var.* 107: 47.

Aston, A.E. 1997. *Idaea vulpinaria atrosignaria* (Lempke) (Lep.: Geometridae) new to north Hampshire. *Entomologist's Rec. J. Var.* 109: 108.

Aston, A.E. 1998. *Digitivalva pulicariae* Klimesch (Lep.: Yponomeutidae) new to North Hampshire. *Entomologist's Rec. J. Var.* 110: 172.

Aston, A.E. 1998b. *Depressaria ultimella* Stt. (Lep.: Oecophoridae) new to North Hampshire. *Entomologist's Rec. J. Var.* 110: 176.

Aston, A.E. 1998c. *Cochylis molliculana* Zell. (Lep.: Tortricidae) new to North Hampshire. *Entomologist's Rec. J. Var.* 110: 183.

Aston, A.E. 1998d. *Blastobasis decolorella* Woll. (Lep.: Blastobasidae) in north-east Hampshire. *Entomologist's Rec. J. Var.* 110: 254.

Aston, A.E. 1998e. *Syncopacma larseniella* Gozm. (Lep.: Gelechiidae) new to North Hampshire. *Entomologist's Rec. J. Var.* 110: 255.

Barker, A., Fuller, M. and Shreeves, W. 2000. *Butterfly Conservation South-Central Regional Action Plan.* Butterfly Conservation.

Beirne, B.P. 1954. *British Pyralid and Plume Moths.* 208 pp. 16 (redrawn) colour plates. Warne. London & New York.

Bond, K.G.M. 1998. First Irish record of *Apomyelois bistriatella subcognata* (Ragonot, 1887) (*neophanes* (Durrant, 1915)) (Lepidoptera: Pyralidae) with a discussion of its reported feeding habits. *Entomologist's Gaz.* 49: 139.

Bradley, J.D. 1985. *Cydia illutana* (Herrich-Schäffer) Lepidoptera: Tortricidae) new to Britain. *Entomologist's Gaz.* 36: 97–101.

Bradley, J.D. 1998. *Checklist of Lepidoptera recorded from the British Isles.* Bradley & Bradley.

Bradley, J.D., Tremewan, W.G. and Smith, A. 1973. *British Tortricoid Moths. Cochylidae and Tortricidae: Tortricinae.* The Ray Society. London.

Bradley, J.D., and Fletcher, D.S. 1979. *A Recorder's Log Book or Label List of British Butterflies and Moths.* Curwen.

Bradley, J.D., Tremewan, W.G. and Smith, A. 1979. *British Tortricoid Moths. Tortricidae: Olethreutinae.* The Ray Society. London.

Brewis, A., Bowman, P. and Rose, F. 1996. *The Flora of Hampshire.* Harley Books. Colchester.

Budd, P.A. and Goater, B. 1998. *Eustixia pupula* Hübner, 1823 (Lepidoptera: Pyralidae, Odontiinae), a New World pyralid new to Britain and Europe. *Entomologist's Gaz.* 49: 169–170.

Burrow, R. 1996. *Dryobota labecula* (Esper) The Oak Rustic (Lep.: Noctuidae) a new breeding species to the British List from the Channel Islands. *Entomologist's Rec. J. Var.* 108: 136–137.

Castle, M.E. (unpublished) Diary, 1956–1964. Copy in possession of Hampshire County Museums Service, Winchester.

Chalmers-Hunt, J.M. and Skinner, B. 1992. The immigration of Lepidoptera to the British Isles in 1990. *Entomologist's Rec. J. Var.* 104: 123–127, 209–218, 231–235.

Chalmers-Hunt, J.M. and Bretherton, R.F. 1993. Lepidoptera immigration to the British Isles in 1987, 1988 and 1989: a supplementary note. *Entomologist's Rec. J. Var.* 105: 27–30.

Clark, J.M. and Eyre, J.A. 1993. *Birds of Hampshire.* 512 pp. Hampshire Ornithological Society. Over Wallop, Hampshire.

Colenutt, S. 1993. BENHS Exhibition, 1992. British Macrolepidoptera. *Br. J. Ent. Nat. Hist.* 6 (1993): 54.

Colenutt, S.R. 1995. *Evergestis limbata* (L.) (Lep.: Pyralidae) new to mainland Britain. *Entomologist's Rec. J. Var.* 107: 197.

Davey, P. 1997. The 1996 insect immigration. *Atropos* 2: 2–13.

Davis, A. 1998. *Blastobasis decolorella* Woll. (Lep.: Blastobasidae) in north-east Hampshire and north-west Surrey. *Entomologist's Rec. J. Var.* 110: 284.

Dickson, R.J. 1994. *Cochylis molliculana* Zeller and *Teleiodes scriptella* (Hübner) (Lepidoptera: Tortricidae and Gelechiidae) in south Hampshire (VC 11) in 1993. *Entomologist's Gaz.* 45: 260.

Dickson, R.J. 1995. *Bankesia douglasii* Stainton (Lep.: Psychidae) in Hampshire. *Entomologist's Rec. J. Var.* 107: 202–203.

Dickson, R.J. 1995b. *Mompha subdivisella* Bradley (Lepidoptera: Momphidae) new to Hampshire. *Entomologist's Gaz.* 46: 242.

Dickson, R.J. 1998, *Euchromius ocellea* (Haworth) and *Microthrix similella* (Zincken) (Lep.: Pyralidae) in Hampshire. *Entomologist's Rec. J. Var.* 110: 298.

Edmunds, R. 1998. *Tachystola acroxantha* (Meyr.) (Lep.: Oecophoridae) – a first record for North Hampshire. *Entomologist's Rec. J. Var.* 110: 83.

Edmunds, R. 1999. *Tachystola acroxantha* (Meyr.) (Lep.: Oecophoridae) – an established colony in North Hampshire. *Entomologist's Rec. J. Var.* 111: 20.

Emmet, A.M., ed. 1979. *A Field Guide to the Smaller British Lepidoptera.* 271 pp. British Entomological & Natural History Society. London.

Emmet, A.M. 1986. *Parornix carpinella* (Frey, 1863) a distinct species from *P. fagivora* (Frey, 1861) (Lep., Gracillariidae). *Entomologist's Rec. J. Var.* 98: 144–146.

Emmet, A.M. 1987. The early stages of *Parornix carpinella* (Frey) and *P. fagivora* (Frey) (Lepidoptera, Gracillariidae). *Entomologist's Rec. J. Var.* 99: 157–159.

Emmet, A.M. 1989. *Phyllonorycter leucographella* (Zeller, 1850) (Lep.: Gracillariidae) in Essex: a species new to Britain. *Entomologist's Rec. J. Var.* 101: 189–194.

Emmet, A.M. 1991. *Phyllonorycter platani* (Staudinger, 1870) (Lepidoptera: Gracillariidae) new to Britain. *Entomologist's Rec. J. Var.* 103: 1.

Emmet, A.M., ed. 1996. *The Moths and Butterflies of Great Britain and Ireland, Vol. 3, Yponomeutidae – Elachistidae.* 452 pp., 17 pl., 9 in colour. Harley Books.

Goater, B. 1974. *The Butterflies and Moths of Hampshire and the Isle of Wight.* Classey.

Goater, B. 1983. New and confirmed records of Lepidoptera in Hampshire and the Isle of Wight since 1974. *Entomologist's Gaz.* 34: 247–255.

Goater, B. 1986. *British Pyralid Moths: A Guide to their Identification.* Harley Books.

Goater, B. 1992. *The Butterflies and Moths of Hampshire and the Isle of Wight: additions and corrections.* UK Nature Conservation No. 7. JNCC.

Goater, B. and Knill-Jones, S.A. 1999. *Herpetogramma licarsisalis* (Walker, 1859) (Lepidoptera: Pyralidae), the Grass Webworm, new to Britain. *Entomologist's Gaz.* 50: 71–74.

Green, D.G. 2000. The Action for Threatened Moths Project: Work in Hampshire and the Isle of Wight during 2000. Hants and IOW Butterfly and Moth Report 2000. Butterfly Conservation. Hampshire Printing Services.

Haggett, G.M. and Smith, C. 1993. *Agrochola haematidea* Duponchel (Lepidoptera: Noctuidae, Cuculliinae) new to Britain. *Entomologist's Gaz.* 44: 183–203.

Huemer, P. and Karsholt, O. 1999. *Microlepidoptera of Europe. Volume 3. Gelechiidae I.* 356 pp., 14 colour pl., 144 figs. Apollo Books. Stenstrup.

Jeffes, M. 1995. A Third British Record of *Etiella zinckenella* Treitschke, 1832 (Lepidoptera: Pyralidae) and other migrants from vc 11. *Entomologist's Rec. J. Var.* 107: 291–292.

Jeffes, M., 2000. Some Notable Records from south-east Dorset. *Atropos* 10: 50.

Johnston J., ed. on behalf of the Hampshire Biodiversity Partnership. 1999. *Hampshire Biodiversity Action Plan (Vol. 1).* Hampshire Printing Services.

Isle of Wight Council. 2000. Wildlife of the Isle of Wight: BAP Audit (2000). Isle of Wight Council, Newport.

Karsholt, O. and Razowski, J., eds. 1996. *The Lepidoptera of Europe. A Distributional Checklist.* 380 pp. Apollo Books. Stenstrup.

Kindred, A. 1954. BENHS Exhibition, 1952. *Proc. Trans. S. Lond. Ent. Nat. Hist. Soc.* 1952–53: 36.

Knill-Jones, S.A. 1990. *Evergestis extimalis* (Scop.) (Lep.: Pyralidae) in the Isle of Wight. *Entomologist's Rec. J. Var.* 102: 304.

Knill-Jones, S.A. 1991. Two species new to the Isle of Wight. *Entomologist's Rec. J. Var.* 103: 158.

Knill-Jones, S.A. 1991b. BENHS Exhibition, 1990. *Br. J. Ent. Nat. Hist.* 4: 30.

Knill-Jones, S.A. 1992. *Elaphria venustula* (Hübn.) – new to the Isle of Wight. *Entomologist's Rec. J. Var.* 104: 256.

Knill-Jones, S.A. 1993. Three species of macro-moths new to the Isle of Wight list taken in 1992, *Entomologist's Rec. J. Var.* 105: 43–44.

Knill-Jones, S.A. 1993b. *Odontosia carmelita* (Esp.) – new to the Isle of Wight. *Entomologist's Rec. J. Var.* 105: 181.

Knill-Jones, S.A. 1994. Noteworthy Butterflies and Moths Recorded at Freshwater in 1992. *Proc. Isle of Wight Nat. Hist. Archaeol. Soc.* 12: 31–33.

Knill-Jones, S.A. 1994b. *Euplagia quadripunctaria* (Poda) and *Lymantria dispar* (Linn.) in the Isle of Wight. *Entomologist's Rec. J. Var.* 106: 28.

Knill-Jones, S.A. 1994c. Three species of Lepidoptera new to the Isle of Wight. *Entomologist's Rec. J. Var.* 106: 77.

Knill-Jones, S.A. 1994d. Two species of Micro-lepidoptera new to the Isle of Wight. *Entomologist's Rec. J. Var.* 106: 114.

Knill-Jones, S.A. 1994e. *Trichoplusia ni* (Hbn.) (Lep. Noctuidae) – a species new to the Isle of Wight. *Entomologist's Rec. J. Var.* 106: 134.

Knill-Jones, S.A. 1994f. Two species of macromoths new to the Isle of Wight. *Entomologist's Rec. J. Var.* 106: 251.

Knill-Jones, S.A. 1995. New species of lepidoptera to the Isle of Wight. *Entomologist's Rec. J. Var.* 107: 76.

Knill-Jones, S.A. 1996. Two species of micro-moth new to the Isle of Wight. *Entomologist's Rec. J. Var.* 108: 18.

Knill-Jones, S.A. 1997. Notable Moths taken in the Isle of Wight during 1994–5. *Proc. Isle of Wight Nat. Hist. Archaeol. Soc.* 13: 75–81.

Knill-Jones, S.A. 1997b. The Portland Ribbon Wave *Idaea degeneraria* Hb. (Lep.: Geometridae) on the Isle of Wight. *Entomologist's Rec. J. Var.* 109: 284.

Knill-Jones, S.A. 1997c. The Channel Islands Pug *Eupithecia ultimaria* (Boisd.) (Lep.: Geometridae) new to the Isle of Wight. *Entomologist's Rec. J. Var.* 109: 286.

Knill-Jones, S.A. 1997d. Recent notable Lepidoptera including *Dendrolimus pini* (Linnaeus) recorded on the Isle of Wight. *Entomologist's Gaz.* 48: 107–109.

Knill-Jones, S.A. 1998. Notable Moths recorded in the Isle of Wight during 1996 and 1997. *Proc. Isle of Wight Nat. Hist. Archaeol. Soc.* 14: 53–58.

Knill-Jones, S.A. 1998b. Late moths in the Isle of Wight during 1997. *Entomologist's Rec. J. Var.* 110: 141.

Knill-Jones, S.A. 1998c. New species of Lepidoptera for the Isle of Wight during 1997. *Entomologist's Rec. J. Var.* 110: 144–145.

Knill-Jones, S.A. 1998d. The Sloe Pug *Chloroclystis chloerata* (Mabile) (*sic.*) (Lep. Geometridae) new to the Isle of Wight. *Entomologist's Rec. J. Var.* 110: 232.

Knill-Jones, S.A. 1999. *Herpetogramma licarsisalis* (Walk.) A Species New to Britain. *Atropos* 6: 31.

Knill-Jones, S.A. 1999b. Notable moths recorded in the Isle of Wight during 1998, including a noctuid new to mainland Britain. Proc. *Isle of Wight Nat. Hist. Archaeol. Soc.* 16: 73–74.

Knill-Jones, S.A. 2000. Notable moths recorded in the Isle of Wight during 1999, including a pyralid new to Britain. *Proc. Isle of Wight Nat. Hist. Archaeol. Soc.* 15: 53–55.

Langmaid, J.R. 1976. *Phyllonorycter heegeriella* (Zeller) in Hampshire. *Entomologist's Rec. J. Var.* 88: 240.

Langmaid, J.R. 1988. *Cydia illutana* H.-S. (Lep.: Tortricidae) in Hampshire. *Entomologist's Rec. J. Var.* 100: 162.

Langmaid, J.R. 1993. *Stigmella samiatella* (Zeller) (Lepidoptera: Nepticulidae) in Hampshire. *Entomologist's Gaz.* 44: 123.

Langmaid, J.R. 1993b. A new tortricid moth for England – *Acleris logiana* (Clerck) (Lepidoptera: Tortricidae) in Hampshire. *Entomologist's Gaz.* 44: 154.

Langmaid, J.R. 1993c. On an unusual huge local abundance of *Mompha langiella* (Hübner) (Lepidoptera: Momphidae) in Hampshire. *Entomologist's Gaz.* 44: 256.

Langmaid, J.R. 1994. A third British record of *Gelechia senticetella* (Staudinger) (Lepidoptera: Gelechiidae). *Entomologist's Gaz.* 45: 36.

Langmaid, J.R. 1994b. *Digitivalva perlepidella* (Stainton) (Lepidoptera: Yponomeutidae) in Hampshire. *Entomologist's Gaz.* 45: 36.

Langmaid, J.R. 1994c. *Cochylis molliculana* Zeller (Lepidoptera: Tortricidae) new to the British fauna. *Entomologist's Gaz.* 45: 255–258.

Langmaid, J.R. 1995. *Paracystola acroxantha* (Meyrick) (Lepidoptera: Oecophoridae) in Hampshire. *Entomologist's Gaz.* 46: 140.

Langmaid, J.R. 1996. *Sitotroga cerealella* (Olivier) (Lepidoptera: Gelechiidae) and *Cryptophlebia leucotreta* (Meyrick (Lepidoptera: Tortricidae) at m.v. light in Hampshire. *Entomologist's Gaz.* 47: 50.

Langmaid, J.R. 1996b. The Channel Islands Pug (*Eupithecia ultimaria* Boisduval) (Lepidoptera: Geometridae) resident in England. *Entomologist's Gaz.* 47: 239–240.

Langmaid, J.R. 1997. *Coleophora deviella* Zeller and *C. aesturiella* Bradley (Lepidoptera: Coleophoridae) in Hampshire. *Entomologist's Gaz.* 48: 1.

Langmaid, J.R. 1997b. Further observations on the biology of *Monochroa moyses* Uffen (Lepidoptera: Gelechiidae). *Entomologist's Rec.* 48: 208.

Langmaid, J.R. 1998. *Ctenoplusia limbirena* (Guenée) (Lepidoptera: Noctuidae) in Hampshire. *Entomologist's Gaz.* 49: 90.

Langmaid, J.R. 1998b. *Cosmopterix scribaiella* Zeller (Lepidoptera: Cosmopterigidae) in Hampshire. *Entomologist's Gaz.* 49: 141.

Langmaid, J.R. 1998c. BENHS Exhibition, 1997. *Br. J. Ent. Nat. Hist.* 11 (1998): 92.

Leverton, R. 2001. *Enjoying Moths.* 276 pp. Poyser Natural History.

Meyrick, E. [1927]. *Revised Handbook of British Lepidoptera.* vi + 914 pp. Watkins & Doncaster. London.

Nash, D.R., Agassiz, D.J.L., Godfray, H.C.J. and Lawton, J.H. 1995. The pattern of spread of invading species: two leaf-mining moths colonizing Great Britain. *J. Anim. Ecol.* 64: 225–233.

Oates, M., Taverner, J., Green, D., *et al.* 2000. *The Butterflies of Hampshire.* Hampshire and Isle of Wight Branch of Butterfly Conservation. Pisces Publications.

Parfitt, R.W. 1999. *Argyresthia trifasciata* Stdgr (Lep.: Yponomeutidae) new to Hampshire. *Entomologist's Rec. J. Var.* 111: 44.

Phillips, J.W. 1991. A further record of *Nascia cilialis* Hb. (Lep.: Pyralidae) in Hampshire. *Entomologist's Rec. J. Var.* 103: 270.

Phillips, J.W. 1998. Three-humped Prominent *Tritophia tritophus*. *Atropos* 4: 73.

Phillips, J. 2000. Reports from Coastal Stations – 1999; Hayling Island, Hampshire. *Atropos* 9: 63.

Pickles, A.J. and Pickles, C.T. 1993. BENHS Exhibition, 1992. *Br. J. Ent. Nat. Hist.* 6 (1993): 62–63.

Plant, C.W. 1998. More on *Blastobasis decolorella* (Woll.) (Lep.: Blastobasidae) in North Hampshire. *Entomologist's Rec. J. Var.* 110: 274.

Potts, P.M. 1988. A report on moth-trapping at Titchfield Haven during 1986 and 1987. Titchfield Haven and Hook-with-Warsash NR. 1985–87 Report. HCC.

Potts, P.M. 1990. *Nascia cilialis* Hübn.) (Lep.: Pyralidae) in Hampshire. *Entomologist's Rec. J. Var.* 102: 191.

Potts, P.M. 1993. *Etiella zinckenella* (Treitschke, 1832) (Lep.: Pyralidae) The second British record and notes on its biology. *Entomologist's Rec. J. Var.* 105: 67–68.

Rogers, T. 2000. The First British Record of Oak Rustic *Dryobota labecula* Esp. *Atropos* 9: 18–19, Pl. 7, fig. 16 (G. Smith).

Sims, I. 1997. *Morophaga choragella* ([Denis & Schiffermüller, 1775]) (Lep.: Tineidae, its distribution and preferred diet in southern England. *Entomologist's Rec. J. Var.* 109: 133–134.

Sims, I. 1997b. *Nemapogon ruricolella* (Stainton, 1849) (Lep.: Tineidae) in southern England. *Entomologist's Rec. J. Var.* 109: 159.

Skinner, B. 1996. Immigrant Lepidoptera in 1992. *Entomologist's Rec. J. Var.* 108: 233–256.

Skinner, B. 1998. *The Colour Identification Guide to Moths of the British Isles.* Second Edition. Viking.

Skinner, B. and Parsons, M. 1998. The Immigration of Lepidoptera to the British Isles in 1994. *Entomologist's Rec. J. Var.* 110: 1–19.

Skinner, B. and Parsons, M. 1998b. The Immigration of Lepidoptera to the British Isles in 1995. *Entomologist's Rec. J. Var.* 110: 197–227.

Skinner, B. and Parsons, M. 1999. The Immigration of Lepidoptera to the British Isles in 1996. *Entomologist's Rec. J. Var.* 111: 153–183.

South, R., Edelsten H.M. and Fletcher, D.S., eds. 1961. *The Moths of the British Isles,* First Series. Warne.

Sterling, D.H. 1994. *Cnephasia genitalana* Pierce & Metcalfe (Lepidoptera: Tortricidae) in Hampshire. *Entomologist's Gaz.* 45: 68.

Sterling, P.H. 1997. *Cosmopterix scribaiella* Zeller (Lepidoptera: Cosmopterigidae) new to the British Isles. *Entomologist's Gaz.* 48: 205–207.

Tilbury, C. 1993. *Calamotropha paludella* (Hübner) (Lepidoptera: Pyralidae) in North Hampshire. *Entomologist's Gaz.* 44: 155.

Townsend, M.C. and Wynne, I.R. 1992. *Elaphria venustula* Hübner and other macrolepidoptera at m.v. light in Hampshire in 1991. *Entomologist's Rec. J. Var.* 104: 296.

Tunmore, M. 1999. An influx of Blossom Underwing *Orthosia miniosa* ([D.&S.]) into the UK. *Atropos* 8: 6.

Walker, D.S. 1998 (unpublished). The Moths and Butterflies of Gosport.

Waring, P. 1992. Wildlife Report, Moths. *British Wildlife* 4(1): 51–53.

Waring, P. 1994. Moth Conservation Project; News Bulletin 5, July 1992–December 1993.

Waring, P. 1998. First record of the Rannoch Looper moth *Semiothisa brunneata* Thunb. (Lep.: Geometridae) for the Isle of Wight. *Entomologist's Rec. J. Var.* 110: 40.

Warne, B.J. 1998. BENHS Exhibition, 1997. *Br. J. Ent. Nat. Hist.* 11 (1998): 95.

Index

Index of English Names